HYMNAL

OF THE

METHODIST EPISCOPAL CHURCH

WITH TUNES.

———————

WESTERN METHODIST BOOK CONCERN.
CINCINNATI: CURTS & JENNINGS, AGENTS.
NEW YORK: EATON & MAINS, AGENTS.

PREFACE TO THE HYMNAL.

THE General Conference of the Methodist Episcopal Church, on the thirtieth day of May, 1876, adopted the following report:—

The Committee on the Revision of the Hymn Book have carefully considered the various papers referred to them, and respectfully report to the General Conference that they are unanimously of the opinion that a thorough revision of the Hymn Book now in use is imperatively demanded. We therefore recommend—

1. That the Board of Bishops be requested to appoint, as soon as practicable, a Committee of fifteen, to whom shall be committed the work of revision.

2. That this Committee be selected with reference to convenience of location for division into three sections for working purposes.

3. That when the work of preparatory revision shall be completed by the several sections, the whole Committee shall be duly notified, and the work of each section shall be revised; and that no hymn now in use shall be excluded without a vote of two thirds of the Committee for its rejection, and that no hymn not now in the collection shall be admitted without a vote of two thirds of the Committee in its favor.

4. That when the Committee have completed their work, they shall submit their report to the Bishops for their approval, and the Bishops approving, they are authorized to commend it to the Church.

5. That after the Committee aforesaid shall have completed their revision of the Hymn Book, and their work has been approved by the Bishops as provided for in item 4, they shall have power to prepare a suitable Hymn and Tune Book for the use of the Church.

6. No compensation shall be paid to the Committee employed in the revisal, except for actual expenses incurred.

In accordance with the foregoing resolution, the Bishops appointed the following persons as

THE COMMITTEE OF REVISION.

Central Section.

James M. Buckley,   Erastus Wentworth,
Richard Wheatley,   John N. Brown,
      Charles E. Hendrickson.

Eastern Section.

Daniel A. Whedon,   William Rice,
Calvin S. Harrington, George Prentice,
      Charles F. Allen.

Western Section.

Francis D. Hemenway, Arthur Edwards,
William Hunter,   Jeremiah H. Bayliss,
      Charles H. Payne.

APPROVAL BY THE BISHOPS.

To the Committee appointed to revise the Hymn Book:—

DEAR BRETHREN—The Bishops, at their late meeting in Cleveland, Ohio, very thoroughly examined the result of the labors of the Committee appointed under authority of the last General Conference, to revise the Hymn Book of the Methodist Episcopal Church.

1. They went through the entire list of the hymns in the book now in use which the Committee has excluded.

2. They thoughtfully considered every revision made in the text of the hymns which the Committee has retained.

3. They read through carefully, and in many cases repeatedly, every new hymn which the Committee has introduced into the Revised Hymn Book.

After the Committee had made a few changes which the Bishops suggested, the following resolution was unanimously adopted, namely:—

Resolved, That we have thoroughly examined, with great satisfaction, the work of the Committee appointed to revise the Hymn Book. We tender to the members of that Committee our thanks; and believe the gratitude of the Church is due these brethren for the labor they have expended, and the wisdom, taste, and good judgment they have shown in preparing this most excellent book.

By order, and on behalf, of the Board of Bishops,

WILLIAM L. HARRIS, *Secretary.*

NEW YORK, *June* 15, 1877.

iv

ADDRESS

UNDER the direction of the General Conference of 1876 this revised edition of our excellent Hymn Book has been prepared. The action of the General Conference, the names of the Committee selected by the Bishops, and the judgment of the Bishops as expressed to the Committee, are herewith presented. You will note the great care which has marked every part of the work, whether in rejecting any of the hymns formerly used, or in changing their phraseology, or in the selection of those which are new. Though perfection is not claimed, yet we believe the present Hymn Book will be considered a great improvement on the preceding one.

We most cordially commend it to you as one of the choicest selections of evangelical hymns ever published; and we trust that it will increase the interest of public worship, give a higher inspiration to social and family services, and aid in private meditation and devotion. As it is published by the authority of the Church, and to meet the wants of the Church, and as the profits will be devoted to religious purposes, we do the more earnestly commend it to your liberal patronage.

We exhort you, dear brethren, to "sing with the spirit" and "with the understanding also," "making melody in your heart to the Lord."

Your affectionate pastors in Christ,

LEVI SCOTT,
MATTHEW SIMPSON,
EDWARD R. AMES,
THOMAS BOWMAN,
WILLIAM L. HARRIS,
RANDOLPH S. FOSTER,
ISAAC W. WILEY,
STEPHEN M. MERRILL,
EDWARD G. ANDREWS,
GILBERT HAVEN,
JESSE T. PECK.

January 12, 1878.

PREFACE TO THE HYMNAL WITH TUNES.

THE Committee appointed by order of the last General Conference to revise the Hymn Book, was also empowered "to prepare a suitable Hymn and Tune Book for the use of the Church;" and this book is presented as the result of its labor. The accepted doctrine of the Church is, that "every person in the congregation ought to sing, not one in ten only." To aid in securing such a consummation has been the prime purpose in the mind of the Committee. It has also been a special aim to prepare a book which would so commend itself to the whole Church as to secure uniformity of use in all our congregations, thus becoming a strong additional bond of union as well as a powerful stimulus in worship. Such a book is quite as much needed as a book of hymns alone.

This book has a superiority over our previous works of this kind in its exact agreement with the Hymnal in the order and consecutive numbering of the hymns. The preservation of this identity has greatly increased the difficulty of adapting all the hymns to suitable tunes. To accomplish this properly, without unduly increasing the size and expense of the book, was not an easy problem; yet it is believed that very few hymns will be found without their appropriate tunes on their own or on opposite pages. In the few instances where this has not been practicable, a familiar tune is suggested, with its page, at the head of the hymn.

The tunes have been taken from the best sources of our own and other countries. They have been selected from a great multitude, and from a great variety of authors, and almost wholly with a view to their availability for congregational use. They are not mere scientific harmonies, but harmonized melodies. Most of them have been tested by long usage, and have become indispensable for popular use. Those that are relatively new will prove, it is believed, as acceptable and popular as the old. The variety is very broad, and yet the music is mainly of a solid, enduring kind. Wherever pages that face each other contain hymns of the same meter it has been the aim to adapt them to one old tune and one less familiar. The number of tunes for particular meters will be found very large, and their character especially excellent. Of the few lighter tunes in the book, it is sufficient to say that they are married to their hymns and cannot well be divorced. The dozen or more of old and fugue tunes that follow the doxologies will be a gratification to many who still enjoy the ancient melodies. The chants, though not numerous, are those very generally used by the universal Church; and it is hoped that they may become more popular and useful among us.

The Committee has been assisted in the preparation of this book by Dr. Eben Tourjée, of Boston, and Mr. Joseph P. Holbrook, of New York, as special musical editors. These names are a sufficient guaranty that the musical department of the work has been done in the best possible manner.

We offer a few suggestions for congregational singing :—

Let all provide themselves with books. Every singer should have a book to himself.

Let all sing ; generally the melody of the tune.

The minister must take and express deep and constant interest in congregational singing ; otherwise it will be a failure.

The chorister must do the same.

There should be a choir or a precentor, and an organ, if possible, to lead the people. The best arrangement is to have the choir and organ in front of the congregation.

Frequent gatherings of the congregation in praise-meetings, and for instruction and practice in learning new tunes, are very desirable. For the sake of variety and freshness, the pastor and chorister should make persistent efforts to encourage the congregation to learn new tunes. The book should be the standard book of the Sunday-school, and should be constantly used in the social meeting as well as in the congregation.

In the hope that the work may stimulate all the people to sing in all the services of the sanctuary, and may contribute somewhat to the spirituality of divine worship through the power of sacred song upon the heart, it is respectfully submitted to the kindly judgment of the Church.

CONTENTS.

HYMNS AND TUNES.

AZMON.   C. M.

CARL GOTTHELF GLASER, ARR. BY LOWELL MASON.

1 *Exultant praise to the Redeemer.*

1 O FOR a thousand tongues, to sing
   My great Redeemer's praise;
The glories of my God and King,
   The triumphs of his grace!

2 My gracious Master and my God,
   Assist me to proclaim,
To spread through all the earth abroad,
   The honors of thy name.

3 Jesus! the name that charms our fears,
   That bids our sorrows cease;
'Tis music in the sinner's ears,
   'Tis life, and health, and peace.

4 He breaks the power of canceled sin,
   He sets the prisoner free;
His blood can make the foulest clean;
   His blood availed for me.

5 He speaks, and, listening to his voice,
   New life the dead receive;
The mournful, broken hearts rejoice;
   The humble poor believe.

6 Hear him, ye deaf; his praise, ye dumb,
   Your loosened tongues employ;
Ye blind, behold your Saviour come;
   And leap, ye lame, for joy.

CHARLES WESLEY.

2   *Worshiping the Lamb.*

1 COME, let us join our cheerful songs
   With angels round the throne;
Ten thousand thousand are their tongues,
   But all their joys are one.

2 "Worthy the Lamb that died," they cry,
   "To be exalted thus!"
"Worthy the Lamb!" our hearts reply,
   "For he was slain for us."

3 Jesus is worthy to receive
   Honor and power divine;
And blessings more than we can give,
   Be, Lord, forever thine.

4 The whole creation join in one,
   To bless the sacred name
Of him that sits upon the throne,
   And to adore the Lamb.

ISAAC WATTS.

SILVER STREET. S. M.

ISAAC SMITH.

3   *The universal King.*

1 COME, sound his praise abroad,
   And hymns of glory sing:
Jehovah is the sovereign God,
   The universal King.

2 He formed the deeps unknown;
   He gave the seas their bound;
The watery worlds are all his own,
   And all the solid ground.

3 Come, worship at his throne,
   Come, bow before the Lord;
We are his works, and not our own;
   He formed us by his word.

4 To-day attend his voice,
   Nor dare provoke his rod;
Come, like the people of his choice,
   And own your gracious God.

ISAAC WATTS.

4   *Song of Moses and the Lamb.*

1 AWAKE, and sing the song
   Of Moses and the Lamb;
Wake, every heart and every tongue,
   To praise the Saviour's name.

2 Sing of his dying love;
   Sing of his rising power;
Sing how he intercedes above
   For those whose sins he bore.

3 Sing on your heavenly way,
   Ye ransomed sinners, sing;
Sing on, rejoicing every day
   In Christ, the eternal King.

4 Soon shall we hear him say,
   "Ye blessed children, come!"
Soon will he call us hence away,
   To our eternal home.

5 There shall each raptured tongue
   His endless praise proclaim;
And sweeter voices tune the song
   Of Moses and the Lamb.

WILLIAM HAMMOND, ALT.

5   *Praise and thanksgiving.*

1 STAND up, and bless the Lord,
   Ye people of his choice;
Stand up, and bless the Lord your God,
   With heart, and soul, and voice.

2 Though high above all praise,
   Above all blessing high,
Who would not fear his holy name,
   And laud, and magnify?

3 O for the living flame
   From his own altar brought,
To touch our lips, our souls inspire,
   And wing to heaven our thought!

4 God is our strength and song,
   And his salvation ours;
Then be his love in Christ proclaimed
   With all our ransomed powers.

5 Stand up, and bless the Lord;
   The Lord your God adore;
Stand up, and bless his glorious name,
   Henceforth, for evermore.

JAMES MONTGOMERY.

WORSHIP.

FELICE GIARDINI.

6 *Invocation of the Trinity.*

1 COME, thou almighty King,
Help us thy name to sing,
  Help us to praise:
Father all-glorious,
O'er all victorious,
Come, and reign over us,
  Ancient of days!

2 Come, thou incarnate Word,
Gird on thy mighty sword,
  Our prayer attend:
Come, and thy people bless,
And give thy word success:
Spirit of holiness,
  On us descend!

3 Come, holy Comforter,
Thy sacred witness bear
  In this glad hour:
Thou who almighty art,
Now rule in every heart,
And ne'er from us depart,
  Spirit of power!

4 To thee, great One and Three,
Eternal praises be
  Hence, evermore:
Thy sovereign majesty
May we in glory see,
And to eternity
  Love and adore!

CHARLES WESLEY.

PACKINGTON. S. M.

REV. JOHN BLACK.

7 *Met in His name.*

1 JESUS, we look to thee,
  Thy promised presence claim;
Thou in the midst of us shalt be,
  Assembled in thy name.

2 Thy name salvation is,
  Which here we come to prove;
Thy name is life, and health, and peace,
  And everlasting love.

3 Not in the name of pride
  Or selfishness we meet;
From nature's paths we turn aside,
  And worldly thoughts forget.

4 We meet the grace to take,
  Which thou hast freely given;
We meet on earth for thy dear sake,
  That we may meet in heaven.

5 Present we know thou art,
  But O thyself reveal!
Now, Lord, let every bounding heart
  The mighty comfort feel.

6 O may thy quickening voice
  The death of sin remove;
And bid our inmost souls rejoice,
  In hope of perfect love.

CHARLES WESLEY.

7

WORSHIP.

8   *General invitation to praise God.*

1 FROM all that dwell below the skies,
Let the Creator's praise arise;
Let the Redeemer's name be sung,
Through every land, by every tongue.

2 Eternal are thy mercies, Lord;
Eternal truth attends thy word:
Thy praise shall sound from shore to shore,
Till suns shall rise and set no more.

3 Your lofty themes, ye mortals, bring;
In songs of praise divinely sing;
The great salvation loud proclaim,
And shout for joy the Saviour's name.

4 In every land begin the song;
To every land the strains belong:
In cheerful sounds all voices raise,
And fill the world with loudest praise.
ISAAC WATTS.

9   *Reverential adoration.*

1 BEFORE Jehovah's awful throne,
Ye nations bow with sacred joy;
Know that the Lord is God alone,
He can create, and he destroy.

2 His sovereign power, without our aid,
Made us of clay, and formed us men;
And when like wandering sheep we strayed,
He brought us to his fold again.

3 We'll crowd thy gates with thankful songs,
High as the heavens our voices raise;
And earth, with her ten thousand tongues,
Shall fill thy courts with sounding praise.

4 Wide as the world is thy command;
Vast as eternity thy love;
Firm as a rock thy truth shall stand,
When rolling years shall cease to move.
ISAAC WATTS, ALT. BY J. WESLEY.

10   *Universal adoration.*

1 O HOLY, holy, holy Lord!
Thou God of hosts, by all adored;
The earth and heavens are full of thee,
Thy light, thy power, thy majesty.

2 Loud hallelujahs to thy name,
Angels and seraphim proclaim:
By all the powers and thrones in heaven,
Eternal praise to thee is given.

3 Apostles join the glorious throng,
And swell the loud triumphant song:
Prophets and martyrs hear the sound,
And spread the hallelujah round.

4 Glory to thee, O God most high!
Father, we praise thy majesty!
The Son, the Spirit, we adore!
One Godhead, blest for evermore.
JOSIAH CONDR.

11   *Invitation to worship.*—Psalm 100.

1 ALL people that on earth do dwell,
Sing to the Lord with cheerful voice:
Him serve with fear, his praise forth tell,
Come ye before him, and rejoice.

2 The Lord, ye know, is God indeed,
Without our aid he did us make;
We are his flock, he doth us feed,
And for his sheep he doth us take.

3 O enter then his gates with praise,
Approach with joy his courts unto:
Praise, laud, and bless his name always,
For it is seemly so to do.

4 For why? the Lord our God is good,
His mercy is forever sure;
His truth at all times firmly stood,
And shall from age to age endure.
WILLIAM KETHE,

8

WORSHIP.

TRURO. L. M.

CHARLES BURNEY.

12 *Praise to the Saviour.*

1 JESUS, thou everlasting King,
Accept the tribute which we bring;
Accept thy well-deserved renown,
And wear our praises as thy crown.

2 Let every act of worship be
Like our espousals, Lord, to thee;
Like the blest hour when from above
We first received the pledge of love.

3 The gladness of that happy day,
O may it ever, ever stay!
Nor let our faith forsake its hold,
Nor hope decline, nor love grow cold.

4 Let every moment, as it flies,
Increase thy praise, improve our joys,
Till we are raised to sing thy name,
At the great supper of the Lamb.
ISAAC WATTS.

13 *The prosperity of the saints.*

1 O RENDER thanks to God above,
The fountain of eternal love,
Whose mercy firm through ages past
Hath stood, and shall forever last.

2 Who can his mighty deeds express,
Not only vast, but numberless?
What mortal eloquence can raise
His tribute of immortal praise?

3 Extend to me that favor, Lord,
Thou to thy chosen dost afford;
When thou return'st to set them free,
Let thy salvation visit me.

4 O may I worthy prove to see
Thy saints in full prosperity,
That I the joyful choir may join,
And count thy people's triumph mine!
TATE AND BRADY.

14 *Welcome to the King of glory.*

1 LIFT up your heads, ye mighty gates!
Behold, the King of glory waits;
The King of kings is drawing near,
The Saviour of the world is here.

2 The Lord is just, a helper tried;
Mercy is ever at his side;
His kingly crown is holiness;
His scepter, pity in distress.

3 O blest the land, the city blest,
Where Christ the ruler is confessed!
O happy hearts and happy homes
To whom this King of triumph comes!

4 Fling wide the portals of your heart;
Make it a temple, set apart
From earthly use for heaven's employ,
Adorned with prayer, and love, and joy.

5 Redeemer, come! I open wide
My heart to thee: here, Lord, abide!
Let me thy inner presence feel,
Thy grace and love in me reveal!

6 So come, my Sovereign! enter in,
Let new and nobler life begin;
Thy Holy Spirit guide us on,
Until the glorious crown be won!
GEORG WEISSEL, TR. BY MISS C. WINKWORTH.

9

DARWALL. H. M.

REV. JOHN D. DARWALL.

15 *Longings for the house of God.*

1 LORD of the worlds above;
　How pleasant and how fair
The dwellings of thy love,
　Thine earthly temples, are!
To thine abode my heart aspires,
With warm desires to see my God.

2 O happy souls that pray
　Where God appoints to hear!
O happy men that pay
　Their constant service there!
They praise thee still; and happy they
That love the way to Zion's hill.

3 They go from strength to strength,
　Through this dark vale of tears,
Till each arrives at length,
　Till each in heaven appears:
O glorious seat! thou, God, our King,
Shalt thither bring our willing feet.

ISAAC WATTS.

16 *The universal King.*

1 YOUNG men and maidens, raise
　Your tuneful voices high;
Old men and children, praise
　The Lord of earth and sky;
Him Three in One, and One in Three,
Extol to all eternity.

2 The universal King
　Let all the world proclaim;
Let every creature sing
　His attributes and name;
Him Three in One, and One in Three,
Extol to all eternity.

3 In his great name alone
　All excellences meet,
Who sits upon the throne,
　And shall forever sit;
Him Three in One, and One in Three,
Extol to all eternity.

4 Glory to God belongs;
　Glory to God be given,
Above the noblest songs
　Of all in earth and heaven;
Him Three in One, and One in Three,
Extol to all eternity.

CHARLES WESLEY.

Doxology.

To God the Father's throne
　Your highest honors raise;
Glory to God the Son;
　To God the Spirit, praise:
With all our powers, eternal King,
Thy everlasting praise we sing.

ISAAC WATTS, ALT.

ARIEL. C. P. M.

ARR. BY LOWELL MASON.

17 *The glory of His grace.*

1 LET all on earth their voices raise,
To sing the great Jehovah's praise,
　And bless his holy name:
His glory let the heathen know,
His wonders to the nations show,
　His saving grace proclaim.

2 He framed the globe; he built the sky;
He made the shining worlds on high,
　And reigns in glory there:
His beams are majesty and light;
His beauties, how divinely bright!
　His dwelling-place, how fair!

3 Come the great day, the glorious hour,
When earth shall feel his saving power,
　All nations fear his name:
Then shall the race of men confess
The beauty of his holiness,
　His saving grace proclaim.

ISAAC WATTS.

18 *God's glorious presence.*

1 THOU God of power, thou God of love,
Whose glory fills the realms above,
　Whose praise archangels sing,
And veil their faces while they cry,
"Thrice holy," to their God most high,
　"Thrice holy," to their King;

2 Thee as our God we too would claim,
And bless the Saviour's precious name,
　Through whom this grace is given:
He bore the curse to sinners due,
He forms their ruined souls anew,
　And makes them heirs of heaven.

3 The veil that hides thy glory rend,
And here in saving power descend,
　And fix thy blest abode;
Here to our hearts thyself reveal,
And let each waiting spirit feel
　The presence of our God.

JOHN WALKER.

19 *The praise of Jesus.*

1 JESUS, thou soul of all our joys,
For whom we now lift up our voice,
　And all our strength exert,
Vouchsafe the grace we humbly claim;
Compose into a thankful frame,
　And tune thy people's heart.

2 While in the heavenly work we join,
Thy glory be our whole design,
　Thy glory, not our own:
Still let us keep this end in view,
And still the pleasing task pursue,
　To please our God alone.

3 Thee let us praise, our common Lord,
And sweetly join, with one accord,
　Thy goodness to proclaim:
Jesus, thyself in us reveal,
And all our faculties shall feel
　Thy harmonizing name.

4 With calmly reverential joy,
O let us all our lives employ
　In setting forth thy love;
And raise in death our triumph higher
And sing, with all the heavenly choir,
　That endless song above.

CHARLES WESLEY.

WORSHIP.

20 *Humble adoration.*

1 HEAVENLY Father, sovereign Lord,
Be thy glorious name adored!
Lord, thy mercies never fail;
Hail, celestial Goodness, hail!

2 Though unworthy of thine ear,
Deign our humble songs to hear;
Purer praise we hope to bring
When around thy throne we sing.

3 While on earth ordained to stay,
Guide our footsteps in thy way,
Till we come to dwell with thee,
Till we all thy glory see.

4 Then, with angel-harps again,
We will wake a nobler strain;
There, in joyful songs of praise,
Our triumphant voices raise.
BENJAMIN WILLIAMS, ALT.

21 *Blessings implored.*

1 LORD, we come before thee now,
At thy feet we humbly bow;
O do not our suit disdain;
Shall we seek thee, Lord, in vain?

2 Lord, on thee our souls depend;
In compassion now descend;
Fill our hearts with thy rich grace,
Tune our lips to sing thy praise.

3 In thine own appointed way,
Now we seek thee, here we stay;
Lord, we know not how to go,
Till a blessing thou bestow.

4 Send some message from thy word,
That may joy and peace afford;
Let thy Spirit now impart
Full salvation to each heart.

5 Comfort those who weep and mourn;
Let the time of joy return;
Those that are cast down lift up;
Make them strong in faith and hope.

6 Grant that all may seek and find
Thee, a gracious God and kind:
Heal the sick, the captive free;
Let us all rejoice in thee.
WILLIAM HAMMOND.

22 *Tribute of praise at parting.*

1 CHRISTIANS, brethren, ere we part,
Every voice and every heart
Join, and to our Father raise
One last hymn of grateful praise.

2 Though we here should meet no more,
Yet there is a brighter shore;
There, released from toil and pain,
There we all may meet again.

3 Now to thee, thou God of heaven,
Be eternal glory given:
Grateful for thy love divine,
May our hearts be ever thine.
H. KIRKE WHITE, ALT.

23 *Concluding prayer and thanksgiving*

1 Now may He who from the dead
Brought the Shepherd of the sheep,
Jesus Christ, our King and Head,
All our souls in safety keep.

2 May he teach us to fulfill
What is pleasing in his sight;
Make us perfect in his will,
And preserve us day and night.

3 To that great Redeemer's praise,
Who the covenant sealed with blood,
Let our hearts and voices raise
Loud thanksgivings to our God.
JOHN NEWTON.

WORSHIP.

MONKLAND. 7.

REV. JOHN B. WILKES.

24 *Saints and angels praising God.*

1 SONGS of praise the angels sang,
Heaven with hallelujahs rang,
When Jehovah's work begun,
When he spake and it was done.

2 Songs of praise awoke the morn,
When the Prince of peace was born:
Songs of praise arose, when he
Captive led captivity.

3 Saints below, with heart and voice,
Still in songs of praise rejoice;
Learning here, by faith and love,
Songs of praise to sing above.

4 Borne upon their latest breath,
Songs of praise shall conquer death;
Then amid eternal joy,
Songs of praise their powers employ.
JAMES MONTGOMERY.

25 *Let all the people praise Him.*

1 THANK and praise Jehovah's name;
For his mercies, firm and sure,
From eternity the same,
To eternity endure.

2 Let the ransomed thus rejoice,
Gathered out of every land,
As the people of his choice,
Plucked from the destroyer's hand.

3 Let the elders praise the Lord,
Him let all the people praise,
When they meet with one accord,
In his courts on holy days.

4 Praise him, ye who know his love;
Praise him from the depths beneath;
Praise him in the heights above;
Praise your Maker, all that breathe.

5 For his truth and mercy stand,
Past, and present, and to be,

Like the years of his right hand,
Like his own eternity.
JAMES MONTGOMERY.

26 *Praise and prayer.*

1 GLORY be to God on high,
God, whose glory fills the sky!
Peace on earth to man forgiven,
Man, the well-beloved of Heaven.

2 Sovereign Father, heavenly King,
Thee we now presume to sing;
Thee with thankful hearts we prove
God of power, and God of love.

3 Christ our Lord and God we own,
Christ, the Father's only Son,
Lamb of God for sinners slain,
Saviour of offending man.

4 Bow thine ear, in mercy bow,
Hear, the world's atonement, thou!
Jesus, in thy name we pray,
Take, O take our sins away.
CHARLES WESLEY.

27 *Praise the Lord.*

1 PRAISE the Lord, his glories show,
Saints within his courts below,
Angels round his throne above,
All that see and share his love.

2 Earth to heaven, and heaven to earth
Tell his wonders, sing his worth;
Age to age, and shore to shore,
Praise him, praise him, evermore!

3 Praise the Lord, his mercies trace;
Praise his providence and grace;
All that he for man hath done;
All he sends us through his Son.

4 Strings and voices, hands and hearts,
In the concert bear your parts;
All that breathe, your Lord adore,
Praise him, praise him, evermore!
HENRY F. LYTE.

2

13

WORSHIP.

Rev. John Black.

28 *The heavenly Guest.*

1 COME, let us who in Christ believe,
Our common Saviour praise:
To him with joyful voices give
The glory of his grace.

2 He now stands knocking at the door
Of every sinner's heart:
The worst need keep him out no more,
Nor force him to depart.

3 Through grace we hearken to thy voice,
Yield to be saved from sin;
In sure and certain hope rejoice,
That thou wilt enter in.

4 Come quickly in, thou heavenly Guest,
Nor ever hence remove;
But sup with us, and let the feast
Be everlasting love.
CHARLES WESLEY.

29 *Blessing on worshipers.*

1 ONCE more we come before our God;
Once more his blessing ask:
O may not duty seem a load,
Nor worship prove a task.

2 Father, thy quickening Spirit send
From heaven, in Jesus' name,
And bid our waiting minds attend,
And put our souls in frame.

3 May we receive the word we hear,
Each in an honest heart;
And keep the precious treasure there,
And never with it part.

4 To seek thee, all our hearts dispose;
To each thy blessings suit;
And let the seed thy servant sows
Produce abundant fruit.
JOSEPH HART.

30 *Expecting the blessing.*

1 SEE, Jesus, thy disciples see,
The promised blessing give;
Met in thy name, we look to thee,
Expecting to receive.

2 Thee we expect, our faithful Lord,
Who in thy name are joined;
We wait, according to thy word,
Thee in the midst to find.

3 With us thou art assembled here,
But O thyself reveal;
Son of the living God, appear!
Let us thy presence feel.

4 Breathe on us, Lord, in this our day,
And these dry bones shall live;
Speak peace into our hearts, and say,
"The Holy Ghost receive."
CHARLES WESLEY.

31 *Infinite grace.*

1 INFINITE excellence is thine,
Thou glorious Prince of grace!
Thy uncreated beauties shine
With never-fading rays.

2 Sinners, from earth's remotest end,
Come bending at thy feet;
To thee their prayers and songs ascend,
In thee their wishes meet.

3 Millions of happy spirits live
On thy exhaustless store;
From thee they all their bliss receive,
And still thou givest more.

4 Thou art their triumph and their joy;
They find their all in thee;
Thy glories will their tongues employ
Through all eternity.
JOHN FAWCETT

WORSHIP.

THOMAS AUGUSTINE ARNE.

32 *The great and effectual door.*

1 JESUS, thou all-redeeming Lord,
  Thy blessing we implore;
Open the door to preach thy word,
  The great, effectual door.

2 Gather the outcasts in, and save
  From sin and Satan's power;
And let them now acceptance have,
  And know their gracious hour.

3 Lover of souls! thou know'st to prize
  What thou hast bought so dear:
Come, then, and in thy people's eyes
  With all thy wounds appear.

4 The hardness of our hearts remove,
  Thou who for all hast died;
Show us the tokens of thy love,
  Thy feet, thy hands, thy side.

5 Ready thou art the blood to apply,
  And prove the record true;
And all thy wounds to sinners cry,
  "I suffered this for you."
                    CHARLES WESLEY.

33 *God, the only object of worship.*

1 O GOD, our strength, to thee our song
  With grateful hearts we raise;
To thee, and thee alone, belong
  All worship, love, and praise.

2 In trouble's dark and stormy hour
  Thine ear hath heard our prayer;
And graciously thine arm of power
  Hath saved us from despair.

3 And thou, O ever gracious Lord,
  Wilt keep thy promise still,

If, meekly hearkening to thy word,
  We seek to do thy will.

4 Led by the light thy grace imparts,
  Ne'er may we bow the knee
To idols, which our wayward hearts
  Set up instead of thee.

5 So shall thy choicest gifts, O Lord,
  Thy faithful people bless;
For them shall earth its stores afford,
  And heaven its happiness.
                    HARRIET AUBER.

34 *Vying with the angels.*

1 A THOUSAND oracles divine
  Their common beams unite,
That sinners may with angels join,
  To worship God aright.

2 Triumphant host! they never cease
  To laud and magnify
The Triune God of holiness,
  Whose glory fills the sky.

3 By faith the upper choir we meet,
  And challenge them to sing
Jehovah on his shining seat,
  Our Maker and our King.

4 But God made flesh is wholly ours,
  And asks our noblest strain;
The Father of celestial powers,
  The Friend of earthborn man!
                    CHARLES WESLEY

Doxology.

To Father, Son, and Holy Ghost,
  The God whom we adore,
Be glory, as it was, is now,
  And shall be evermore!
                    TATE AND BRADY.

WORSHIP.

MAINZER. L. M.

JOSEPH MAINZER.

35 *Grace, pardon, and life.*

1 FATHER of heaven, whose love profound
A ransom for our souls hath found,
Before thy throne we sinners bend;
To us thy pardoning love extend.

2 Almighty Son, incarnate Word,
Our Prophet, Priest, Redeemer, Lord,
Before thy throne we sinners bend;
To us thy saving grace extend.

3 Eternal Spirit, by whose breath
The soul is raised from sin and death,
Before thy throne we sinners bend;
To us thy quickening power extend.

4 Jehovah! Father, Spirit, Son,
Mysterious Godhead! Three in One!
Before thy throne we sinners bend;
Grace, pardon, life, to us extend.

JOHN COOPER.

36 *True worship every-where accepted.*

1 O THOU to whom, in ancient time,
The lyre of Hebrew bards was strung,
Whom kings adored in song sublime,
And prophets praised with glowing tongue

2 Not now on Zion's height alone
The favored worshiper may dwell,
Nor where, at sultry noon, thy Son
Sat weary by the patriarch's well.

3 From every place below the skies,
The grateful song, the fervent prayer,
The incense of the heart may rise
To heaven, and find acceptance there.

4 O Thou to whom, in ancient time,
The holy prophet's harp was strung,
To thee at last in every clime,
Shall temples rise and praise be sung.

JOHN PIERPONT.

WARD. L. M.

SCOTCH TUNE, ARR. BY LOWELL MASON.

37 *Trembling aspiration.*

1 O THOU, whom all thy saints adore,
We now with all thy saints agree,
And bow our inmost souls before
Thy glorious, awful Majesty.

2 We come, great God, to seek thy face,
And for thy loving-kindness wait;
And O how dreadful is this place!
'Tis God's own house, 'tis heaven's gate.

3 Tremble our hearts to find thee nigh;
To thee our trembling hearts aspire;

And lo! we see descend from high
The pillar and the flame of fire.

4 Still let it on the assembly stay,
And all the house with glory fill;
To Canaan's bounds point out the way,
And lead us to thy holy hill.

5 There let us all with Jesus stand,
And join the general Church above,
And take our seats at thy right hand,
And sing thine everlasting love.

CHARLES WESLEY.

16

MILLER.   L. M.   C. P. E. BACH, ARR. BY DR. MILLER.

38   *Solemn adoration.*

1 ETERNAL Power, whose high abode
Becomes the grandeur of a God,
Infinite lengths beyond the bounds
Where stars revolve their little rounds!

2 Thee while the first archangel sings,
He hides his face behind his wings,
And ranks of shining thrones around
Fall worshiping, and spread the ground.

3 Lord, what shall earth and ashes do?
We would adore our Maker too;
From sin and dust to thee we cry,
The Great, the Holy, and the High.

4 Earth, from afar, hath heard thy fame,
And worms have learned to lisp thy name:
But O! the glories of thy mind
Leave all our soaring thoughts behind.

5 God is in heaven, and men below:
Be short our tunes; our words be few;
A solemn reverence checks our songs,
And praise sits silent on our tongues.
                                    ISAAC WATTS.

39   *Living bread.*

1 THY presence, gracious God, afford;
Prepare us to receive thy word:
Now let thy voice engage our ear,
And faith be mixed with what we hear.

2 Distracting thoughts and cares remove,
And fix our hearts and hopes above:
With food divine may we be fed,
And satisfied with living bread.

3 To us the sacred word apply
With sovereign power and energy;
And may we, in thy faith and fear,
Reduce to practice what we hear.

4 Father, in us thy Son reveal;
Teach us to know and do thy will:
Thy saving power and love display,
And guide us to the realms of day.
                                    JOHN FAWCETT

40   *God revealed to faith.*

1 NOT here, as to the prophet's eye,
   The Lord upon his throne appears;
Nor seraphim responsive cry,
   "Holy! thrice holy!" in our ears:

2 Yet God is present in this place,
   Veiled in serener majesty;
So full of glory, truth, and grace,
   That faith alone such light can see.

3 Nor, as he in the temple taught,
   Is Christ within these walls revealed,
When blind, and deaf, and dumb were
      brought,
   Lepers and lame, and all were healed:

4 Yet here, when two or three shall meet,
   Or thronging multitudes are found,
All may sit down at Jesus' feet,
   And hear from him the joyful sound.

5 Send forth the seraphim, O Lord,
   To touch thy servants' lips with fire:
Saviour, give them thy faithful word;
   Come, Holy Ghost, their hearts inspire.
                                    JAMES MONTGOMERY.

WAUGH. S. M.

REV. RALPH HARRISON.

41 *Glory begun below.*

1 COME, ye that love the Lord,
  And let your joys be known;
Join in a song with sweet accord,
  While ye surround his throne.

2 Let those refuse to sing
  Who never knew our God,
But servants of the heavenly King
  May speak their joys abroad.

3 The God that rules on high,
  That all the earth surveys,
That rides upon the stormy sky,
  And calms the roaring seas;

4 This awful God is ours,
  Our Father and our Love;
He will send down his heavenly powers,
  To carry us above.

5 There we shall see his face,
  And never, never sin;
There, from the rivers of his grace,
  Drink endless pleasures in:

6 Yea, and before we rise
  To that immortal state,
The thoughts of such amazing bliss
  Should constant joys create.

7 The men of grace have found
  Glory begun below;
Celestial fruit on earthly ground
  From faith and hope may grow:

8 Then let our songs abound,
  And every tear be dry;
We're marching through Immanuel's
    ground,
  To fairer worlds on high.

ISAAC WATTS, ALT. BY J. WESLEY.

42 *Creating love and redeeming grace.*

1 FATHER, in whom we live,
  In whom we are, and move,
The glory, power, and praise receive
  Of thy creating love.

2 Let all the angel throng
  Give thanks to God on high,
While earth repeats the joyful song,
  And echoes to the sky.

3 Incarnate Deity,
  Let all the ransomed race
Render in thanks their lives to thee,
  For thy redeeming grace.

4 The grace to sinners showed,
  Ye heavenly choirs proclaim,
And cry, "Salvation to our God,
  Salvation to the Lamb!"

CHARLES WESLEY.

43 *The sacrifice of praise.*

1 WITH joy we lift our eyes
  To those bright realms above,
That glorious temple in the skies,
  Where dwells eternal Love.

2 Before thy throne we bow,
  O thou almighty King;
Here we present the solemn vow,
  And hymns of praise we sing.

3 While in thy house we kneel,
  With trust and holy fear,
Thy mercy and thy truth reveal,
  And lend a gracious ear.

4 Lord, teach our hearts to pray,
  And tune our lips to sing;
Nor from thy presence cast away
  The sacrifice we bring.

THOMAS JERVIS.

MALVERN. L. M.

LOWELL MASON.

44   *The great Shepherd with his flock.*

1 JESUS, where'er thy people meet,
There they behold thy mercy-seat;
Where'er they seek thee, thou art found,
And every place is hallowed ground.

2 For thou, within no walls confined,
Dost dwell with those of humble mind;
Such ever bring thee where they come,
And, going, take thee to their home.

3 Great Shepherd of thy chosen few,
Thy former mercies here renew;
Here, to our waiting hearts, proclaim
The sweetness of thy saving name.

4 Here may we prove the power of prayer
To strengthen faith and sweeten care;
To teach our faint desires to rise,
And bring all heaven before our eyes.

WILLIAM COWPER.

45   *Blest hour of prayer.*

BLEST hour, when mortal man retires
To hold communion with his God;
To send to Heaven his warm desires,
And listen to the sacred word.

Blest hour, when God himself draws nigh,
Well pleased his people's voice to hear;
To hush the penitential sigh,
And wipe away the mourner's tear.

3 Blest hour, for, where the Lord resorts,
Foretastes of future bliss are given;
And mortals find his earthly courts
The house of God, the gate of heaven.

4 Hail, peaceful hour! supremely blest
Amid the hours of worldly care;
The hour that yields the spirit rest,
That sacred hour, the hour of prayer.

5 And when my hours of prayer are past
And this frail tenement decays,
Then may I spend in heaven at last
A never-ending hour of praise.

THOMAS RAFFLES.

46   *For Zion's peace.*

1 O THOU, our Saviour, Brother, Friend,
Behold a cloud of incense rise;
The prayers of saints to heaven ascend,
Grateful, accepted sacrifice.

2 Regard our prayers for Zion's peace;
Shed in our hearts thy love abroad;
Thy gifts abundantly increase;
Enlarge, and fill us all with God.

3 Before thy sheep, great Shepherd, go
And guide into thy perfect will;
Cause us thy hallowed name to know;
The work of faith in us fulfill.

4 Help us to make our calling sure;
O let us all be saints indeed,
And pure, as thou thyself art pure,
Conformed in all things to our Head.

5 Take the dear purchase of thy blood;
Thy blood shall wash us white as snow
Present us sanctified to God,
And perfected in love below.

CHARLES WESLEY.

WAVERTREE. L. M. 6l. W. Sdccms

47 *Lo! God is here.*

1 Lo! God is here! let us adore,
  And own how dreadful is this place;
Let all within us feel his power,
  And silent bow before his face;
Who know his power, his grace who prove,
Serve him with awe, with reverence love.

2 Lo! God is here! him day and night
  United choirs of angels sing:
To him, enthroned above all height,
  Heaven's host their noblest praises bring;
Disdain not, Lord, our meaner song,
Who praise thee with a stammering tongue.

3 Being of beings, may our praise
  Thy courts with grateful fragrance fill;
Still may we stand before thy face,
  Still hear and do thy sovereign will;
To thee may all our thoughts arise,
Ceaseless, accepted sacrifice.

GERHARD TERSTEEGEN. TR. BY J. WESLEY.

48 *Holy, holy, holy, Lord God of Sabaoth.*

1 INFINITE God, to thee we raise
Our hearts in solemn songs of praise;
By all thy works on earth adored,
We worship thee, the common Lord;
The everlasting Father own,
And bow our souls before thy throne.

2 Thee all the choir of angels sings,
The Lord of hosts, the King of kings;
Cherubs proclaim thy praise aloud,
And seraphs shout the Triune God;
And "Holy, holy, holy," cry,
"Thy glory fills both earth and sky."

3 Father of endless majesty,
All might and love we render thee;
Thy true and only Son adore,
The same in dignity and power;
And God the Holy Ghost declare,
The saints' eternal Comforter.

CHARLES WESLEY.

HEBRON. L. M. LOWELL MASON.

49 *Lift up our hearts to Thee.*

1 O CHRIST, who hast prepared a place
For us around thy throne of grace,
We pray thee, lift our hearts above,
And draw them with the cords of love.

2 Source of all good, thou, gracious Lord,
Art our exceeding great reward;
How transient is our present pain,
How boundless our eternal gain!

3 With open face and joyful heart,
We then shall see thee as thou art:
Our love shall never cease to glow,
Our praise shall never cease to flow.

4 Thy never-failing grace to prove,
A surety of thine endless love,
Send down thy Holy Ghost, to be
The raiser of our souls to thee.

SANTOLIUS VICTORINUS. TR. BY J. CHANDLER.

ELLACOMBE. 7, 6.

ST. GALL'S COLLECTION.

50 *Show mercy.*

1 O GOD, to us show mercy,
  And bless us in thy grace;
Cause thou to shine upon us
  The brightness of thy face:

2 That so throughout all nations
  Thy way may be well known,
And unto every people
  Thy saving health be shown.

3 O God, let people praise thee,
  Let all the people praise;
O let the nations joyful
  Their songs of gladness raise:

4 For thou shalt judge the people
  In truth and righteousness;
And on the earth all nations
  Shall thy just rule confess.

5 O God, let people praise thee;
  Thy praises let them sing;
And then in rich abundance
  The earth her fruit shall bring:

6 The Lord our God shall bless us,
  God shall his blessing send;
And people all shall fear him
  To earth's remotest end.

UNKNOWN.

LYONS. 10, 11.

FRANCIS JOSEPH HAYDN.

51 *Thanksgiving for infinite love.*

1 Ye servants of God, your Master proclaim,
And publish abroad his wonderful name;
The name all-victorious of Jesus extol;
His kingdom is glorious, and rules over all.

2 God ruleth on high, almighty to save;
And still he is nigh; his presence we have:
The great congregation his triumph shall sing,
Ascribing salvation to Jesus, our King.

3 "Salvation to God, who sits on the throne,"
Let all cry aloud, and honor the Son:
The praises of Jesus the angels proclaim,
Fall down on their faces, and worship the Lamb.

4 Then let us adore, and give him his right,
All glory and power, all wisdom and might,
All honor and blessing, with angels above,
And thanks never ceasing for infinite love.

CHARLES WESLEY.

GREENVILLE. 8, 7, 4. JEAN JACQUES ROUSSEAU.

52 *For the fullness of peace and joy.*

1 LORD, dismiss us with thy blessing,
  Fill our hearts with joy and peace;
Let us each, thy love possessing,
  Triumph in redeeming grace;
    O refresh us,
  Traveling through this wilderness.

2 Thanks we give, and adoration,
  For thy gospel's joyful sound;
May the fruits of thy salvation
  In our hearts and lives abound;
    May thy presence
  With us evermore be found.

3 So, whene'er the signal's given
  Us from earth to call away,
Borne on angels' wings to heaven,
  Glad the summons to obey,
    May we ever
  Reign with Christ in endless day.
                    WALTER SHIRLEY.

53 *The apostolic benediction.*

MAY the grace of Christ our Saviour,
  And the Father's boundless love,
With the Holy Spirit's favor,
  Rest upon us from above:
Thus may we abide in union
  With each other and the Lord;
And possess, in sweet communion,
  Joys which earth cannot afford.
                    JOHN NEWTON.

54 *Heavenly joy anticipated.*

1 IN thy name, O Lord, assembling,
  We, thy people, now draw near:
Teach us to rejoice with trembling;
  Speak, and let thy servants hear:
    Hear with meekness,
  Hear thy word with godly fear.

2 While our days on earth are lengthened
  May we give them, Lord, to thee:
Cheered by hope, and daily strengthened,
  May we run, nor weary be,
    Till thy glory
  Without cloud in heaven we see.

3 There, in worship purer, sweeter,
  All thy people shall adore;
Sharing then in rapture greater
  Than they could conceive before:
    Full enjoyment,
  Full and pure, for evermore.
                    THOMAS KELLY

55 *For a blessing on the word.*

1 COME, thou soul-transforming Spirit,
  Bless the sower and the seed;
Let each heart thy grace inherit;
  Raise the weak, the hungry feed;
    From the gospel
  Now supply thy people's need.

2 O may all enjoy the blessing
  Which thy word's designed to give;
Let us all, thy love possessing,
  Joyfully the truth receive,
    And forever
  To thy praise and glory live.
                    JONATHAN EVANS

RATHBUN.   8, 7.   ITHAMAR CONKEY.

56   *Isaiah's vision.*

1 ROUND the Lord, in glory seated,
   Cherubim and seraphim
Filled his temple, and repeated
   Each to each the alternate hymn:

2 "Lord, thy glory fills the heaven;
   Earth is with its fullness stored;
Unto thee be glory given,
   Holy, holy, holy Lord."

3 Heaven is still with glory ringing;
   Earth takes up the angels' cry,
"Holy, holy, holy," singing,
   "Lord of hosts, Lord God most high."

4 With his seraph train before him,
   With his holy Church below,
Thus unite we to adore him:
   Bid we thus our anthem flow:

5 "Lord, thy glory fills the heaven;
   Earth is with its fullness stored;
Unto thee be glory given,
   Holy, holy, holy Lord."

                              RICHARD MANT.

57   *Exhortation to praise God.*

1 PRAISE the Lord! ye heavens, adore him;
   Praise him, angels, in the height;
Sun and moon, rejoice before him;
   Praise him, all ye stars of light.

2 Praise the Lord, for he hath spoken;
   Worlds his mighty voice obeyed;
Laws which never shall be broken,
   For their guidance he hath made.

3 Praise the Lord, for he is glorious;
   Never shall his promise fail;
God hath made his saints victorious;
   Sin and death shall not prevail.

4 Praise the God of our salvation;
   Hosts on high his power proclaim;
Heaven and earth, and all creation,
   Laud and magnify his name.
                              JOHN KEMPTHORNE.

58   *Glory to the Lamb.*

1 HARK! the notes of angels, singing,
   "Glory, glory to the Lamb!"
All in heaven their tribute bringing,
   Raising high the Saviour's name.

2 Ye for whom his life was given,
   Sacred themes to you belong:
Come, assist the choir of heaven;
   Join the everlasting song.

3 See! the angelic hosts have crowned him,
   Jesus fills the throne on high;
Countless myriads, hovering round him,
   With his praises rend the sky.

4 Filled with holy emulation,
   Let us vie with those above:
Sweet the theme, a free salvation,
   Fruit of everlasting love.

5 Endless life in him possessing,
   Let us praise his precious name;
Glory, honor, power, and blessing,
   Be forever to the Lamb.
                              THOMAS KELU

59   *Dismission.*

LORD, dismiss us with thy blessing,
   Bid us now depart in peace;
Still on heavenly manna feeding,
   Let our faith and love increase:
Fill each breast with consolation,
   Up to thee our hearts we raise:
When we reach our blissful station,
   Then we'll give thee nobler praise.
                              EDWIN SMYTHE

23

BELMONT.   C. M.   SAMUEL WEBBE.

60   *Confession, prayer, and praise.*

1 LORD, when we bend before thy throne,
    And our confessions pour,
O may we feel the sins we own,
    And hate what we deplore.

2 Our contrite spirits pitying see;
    True penitence impart;
And let a healing ray from thee
    Beam peace into each heart.

3 When we disclose our wants in prayer,
    May we our wills resign;
And not a thought our bosom share
    Which is not wholly thine.

4 And when, with heart and voice, we strive
    Our grateful hymns to raise,
Let love divine within us live,
    And fill our souls with praise.

Then, on thy glories while we dwell,
    Thy mercies we'll review;
With love divine transported, tell—
    Thou, God, art Father too!
                            JOSEPH D. CARLYLE.

61   *Divine guidance, and rest.*

1 BEFORE thy mercy-seat, O Lord,
    Behold, thy servants stand,
To ask the knowledge of thy word,
    The guidance of thy hand.

2 Let thy eternal truths, we pray,
    Dwell richly in each heart;
That from the safe and narrow way
    We never may depart.

3 Lord, from thy word remove the seal,
    Unfold its hidden store;
And, as we read, O may we feel
    Its value more and more.

4 Help us to see the Saviour's love
    Beaming from every page;
And let the thoughts of joys above
    Our inmost souls engage.

5 Thus while thy word our footsteps
        guides,
    Shall we be truly blest;
And safe arrive where love provides
    An everlasting rest.
                            WILLIAM H. BATHURST.

62   *For a benediction on the truth.*

1 O GOD, by whom the seed is given,
    By whom the harvest blest;
Whose word, like manna showered from
        heaven,
    Is planted in our breast;

2 Preserve it from the passing feet,
    And plunderers of the air,
The sultry sun's intenser heat,
    And weeds of worldly care.

3 Though buried deep, or thinly strown,
    Do thou thy grace supply:
The hope in earthly furrows sown
    Shall ripen in the sky.
                            REGINALD HEBER.

24

WORSHIP.

63   *The glories of our King.*

1 COME, ye that love the Saviour's name,
  And joy to make it known,
The Sovereign of your hearts proclaim,
  And bow before his throne.

2 Behold your Lord, your Master, crowned
  With glories all divine;
And tell the wondering nations round
  How bright those glories shine.

3 When, in his earthly courts, we view
  The glories of our King,
We long to love as angels do,
  And wish like them to sing.

4 And shall we long and wish in vain?
  Lord, teach our songs to rise:
Thy love can animate the strain,
  And bid it reach the skies.
                    ANNE STEELE.

64   *The Desire of all nations.*

1 COME, thou Desire of all thy saints,
  Our humble strains attend,
While, with our praises and complaints,
  Low at thy feet we bend.

2 How should our songs, like those above,
  With warm devotion rise!
How should our souls, on wings of love,
  Mount upward to the skies!

3 Come, Lord, thy love alone can raise
  In us the heavenly flame;
Then shall our lips resound thy praise,
  Our hearts adore thy name.

4 Now, Saviour, let thy glory shine,
  And fill thy dwellings here,
Till life, and love, and joy divine,
  A heaven on earth appear.

5 Then shall our hearts, enraptured, say
  "Come, great Redeemer, come,
And bring the bright, the glorious day,
  That calls thy children home."
                    ANNE STEELE.

65   *Invoking divine blessings.*

1 WITHIN thy house, O Lord our God,
  In majesty appear;
Make this a place of thine abode,
  And shed thy blessings here.

2 As we thy mercy-seat surround,
  Thy Spirit, Lord, impart;
And let thy gospel's joyful sound,
  With power reach every heart.

3 Here let the blind their sight obtain;
  Here give the mourner rest;
Let Jesus here triumphant reign,
  Enthroned in every breast.

4 Here let the voice of sacred joy
  And fervent prayer arise,
Till higher strains our tongues employ,
  In realms beyond the skies.
                    UNKNOWN.

WORSHIP.

DUKE STREET. L. M.

John Hatton.

66 *Jesus reigns.*

1 COME, let us tune our loftiest song,
  And raise to Christ our joyful strain;
Worship and thanks to him belong,
  Who reigns, and shall forever reign.

2 His sovereign power our bodies made;
  Our souls are his immortal breath.;
And when his creatures sinned, he bled,
  To save us from eternal death.

3 Burn every breast with Jesus' love;
  Bound every heart with rapturous joy;
And saints on earth, with saints above,
  Your voices in his praise employ.

4 Extol the Lamb with loftiest song,
  Ascend for him our cheerful strain;
Worship and thanks to him belong,
  Who reigns, and shall forever reign.
  ROBERT A. WEST.

67 *The bond of love.*

1 PRAISE waits in Zion, Lord, for thee:
  Thy saints adore thy holy name;
Thy creatures bend the obedient knee,
  And humbly now thy presence claim.

2 Eternal Source of truth and light,
  To thee we look, on thee we call;
Lord, we are nothing in thy sight,
  But thou to us art all in all.

3 Still may thy children in thy word
  Their common trust and refuge see;
O bind us to each other, Lord,
  By one great bond,—the love of thee.

4 Here, at the portal of thy house,
  We leave our mortal hopes and fears;
Accept our prayers and bless our vows,
  And dry our penitential tears.

5 So shall our sun of hope arise,
  With brighter still and brighter ray,
Till thou shalt bless our longing eyes
  With beams of everlasting day.
  SIR J. E. SMITH.

68 *The praises of Jehovah.*

1 SERVANTS of God, in joyful lays,
  Sing ye the Lord Jehovah's praise;
His glorious name let all adore,
  From age to age, for evermore.

2 Blest be that name, supremely blest.
  From the sun's rising to its rest;
Above the heavens his power is known,
  Through all the earth his goodness shown.

3 Who is like God? so great, so high,
  He bows himself to view the sky;
And yet, with condescending grace
  Looks down upon the human race.

4 He hears the uncomplaining moan
  Of those who sit and weep alone;
He lifts the mourner from the dust,
  In him the poor may safely trust.

5 O then, aloud, in joyful lays,
  Sing to the Lord Jehovah's praise;
His saving name let all adore,
  From age to age, for evermore.
  JAMES MONTGOMERY.

GILEAD. L. M.   Etienne Henri Mehul

69 *Joy of public worship.*

1 GREAT God, attend, while Zion sings
The joy that from thy presence springs;
To spend one day with thee on earth
Exceeds a thousand days of mirth.

2 Might I enjoy the meanest place
Within thy house, O God of grace,
Not tents of ease, nor thrones of power,
Should tempt my feet to leave thy door.

3 God is our sun, he makes our day;
God is our shield, he guards our way
From all assaults of hell and sin,
From foes without, and foes within.

4 All needful grace will God bestow,
And crown that grace with glory too;
He gives us all things, and withholds
No real good from upright souls.

5 O God, our King, whose sovereign sway
The glorious hosts of heaven obey,
And devils at thy presence flee;
Blest is the man that trusts in thee.
                                    ISAAC WATTS.

70   *The eternal God exalted.*

1 ETERNAL God, celestial King,
Exalted be thy glorious name;
Let hosts in heaven thy praises sing,
  And saints on earth thy love proclaim.

2 My heart is fixed on thee, my God;
I rest my hope on thee alone;
I'll spread thy sacred truths abroad,
  To all mankind thy love make known.

3 Awake, my tongue; awake, my lyre;
  With morning's earliest dawn arise;
To songs of joy my soul inspire,
  And swell your music to the skies.

4 With those who in thy grace abound.
  To thee I'll raise my thankful voice;
Till every land the earth around,
  Shall hear, and in thy name rejoice.
                              WILLIAM WRANGHAM.

71   *Hosanna to the living Lord.*

1 HOSANNA to the living Lord!
Hosanna to the incarnate Word!
To Christ, Creator, Saviour, King,
Let earth, let heaven, hosanna sing.

2 "Hosanna, Lord!" thine angels cry,
"Hosanna, Lord!" thy saints reply;
Above, beneath us, and around,
The dead and living swell the sound.

3 O Saviour, with protecting care,
Return to this, thy house of prayer,
Assembled in thy sacred name,
Where we thy parting promise claim.

4 But chiefest in our cleansèd breast,
Eternal, bid thy Spirit rest,
And make our secret soul to be
A temple pure, and worthy thee.

5 So, in the last and dreadful day,
When earth and heaven shall melt away
Thy flock, redeemed from sinful stain,
Shall swell the sound of praise again.
                              REGINALD HEBER.

27

MENDEBRAS. 7, 6. GERMAN MELODY, ARR. BY LOWELL MASON.

72 *Day of rest and gladness.*

1 O DAY of rest and gladness,
  O day of joy and light,
O balm of care and sadness,
  Most beautiful, most bright:
On thee, the high and lowly,
  Through ages joined in tune,
Sing "Holy, holy, holy,"
  To the great God Triune.

2 On thee, at the creation,
  The light first had its birth;
On thee, for our salvation,
  Christ rose from depths of earth,
On thee, our Lord, victorious,
  The Spirit sent from heaven;
And thus on thee, most glorious,
  A triple light was given.

3 To-day on weary nations
  The heavenly manna falls;
To holy convocations
  The silver trumpet calls,
Where gospel light is glowing
  With pure and radiant beams,
And living water flowing
  With soul-refreshing streams.

4 New graces ever gaining
  From this our day of rest,
We reach the rest remaining
  To spirits of the blest;
To Holy Ghost be praises,
  To Father, and to Son,
The Church her voice upraises
  To thee, blest Three in One.
                    CHRISTOPHER WORDSWORTH.

WARSAW. H. M. THOMAS CLARK.

73 *Joyful homage.*

1 AWAKE, ye saints, awake!
  And hail this sacred day:
In loftiest songs of praise
  Your joyful homage pay:
Come, bless the day that God hath blest,
The type of heaven's eternal rest.

2 On this auspicious morn
  The Lord of life arose;

He burst the bars of death,
  And vanquished all our foes;
And now he pleads our cause above,
And reaps the fruit of all his love.

3 All hail, triumphant Lord!
  Heaven with hosannas rings,
  And earth, in humbler strains,
  Thy praise responsive sings:
Worthy the Lamb, that once was slain,
Through endless years to live and reign.
          ELIZABETH SCOTT, ALT. BY T. COTTERILL.

MERTON.   C. M.

HENRY KEMBLE OLIVER.

74   *Sabbath and sanctuary joys.*

1 WITH joy we hail the sacred day,
  Which God has called his own;
With joy the summons we obey,
  To worship at his throne.

2 Thy chosen temple, Lord, how fair!
  As here thy servants throng
To breathe the humble, fervent prayer,
  And pour the grateful song.

3 Spirit of grace! O deign to dwell
  Within thy Church below;
Make her in holiness excel,
  With pure devotion glow.

4 Let peace within her walls be found;
  Let all her sons unite,
To spread with holy zeal around
  Her clear and shining light.

5 Great God, we hail the sacred day,
  Which thou hast called thine own;
With joy the summons we obey
  To worship at thy throne.

HARRIET AUBER.

75   *Easter Sunday.*

1 THE Lord of Sabbath let us praise,
  In concert with the blest,
Who, joyful, in harmonious lays
  Employ an endless rest.

2 Thus, Lord, while we remember thee,
  We blest and pious grow;
By hymns of praise we learn to be
  Triumphant here below.

3 On this glad day a brighter scene
  Of glory was displayed,
By the eternal Word, than when
  This universe was made.

4 He rises, who mankind has bought
  With grief and pain extreme:

'Twas great to speak the world from naught;
  'Twas greater to redeem.

SAMUEL WESLEY, JR.

76   *We will rejoice, and be glad in it.*

1 THIS is the day the Lord hath made:
  O earth, rejoice and sing;
Let songs of triumph hail the morn;
  Hosanna to our King!

2 The Stone the builders set at naught,
  That Stone has now become
The sure foundation and the strength
  Of Zion's heavenly dome.

3 Christ is that Stone, rejected once,
  And numbered with the slain;
Now raised in glory, o'er his Church
  Eternally to reign.

4 This is the day the Lord hath made:
  O earth, rejoice and sing;
With songs of triumph hail the morn;
  Hosanna to our King!

HARRIET AUBER.

77   *Sabbath light.*

1 AGAIN the Lord of life and light
  Awakes the kindling ray,
Dispels the darkness of the night,
  And pours increasing day.

2 O what a night was that which wrapt
  A guilty world in gloom!
O what a sun, which broke this day
  Triumphant from the tomb!

3 This day be grateful homage paid,
  And loud hosannas sung;
Let gladness dwell in every heart,
  And praise on every tongue.

4 Ten thousand thousand lips shall join
  To hail this happy morn,
Which scatters blessings from its wings
  On nations yet unborn.

MRS. ANNA L. BARBAULD.

3

OVERBERG.   L. M.
JOHANN CHRISTIAN HEINRICH RINK.

78 *Ardent hope of heavenly rest.*

1 LORD of the Sabbath, hear our vows,
On this thy day, in this thy house,
And own, as grateful sacrifice,
The songs which from thy servants rise.

2 Thine earthly Sabbaths, Lord, we love;
But there's a nobler rest above;
To that our laboring souls aspire
With ardent hope and strong desire.

3 No more fatigue, no more distress,
Nor sin nor hell, shall reach the place;
No sighs shall mingle with the songs,
Which warble from immortal tongues,

4 No rude alarms of raging foes,
No cares to break the long repose;
No midnight shade, no clouded sun,
But sacred, high, eternal noon.

O long-expected day, begin!
Dawn on these realms of woe and sin;
Fain would we leave this weary road,
And sleep in death, to rest with God.
                                PHILIP DODDRIDGE.

79 *Sabbath evening: Thy kingdom come.*

MILLIONS within thy courts have met,
Millions this day before thee bowed;
Their faces Zionward were set,
Vows with their lips to thee they vowed.

2 But thou, soul-searching God! hast known
The hearts of all that bent the knee;
And hast accepted those alone,
Who in the spirit worshiped thee.

3 People of many a tribe and tongue,
Of various languages and lands,
Have heard thy truth, thy glory sung,
And offered prayer with holy hands.

4 And not a prayer, a tear, a sigh,
Hath failed this day some suit to gain:
To those in trouble thou wert nigh;
Not one hath sought thy face in vain.

5 Yet one prayer more;—and be it one
In which both heaven and earth accord:—
Fulfill thy promise to thy Son:
Let all that breathe call Jesus Lord!
                                JAMES MONTGOMERY.

80 *Sabbath evening rest.*

1 SWEET is the light of Sabbath eve,
And soft the sunbeams lingering there
For these blest hours the world I leave,
Waited on wings of faith and prayer.

2 The time how lovely and how still!
Peace shines and smiles on all below;
The plain, the stream, the wood, the hill,
All fair with evening's setting glow.

3 Season of rest! the tranquil soul
Feels the sweet calm, and melts to love
And while these sacred moments roll,
Faith sees the smiling heaven above.

4 Nor will our days of toil be long;
Our pilgrimage will soon be trod;
And we shall join the ceaseless song,
The endless Sabbath of our God.
                                JAMES EDMESTON.

ROCKINGHAM.   L. M.   LOWELL MASON.

81   *Delights of the Sabbath.*

1 SWEET is the work, my God, my King,
To praise thy name, give thanks, and sing;
To show thy love by morning light,
And talk of all thy truth by night.

2 Sweet is the day of sacred rest;
No mortal cares shall seize my breast;
O may my heart in tune be found,
Like David's harp of solemn sound.

3 When grace has purified my heart,
Then I shall share a glorious part;
And fresh supplies of joy be shed,
Like holy oil, to cheer my head.

4 Then shall I see, and hear, and know
All I desired or wished below;
And every power find sweet employ
In that eternal world of joy.
                                ISAAC WATTS.

82   *Pledge of glorious rest.*

1 RETURN, my soul, enjoy thy rest;
Improve the day thy God hath blest:
Another six days' work is done;
Another Sabbath is begun.

2 O that our thoughts and thanks may rise,
As grateful incense to the skies,
And draw from Christ that sweet repose,
Which none but he that feels it knows!

3 This heavenly calm within the breast
Is the dear pledge of glorious rest,
Which for the Church of God remains;
The end of cares, the end of pains.

4 In holy duties, let the day,
In holy comforts pass away;
How sweet a Sabbath thus to spend,
In hope of one that ne'er shall end!
                                JOSEPH STENNETT.

83   *Hailing the Sabbath's return.*

1 MY opening eyes with rapture see
The dawn of this returning day;
My thoughts, O God, ascend to thee,
While thus my early vows I pay.

2 I yield my heart to thee alone,
Nor would receive another guest:
Eternal King, erect thy throne,
And reign sole monarch in my breast.

3 O bid this trifling world retire,
And drive each carnal thought away;
Nor let me feel one vain desire,
One sinful thought, through all the day

4 Then, to thy courts when I repair,
My soul shall rise on joyful wing;
The wonders of thy love declare,
And join the strains which angels sing.
                                JAMES HUTTON.

84   *Undisturbed devotion.*

1 FAR from my thoughts, vain world, be
gone!
Let my religious hours alone:
Fain would mine eyes my Saviour see;
I wait a visit, Lord, from thee.

2 O warm my heart with holy fire,
And kindle there a pure desire:
Come, sacred Spirit, from above,
And fill my soul with heavenly love.

3 Blest Saviour, what delicious fare!
How sweet thine entertainments are!
Never did angels taste above
Redeeming grace and dying love.

4 Hail, great Immanuel, all divine!
In thee thy Father's glories shine;
Thy glorious name shall be adored,
And every tongue confess thee Lord.
                                ISAAC WATTS.

LISBON.   S. M.

DANIEL READ.

85 *The Sabbath welcome.*

1 WELCOME, sweet day of rest,
  That saw the Lord arise;
Welcome to this reviving breast,
  And these rejoicing eyes!

2 The King himself comes near,
  And feasts his saints to-day;
Here we may sit, and see him here,
  And love, and praise, and pray.

3 One day in such a place,
  Where thou, my God, art seen,
Is sweeter than ten thousand days
  Of pleasurable sin.

4 My willing soul would stay
  In such a frame as this,
And sit and sing herself away
  To everlasting bliss.

ISAAC WATTS.

86 *Day of light, rest, peace, prayer.*

1 THIS is the day of light:
  Let there be light to-day;
O Day-spring, rise upon our night,
  And chase its gloom away.

2 This is the day of rest:
  Our failing strength renew;
On weary brain and troubled breast
  Shed thou thy freshening dew.

3 This is the day of peace:
  Thy peace our spirits fill;
Bid thou the blasts of discord cease,
  The waves of strife be still.

4 This is the day of prayer:
  Let earth to heaven draw near;
Lift up our hearts to seek thee there;
  Come down to meet us here.

5 This is the first of days:
  Send forth thy quickening breath,
And wake dead souls to love and praise
  O Vanquisher of death!

JOHN ELLERTON.

87 *The eternal Sabbath.*

1 HAIL to the Sabbath day!
  The day divinely given,
When men to God their homage pay,
  And earth draws near to heaven.

2 Lord, in this sacred hour,
  Within thy courts we bend,
And bless thy love, and own thy power,
  Our Father and our Friend.

3 But thou art not alone
  In courts by mortals trod;
Nor only is the day thine own
  When man draws near to God:

4 Thy temple is the arch
  Of yon unmeasured sky;
Thy Sabbath, the stupendous march
  Of vast eternity.

5 Lord, may that holier day
  Dawn on thy servants' sight;
And purer worship may we pay
  In heaven's unclouded light.

STEPHEN G. BULFINCH.

SABBATH MORN. 7, 6l.

LOWELL MASON.

Show thy reconciléd face,
  Take away our sin and shame;
From our worldly cares set free,
  May we rest this day in thee.

3 Here we come thy name to praise;
  May we feel thy presence near:
May thy glory meet our eyes,
  While we in thy house appear:
Here afford us, Lord, a taste
Of our everlasting feast.

4 May thy gospel's joyful sound
  Conquer sinners, comfort saints;
Make the fruits of grace abound,
  Bring relief for all complaints:
Thus may all our Sabbaths prove,
Till we join the Church above.

JOHN NEWTON.

88 *Safely through another week.*
1 SAFELY through another week,
  God has brought us on our way;
Let us now a blessing seek,
  Waiting in his courts to-day:
Day of all the week the best,
Emblem of eternal rest.

2 While we pray for pardoning grace,
  Through the dear Redeemer's name,

THATCHER. S. M.

GEORGE FREDERICK HANDEL.

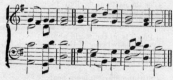

And, joyful in the house of prayer,
  Bend at the mercy-seat.

3 Pray for Jerusalem,
  The city of our God;
Lord, send thy blessing down to them
  That love the dear abode.

4 Within these walls may peace
  And harmony be found;
Zion, in all thy palaces,
  Prosperity abound!

89 *Gladness in the house of prayer.*
1 GLAD was my heart to hear
  My old companions say,
"Come, in the house of God appear,
  For 'tis a holy day."

2 Thither the tribes repair,
  Where all are wont to meet;

5 For friends and brethren dear,
  Our prayer shall never cease:
Oft as they meet for worship here,
  God send his people peace!

JAMES MONTGOMERY.

DIJON.   7.

GERMAN EVENING HYMN.

90   *Immortality and light.*

1 DAY of God, thou blessed day,
At thy dawn the grave gave way
To the power of Him within,
Who had, sinless, bled for sin.

2 Thine the radiance to illume
First, for man, the dismal tomb,
When its bars their weakness owned,
There revealing death dethroned.

3 Then the Sun of righteousness
Rose, a darkened world to bless,
Bringing up from mortal night
Immortality and light.

4 Day of glory, day of power,
Sacred be thine every hour;
Emblem, earnest, of the rest
That remaineth for the blest.
                    HANNAH F. GOULD.

91   *The first of days.*

1 ON this day, the first of days,
God the Father's name we praise;
Who, creation's Lord and Spring,
Did the world from darkness bring.

2 On this day the Eternal Son
Over death his triumph won;
On this day the Spirit came
With his gifts of living flame.

3 O that fervent love to-day
May in every heart have sway,
Teaching us to praise aright
God the source of life and light!

4 God, the blessed Three in One,
Dwell within my heart alone;
Thou dost give thyself to me,
May I give myself to thee.
                    SIR HENRY W. BAKER

92   *Sabbath evening.*

1 SOFTLY fades the twilight ray
Of the holy Sabbath day;
Gently as life's setting sun,
When the Christian's course is run.

2 Night her solemn mantle spreads
O'er the earth as daylight fades;
All things tell of calm repose,
At the holy Sabbath's close.

3 Peace is on the world abroad;
'Tis the holy peace of God,
Symbol of the peace within
When the spirit rests from sin.

4 Still the Spirit lingers near,
Where the evening worshiper
Seeks communion with the skies,
Pressing onward to the prize.

5 Saviour, may our Sabbaths be
Days of joy and peace in thee,
Till in heaven our souls repose,
Where the Sabbath ne'er shall close.
                    SAMUEL F. SMITH.

34

EVENTIDE. 10. WILLIAM HENRY MONK.

93 *Abide with me.*

1 ABIDE with me! Fast falls the eventide,
The darkness deepens—Lord, with me abide!
When other helpers fail, and comforts flee,
Help of the helpless, O abide with me!

2 Swift to its close ebbs out life's little day;
Earth's joys grow dim, its glories pass away;
Change and decay in all around I see;
O thou, who changest not, abide with me!

3 I need thy presence every passing hour;
What but thy grace can foil the tempter's power?
Who, like thyself, my guide and stay can be?
Through cloud and sunshine, Lord, abide with me!

4 I fear no foe, with thee at hand to bless;
Ills have no weight, and tears no bitterness;
Where is death's sting? where, grave, thy victory?
I triumph still, if thou abide with me.

5 Hold thou thy cross before my closing eyes;
Shine through the gloom and point me to the skies;
Heaven's morning breaks, and earth's vain shadows flee;
In life, in death, O Lord, abide with me!
HENRY F. LYTE.

94 *Parting hymn of praise.*

1 SAVIOUR, again to thy dear name we raise,
With one accord, our parting hymn of praise;
We stand to bless thee ere our worship cease,
Then, lowly kneeling, wait thy word of peace.

2 Grant us thy peace upon our homeward way;
With thee began, with thee shall end the day;
Guard thou the lips from sin, the hearts from shame,
That in this house have called upon thy name.

3 Grant us thy peace, Lord, through the coming night,
Turn thou for us its darkness into light,
From harm and danger keep thy children free,
For dark and light are both alike to thee.

4 Grant us thy peace throughout our earthly life,
Our balm in sorrow, and our stay in strife;
Then, when thy voice shall bid our conflict cease,
Call us, O Lord, to thine eternal peace.
JOHN ELLERTON.

PETERBORO'. C. M.

REV. RALPH HARRIS, N.

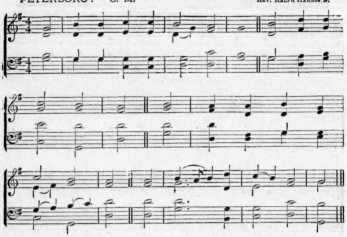

95 *Renewed consecration.*

1 ONCE more, my soul, the rising day
    Salutes thy waking eyes;
Once more, my voice, thy tribute pay
    To Him that rules the skies.

2 Night unto night his name repeats,
    The day renews the sound,
Wide as the heavens on which he sits
    To turn the seasons round.

3 'Tis he supports my mortal frame;
    My tongue shall speak his praise;
My sins might rouse his wrath to flame,
    But yet his wrath delays.

4 Great God, let all my hours be thine,
    Whilst I enjoy the light;
Then shall my sun in smiles decline,
    And bring a peaceful night.
                        ISAAC WATTS.

96 *Morning supplications.*

1 AWAKE, my soul, to meet the day;
    Unfold thy drowsy eyes,
And burst the heavy chain that binds
    Thine active faculties.

2 God's guardian shield was round me
        spread
    In my defenseless sleep:
Let him have all my waking hours
    Who doth my slumbers keep.

3 Pardon, O God, my former sloth,
    And arm my soul with grace,

As, rising, now I seal my vows
    To prosecute thy ways.

4 Bright Sun of righteousness, arise;
    Thy radiant beams display;
And guide my dark, bewildered soul
    To everlasting day.
                        PHILIP DODDRIDGE.

97 *Angelic guardianship.*

1 ALL praise to Him who dwells in bliss,
    Who made both day and night;
Whose throne is in the vast abyss
    Of uncreated light.

2 Each thought and deed his piercing eyes
    With strictest search survey;
The deepest shades no more disguise,
    Than the full blaze of day.

3 Whom thou dost guard, O King of kings,
    No evil shall molest;
Under the shadow of thy wings
    Shall they securely rest.

4 Thy angels shall around their beds
    Their constant stations keep;
Thy faith and truth shall shield their heads,
    For thou dost never sleep.

5 May we with calm and sweet repose,
    And heavenly thoughts refreshed,
Our eyelids with the morn unclose,
    And bless thee, ever blest.
                        CHARLES WESLEY.

WARWICK.   C. M.   Samuel Stanley.

98   *Preparation for public worship.*

1 LORD, in the morning thou shalt hear
    My voice ascending high:
To thee will I direct my prayer,
    To thee lift up mine eye:

2 Up to the hills where Christ is gone,
    To plead for all his saints,
Presenting, at the Father's throne,
    Our songs and our complaints.

3 Thou art a God before whose sight
    The wicked shall not stand;
Sinners shall ne'er be thy delight,
    Nor dwell at thy right hand.

4 Now to thy house will I resort,
    To taste thy mercies there:
I will frequent thy holy court,
    And worship in thy fear.

5 O may thy spirit guide my feet
    In ways of righteousness;
Make every path of duty straight,
    And plain before my face.
                                ISAAC WATTS.

99   *Warmest thanks.*

1 Now from the altar of our hearts,
    Let warmest thanks arise;
Assist us, Lord, to offer up
    Our evening sacrifice.

2 This day God was our sun and shield,
    Our keeper and our guide;
His care was on our weakness shown,
    His mercies multiplied.

3 Minutes and mercies multiplied,
    Have made up all this day;
Minutes came quick, but mercies were
    More swift and free than they.

4 New time, new favors, and new joys,
    Do a new song require:
Till we shall praise thee as we would,
    Accept our hearts' desire.
                                JOHN MASON

100   *Grateful praise.*

1 LORD of my life, O may thy praise
    Employ my noblest powers,
Whose goodness lengthens out my days,
    And fills the circling hours.

2 While many spent the night in sighs,
    And restless pains and woes,
In gentle sleep I closed my eyes,
    And undisturbed repose.

3 O let the same almighty care
    My waking hours attend;
From every danger, every snare,
    My heedless steps defend.
                                ANNE STEELE.

101   *The Christian home.*

1 HAPPY the home when God is there,
    And love fills every breast;
When one their wish and one their prayer
    And one their heavenly rest.

2 Happy the home where Jesus' name
    Is sweet to every ear;
Where children early lisp his fame,
    And parents hold him dear.

3 Happy the home where prayer is heard,
    And praise is wont to rise;
Where parents love the sacred word,
    And live but for the skies.

4 Lord, let us in our homes agree,
    This blessed peace to gain;
Unite our hearts in love to thee,
    And love to all will reign.
                                UNKNOWN

HURSLEY.   L. M.   PETER RITTER, ARR. BY WILLIAM HENRY MONK.

102   *Abide with us.*

1 SUN of my soul, thou Saviour dear,
It is not night if thou be near;
O may no earthborn cloud arise
To hide thee from thy servant's eyes.

2 When the soft dews of kindly sleep
My wearied eyelids gently steep,
Be my last thought, how sweet to rest
Forever on my Saviour's breast.

3 Abide with me from morn till eve,
For without thee I cannot live;
Abide with me when night is nigh,
For without thee I dare not die.

4 If some poor wandering child of thine
Have spurned, to-day, the voice divine,
Now, Lord, the gracious work begin;
Let him no more lie down in sin.

5 Watch by the sick; enrich the poor
With blessings from thy boundless store;
Be every mourner's sleep to-night,
Like infant's slumbers, pure and light.

6 Come near and bless us when we wake,
Ere through the world our way we take;
Till in the ocean of thy love,
We lose ourselves in heaven above.
                                JOHN KEBLE.

103   *Morning mercies, daily discipline.*

1 NEW every morning is the love
Our wakening and uprising prove;
Through sleep and darkness safely brought,
Restored to life, and power, and thought,

2 New mercies, each returning day,
Hover around us while we pray;
New perils past, new sins forgiven,
New thoughts of God, new hopes of
        heaven.

3 If on our daily course our mind
Be set to hallow all we find,
New treasures still of countless price
God will provide for sacrifice.

4 The trivial round, the common task,
Will furnish all we ought to ask,—
Room to deny ourselves, a road
To bring us daily nearer God.

5 Only, O Lord, in thy dear love
Fit us for perfect rest above;
And help us this, and every day,
To live more nearly as we pray.
                                JOHN KEBLE.

104   *Morning and evening mercies.*

1 MY God, how endless is thy love!
Thy gifts are every evening new;
And morning mercies from above,
Gently distill like early dew.

2 Thou spread'st the curtains of the night,
Great Guardian of my sleeping hours,
Thy sovereign word restores the light,
And quickens all my drowsy powers.

3 I yield my powers to thy command;
To thee I consecrate my days;
Perpetual blessings from thy hand
Demand perpetual songs of praise.
                                ISAAC WATTS.

EVENING HYMN.   L. M.   * THOMAS TALLIS.

105   *Evening hymn.*

1 GLORY to thee, my God, this night,
For all the blessings of the light:
Keep me, O keep me, King of kings,
Beneath the shadow of thy wings.

2 Forgive me, Lord, for thy dear Son,
The ill which I this day have done;
That with the world, myself, and thee,
I, ere I sleep, at peace may be.

3 Teach me to live, that I may dread
The grave as little as my bed;
Teach me to die, that so I may
Rise glorious at the judgment-day.

4 O let my soul on thee repose,
And may sweet sleep mine eyelids close;
Sleep, which shall me more vigorous make,
To serve my God, when I awake.

5 Lord, let my soul forever share
The bliss of thy paternal care:
'Tis heaven on earth, 'tis heaven above,
To see thy face, and sing thy love.
THOMAS KEN.

106   *Morning hymn.*

1 AWAKE, my soul, and with the sun
Thy daily stage of duty run;
Shake off dull sloth, and joyful rise
To pay thy morning sacrifice.

2 Wake, and lift up thyself, my heart,
And with the angels bear thy part,
Who all night long unwearied sing
High praises to the eternal King.

3 All praise to thee, who safe hast kept,
And hast refreshed me while I slept:
Grant, Lord, when I from death shall wake,
I may of endless life partake.

4 Lord, I my vows to thee renew :
Disperse my sins as morning dew;
Guard my first springs of thought and will,
And with thyself my spirit fill.

5 Direct, control, suggest this day,
All I design, or do, or say;
That all my powers, with all their might,
In thy sole glory may unite.
THOMAS KEN.

107   *Morning prayer.*

1 Now doth the sun ascend the sky,
And wake creation with its ray;
Keep us from sin, O Lord most high,
Through all the actions of the day.

2 Curb thou for us the unruly tongue;
Teach us the way of peace to prize;
And close our eyes against the throng
Of earth's absorbing vanities.

3 O may our hearts be pure within;
No cherished madness vex the soul :
May abstinence the flesh restrain,
And its rebellious pride control.

4 So when the evening stars appear,
And in their train the darkness bring,
May we, O Lord, with conscience clear,
Our praise to thy pure glory sing.
AMBROSE OF MILAN.   TR. BY E. CASWALL.

39

WORSHIP—MORNING AND EVENING.

HEBRON. L. M.

LOWELL MASON.

108   *Evening meditations.*

1 THUS far the Lord hath led me on,
  Thus far his power prolongs my days;
And every evening shall make known
  Some fresh memorial of his grace.

2 Much of my time has run to waste,
  And I, perhaps, am near my home;
But he forgives my follies past,
  And gives me strength for days to come.

3 I lay my body down to sleep;
  Peace is the pillow for my head;
While well-appointed angels keep
  Their watchful stations round my bed.

4 Thus, when the night of death shall come,
  My flesh shall rest beneath the ground,
And wait thy voice to rouse my tomb,
  With sweet salvation in the sound.

ISAAC WATTS.

109   *Evening prayer.*

1 AGAIN as evening's shadow falls,
  We gather in these hallowed walls;
And vesper hymn and vesper prayer
  Rise mingling on the holy air.

2 May struggling hearts that seek release
  Here find the rest of God's own peace;
And, strengthened here by hymn and prayer,
  Lay down the burden and the care.

3 O God, our light! to thee we bow;
  Within all shadows standest thou;
Give deeper calm than night can bring;
  Give sweeter songs than lips can sing.

4 Life's tumult we must meet again,
  We cannot at the shrine remain;
But in the Spirit's secret cell
  May hymn and prayer forever dwell.

SAMUEL LONGFELLOW.

[L. M. 6l. Tune, Yoakley. Page 176.]

110   *The soul's Advocate.*

1 WHEN, streaming from the eastern skies,
The morning light salutes mine eyes,
O Sun of righteousness divine!
On me with beams of mercy shine;
O chase the clouds of guilt away,
And turn my darkness into day.

2 And when to heaven's all-glorious King
My morning sacrifice I bring,
And, mourning o'er my guilt and shame,
Ask mercy in my Saviour's name;
Then, Jesus, cleanse me with thy blood,
And be my Advocate with God.

3 When each day's scenes and labors close,
And wearied nature seeks repose,
With pardoning mercy richly blest,
Guard me, my Saviour, while I rest;
And, as each morning sun shall rise,
O lead me onward to the skies.

4 And at my life's last setting sun,
My conflicts o'er, my labors done,
Jesus, thy heavenly radiance shed,
To cheer and bless my dying bed;
And, from death's gloom my spirit raise,
To see thy face, and sing thy praise.

WILLIAM SHRUBSOLE, JR.

40

KENTUCKY.   S. M.

JEREMIAH INGALLS.

111   *The Day-star.*

1 WE lift our hearts to thee,
　O Day-star from on high!
The sun itself is but thy shade,
　Yet cheers both earth and sky.

2 O let thy rising beams
　The night of sin disperse,—
The mists of error and of vice
　Which shade the universe.

3 How beauteous nature now!
　How dark and sad before!
With joy we view the pleasing change,
　And nature's God adore.

4 O may no gloomy crime
　Pollute the rising day;
Or Jesus' blood, like evening dew,
　Wash all the stains away.

5 May we this life improve,
　To mourn for errors past;
And live this short revolving day
　As if it were our last.

JOHN WESLEY.

112   *Devout gratitude.*

1 SEE how the morning sun
　Pursues his shining way;
And wide proclaims his Maker's praise,
　With every brightening ray.

2 Thus would my rising soul
　Its heavenly Parent sing,
And to its great Original
　The humble tribute bring.

3 Serene I laid me down,
　Beneath his guardian care;
I slept, and I awoke, and found
　My kind Preserver near.

4 My life I would anew
　Devote, O Lord, to thee;
And in thy service I would spend
　A long eternity.

ELIZABETH SCOTT.

113   *Evening meditation.*

1 THE day is past and gone,
　The evening shades appear;
O may we all remember well
　The night of death draws near.

2 We lay our garments by,
　Upon our beds to rest;
So death will soon disrobe us all
　Of what we 've here possessed.

3 Lord, keep us safe this night,
　Secure from all our fears;
May angels guard us while we sleep,
　Till morning light appears.

4 And when we early rise,
　And view the unwearied sun,
May we set out to win the prize,
　And after glory run.

5 And when our days are past,
　And we from time remove,
O may we in thy bosom rest,
　The bosom of thy love.

JOHN LELAND.

[C. M. Tune, Evan. Page 156.]

114   *Protection invoked.*

1 IN mercy, Lord, remember me,
　Through all the hours of night,
And grant to me most graciously
　The safeguard of thy might.

2 With cheerful heart I close mine eyes,
　Since thou wilt not remove;
O in the morning let me rise
　Rejoicing in thy love.

3 Or if this night should prove my last,
　And end my transient days,
Lord, take me to thy promised rest,
　Where I may sing thy praise.

JOHN F. HERZOG.

STOCKWELL. 8, 7. DARIUS ELIOT JONES.

115 *Memories of the dead.*

1 SILENTLY the shades of evening
  Gather round my lowly door;
Silently they bring before me
  Faces I shall see no more.

2 O the lost, the unforgotten,
  Though the world be oft forgot!
O the shrouded and the lonely,
  In our hearts they perish not!

3 Living in the silent hours,
  Where our spirits only blend,
They, unlinked with earthly trouble,
  We, still hoping for its end.

4 How such holy memories cluster,
  Like the stars when storms are past.
Pointing up to that fair heaven
  We may hope to gain at last.
                        CHRISTOPHER C. COX.

116 *Trust in God's care.*

1 SAVIOUR, breathe an evening blessing,
  Ere repose our spirits seal;
Sin and want we come confessing;
  Thou canst save and thou canst heal.

2 Though destruction walk around us,
  Though the arrows past us fly,
Angel guards from thee surround us;
  We are safe, if thou art nigh.

3 Though the night be dark and dreary,
  Darkness cannot hide from thee;
Thou art he who, never weary,
  Watchest where thy people be.

4 Should swift death this night o'ertake us,
  And our couch become our tomb,
May the morn in heaven awake us,
  Clad in light and deathless bloom.
                        JAMES EDMESTON.

MERCY. 7. LOUIS MOREAU GOTTSCHALK, ARR. BY E P. PARKER.

117 *Communion with God.*

1 SOFTLY now the light of day
Fades upon our sight away;
Free from care, from labor free,
Lord, we would commune with thee.

2 Thou, whose all-pervading eye
Naught escapes, without, within,

Pardon each infirmity,
  Open fault, and secret sin.

3 Soon from us the light of day
Shall forever pass away;
Then, from sin and sorrow free,
Take us, Lord, to dwell with thee.
                        GEORGE W. DOANE.

TRINITY.   8, 7, 7.   HILLER'S "CHORALBUCH."

118   *The Apostles' Creed.*

1 WE all believe in one true God,
    Father, Son, and Holy Ghost,
Strong Deliverer in our need,
    Praised by all the heavenly host,
By whose mighty power alone
All is made, and wrought, and done.

2 And we believe in Jesus Christ,
    Son of man and Son of God;

Who, to raise us up to heaven,
    Left his throne and bore our load;
By whose cross and death are we
Rescued from our misery.

3 And we confess the Holy Ghost,
    Who from both forever flows;
Who upholds and comforts us
    In the midst of fears and woes.
Blest and holy Trinity,
Praise shall aye be brought to thee!
    T. CLAUSNITZER.   TR. BY MISS C. WINKWORTH.

NASHVILLE.   L. P. M.

ADAPTED BY LOWELL MASON.

119   *Divine condescension.*

O GOD, of good the unfathomed sea!
Who would not give his heart to thee?
    Who would not love thee with his might?
O Jesus, lover of mankind,
Who would not his whole soul and mind,
    With all his strength, to thee unite?

2 Thou shin'st with everlasting rays;
Before the insufferable blaze
    Angels with both wings veil their eyes;
Yet free as air thy bounty streams,
On all thy works thy mercy's beams,
    Diffusive as thy sun's, arise.

3 Astonished at thy frowning brow,
Earth, hell, and heaven's strong pillars bow:
    Terrible majesty is thine!
Who then can that vast love express
Which bows thee down to me,—who less
    Than nothing am, till thou art mine!

4 High throned on heaven's eternal hill,
In number, weight, and measure, still
    Thou sweetly orderest all that is;
And yet thou deign'st to come to me,
And guide my steps, that I, with thee
    Enthroned, may reign in endless bliss.
    JOHANN A. SCHEFFLER.   TR. BY J. WESLEY.

OXFORD.   C. M.

WILLIAM COOMBS.

120   *Te Deum laudamus.*

1 O GOD, we praise thee, and confess
   That thou the only Lord
And everlasting Father art,
   By all the earth adored.

2 To thee all angels cry aloud;
   To thee the powers on high,
Both cherubim and seraphim,
   Continually do cry;

3 "O holy, holy, holy Lord,
   Whom heavenly hosts obey,
The world is with the glory filled
   Of thy majestic sway."

4 The apostles' glorious company,
   And prophets crowned with light,
With all the martyrs' noble host,
   Thy constant praise recite.

5 The holy Church throughout the world,
   O Lord, confesses thee,
That thou eternal Father art,
   Of boundless majesty.

NAHUM TATE.

121   *One God in Three Persons.*

1 HAIL, Father, Son, and Holy Ghost,
   One God in Persons Three;
Of thee we make our joyful boast,
   And homage pay to thee.

2 Present alike in every place,
   Thy Godhead we adore;
Beyond the bounds of time and space
   Thou dwellest evermore.

3 In wisdom infinite thou art,
   Thine eye doth all things see;
And every thought of every heart
   Is fully known to thee.

4 Thou lov'st whate'er thy hands have
      made;
   Thy goodness we rehearse,
In shining characters displayed
   Throughout the universe.

5 Wherefore let every creature give
   To thee the praise designed;
But chiefly, Lord, the thanks receive,
   The hearts, of all mankind.

CHARLES WESLEY.

122   *All Thy works shall praise thee.*
      Ps. 145:10.

1 THERE seems a voice in every gale,
   A tongue in every flower,
Which tells, O Lord, the wondrous tale
   Of thy almighty power;
The birds, that rise on quivering wing,
   Proclaim their Maker's praise,
And all the mingling sounds of spring
   To thee an anthem raise.

2 Shall I be mute, great God, alone
   'Midst nature's loud acclaim?
Shall not my heart, with answering tone,
   Breathe forth thy holy name?
All nature's debt is small to mine;
   Nature shall cease to be;
Thou gavest—proof of love divine—
   Immortal life to me.

MRS. AMELIA OPIE.

BEMERTON.   C. M.

HENRY WELLINGTON GREATOREX.

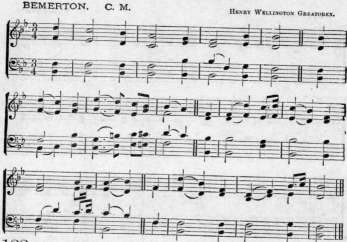

123   *Omniscience.*

1 LORD, all I am is known to thee;
  In vain my soul would try
To shun thy presence, or to flee
  The notice of thine eye.

2 Thy all-surrounding sight surveys
  My rising and my rest,
My public walks, my private ways,
  The secrets of my breast.

3 My thoughts lie open to thee, Lord,
  Before they're formed within;
And ere my lips pronounce the word,
  Thou know'st the sense I mean.

4 O wondrous knowledge, deep and high!
  Where can a creature hide?
Within thy circling arms I lie,
  Beset on every side.

5 So let thy grace surround me still,
  And like a bulwark prove,
To guard my soul from every ill,
  Secured by sovereign love.

ISAAC WATTS.

124   *The Author of every perfect gift.*

1 FATHER, to thee my soul I lift;
  My soul on thee depends;
Convinced that every perfect gift
  From thee alone descends.

2 Mercy and grace are thine alone,
  And power and wisdom too:
Without the Spirit of thy Son,
  We nothing good can do.

3 We cannot speak one useful word,
  One holy thought conceive,
Unless, in answer to our Lord,
  Thyself the blessing give.

4 His blood demands the purchased grace:
  His blood's availing plea
Obtained the help for all our race,
  And sends it down to me.

5 From thee, through Jesus we receive
  The power on thee to call,
In whom we are, and move, and live;
  Our God is all in all.

CHARLES WESLEY.

125   *My Father.*

1 O GOD, thy power is wonderful,
  Thy glory passing bright;
Thy wisdom, with its deep on deep
  A rapture to the sight.

2 I see thee in the eternal years
  In glory all alone,
Ere round thine uncreated fires
  Created light had shone.

3 I see thee walk in Eden's shade,
  I see thee all through time;
Thy patience and compassion seem
  New attributes sublime.

4 I see thee when the doom is o'er,
  And outworn time is done,
Still, still incomprehensible,
  O God, yet not alone.

5 Angelic spirits, countless souls,
  Of thee have drunk their fill;
And to eternity will drink
  Thy joy and glory still.

6 O little heart of mine! shall pain
  Or sorrow make thee moan,
When all this God is all for thee,
  A Father all thine own?

FREDERICK W. FABER.

4   45

ALL SAINTS. L. M.

WILLIAM KNAPP.

126 FIRST PART.
The Unsearchable.

1 O GOD, thou bottomless abyss!
  Thee to perfection who can know?
O height immense! what words suffice
  Thy countless attributes to show?

2 Greatness unspeakable is thine;
  Greatness, whose undiminished ray,
When short-lived worlds are lost, shall shine,
  When earth and heaven are fled away.

3 Unchangeable, all-perfect Lord,
  Essential life's unbounded sea,
What lives and moves, lives by thy word;
  It lives, and moves, and is, from thee.

4 High is thy power above all height;
  Whate'er thy will decrees is done;
Thy wisdom, equal to thy might,
  Only to thee, O God, is known!
        ERNEST LANGE. TR. BY J. WESLEY.

127 SECOND PART.
Wisdom, love, power.

1 THINE, Lord, is wisdom, thine alone;
  Justice and truth before thee stand;
Yet, nearer to thy sacred throne,
  Mercy withholds thy lifted hand.

2 Each evening shows thy tender love,
  Each rising morn thy plenteous grace;
Thy wakened wrath doth slowly move,
  Thy willing mercy flies apace.

3 To thy benign, indulgent care,
  Father, this light, this breath, we owe;
And all we have, and all we are,
  From thee, great Source of being, flow.

4 Thrice Holy! thine the kingdom is,
  The power omnipotent is thine;
And when created nature dies,
  Thy never-ceasing glories shine.
        ERNEST LANGE. TR. BY J. WESLEY.

128 *Immanuel, God with us.*

1 ETERNAL depth of love divine,
  In Jesus, God with us, displayed;
How bright thy beaming glories shine!
  How wide thy healing streams are
    spread!

2 With whom dost thou delight to dwell?
  Sinners, a vile and thankless race!
O God, what tongue aright can tell
  How vast thy love, how great thy
    grace!

3 The dictates of thy sovereign will
  With joy our grateful hearts receive;
All thy delight in us fulfill;
  Lo, all we are to thee we give.

4 To thy sure love, thy tender care,
  Our flesh, soul, spirit, we resign;
O fix thy sacred presence there,
  And seal the abode forever thine.
        NICOLAUS L. ZINZENDORF. TR. BY J. WESLEY.

129 *For the grace of the Holy Trinity.*

1 BLEST Spirit, one with God above,
  Thou source of life and holy love,
O cheer us with thy sacred beams,
  Refresh us with thy plenteous streams.

2 O may our lips confess thy name,
  Our holy lives thy power proclaim;
With love divine our hearts inspire,
  And fill us with thy holy fire.

3 O holy Father, holy Son,
  And Holy Spirit, Three in One,
Thy grace devoutly we implore;
  Thy name be praised for evermore.
        FROM THE LATIN. TR. BY J. CHANDLER.

GOD—BEING AND ATTRIBUTES.

HAMBURG. L. M.   Arr. from a Gregorian Chant, by Lowell Mason.

130   *Incomprehensible glory.*

1 GOD is the name my soul adores,
  The almighty Three, the eternal One;
Nature and grace, with all their powers,
  Confess the Infinite Unknown.

2 Thy voice produced the sea and spheres,
  Bade the waves roar, the planets shine;
But nothing like thyself appears
  Through all these spacious works of thine.

3 Still restless nature dies and grows;
  From change to change the creatures run:
Thy being no succession knows,
  And all thy vast designs are one.

4 A glance of thine runs through the globe,
  Rules the bright worlds, and moves their
      frame;
Of light thou form'st thy dazzling robe;
  Thy ministers are living flame.

5 How shall polluted mortals dare
  To sing thy glory or thy grace?
Beneath thy feet we lie afar,
  And see but shadows of thy face.

6 Who can behold the blazing light?
  Who can approach consuming flame?
None but thy wisdom knows thy might;
  None but thy word can speak thy name.
                  ISAAC WATTS.

131   *Jehovah's holiness.*

1 HOLY as thou, O Lord, is none;
Thy holiness is all thine own;
A drop of that unbounded sea
Is ours,—a drop derived from thee:

2 And when thy purity we share,
Thine only glory we declare;
And, humbled into nothing, own,
Holy and pure is God alone.

3 Sole, self-existing God and Lord,
By all thy heavenly hosts adored,
Let all on earth bow down to thee,
And own thy peerless majesty:

4 Thy power unparalleled confess,
Established on the rock of peace;
The rock that never shall remove,
The rock of pure, almighty love.
                  CHARLES WESLEY.

132   *From everlasting to everlasting.*

1 ERE mountains reared their forms sub-
     lime,
  Or heaven and earth in order stood,
Before the birth of ancient time,
  From everlasting thou art God.

2 A thousand ages, in their flight,
  With thee are as a fleeting day;
Past, present, future, to thy sight
  At once their various scenes display.

3 But our brief life's a shadowy dream,
  A passing thought that soon is o'er,
That fades with morning's earliest beam,
  And fills the musing mind no more.

4 To us, O Lord, the wisdom give
  Each passing moment so to spend,
That we at length with thee may live
  Where life and bliss shall never end.
                  HARRIET AUBER.

LUTON.   L. M.   REV. GEORGE BURDER.

133   *Omnipotence and wisdom.*

1 COME, O my soul, in sacred lays,
Attempt thy great Creator's praise:
But O what tongue can speak his fame?
What mortal verse can reach the theme?

2 Enthroned amid the radiant spheres,
He glory like a garment wears;
To form a robe of light divine,
Ten thousand suns around him shine.

3 In all our Maker's grand designs,
Omnipotence, with wisdom, shines;
His works, through all this wondrous frame,
Declare the glory of his name.

4 Raised on devotion's lofty wing,
Do thou, my soul, his glories sing;
And let his praise employ thy tongue,
Till listening worlds shall join the song.
                                    THOMAS BLACKLOCK.

134   *The Lord is King.*

1 THE Lord is King! lift up thy voice,
O earth, and all ye heavens, rejoice!
From world to world the joy shall ring,
The Lord omnipotent is King.

2 The Lord is King! child of the dust,
The Judge of all the earth is just;
Holy and true are all his ways:
Let every creature speak his praise.

3 He reigns! ye saints, exalt your strains;
Your God is King, your Father reigns;
And he is at the Father's side,
The Man of love, the Crucified.

4 Come, make your wants, your burdens
        known,
He will present them at the throne;
And angel bands are waiting there
His messages of love to bear.

5 O when his wisdom can mistake,
His might decay, his love forsake,
Then may his children cease to sing,
The Lord omnipotent is King.
                                    JOSIAH CONDER.

135   *Omnipresence.*

1 LORD of all being! throned afar,
Thy glory flames from sun and star;
Center and soul of every sphere,
Yet to each loving heart how near!

2 Sun of our life, thy quickening ray
Sheds on our path the glow of day;
Star of our hope, thy softened light
Cheers the long watches of the night.

3 Our midnight is thy smile withdrawn
Our noontide is thy gracious dawn;
Our rainbow arch thy mercy's sign,
All, save the clouds of sin, are thine!

4 Lord of all life, below, above,
Whose light is truth, whose warmth is love,
Before thy ever-blazing throne
We ask no luster of our own.

5 Grant us thy truth to make us free,
And kindling hearts that burn for thee,
Till all thy living altars claim
One holy light, one heavenly flame.
                                    OLIVER W. HOLMES.

GOD—BEING AND ATTRIBUTES.

NICÆA. 11, 12, 10. REV. JOHN BACCHUS DYKES.

136 *Holy, holy, holy.*

1 HOLY, holy, holy, Lord God Almighty!
  Early in the morning our song shall rise
    to thee;
Holy, holy, holy, merciful and mighty,
  God in Three Persons, blessed Trinity!

2 Holy, holy, holy! all the saints adore thee,
  Casting down their golden crowns around
    the glassy sea;
Cherubim and seraphim falling down be-
    fore thee,
  Which wert, and art, and evermore shalt be.

3 Holy, holy, holy! though the darkness
    hide thee,
  Though the eye of sinful man thy glory
    may not see;
Only thou art holy; there is none beside
    thee,
  Perfect in power, in love, and purity.

4 Holy, holy, holy, Lord God Almighty!
  All thy works shall praise thy name, in
    earth, and sky, and sea;
Holy, holy, holy, merciful and mighty,
  God in Three Persons, blessed Trinity!
                          REGINALD HEBER.

UXBRIDGE. L. M. LOWELL MASON.

137 *The Trinity adored.*

1 O HOLY, holy, holy Lord,
  Bright in thy deeds and in thy name,
Forever be thy name adored,
  Thy glories let the world proclaim.

2 O Jesus, Lamb once crucified
  To take our load of sins away,
Thine be the hymn that rolls its tide
  Along the realms of upper day.

3 O Holy Spirit from above,
  In streams of light and glory given,
Thou source of ecstasy and love,
  Thy praises ring through earth and
    heaven.

4 O God Triune, to thee we owe
  Our every thought, our every song;
And ever may thy praises flow
  From saint and seraph's burning tongue.
                        JAMES W. EASTBURN.

49

CREATION. L. M. D.

Francis Joseph Haydn.

138 *The heavens declare His glory.*

1 THE spacious firmament on high,
With all the blue ethereal sky,
And spangled heavens, a shining frame,
Their great Original proclaim:
The unwearied sun, from day to day,
Does his Creator's power display,
And publishes to every land
The work of an almighty hand.

2 Soon as the evening shades prevail,
The moon takes up the wondrous tale,
And nightly, to the listening earth,
Repeats the story of her birth;
While all the stars that round her burn,
And all the planets in their turn,
Confirm the tidings as they roll,
And spread the truth from pole to pole.

3 What though in solemn silence all
Move round the dark terrestrial ball?
What though no real voice nor sound
Amid the radiant orbs be found?
In reason's ear they all rejoice,
And utter forth a glorious voice;
Forever singing as they shine,
"The hand that made us is divine."
JOSEPH ADDISON.

139 *Jehovah's sovereignty.*

1 FATHER of all, whose powerful voice
Called forth this universal frame!
Whose mercies over all rejoice,
Through endless ages still the same;
Thou by thy word upholdest all;
Thy bounteous love to all is showed:
Thou hear'st thy every creature's call,
And fillest every mouth with good.

2 In heaven thou reign'st enthroned in light,
Nature's expanse before thee spread;
Earth, air, and sea, before thy sight,
And hell's deep gloom, are open laid:
Wisdom, and might, and love are thine:
Prostrate before thy face we fall,
Confess thine attributes divine,
And hail thee sovereign Lord of all.

3 Blessing and honor, praise and love,
Co-equal, co-eternal Three,
In earth below, in heaven above,
By all thy works, be paid to thee.
Let all who owe to thee their birth,
In praises every hour employ;
Jehovah reigns! be glad, O earth,
And shout, ye morning stars, for joy!
JOHN WESLEY.

LYONS. 10, 11.   FRANCIS JOSEPH HAYDN.

140 *Worshiping the King.*

1 O WORSHIP the King all-glorious above,
And gratefully sing his wonderful love;
Our Shield and Defender, the Ancient of days,
Pavilioned in splendor, and girded with praise.

2 O tell of his might, and sing of his grace,
Whose robe is the light, whose canopy space;
His chariots of wrath the deep thunder-clouds form,
And dark is his path on the wings of the storm.

3 Thy bountiful care what tongue can recite?
It breathes in the air, it shines in the light,
It streams from the hills, it descends to the plain,
And sweetly distills in the dew and the rain.

4 Frail children of dust, and feeble as frail,
In thee do we trust, nor find thee to fail;
Thy mercies how tender! how firm to the end!
Our Maker, Defender, Redeemer, and Friend.
                                    SIR ROBERT GRANT.

141 *The Lord will provide.*

1 THOUGH troubles assail, and dangers affright,
Though friends should all fail, and foes all unite,
Yet one thing secures us, whatever betide,
The promise assures us, "The Lord will provide."

2 The birds, without barn or store-house, are fed;
From them let us learn to trust for our bread:
His saints what is fitting shall ne'er be denied,
So long as 'tis written, "The Lord will provide."

3 When Satan appears to stop up our path
And fills us with fears, we triumph by faith;
He cannot take from us, though oft he has tried,
The heart-cheering promise, "The Lord will provide."

4 He tells us we're weak, our hope is in vain;
The good that we seek we ne'er shall obtain:
But when such suggestions our graces have tried,
This answers all questions, "The Lord will provide."

5 No strength of our own, nor goodness we claim;
Our trust is all thrown on Jesus's name:
In this our strong tower for safety we hide;
The Lord is our power, "The Lord will provide."

6 When life sinks apace, and death is in view,
The word of his grace shall comfort us through:
Not fearing or doubting, with Christ on our side,
We hope to die shouting, "The Lord will provide."
                                    JOHN NEWTON.

MILLENNIUM.   H. M.   ENGLISH.

142   *Wondrous condescension.*

1 THE Lord Jehovah reigns,
   His throne is built on high;
The garments he assumes
   Are light and majesty:
His glories shine with beams so bright,
No mortal eye can bear the sight.

2 The thunders of his hand
   Keep the wide world in awe;
His wrath and justice stand
   To guard his holy law;
And where his love resolves to bless,
His truth confirms and seals the grace.

3 Through all his mighty works
   Amazing wisdom shines;
Confounds the powers of hell,
   And all their dark designs;
Strong is his arm, and shall fulfill
His great decrees and sovereign will.

4 And will this sovereign King
   Of glory condescend,
And will he write his name,
   My Father and my Friend?
I love his name, I love his word;
Join all my powers to praise the Lord.
                              ISAAC WATTS.

DAVID.   8.   GEORGE FREDERICK HANDEL.

143   *The changeless Friend.*

1 THIS God is the God we adore,
   Our faithful, unchangeable friend,
Whose love is as great as his power,
   And neither knows measure nor end:

2 'Tis Jesus, the first and the last,
   Whose Spirit shall guide us safe home;
We'll praise him for all that is past,
   And trust him for all that's to come.
                              JOSEPH HART.

DIX.   7, 6l.

FROM THE GERMAN, ARR. BY WM. H. MONK.

144   *Praise to the Trinity.*

1 HOLY, holy, holy Lord,
  God of hosts, eternal King,
By the heavens and earth adored;
  Angels and archangels sing,
Chanting everlastingly
To the blessed Trinity.

2 Since by thee were all things made,
  And in thee do all things live,
Be to thee all honor paid;
  Praise to thee let all things give,
Singing everlastingly
To the blessed Trinity.

3 Thousands, tens of thousands, stand,
  Spirits blest, before the throne,
Speeding thence at thy command,
  And, when thy commands are done,
Singing everlastingly
To the blessed Trinity.

4 Cherubim and seraphim
  Veil their faces with their wings;
Eyes of angels are too dim
  To behold the King of kings,
While they sing eternally
To the blessed Trinity.

5 Thee apostles, prophets thee,
  Thee the noble martyr band,
Praise with solemn jubilee,
  Thee, the Church in every land;
Singing everlastingly
To the blessed Trinity.

6 Hallelujah! Lord, to thee,
  Father, Son, and Holy Ghost;
Godhead One, and Persons Three;
  Join us with the heavenly host,
Singing everlastingly
To the blessed Trinity.
                    CHRISTOPHER WORDSWORTH.

145   *Worship the Creator.*

1 LET us with a gladsome mind
Praise the Lord, for he is kind,
For his mercies shall endure,
Ever faithful, ever sure.
Let us sound his name abroad,
For of gods he is the God,
Who by wisdom did create
Heaven's expanse and all its state.

2 Did the solid earth ordain
How to rise above the main;
Who, by his commanding might,
Filled the new-made world with light;
Caused the golden-tresséd sun
All the day his course to run;
And the moon to shine by night,
'Mid her spangled sisters bright.

3 All his creatures God doth feed,
His full hand supplies their need;
He hath with a pitying eye
Looked upon our misery:
Let us, therefore, warble forth
His high majesty and worth,
For his mercies shall endure,
Ever faithful, ever sure.
                    JOHN MILTON.

STEPHENS.　C. M.

WILLIAM JONES.

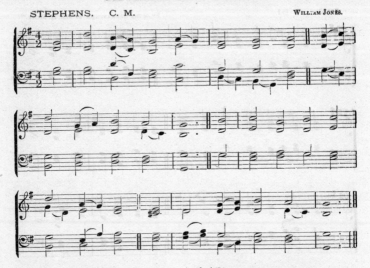

146 *Glory, mercy, grace.*

1 FATHER, how wide thy glory shines,
　How high thy wonders rise!
Known through the earth by thousand
　signs,
　By thousands through the skies.

2 Those mighty orbs proclaim thy power;
　Their motions speak thy skill:
And on the wings of every hour
　We read thy patience still.

3 Part of thy name divinely stands
　On all thy creatures writ;
They show the labor of thy hands,
　Or impress of thy feet;

4 But when we view thy strange design
　To save rebellious worms,
Where vengeance and compassion join
　In their divinest forms;

5 Here the whole Deity is known,
　Nor dares a creature guess
Which of the glories brighter shone,
　The justice or the grace.

6 Now the full glories of the Lamb
　Adorn the heavenly plains;
Bright seraphs learn Immanuel's name,
　And try their choicest strains.

7 O may I bear some humble part
　In that immortal song!
Wonder and joy shall tune my heart,
　And love command my tongue.
ISAAC WATTS.

147 *Majesty and love of God.*

1 MY God, how wonderful thou art,
　Thy majesty how bright,
How beautiful thy mercy-seat
　In depths of burning light!

2 How dread are thine eternal years,
　O everlasting Lord,
By prostrate spirits day and night
　Incessantly adored!

3 How beautiful, how beautiful,
　The sight of thee must be,
Thine endless wisdom, boundless power,
　And awful purity!

4 O how I fear thee, living God,
　With deepest, tenderest fears,
And worship thee with trembling hope,
　And penitential tears.

5 Yet I may love thee too, O Lord,
　Almighty as thou art;
For thou hast stooped to ask of me
　The love of my poor heart.

6 No earthly father loves like thee,
　No mother half so mild
Bears and forbears, as thou hast done
　With me, thy sinful child.

7 Father of Jesus, love's reward!
　What rapture will it be,
Prostrate before thy throne to lie,
　And gaze, and gaze on thee!
FREDERICK W. FABER.

WELLESLEY.   8, 7.   Lizzie S. Tourjée.

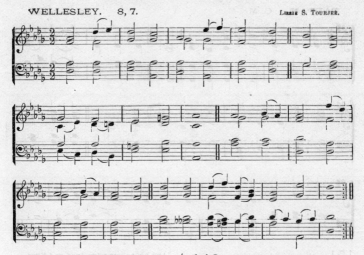

148 *God's glory in creation and re-*
              demption.

1 MIGHTY God! while angels bless thee,
    May a mortal lisp thy name?
Lord of men, as well as angels,
    Thou art every creature's theme:
Lord of every land and nation,
    Ancient of eternal days!
Sounded through the wide creation
    Be thy just and awful praise.

2 For the grandeur of thy nature,
    Grand beyond a seraph's thought;
For the wonders of creation,
    Works with skill and kindness wrought;
For thy providence, that governs
    Through thine empire's wide domain,
Wings an angel, guides a sparrow;
    Blessed be thy gentle reign!

3 For thy rich, thy free redemption,
    Bright, though veiled in darkness long,
Thought is poor, and poor expression;
    Who can sing that wondrous song?
Brightness of the Father's glory!
    Shall thy praise unuttered lie?
Break, my tongue, such guilty silence,
    Sing the Lord who came to die:—

4 From the highest throne of glory,
    To the cross of deepest woe,
Came to ransom guilty captives:
    Flow, my praise, forever flow!
Re-ascend, immortal Saviour;
    Leave thy footstool, take thy throne;
Thence return and reign forever;
    Be the kingdom all thine own!
                          ROBERT ROBINSON.

149   *The wideness of God's mercy.*

1 THERE's a wideness in God's mercy,
    Like the wideness of the sea:
There's a kindness in his justice,
    Which is more than liberty.

2 There is welcome for the sinner,
    And more graces for the good;
There is mercy with the Saviour;
    There is healing in his blood.

3 For the love of God is broader
    Than the measure of man's mind;
And the heart of the Eternal
    Is most wonderfully kind.

4 If our love were but more simple,
    We should take him at his word;
And our lives would be all sunshine
    In the sweetness of our Lord.
                       FREDERICK W. FABER.

150   *Unchanging wisdom and love.*

1 GOD is love; his mercy brightens
    All the path in which we rove;
Bliss he wakes and woe he lightens;
    God is wisdom, God is love.

2 Chance and change are busy ever;
    Man decays, and ages move;
But his mercy waneth never;
    God is wisdom, God is love.

3 E'en the hour that darkest seemeth
    Will his changeless goodness prove;
From the gloom his brightness streameth,
    God is wisdom, God is love.

4 He with earthly cares entwineth
    Hope and comfort from above;
Every-where his glory shineth;
    God is wisdom, God is love.
                        SIR JOHN BOWRING.

GOD—BEING AND ATTRIBUTES.

TAPPAN.   C. M.   * George Kingsley.

* George Kingsley.

151   *Majesty and providence.*

1 THE Lord our God is clothed with might,
  The winds obey his will;
He speaks, and in his heavenly height
  The rolling sun stands still.

2 Rebél, ye waves, and o'er the land
  With threatening aspect roar;
The Lord uplifts his awful hand,
  And chains you to the shore.

3 Ye winds of night, your force combine;
  Without his high behest,
Ye shall not, in the mountain pine,
  Disturb the sparrow's nest.

4 His voice sublime is heard afar;
  In distant peals it dies;
He yokes the whirlwind to his car,
  And sweeps the howling skies.

5 Ye sons of earth, in reverence bend;
  Ye nations, wait his nod;
And bid the choral song ascend
  To celebrate our God.
                              H. KIRKE WHITE.

152   *The Lord is King.*

1 THE Lord descended from above,
  And bowed the heavens most high,
And underneath his feet he cast
  The darkness of the sky.

2 On cherubim and seraphim
  Full royally he rode,
And on the wings of mighty winds
  Came flying all abroad.

3 He sat serene upon the floods,
  Their fury to restrain;

And he, as sovereign Lord and King,
  For evermore shall reign.

4 Give glory to his awful name,
  And honor him alone;
Give worship to his majesty
  Upon his holy throne.
                              THOMAS STERNHOLD.

153   *Praise from all creation.*

1 PRAISE ye the Lord, ye immortal choirs
  That fill the worlds above;
Praise him who formed you of his fires,
  And feeds you with his love.

2 Shine to his praise, ye crystal skies,
  The floor of his abode;
Or veil in shades your thousand eyes
  Before your brighter God.

3 Thou restless globe of golden light,
  Whose beams create our days,
Join with the silver queen of night,
  To own your borrowed rays.

4 Thunder and hail, and fire and storms,
  The troops of his command,
Appear in all your dreadful forms,
  And speak his awful hand.

5 Shout to the Lord, ye surging seas,
  In your eternal roar;
Let wave to wave resound his praise,
  And shore reply to shore.

6 Thus while the meaner creatures sing,
  Ye mortals, catch the sound;
Echo the glories of your King
  Through all the nations round.
                              ISAAC WATTS.

GOD—PROVIDENCE.

BELMONT. C. M. SAMUEL WEBBE.

154 *Goodness and mercy.*

1 LET every tongue thy goodness speak,
  Thou sovereign Lord of all;
Thy strengthening hands uphold the weak,
  And raise the poor that fall.

2 When sorrows bow the spirit down,
  When virtue lies distressed,
Beneath the proud oppressor's frown,
  Thou giv'st the mourner rest.

3 Thou know'st the pains thy servants feel,
  Thou hear'st thy children's cry;
And their best wishes to fulfill,
  Thy grace is ever nigh.

4 Thy mercy never shall remove
  From men of heart sincere:
Thou sav'st the souls whose humble love
  Is joined with holy fear.

5 My lips shall dwell upon thy praise,
  And spread thy fame abroad;
Let all the sons of Adam raise
  The honors of their God.

ISAAC WATTS.

155 *The angelic guard.*

1 WHICH of the monarchs of the earth
  Can boast a guard like ours,
Encircled from our second birth
  With all the heavenly powers?

2 Myriads of bright, cherubic bands,
  Sent by the King of kings,
Rejoice to bear us in their hands,
  And shade us with their wings.

3 Angels, where'er we go, attend
  Our steps, whate'er betide;

With watchful care their charge defend,
  And evil turn aside.

4 Our lives those holy angels keep
  From every hostile power;
And, unconcerned, we sweetly sleep,
  As Adam in his bower.

5 And when our spirits we resign,
  On outstretched wings they bear,
And lodge us in the arms divine,
  And leave us ever there.

CHARLES WESLEY.

156 *The twenty-third Psalm.*

1 THE Lord's my Shepherd, I'll not want:
  He makes me down to lie
In pastures green; he leadeth me
  The quiet waters by.

2 My soul he doth restore again;
  And me to walk doth make
Within the paths of righteousness,
  E'en for his own name's sake.

3 Yea, though I walk through death's dark
      vale,
  Yet will I fear no ill;
For thou art with me, and thy rod
  And staff me comfort still.

4 A table thou hast furnished me
  In presence of my foes;
My head thou dost with oil anoint,
  And my cup overflows.

5 Goodness and mercy all my life
  Shall surely follow me;
And in God's house for evermore
  My dwelling-place shall be.

FRANCIS ROUS

57

GOD—PROVIDENCE.

DUNDEE.   C. M.

GUILLAUME FRANC.

157 *Rejoicing in deliverance.*

1 O THOU, who, when we did complain,
    Didst all our griefs remove,
O Saviour, do not now disdain
    Our humble praise and love.

2 Since thou a pitying ear didst give,
    And hear us when we prayed,
We'll call upon thee while we live,
    And never doubt thy aid.

3 Pale death, with all his ghastly train,
    Our souls encompassed round;
Anguish, and sin, and dread, and pain,
    On every side we found.

4 To thee, O Lord of life, we prayed,
    And did for succor flee:
"O save," in our distress we said,
    "The souls that trust in thee."

5 How good thou art! how large thy
        grace!
    How ready to forgive!
Thy mercies crown our fleeting days;
    And by thy love we live.

6 Our eyes no longer drowned in tears,
    Our feet from falling free,
Redeemed from death and guilty fears,
    O Lord, we'll live to thee.
                              CHARLES WESLEY.

158   *The sure refuge.*

1 THERE is a safe and secret place
    Beneath the wings divine,
Reserved for all the heirs of grace;
    O be that refuge mine!

2 The least and feeblest there may bide,
    Uninjured and unawed;

While thousands fall on every side,
    He rests secure in God.

3 The angels watch him on his way,
    And aid with friendly arm;
And Satan, roaring for his prey,
    May hate, but cannot harm.

4 He feeds in pastures large and fair
    Of love and truth divine:
O child of God, O glory's heir,
    How rich a lot is thine!

5 A hand almighty to defend,
    An ear for every call,
An honored life, a peaceful end,
    And heaven to crown it all!
                              HENRY F. LYTE.

159   *The only source of blessing.*

1 JEHOVAH, God, thy gracious power
    On every hand we see;
O may the blessings of each hour
    Lead all our thoughts to thee.

2 If on the wings of morn we speed,
    To earth's remotest bound,
Thy hand will there our footsteps lead,
    Thy love our path surround.

3 Thy power is in the ocean deeps,
    And reaches to the skies;
Thine eye of mercy never sleeps,
    Thy goodness never dies.

4 From morn till noon—till latest eve,
    Thy hand, O God, we see;
And all the blessings we receive,
    Proceed alone from thee.
                              JOHN THOMSON.

GOD—PROVIDENCE.

MANOAH. C. M.

FROM MEHUL AND HAYDN.

160   *Gratitude.*

1 WHEN all thy mercies, O my God,
  My rising soul surveys,
Transported with the view, I'm lost
  In wonder, love, and praise.

2 O how can words with equal warmth
  The gratitude declare,
That glows within my ravished heart?
  But thou canst read it there.

3 To all my weak complaints and cries,
  Thy mercy lent an ear,
Ere yet my feeble thoughts had learned
  To form themselves in prayer.

4 When in the slippery paths of youth,
  With heedless steps I ran,
Thine arm, unseen, conveyed me safe,
  And led me up to man.

5 Through hidden dangers, toils, and
    deaths,
  It gently cleared my way;
And through the pleasing snares of vice,
  More to be feared than they.

6 Through every period of my life
  Thy goodness I'll pursue;
And after death, in distant worlds,
  The pleasing theme renew.

7 Through all eternity to thee
  A grateful song I'll raise;
But O, eternity's too short
  To utter all thy praise.

                JOSEPH ADDISON.

161   *Verily, thou art a God that hidest thyself.*—Isa. 45:15.

1 GOD moves in a mysterious way
  His wonders to perform;
He plants his footsteps in the sea,
  And rides upon the storm.

2 Deep in unfathomable mines
  Of never-failing skill,
He treasures up his bright designs,
  And works his sovereign will.

3 Ye fearful saints, fresh courage take:
  The clouds ye so much dread
Are big with mercy, and shall break
  In blessings on your head.

4 Judge not the Lord by feeble sense,
  But trust him for his grace;
Behind a frowning providence
  He hides a smiling face.

5 His purposes will ripen fast,
  Unfolding every hour:
The bud may have a bitter taste,
  But sweet will be the flower.

6 Blind unbelief is sure to err,
  And scan his work in vain:
God is his own interpreter,
  And he will make it plain.

                WILLIAM COWPER.

Doxology.

To Father, Son, and Holy Ghost,
  The God whom we adore,
Be glory, as it was, is now,
  And shall be evermore!

                TATE AND BRADY.

GOD—PROVIDENCE.

HAMBURG.   L. M.   ARR. FROM A GREGORIAN CHANT BY LOWELL MASON.

162   *Crowning God with praise.*

1 KINGDOMS and thrones to God belong;
Crown him, ye nations, in your song:
His wondrous names and powers rehearse;
His honors shall enrich your verse.

2 He shakes the heavens with loud alarms;
How terrible is God in arms!
In Israel are his mercies known,
Israel is his peculiar throne.

3 Proclaim him King, pronounce him blest;
He's your defense, your joy, your rest:
When terrors rise and nations faint,
God is the strength of every saint.
ISAAC WATTS.

163   *God's presence with his people.*

1 WHEN Israel, of the Lord beloved,
  Out from the land of bondage came,
Her fathers' God before her moved,
  An awful guide, in smoke and flame.

2 By day, along the astonished lands
  The cloudy pillar glided slow;
By night, Arabia's crimsoned sands
  Returned the fiery column's glow.

3 Thus present still, though now unseen,
  When brightly shines the prosperous day,
Be thoughts of thee a cloudy screen,
  To temper the deceitful ray.

4 And O, when gathers on our path,
  In shade and storm, the frequent night,
Be thou, long-suffering, slow to wrath,
  A burning and a shining light.
SIR WALTER SCOTT.

164   *The great Provider.*

1 PEACE, troubled soul, thou need'st not fear;
Thy great Provider still is near;

Who fed thee last, will feed thee still:
Be calm, and sink into his will.

2 The Lord, who built the earth and sky,
In mercy stoops to hear thy cry;
His promise all may freely claim:
Ask and receive in Jesus' name.

3 Without reserve give Christ your heart;
Let him his righteousness impart;
Then all things else he'll freely give;
With him you all things shall receive.

4 Thus shall the soul be truly blest,
That seeks in God his only rest;
May I that happy person be,
In time and in eternity.
SAMUEL ECKING.

165   *God our shield.*

1 The tempter to my soul hath said,
  "There is no help in God for thee:"
Lord, lift thou up thy servant's head;
  My glory, shield, and solace be.

2 Thus to the Lord I raised my cry:
  He heard me from his holy hill;
At his command the waves rolled by;
  He beckoned, and the winds were still.

3 I laid me down and slept,—I woke;
  Thou, Lord, my spirit didst sustain;
Bright from the east the morning broke,
  Thy comforts rose on me again.

4 I will not fear, though arméd throngs
  Surround my steps in all their wrath;
Salvation to the Lord belongs;
  His presence guards his people's path.
JAMES MONTGOMERY.

FORTRESS. 8, 7, 6.

MARTIN LUTHER.

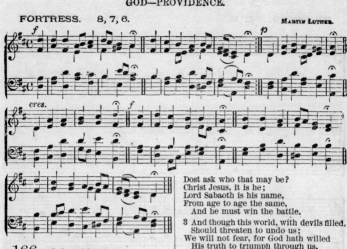

Dost ask who that may be?
Christ Jesus, it is he;
Lord Sabaoth is his name,
From age to age the same,
  And he must win the battle.

3 And though this world, with devils filled,
  Should threaten to undo us;
We will not fear, for God hath willed
  His truth to triumph through us.
The Prince of darkness grim—
We tremble not for him;
His rage we can endure,
For lo! his doom is sure,
  One little word shall fell him.

166 *God a mighty fortress.*

1 A MIGHTY fortress is our God,
  A bulwark never failing:
Our Helper he; amid the flood
  Of mortal ills prevailing.
For still our ancient foe
Doth seek to work us woe;
His craft and power are great,
And, armed with cruel hate,
  On earth is not his equal.

2 Did we in our own strength confide,
  Our striving would be losing;
Were not the right man on our side,
  The man of God's own choosing.

4 That word above all earthly powers
  No thanks to them—abideth;
The Spirit and the gifts are ours
  Through him who with us sideth.
Let goods and kindred go,
This mortal life also:
The body they may kill:
God's truth abideth still,
  His kingdom is forever.

MARTIN LUTHER. TR. BY F. H. HEDGE.

ZEPHYR. L. M.

WILLIAM BATCHELDER BRADBURY.

Ye heavenly guides, speed not away,
God willeth you with us to stay.

3 But chiefly at its journey's end
'Tis yours the spirit to befriend,
And whisper to the faithful heart,
"O Christian soul, in peace depart."

4 Blest Jesus, thou whose groans and tears
Have sanctified frail nature's fears,
To earth in bitter sorrow weighed,
Thou didst not scorn thine angel's aid.

5 An angel guard to us supply,
When on the bed of death we lie;
And by thine own almighty power
O shield us in the last dread hour.

167 *God's messengers of love.*

1 THEY come, God's messengers of love,
They come from realms of peace above,
From homes of never-fading light,
From blissful mansions ever bright.

2 They come to watch around us here,
To soothe our sorrow, calm our fear:

ROBERT CAMPBELL.

GOD—PROVIDENCE.

ST. PETER. **L. M.** *ARR. FROM A GERMAN CHORAL.*

168 *Security in God.*

1 GOD is our refuge and defense;
In trouble our unfailing aid:
Secure in his omnipotence,
What foe can make our souls afraid?

2 Yea, though the earth's foundations rock,
And mountains down the gulf be hurled,
His people smile amid the shock:
They look beyond this transient world,

3 There is a river pure and bright,
Whose streams make glad the heavenly plains;
Where, in eternity of light,
The city of our God remains.

4 Built by the word of his command,
With his unclouded presence blest,
Firm as his throne the bulwarks stand;
There is our home, our hope, our rest.
JAMES MONTGOMERY.

69 *The Saviour's tender care.*

GOD of my life, whose gracious power
Through varied deaths my soul hath led,
turned aside the fatal hour,
Or lifted up my sinking head;

In all my ways thy hand I own,
Thy ruling providence I see;
Assist me still my course to run,
And still direct my paths to thee.

Whither, O whither should I fly,
But to my loving Saviour's breast?
Secure within thine arms to lie,
And safe beneath thy wings to rest.

4 I have no skill the snare to shun,
But thou, O Christ, my wisdom art:
I ever into ruin run,
But thou art greater than my heart.

5 Foolish, and impotent, and blind,
Lead me a way I have not known;
Bring me where I my heaven may find,
The heaven of loving thee alone.
CHARLES WESLEY.

170 *Quietness and assurance.*

1 How do Thy mercies close me round!
Forever be thy name adored;
I blush in all things to abound;
The servant is above his Lord.

2 Inured to poverty and pain,
A suffering life my Master led;
The Son of God, the Son of man,
He had not where to lay his head.

3 But lo! a place he hath prepared
For me, whom watchful angels keep;
Yea, he himself becomes my guard;
He smooths my bed, and gives me sleep:

4 Jesus protects; my fears, be gone;
What can the Rock of ages move?
Safe in thy arms I lay me down,
Thine everlasting arms of love.

5 While thou art intimately nigh,
Who, who shall violate my rest?
Sin, earth, and hell I now defy:
I lean upon my Saviour's breast.

6 I rest beneath the Almighty's shade;
My griefs expire, my troubles cease;
Thou, Lord, on whom my soul is stayed,
Wilt keep me still in perfect peace.
CHARLES WESLEY.

ZION.   8, 7, 4.

THOMAS HASTINGS.

171   *The pilgrim's Guide.*

1 GUIDE me, O thou great Jehovah,
   Pilgrim through this barren land:
I am weak, but thou art mighty;
   Hold me with thy powerful hand:
      Bread of heaven,
   Feed me till I want no more.

2 Open now the crystal fountain,
   Whence the healing waters flow;

Let the fiery, cloudy pillar,
   Lead me all my journey through:
      Strong Deliverer,
   Be thou still my strength and shield.

3 When I tread the verge of Jordan,
   Bid my anxious fears subside;
Bear me through the swelling current;
   Land me safe on Canaan's side:
      Songs of praises
I will ever give to thee.

WILLIAM WILLIAMS.

MAGATA.   S. M.

* REV. JOHN BLACK.

172   *Infinite compassion.*

1 MY soul, repeat His praise,
   Whose mercies are so great;
Whose anger is so slow to rise,
   So ready to abate.

2 High as the heavens are raised
   Above the ground we tread,
So far the riches of his grace
   Our highest thoughts exceed.

3 His power subdues our sins;
   And his forgiving love,
Far as the east is from the west,
   Doth all our guilt remove.

4 The pity of the Lord,
   To those that fear his name,
Is such as tender parents feel;
   He knows our feeble frame.

5 Our days are as the grass,
   Or like the morning flower:
If one sharp blast sweep o'er the field
   It withers in an hour.

6 But thy compassions, Lord,
   To endless years endure;
And children's children ever find
   Thy words of promise sure.

ISAAC WATTS.

GOD—PROVIDENCE.

HAYDN. S. M.   FRANCIS JOSEPH HAYDN.

173   *Omnipotent goodness.*

1 AWAY, my needless fears,
   And doubts no longer mine;
A ray of heavenly light appears,
   A messenger divine.

2 Thrice comfortable hope,
   That calms my troubled breast;
My Father's hand prepares the cup,
   And what he wills is best.

3 If what I wish is good,
   And suits the will divine,
By earth and hell in vain withstood,
   I know it shall be mine.

4 Still let them counsel take
   To frustrate his decree;
They cannot keep a blessing back,
   By Heaven designed for me.

5 Here then I doubt no more,
   But in his pleasure rest,
Whose wisdom, love, and truth, and power,
   Engage to make me blest.
                    CHARLES WESLEY.

174   *Through a glass, darkly.*
             1 Cor. 13: 12.

1 THY way is in the sea;
   Thy paths we cannot trace;
Nor solve, O Lord, the mystery
   Of thy unbounded grace.

2 Here the dark veils of sense
   Our captive souls surround;
Mysterious deeps of providence
   Our wondering thoughts confound.

3 As through a glass we see
   The wonders of thy love;
How little do we know of thee,
   Or of the joys above!

4 In part we know thy will,
   And bless thee for the sight:
Soon will thy love the rest reveal
   In glory's clearer light.

5 With joy shall we survey
   Thy providence and grace;
And spend an everlasting day
   In wonder, love, and praise.
                 JOHN FAWCETT, ALT.

175   *Delight in God.*

1 LORD, I delight in thee,
   And on thy care depend;
To thee in every trouble flee,
   My best, my only Friend.

2 When nature's streams are dried,
   Thy fullness is the same;
With this will I be satisfied,
   And glory in thy name.

3 Who made my heaven secure,
   Will here all good provide:
While Christ is rich, can I be poor?
   What can I want beside?

4 I cast my care on thee!
   I triumph and adore:
Henceforth my great concern shall be
   To love and please thee more.
                 JOHN RYLAND. ALT.

GOD—PROVIDENCE.

DENNIS.   S. M.   Hans George Naegeli

176   *Thy gentleness hath made me great.*

Ps. 18: 35.

1 How gentle God's commands!
   How kind his precepts are!
Come, cast your burdens on the Lord,
   And trust his constant care.

2 Beneath his watchful eye
   His saints securely dwell;
That hand which bears all nature up
   Shall guard his children well.

3 Why should this anxious load
   Press down your weary mind?
Haste to your heavenly Father's throne,
   And sweet refreshment find.

4 His goodness stands approved,
   Unchanged from day to day:
I'll drop my burden at his feet,
   And bear a song away.

PHILIP DODDRIDGE.

177   *Afflictions blessed.*

1 How tender is thy hand,
   O thou most gracious Lord!
Afflictions came at thy command,
   And left us at thy word.

2 How gentle was the rod
   That chastened us for sin!
How soon we found a smiling God
   Where deep distress had been!

3 A Father's hand we felt,
   A Father's love we knew:
'Mid tears of penitence we knelt,
   And found his promise true.

4 Now will we bless the Lord,
   And in his strength confide:
Forever be his name adored,
   For there is none beside.

THOMAS MASTINGS.

178   *All things in Christ.*

1 THOU very-present Aid
   In suffering and distress,
The mind which still on thee is stayed,
   Is kept in perfect peace.

2 The soul by faith reclined
   On the Redeemer's breast,
'Mid raging storms, exults to find
   An everlasting rest.

3 Sorrow and fear are gone,
   Whene'er thy face appears;
It stills the sighing orphan's moan
   And dries the widow's tears.

4 It hallows every cross;
   It sweetly comforts me;
Makes me forget my every loss,
   And find my all in thee.

5 Jesus, to whom I fly,
   Doth all my wishes fill;
What though created streams are dry,
   I have the fountain still.

6 Stripped of each earthly friend,
   I find them all in one;
And peace and joy which never end,
   And heaven, in Christ alone.

CHARLES WESLEY.

PORTUGUESE HYMN. 11.

UNKNOWN.

179 *The Lord is my Shepherd.*

1 THE Lord is my Shepherd, no want shall I know;
  I feed in green pastures, safe-folded I rest;
He leadeth my soul where the still waters flow,
  Restores me when wandering, redeems when oppressed.

2 Through the valley and shadow of death though I stray,
  Since thou art my guardian, no evil I fear;

Thy rod shall defend me, thy staff be my stay;
  No harm can befall, with my Comforter near.

3 In the midst of affliction my table is spread;
  With blessings unmeasured my cup runneth o'er;
With perfume and oil thou anointest my head;
  O what shall I ask of thy providence more?

4 Let goodness and mercy, my bountiful God,
  Still follow my steps till I meet thee above;
I seek—by the path which my forefathers trod,
  Through the land of their sojourn—thy kingdom of love.

JAMES MONTGOMERY.

RAKEM. L. M. 61.

ISAAC BEVERLY WOODBURY.

180 *The Shepherd of Israel.*

1 THE Lord my pasture shall prepare,
And feed me with a shepherd's care;
His presence shall my wants supply,
And guard me with a watchful eye;
My noonday walks he shall attend,
And all my midnight hours defend.

2 When in the sultry glebe I faint,
Or on the thirsty mountain pant,

To fertile vales and dewy meads,
My weary, wandering steps he leads,
Where peaceful rivers, soft and slow,
Amid the verdant landscape flow.

3 Though in a bare and rugged way,
Through devious, lonely wilds I stray,
Thy bounty shall my pains beguile;
The barren wilderness shall smile,
With sudden greens and herbage crowned,
And streams shall murmur all around.

4 Though in the paths of death I tread,
With gloomy horrors overspread,
My steadfast heart shall fear no ill.
For thou, O Lord, art with me still;
Thy friendly crook shall give me aid,
And guide me through the dreadful shade.

JOSEPH ADDISON.

ST. JAMES. 7, 6.

FROM LINDEMAN'S KORAL BOK.

181 *The glories of Christ's kingdom.*

1 Hail, to the Lord's Anointed,
   Great David's greater Son!
Hail, in the time appointed,
   His reign on earth begun!
He comes to break oppression,
   To set the captive free;
To take away transgression,
   And rule in equity.

2 He comes with succor speedy
   To those who suffer wrong;
To help the poor and needy,
   And bid the weak be strong;
To give them songs for sighing,
   Their darkness turn to light,
Whose souls, condemned and dying,
   Were precious in his sight.

3 He shall descend like showers
   Upon the fruitful earth,
And love and joy, like flowers,
   Spring in his path to birth:
Before him, on the mountains,
   Shall peace, the herald, go,
And righteousness, in fountains,
   From hill to valley flow.

4 To him shall prayer unceasing,
   And daily vows ascend;
His kingdom still increasing,
   A kingdom without end:
The tide of time shall never
   His covenant remove;
His name shall stand forever;
   That name to us is Love.
                        JAMES MONTGOMERY.

DIX. 7. 6l.

ARR. BY WILLIAM HENRY MONK.

182   *The guiding star.*

1 As with gladness men of old
Did the guiding star behold;
As with joy they hailed its light,
Leading onward, beaming bright;
So, most gracious Lord, may we
Evermore be led to thee.

2 As with joyful steps they sped
To that lowly manger-bed,

There to bend the knee before
Him whom heaven and earth adore;
So may we with willing feet
Ever seek the mercy-seat.

3 As they offered gifts most rare
At that manger rude and bare;
So may we with holy joy,
Pure, and free from sin's alloy,
All our costliest treasures bring,
Christ, to thee, our heavenly King.

4 Holy Jesus, every day
Keep us in the narrow way;
And, when earthly things are past,
Bring our ransomed souls at last
Where they need no star to guide,
Where no clouds thy glory hide.
                        WILLIAM C. DIX.

ANTIOCH. C. M.

* ARR. FROM GEORGE FREDERICK HANDEL.

183 *Joy to the world.*

1 JOY to the world! the Lord is come;
  Let earth receive her King;
Let every heart prepare him room,
  And heaven and nature sing.

2 Joy to the world! the Saviour reigns;
  Let men their songs employ;
While fields and floods, rocks, hills, and plains,
  Repeat the sounding joy.

3 No more let sin and sorrow grow,
  Nor thorns infest the ground;
He comes to make his blessings flow
  Far as the curse is found.

4 He rules the world with truth and grace,
  And makes the nations prove
The glories of his righteousness,
  And wonders of his love.

ISAAC WATTS.

184 *Wonderful, Counselor.*—Isa. 9: 6.

1 To us a Child of hope is born,
  To us a Son is given;
Him shall the tribes of earth obey,
  Him, all the hosts of heaven.

2 His name shall be the Prince of peace,
  For evermore adored;
The Wonderful, the Counselor,
  The great and mighty Lord.

3 His power, increasing, still shall spread;
  His reign no end shall know;

Justice shall guard his throne above,
  And peace abound below.

4 To us a Child of hope is born,
  To us a Son is given;
The Wonderful, the Counselor,
  The mighty Lord of heaven.

JOHN MORRISON.

185 *The Saviour's advent.*

1 HARK, the glad sound! the Saviour
    comes,
  The Saviour promised long;
Let every heart prepare a throne,
  And every voice a song.

2 He comes, the prisoner to release,
  In Satan's bondage held;
The gates of brass before him burst,
  The iron fetters yield.

3 He comes, from thickest films of vice
  To clear the mental ray,
And on the eyes oppressed with night
  To pour celestial day.

4 He comes, the broken heart to bind,
  The wounded soul to cure,
And, with the treasures of his grace,
  To enrich the humble poor.

5 Our glad hosannas, Prince of peace,
  Thy welcome shall proclaim,
And heaven's eternal arches ring
  With thy beloved name.

PHILIP DODDRIDGE.

HANOVER.   11, 1C.

JOHANN C. W. A. MOZART.

186   *The star in the East.*

1 BRIGHTEST and best of the sons of the
      morning,
   Dawn on our darkness, and lend us thine
      aid;
Star of the East, the horizon adorning,
   Guide where our infant Redeemer is laid.

2 Cold on his cradle the dew-drops are shin-
      ing;
   Low lies his bed with the beasts of the
      stall;
Angels adore him, in slumber reclining,—
   Maker, and Monarch, and Saviour of all.

3 Say, shall we yield him, in costly devo-
      tion,
   Odors of Edom and offerings divine?
Gems of the mountain, and pearls of the
      ocean,
   Myrrh from the forest, and gold from the
      mine?

4 Vainly we offer each ample oblation;
   Vainly with gifts would his favor secure;
Richer by far is the heart's adoration;
   Dearer to God are the prayers of the poor.
                              REGINALD HEBER.

MISSIONARY CHANT.   L. M.

HEINRICH CHRISTOPHER ZEUNER.

187   *Star of Bethlehem.*

1 WHEN, marshaled on the nightly plain,
   The glittering host bestud the sky,
One star alone of all the train
   Can fix the sinner's wandering eye.

2 Hark! hark! to God the chorus breaks,
   From every host, from every gem;
But one alone the Saviour speaks,
   It is the Star of Bethlehem.

3 Once on the raging seas I rode,
   The storm was loud, the night was dark,
The ocean yawned, and rudely blowed
   The wind that tossed my foundering bark.

4 Deep horror then my vitals froze;
   Death-struck, I ceased the tide to stem;
When suddenly a star arose,
   It was the Star of Bethlehem.

5 It was my guide, my light, my all,
   It bade my dark forebodings cease;
And, through the storm and danger's thrall
   It led me to the port of peace.

6 Now safely moored, my perils o'er,
   I'll sing, first in night's diadem,
For ever and for evermore,
   The Star, the Star of Bethlehem.
                              H. KIRKE WHITE.

WILMOT. 8, 7.

CARL MARIA VON WEBER.

188   *Peace on earth, good-will to men.*

1 HARK! what mean those holy voices,
  Sweetly sounding through the skies?
Lo! the angelic host rejoices;
  Heavenly hallelujahs rise.

2 Listen to the wondrous story,
  Which they chant in hymns of joy:
" Glory in the highest, glory,
  Glory be to God most high!

3 " Peace on earth, good-will from heaven,
  Reaching far as man is found;

Souls redeemed and sins forgiven!
  Loud our golden harps shall sound.

4 " Christ is born, the great Anointed;
  Heaven and earth his praises sing;
O receive whom God appointed,
  For your Prophet, Priest, and King.

5 " Hasten, mortals, to adore him;
  Learn his name, and taste his joy;
Till in heaven ye sing before him,
  ' Glory be to God most high!' "
                            JOHN CAWOOD.

HELMSLEY. 8, 7, 4.

REV. THOMAS OLIVERS.

189   *Adoring the holy Child.*

1 ANGELS, from the realms of glory,
  Wing your flight o'er all the earth;
Ye who sang creation's story,
  Now proclaim Messiah's birth:
    Come and worship,
  Worship Christ, the newborn King.

2 Shepherds, in the field abiding,
  Watching o'er your flocks by night,
God with man is now residing;
  Yonder shines the infant light:
    Come and worship,
  Worship Christ, the newborn King.

3 Sages, leave your contemplations,
  Brighter visions beam afar;

Seek the great Desire of nations;
  Ye have seen his natal star:
    Come and worship,
  Worship Christ, the newborn King.

4 Saints, before the altar bending,
  Watching long in hope and fear,
Suddenly the Lord, descending,
  In his temple shall appear:
    Come and worship,
  Worship Christ, the newborn King.

5 Sinners, wrung with true repentance,
  Doomed for guilt to endless pains,
Justice now revokes the sentence,
  Mercy calls you,—break your chains:
    Come and worship,
  Worship Christ, the newborn King.
                        JAMES MONTGOMERY.

HERALD ANGELS.   7. D.   FELIX MENDELSSOHN-BARTHOLDY.

190   *God incarnate.*

1 HARK! the herald-angels sing,
"Glory to the newborn King;
Peace on earth, and mercy mild;
God and sinners reconciled."

2 Joyful, all ye nations, rise,
Join the triumphs of the skies;
With angelic hosts proclaim,
"Christ is born in Bethlehem."

3 Christ, by highest heaven adored,
Christ, the everlasting Lord;
Veiled in flesh the Godhead see;
Hail, incarnate Deity!

4 Hail the heaven-born Prince of peace!
Hail the Sun of righteousness!
Light and life to all he brings,
Risen with healing in his wings.

CHARLES WESLEY.

191   *Prince of peace.*

1 BRIGHT and joyful is the morn,
For to us a Child is born;
From the highest realms of heaven,
Unto us a Son is given.

2 On his shoulder he shall bear
Power and majesty, and wear,
On his vesture and his thigh,
Names most awful, names most high.

3 Wonderful in counsel he,
Christ, the incarnate Deity;
Sire of ages, ne'er to cease;
King of kings, and Prince of peace.

4 Come and worship at his feet;
Yield to him the homage meet;
From the manger to the throne,
Homage due to God alone.

JAMES MONTGOMERY.

CHRIST—INCARNATION AND BIRTH.

CHRISTMAS. C. M.
GEORGE FREDERICK HANDEL.

192 *Good tidings of great joy.*—Luke 2: 10.

1 WHILE shepherds watched their flocks by
    night,
  All seated on the ground,
The angel of the Lord came down,
  And glory shone around.

2 "Fear not," said he,—for mighty dread
  Had seized their troubled mind,—
"Glad tidings of great joy I bring,
  To you and all mankind.

3 "To you, in David's town, this day
  Is born, of David's line,
The Saviour, who is Christ the Lord;
  And this shall be the sign:

4 "The heavenly babe you there shall find
  To human view displayed,
All meanly wrapped in swathing-bands,
  And in a manger laid."

5 Thus spake the seraph; and forthwith
  Appeared a shining throng,
Of angels, praising God on high,
  Who thus addressed their song:

6 "All glory be to God on high,
  And to the earth be peace:
Good-will henceforth from heaven to men,
  Begin and never cease."
  TATE AND BRADY.

193 *Glory to God in the highest.*

1 MORTALS, awake, with angels join,
  And chant the solemn lay;

Joy, love, and gratitude combine,
  To hail the auspicious day.

2 In heaven the rapturous song began,
  And sweet seraphic fire
Through all the shining legions ran,
  And strung and tuned the lyre.

3 Swift through the vast expanse it flew,
  And loud the echo rolled;
The theme, the song, the joy, was new,
  'Twas more than heaven could hold.

4 Down through the portals of the sky
  The impetuous torrent ran;
And angels flew, with eager joy,
  To bear the news to man.

5 Hark! the cherubic armies shout,
  And glory leads the song:
Good-will and peace are heard through-
    out
  The harmonious heavenly throng.

6 With joy the chorus we repeat,
  "Glory to God on high!"
Good-will and peace are now complete,
  Jesus was born to die.

7 Hail, Prince of life, forever hail!
  Redeemer, Brother, Friend!
Though earth, and time, and life shall
    fail,
  Thy praise shall never end.
  SAMUEL MEDLEY.

CAROL. C. M. D.
RICHARD STORRS WILLIS.

CAROL.   C. M.   (Concluded.)

FINE.

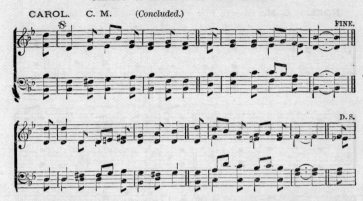

D. S.

194   *Christmas carol.*

1 IT came upon the midnight clear,
  That glorious song of old,
From angels bending near the earth
  To touch their harps of gold;
"Peace on the earth, good-will to men,
  From heaven's all-gracious King."
The world in solemn stillness lay
  To hear the angels sing.

2 Still through the cloven skies they come
  With peaceful wings unfurled,
And still their heavenly music floats
  O'er all the weary world;
Above its sad and lowly plains
  They bend on hovering wing,
And ever o'er its Babel sounds
  The blessed angels sing.

3 But with the woes of sin and strife
  The world has suffered long;
Beneath the angel-strain have rolled
  Two thousand years of wrong;
And man, at war with man, hears not
  The love song which they bring:
O hush the noise, ye men of strife,
  And hear the angels sing!

4 And ye, beneath life's crushing load,
  Whose forms are bending low,
Who toil along the climbing way
  With painful steps and slow,
Look now! for glad and golden hours
  Come swiftly on the wing:
O rest beside the weary road,
  And hear the angels sing!

5 For lo! the days are hastening on
  By prophet-bards foretold,
When with the ever-circling years
  Comes round the age of gold;
When peace shall over all the earth
  Its ancient splendors fling,
And the whole world give back the song
  Which now the angels sing.

EDMUND H. SEARS.

195   *Christmas anthem.*

1 CALM on the listening ear of night,
  Come heaven's melodious strains,
Where wild Judea stretches far
  Her silver-mantled plains;
Celestial choirs from courts above
  Shed sacred glories there;
And angels, with their sparkling lyres,
  Make music on the air.

2 The answering hills of Palestine
  Send back the glad reply,
And greet from all their holy heights
  The Dayspring from on high:
O'er the blue depths of Galilee
  There comes a holier calm;
And Sharon waves in solemn praise
  Her silent groves of palm.

3 "Glory to God!" the lofty strain
  The realm of ether fills;
How sweeps the song of solemn joy
  O'er Judah's sacred hills!
"Glory to God!" the sounding skies
  Loud with their anthems ring:
"Peace on the earth; good-will to men,
  From heaven's eternal King."

4 Light on thy hills, Jerusalem!
  The Saviour now is born!
More bright on Bethlehem's joyous plains
  Breaks the first Christmas morn;
And brighter on Moriah's brow,
  Crowned with her temple spires,
Which first proclaim the newborn light,
  Clothed with its orient fires.

5 This day shall Christian tongues be mute.
  And Christian hearts be cold?
O catch the anthem that from heaven
  O'er Judah's mountains rolled!
When nightly burst from seraph-harps
  The high and solemn lay,—
"Glory to God; on earth be peace;
  Salvation comes to-day!"

EDMUND H. SEARS.

NOEL.   C. M.   LOWELL MASON.

196   *Patience of Jesus.*

1 WHAT grace, O Lord, and beauty shone
    Around thy steps below!
What patient love was seen in all
    Thy life and death of woe!

2 For, ever on thy burdened heart
    A weight of sorrow hung;
Yet no ungentle, murmuring word
    Escaped thy silent tongue.

3 Thy foes might hate, despise, revile,
    Thy friends unfaithful prove;
Unwearied in forgiveness still,
    Thy heart could only love.

4 O give us hearts to love like thee,
    Like thee, O Lord, to grieve
Far more for others' sins, than all
    The wrongs that we receive.

5 One with thyself, may every eye
    In us, thy brethren, see
That gentleness and grace that spring
    From union, Lord, with thee.
                        SIR EDWARD DENNY.

197   *A present help.*

1 WE may not climb the heavenly steeps
    To bring the Lord Christ down;
In vain we search the lowest deeps,
    For him no depths can drown.

2 But warm, sweet, tender, even yet
    A present help is he;
And faith has yet its Olivet,
    And love its Galilee.

3 The healing of the seamless dress
    Is by our beds of pain;
We touch him in life's throng and press,
    And we are whole again.

4 Through him the first fond prayers are said
    Our lips of childhood frame;
The last low whispers of our dead
    Are burdened with his name.

5 O Lord and Master of us all,
    Whate'er our name or sign,
We own thy sway, we hear thy call,
    We test our lives by thine!
                        JOHN G. WHITTIER.

198   *The Transfiguration.*

1 THE chosen three, on mountain height,
    While Jesus bowed in prayer,
Beheld his vesture glow with light,
    His face shine wondrous fair.

2 And lo! with the transfigured Lord,
    Leader and seer they saw;
With Carmel's hoary prophet stood
    The giver of the law.

3 From the low-bending cloud above,
    Whence radiant brightness shone,
Spake out the Father's voice of love,
    "Hear my beloved Son!"

4 Lord, lead us to the mountain height;
    To prayer's transfiguring glow;
And clothe us with the Spirit's might
    For grander work below.
                        DAVID H. ELA.

CHRIST—LIFE AND CHARACTER.

AMES.   L. M.   FROM SIGISMUND NEUKOMM, ARR. BY LOWELL MASON.

199   *The Transfiguration.*

1 O WONDROUS type! O vision fair
Of glory that the Church shall share,
Which Christ upon the mountain shows,
Where brighter than the sun he glows!

2 From age to age the tale declare,
How with the three disciples there,
Where Moses and Elias meet,
The Lord holds converse high and sweet.

3 With shining face and bright array,
Christ deigns to manifest to-day
What glory shall be theirs above,
Who joy in God with perfect love.

4 And faithful hearts are raised on high
By this great vision's mystery;
For which in joyful strains we raise
The voice of prayer, the hymn of praise.

5 O Father, with the Eternal Son,
And Holy Spirit, ever One,
Vouchsafe to bring us by thy grace
To see thy glory face to face.
SARUM BREVIARY. TR. BY J. M. NEALE.

200   *Hermon.*

1 O MASTER, it is good to be
High on the mountain here with thee,
Where stand revealed to mortal gaze
Those glorious saints of other days,
Who once received on Horeb's height
The eternal laws of truth and right,
Or caught the still small whisper, higher
Than storm, than earthquake, or than fire.

2 O Master, it is good to be
Entranced, enwrapt, alone with thee;
And watch thy glistering raiment glow
Whiter than Hermon's whitest snow;
The human lineaments that shine
Irradiant with a light divine;
Till we too change from grace to grace,
Gazing on that transfigured face.

3 O Master, it is good to be
Here on the holy mount with thee:
When darkling in the depths of night,
When dazzled with excess of light,

We bow before the heavenly voice
That bids bewildered souls rejoice,
Though love wax cold, and faith be dim,
"This is my Son, O hear ye him."
ARTHUR P. STANLEY.

201   *Receive thy sight.*—Luke 18: 42.

1 WHEN the blind suppliant in the way,
By friendly hands to Jesus led,
Prayed to behold the light of day,
"Receive thy sight," the Saviour said.

2 At once he saw the pleasant rays
That lit the glorious firmament;
And, with firm step and words of praise,
He followed where the Master went.

3 Look down in pity, Lord, we pray,
On eyes oppressed by moral night,
And touch the darkened lids, and say
The gracious words, "Receive thy sight."

4 Then, in clear daylight, shall we see
Where walked the sinless Son of God;
And, aided by new strength from thee,
Press onward in the path he trod.
WILLIAM C. BRYANT.

202   *Meekness of Christ.*

1 How beauteous were the marks divine,
That in thy meekness used to shine,
That lit thy lonely pathway, trod
In wondrous love, O Son of God!

2 O who like thee, so mild, so bright,
Thou Son of man, thou Light of light?
O who like thee did ever go
So patient, through a world of woe?

3 O who like thee so humbly bore
The scorn, the scoffs of men, before?
So meek, so lowly, yet so high,
So glorious in humility?

4 And death, that sets the prisoner free,
Was pang, and scoff, and scorn to thee;
Yet love through all thy torture glowed
And mercy with thy life-blood flowed.

5 O wondrous Lord, my soul would be
Still more and more conformed to thee,
And learn of thee, the lowly One,
And like thee, all my journey run.
A. CLEVELAND COXE.

ST. JOSEPH. 8, 7, 7.

H. H. STATHAM.

203 *The tears of Jesus.*

1 JESUS wept! those tears are over,
But his heart is still the same;
Kinsman, Friend, and elder Brother,
Is his everlasting name.
    Saviour, who can love like thee,
    Gracious One of Bethany?

2 When the pangs of trial seize us,
When the waves of sorrow roll,
I will lay my head on Jesus,
Pillow of the troubled soul.
    Surely, none can feel like thee,
    Weeping One of Bethany!

3 Jesus wept! and still in glory,
He can mark each mourner's tear;
Living to retrace the story
Of the hearts he solaced here.
    Lord, when I am called to die,
    Let me think of Bethany.

4 Jesus wept! that tear of sorrow
Is a legacy of love;
Yesterday, to-day, to-morrow,
He the same doth ever prove.
    Thou art all in all to me,
    Living One of Bethany!

SIR EDWARD DENNY.

RATHBUN. 8, 7.

ITHAMAR CONKEY.

204 *Glorying in the cross.*

1 IN the cross of Christ I glory,
Towering o'er the wrecks of time;
All the light of sacred story
Gathers round its head sublime.

2 When the woes of life o'ertake me,
Hopes deceive, and fears annoy,
Never shall the cross forsake me;
Lo! it glows with peace and joy.

3 When the sun of bliss is beaming
Light and love upon my way,

From the cross the radiance streaming
Adds more luster to the day.

4 Bane and blessing, pain and pleasure,
By the cross are sanctified;
Peace is there, that knows no measure,
Joys that through all time abide.

5 In the cross of Christ I glory,
Towering o'er the wrecks of time;
All the light of sacred story
Gathers round its head sublime.

SIR JOHN BOWRING.

ALETTA.   7.   WILLIAM BATCHELDER BRADBURY.

205   *Lessons of the cross.*

1 NEVER further than Thy cross:
  Never higher than thy feet:
Here earth's precious things seem dross:
  Here earth's bitter things grow sweet.

2 Gazing thus our sin we see,
  Learn thy love while gazing thus;
Sin, which laid the cross on thee,
  Love, which bore the cross for us.

3 Here we learn to serve and give,
  And, rejoicing, self deny;
Here we gather love to live,
  Here we gather faith to die.

4 Pressing onward as we can,
  Still to this our hearts must tend;
Where our earliest hopes began,
  There our last aspirings end;

5 Till amid the hosts of light,
  We in thee redeemed, complete.

Through thy cross made pure and white,
Cast our crowns before thy feet.
MRS. ELIZABETH CHARLES.

206   *Sinai, Tabor, Calvary.*

1 WHEN on Sinai's top I see
God descend, in majesty,
To proclaim his holy law,
All my spirit sinks with awe.

2 When, in ecstasy sublime,
Tabor's glorious steep I climb,
At the too transporting light,
Darkness rushes o'er my sight.

3 When on Calvary I rest,
God, in flesh made manifest,
Shines in my Redeemer's face,
Full of beauty, truth, and grace.

4 Here I would forever stay,
Weep and gaze my soul away;
Thou art heaven on earth to me,
Lovely, mournful Calvary.
JAMES MONTGOMERY.

DYER.   C. M.   HARVEY C. CAMP.

207   *The second Man is the Lord from
heaven.*—1 Cor. 15: 47.

1 PRAISE to the Holiest in the height,
  And in the depth be praise;
In all his words most wonderful,
  Most sure in all his ways.

2 O loving wisdom of our God!
  When all was sin and shame,

A second Adam to the fight
  And to the rescue came.

3 O wisest love! that flesh and blood,
  Which did in Adam fail,
Should strive afresh against the foe,
  Should strive and should prevail.

4 O generous love! that he, who smote
  In Man for man the foe,
The double agony in Man
  For man should undergo;

5 And in the garden secretly,
  And on the cross on high,
Should teach his brethren, and inspire
  To suffer and to die.
JOHN H. NEWMAN.

6   77

GERMANY. L. M.

LUDWIG VON BEETHOVEN.

208 *The power of the cross.*

1 WE sing the praise of Him who died,
Of him who died upon the cross;
The sinner's hope let men deride,
For this we count the world but loss.

2 Inscribed upon the cross we see,
In shining letters, "God is Love;"
He bears our sins upon the tree,
He brings us mercy from above.

3 The cross! it takes our guilt away;
It holds the fainting spirit up;
It cheers with hope the gloomy day,
And sweetens every bitter cup.

4 It makes the coward spirit brave,
And nerves the feeble arm for fight;
It takes its terror from the grave,
And gilds the bed of death with light:

5 The balm of life, the cure of woe,
The measure and the pledge of love,
The sinner's refuge here below,
The angels' theme in heaven above.
THOMAS KELLY.

209 *The hidings of the Father's face.*

1 FROM Calvary a cry was heard,
A bitter and heart-rending cry;
My Saviour! every mournful word
Bespeaks thy soul's deep agony.

2 A horror of great darkness fell
On thee, thou spotless, holy One!
And all the swarming hosts of hell
Conspired to tempt God's only Son.

3 The scourge, the thorns, the deep disgrace,
These thou couldst bear, nor once repine;

But when Jehovah veiled his face,
Unutterable pangs were thine.

4 Let the dumb world its silence break
Let pealing anthems rend the sky;
Awake, my sluggish soul, awake!
He died, that we might never die.

5 Lord, on thy cross I fix mine eye:
If e'er I lose its strong control,
O let that dying, piercing cry,
Melt and reclaim my wandering soul.
J. W. CUNNINGHAM.

210 *Atonement made.*

1 'TIS finished! the Messiah dies,—
Cut off for sins, but not his own;
Accomplished is the sacrifice,
The great redeeming work is done.

2 'Tis finished! all the debt is paid;
Justice divine is satisfied;
The grand and full atonement made;
Christ for a guilty world hath died

3 The veil is rent; in him alone
The living way to heaven is seen;
The middle wall is broken down,
And all mankind may enter in.

4 The types and figures are fulfilled;
Exacted is the legal pain;
The precious promises are sealed;
The spotless Lamb of God is slain.

5 Death, hell, and sin are now subdued
All grace is now to sinners given;
And, lo! I plead the atoning blood,
And in thy right I claim my heaven.
CHARLES WESLEY.

EUCHARIST. L. M.

ISAAC BAKER WOODBURY.

211 *Glorying in the cross.*

1 WHEN I survey the wondrous cross
  On which the Prince of glory died,
My richest gain I count but loss,
  And pour contempt on all my pride.

2 Forbid it, Lord, that I should boast,
  Save in the death of Christ, my God;
All the vain things that charm me most,
  I sacrifice them to his blood.

3 See, from his head, his hands, his feet,
  Sorrow and love flow mingled down:
Did e'er such love and sorrow meet,
  Or thorns compose so rich a crown?

4 Were the whole realm of nature mine,
  That were a present far too small;
Love so amazing, so divine,
  Demands my soul, my life, my all.
                ISAAC WATTS.

212 *Christ crucified.*

1 EXTENDED on a cursèd tree,
  Covered with dust, and sweat, and blood,
See there, the King of glory see!
  Sinks and expires the Son of God.

2 Who, who, my Saviour, this hath done?
  Who could thy sacred body wound?
No guilt thy spotless heart hath known,
  No guile hath in thy lips been found.

3 I, I alone have done the deed;
  'Tis I thy sacred flesh have torn;
My sins have caused thee, Lord, to bleed,
  Pointed the nail, and fixed the thorn.

4 For me the burden to sustain
  Too great, on thee, my Lord, was laid:
To heal me, thou hast borne my pain;
  To bless me, thou a curse wast made.

5 My Saviour, how shall I proclaim,
  How pay the mighty debt I owe?
Let all I have, and all I am,
  Ceaseless, to all, thy glory show.

6 Still let thy tears, thy groans, thy sighs,
  O'erflow my eyes, and heave my breast,
Till, loosed from flesh and earth, I rise,
  And ever in thy bosom rest.
      PAUL GERHARDT. TR. BY J. WESLEY.

213 *Gazing on the cross.*

1 LORD JESUS, when we stand afar
  And gaze upon thy holy cross,
In love of thee and scorn of self,
  O may we count the world as loss.

2 When we behold thy bleeding wounds,
  And the rough way that thou hast trod,
Make us to hate the load of sin
  That lay so heavy on our God.

3 O holy Lord! uplifted high
  With outstretched arms, in mortal woe,
Embracing in thy wondrous love
  The sinful world that lies below!

4 Give us an ever-living faith
  To gaze beyond the things we see;
And in the mystery of thy death
  Draw us and all men after thee!
           WILLIAM W. HOW.

COMMUNION.   C. M.   Stephen Jenks.

214   *Godly sorrow at the cross.*

1 ALAS! and did my Saviour bleed?
  And did my Sovereign die?
Would he devote that sacred head
  For such a worm as I?

2 Was it for crimes that I have done,
  He groaned upon the tree?
Amazing pity! grace unknown!
  And love beyond degree!

3 Well might the sun in darkness hide,
  And shut his glories in,
When Christ, the mighty Maker, died,
  For man the creature's sin.

4 Thus might I hide my blushing face
  While his dear cross appears;
Dissolve my heart in thankfulness,
  And melt mine eyes to tears.

5 But drops of grief can ne'er repay
  The debt of love I owe:
Here, Lord, I give myself away,—
  'Tis all that I can do.

ISAAC WATTS.

215   *He died for thee.*

1 BEHOLD the Saviour of mankind
  Nailed to the shameful tree;
How vast the love that him inclined
  To bleed and die for thee!

2 Hark! how he groans, while nature shakes,
  And earth's strong pillars bend:
The temple's veil in sunder breaks,
  The solid marbles rend.

3 'Tis done! the precious ransom's paid!
  "Receive my soul!" he cries:
See where he bows his sacred head;
  He bows his head, and dies!

4 But soon he'll break death's envious chain
  And in full glory shine:
O Lamb of God, was ever pain,
  Was ever love, like thine?

SAMUEL WESLEY.

216   *God manifest in the flesh.*

1 WITH glorious clouds encompassed round
  Whom angels dimly see,
Will the Unsearchable be found,
  Or God appear to me?

2 Will he forsake his throne above,
  Himself to worms impart?
Answer, thou Man of grief and love,
  And speak it to my heart.

3 In manifested love explain
  Thy wonderful design;
What meant, thou suffering Son of man
  Thy streaming blood divine?

4 Didst thou not in our flesh appear,
  And live and die below,
That I might now perceive thee near,
  And my Redeemer know?

5 Might view the Lamb in his own light,
  Whom angels dimly see;
And gaze, transported at the sight,
  To all eternity!

CHARLES WESLEY.

OLIVES' BROW. L. M.

WILLIAM BATCHELDER BRADBURY.

217 *Christ in Gethsemane.*

1 'Tis midnight; and on Olives' brow
   The star is dimmed that lately shone:
'Tis midnight; in the garden, now,
   The suffering Saviour prays alone.

2 'Tis midnight; and from all removed,
   The Saviour wrestles lone with fears;
E'en that disciple whom he loved
   Heeds not his Master's grief and tears.

3 'Tis midnight; and for others' guilt
   The Man of sorrows weeps in blood;
Yet he that hath in anguish knelt
   Is not forsaken by his God.

4 'Tis midnight; and from ether-plains
   Is borne the song that angels know;
Unheard by mortals are the strains
   That sweetly soothe the Saviour's woe.
                        WILLIAM B. TAPPAN.

218 *Prophecy fulfilled.*

1 "'Tis finished!" so the Saviour cried,
   And meekly bowed his head and died:
'Tis finished! yes, the race is run;
   The battle fought; the victory won.

2 'Tis finished! all that Heaven foretold
   By prophets in the days of old;
And truths are opened to our view,
   That kings and prophets never knew.

3 'Tis finished! Son of God, thy power
   Hath triumphed in this awful hour;
And yet our eyes with sorrow see
   That life to us was death to thee.

4 'Tis finished! let the joyful sound
   Be heard through all the nations round;
'Tis finished! let the triumph rise
   And swell the chorus of the skies!
                        SAMUEL STENNETT, ALT.

HERMON. C. M.

LOWELL MASON.

219 *Hail, holy cross!*

1 THE royal banner is unfurled,
   The cross is reared on high,
On which the Saviour of the world
   Is stretched in agony.

2 See! through his holy hands and feet
   The cruel nails they drive:
Our ransom thus is made complete,
   Our souls are saved alive.

3 And see! the spear hath pierced his side,
   And shed that sacred flood,

That holy reconciling tide,
   The water and the blood.

4 Hail, holy cross! from thee we learn
   The only way to heaven;
And O, to thee may sinners turn.
   And look, and be forgiven!

5 Jehovah, we thy name adore,
   In thee we will rejoice,
And sing, till time shall be no more,
   The triumphs of the cross.
   VENANTIUS FORTUNATUS. TR. BY J. CHANDLER.

SELENA.   L. M. 6l.   ISAAC BAKER WOODBURY.

220   *Transcendent love.*

1 O LOVE divine, what hast thou done!
    The incarnate God hath died for me!
The Father's co-eternal Son,
    Bore all my sins upon the tree!
The Son of God for me hath died:
My Lord, my Love, is crucified.

2 Behold him, all ye that pass by,—
    The bleeding Prince of life and peace!
Come, sinners, see your Saviour die,
    And say, was ever grief like his?
Come, feel with me his blood applied:
My Lord, my Love, is crucified:

3 Is crucified for me and you,
    To bring us rebels back to God:
Believe, believe the record true,
    Ye all are bought with Jesus' blood:
Pardon for all flows from his side:
My Lord, my Love, is crucified.

4 Then let us sit beneath his cross,
    And gladly catch the healing stream;
All things for him account but loss,
    And give up all our hearts to him:
Of nothing think or speak beside,—
My Lord, my Love is crucified.

CHARLES WESLEY.

221   *Sovereign love.*

1 WOULD Jesus have the sinner die?
    Why hangs he then on yonder tree?
What means that strange expiring cry?
    Sinners, he prays for you and me;
"Forgive them, Father, O forgive!
They know not that by me they live."

2 Jesus, descended from above,
    Our loss of Eden to retrieve,
Great God of universal love,
    If all the world through thee may live,
In us a quickening spirit be,
And witness thou hast died for me.

3 Thou loving, all-atoning Lamb,
    Thee—by thy painful agony,
Thy bloody sweat, thy grief and shame,
    Thy cross and passion on the tree,
Thy precious death and life—I pray,
Take all, take all my sins away.

4 O let thy love my heart constrain!
    Thy love, for every sinner free,
That every fallen son of man
    May taste the grace that found out me;
That all mankind with me may prove
Thy sovereign, everlasting love.

CHARLES WESLEY.

MUNICH. 7, 6.

ARR. MENDELSSOHN.

Lo, here I fall, my Saviour!
  'Tis I deserve thy place;
Look on me with thy favor,
  Vouchsafe to me thy grace.

3 What language shall I borrow
  To thank thee, dearest Friend,
For this, thy dying sorrow,
  Thy pity without end?
O make me thine forever;
  And should I fainting be,
Lord, let me never, never,
  Outlive my love to thee.

4 Be near me when I'm dying,
  O show thy cross to me;
And, for my succor flying,
  Come, Lord, and set me free:
These eyes, new faith receiving,
  From Jesus shall not move;
For he who dies believing,
  Dies safely, through thy love.

BERNARD OF CLAIRVAUX, PAUL GERHARDT.
TR. BY J. W. ALEXANDER.

222   *Crowned with thorns.*

1 O SACRED Head, now wounded,
  With grief and shame weighed down,
Now scornfully surrounded
  With thorns, thine only crown;
O sacred Head, what glory,
  What bliss, till now was thine!
Yet, though despised and gory,
  I joy to call thee mine.

2 What thou, my Lord, hast suffered
  Was all for sinners' gain:
Mine, mine was the transgression,
  But thine the deadly pain:

PASSION CHORALE. 7, 6.

HANS LEO. HASSLER.

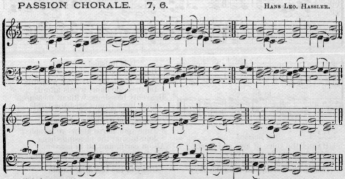

GETHSEMANE. 7, 6l.

RICHARD REDHEAD.

223 *Christ our exemplar.*

1 Go to dark Gethsemane,
 Ye that feel the tempter's power;
Your Redeemer's conflict see,
 Watch with him one bitter hour;
Turn not from his griefs away,
Learn of Jesus Christ to pray.

2 Follow to the judgment-hall;
 View the Lord of life arraigned;
O the wormwood and the gall!
 O the pangs his soul sustained!
Shun not suffering, shame, or loss;
Learn of him to bear the cross.

3 Calvary's mournful mountain climb;
 There, adoring at his feet,
Mark that miracle of time,
 God's own sacrifice complete:
"It is finished!" hear him cry;
Learn of Jesus Christ to die.

4 Early hasten to the tomb,
 Where they laid his breathless clay;
All is solitude and gloom;
 Who hath taken him away?
Christ is risen; he meets our eyes;
Saviour, teach us so to rise!

JAMES MONTGOMERY.

CALVARY. 8, 7, 4.

SAMUEL STANLEY.

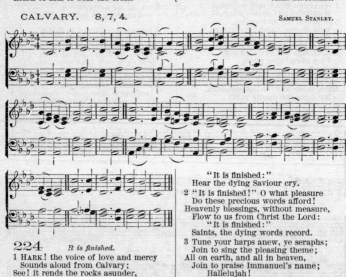

224 *It is finished.*

1 HARK! the voice of love and mercy
 Sounds aloud from Calvary;
See! it rends the rocks asunder,
 Shakes the earth, and veils the sky;
 "It is finished:"
 Hear the dying Saviour cry.

2 "It is finished!" O what pleasure
 Do these precious words afford!
Heavenly blessings, without measure,
 Flow to us from Christ the Lord:
 "It is finished:"
 Saints, the dying words record.

3 Tune your harps anew, ye seraphs;
 Join to sing the pleasing theme;
All on earth, and all in heaven,
 Join to praise Immanuel's name;
 Hallelujah!
 Glory to the bleeding Lamb.

JONATHAN EVANS.

SUMMERSIDE. 8, 7. D.

* REV. JOHN BLACK.

225 *Easter anthem.*

1 SING with all the sons of glory,
   Sing the resurrection song!
Death and sorrow, earth's dark story,
   To the former days belong:
All around the clouds are breaking,
   Soon the storms of time shall cease,
In God's likeness, man awaking,
   Knows the everlasting peace.

2 O what glory, far exceeding
   All that eye has yet perceived!
Holiest hearts for ages pleading,
   Never that full joy conceived.
God has promised, Christ prepares it,
   There on high our welcome waits;
Every humble spirit shares it,
   Christ has passed the eternal gates.

3 Life eternal! heaven rejoices,
   Jesus lives who once was dead;
Join, O man, the deathless voices,
   Child of God, lift up thy head!
Patriarchs from the distant ages,
   Saints all longing for their heaven,
Prophets, psalmists, seers and sages,
   All await the glory given.

4 Life eternal! O what wonders
   Crowd on faith; what joy unknown,

When, amidst earth's closing thunders,
   Saints shall stand before the throne!
O to enter that bright portal,
   See that glowing firmament,
Know, with thee, O God immortal,
   "Jesus Christ whom thou hast sent!"
                              WILLIAM J. IRONS.

226 *Jesus, victor over death.*

1 COME, ye saints, look here and wonder;
   See the place where Jesus lay:
He has burst his bands asunder;
   He has borne our sins away;
      Joyful tidings!
   Yes, the Lord has risen to-day.

2 Jesus triumphs! sing ye praises;
   By his death he overcame:
Thus the Lord his glory raises,
   Thus he fills his foes with shame:
      Sing ye praises!
   Praises to the Victor's name.

3 Jesus triumphs! countless legions
   Come from heaven to meet their King;
Soon, in yonder blessed regions,
   They shall join his praise to sing:
      Songs eternal
   Shall through heaven's high arches ring.
                              THOMAS KELLY.

RESURRECTION. 10, 11, 12. *ARR. FROM JOHN EDGAR GOULD.

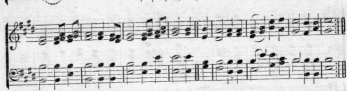

227 *The voice of triumph.*

1 LIFT your glad voices in triumph on high,
For Jesus hath risen, and man shall not die;
Vain were the terrors that gathered around him,
And short the dominion of death and the grave;
He burst from the fetters of darkness that bound him,
Resplendent in glory, to live and to save:
Loud was the chorus of angels on high,—
The Saviour hath risen, and man shall not die.

2 Glory to God, in full anthems of joy;
The being he gave us death cannot destroy;
Sad were the life we may part with to-morrow,
If tears were our birthright, and death were our end;
But Jesus hath cheered the dark valley of sorrow,
And bade us, immortal, to heaven ascend:
Lift then your voices in triumph on high,
For Jesus hath risen, and man shall not die.

HENRY WARE, JR.

TAMAR. C. M. ISAAC BAKER WOODBURY.

228 *Christ, the Conqueror.*

1 WELCOME, thou Victor in the strife,
Now welcome from the cave!
To-day we triumph in thy life
Around thine empty grave.

2 Our enemy is put to shame,
His short-lived triumph o'er;
Our God is with us, we exclaim,
We fear our foe no more.

3 O let thy conquering banner wave
O'er hearts thou makest free,
And point the path that from the grave
Leads heavenward up to thee.

4 We bury all our sin and crime
Deep in our Saviour's tomb,
And seek the treasure there, that time
Nor change can e'er consume.

5 We die with thee: O let us live
Henceforth to thee aright;
The blessings thou hast died to give
Be daily in our sight.

6 Fearless we lay us in the tomb,
And sleep the night away,
If thou art there to break the gloom,
And call us back to day.

BENJAMIN SCHMOLKE, TR. BY MISS C. WINKWORTH.

DORT. 6, 4.

LOWELL MASON.

229 *Ascension hymn.*

RISE, glorious Conqueror, rise
Into thy native skies;
　　Assume thy right;
And where in many a fold
The clouds are backward rolled,
Pass through those gates of gold,
　　And reign in light!

2 Victor o'er death and hell,
Cherubic legions swell
　　The radiant train:
Praises all heaven inspire;
Each angel sweeps his lyre,
And claps his wings of fire,
　　Thou Lamb once slain!

3 Enter, incarnate God!
No feet but thine have trod
　　The serpent down:
Blow the full trumpets, blow,
Wider yon portals throw,
Saviour, triumphant, go,
　　And take thy crown!

4 Lion of Judah, hail!
And let thy name prevail
　　From age to age:
Lord of the rolling years,
Claim for thine own the spheres,
For thou hast bought with tears
　　Thy heritage.

MATTHEW BRIDGES.

MENDEBRAS. 7, 6.

GERMAN MELODY, ARR. BY LOWELL MASON.

230 *Resurrection hymn.*

1 THE day of resurrection!
　　Earth, tell it out abroad!
The passover of gladness,
　　The passover of God!
From death to life eternal,
　　From earth unto the sky,
Our Christ hath brought us over,
　　With hymns of victory.

2 Our hearts be pure from evil,
　　That we may see aright
The Lord in rays eternal
　　Of resurrection light;

And, listening to his accents,
　　May hear, so calm and plain,
His own "All hail!'" and, hearing,
　　May raise the victor-strain.

3 Now let the heavens be joyful!
　　Let earth her song begin!
Let the round world keep triumph,
　　And all that is therein!
Invisible and visible,
　　Their notes let all things blend,
For Christ the Lord hath risen,
　　Our Joy that hath no end.

JOHN OF DAMASCUS. TR. BY J. M. NEALE.

BAPTISTE. 11.

JOHN BAPTIST. CALKIN.

231 *Easter chant.*

1 WELCOME, happy morning! age to age shall say:
Hell to-day is vanquished, heaven is won to-day!
Lo, the dead is living, God for evermore!
Him, their true Creator, all his works adore.

2 Earth with joy confesses, clothing her for spring,
All good gifts returned with her returning King:
Bloom in every meadow, leaves on every bough,
Speak his sorrows ended, hail his triumph now.

3 Maker and Redeemer, life and health of all,
Thou, from heaven beholding human nature's fall,

Of the Father's Godhead true and only Son,
Manhood to deliver, manhood didst put on.

4 Thou, of life the author, death didst undergo,
Tread the path of darkness, saving strength to show;
Come then, true and faithful, now fulfill thy word,
'Tis thine own third morning, rise, my buried Lord!

5 Loose the souls long-prisoned, bound with Satan's chain;
All that now is fallen raise to life again;
Show thy face in brightness, bid the nations see,
Bring again our daylight; day returns with thee!

VENANTIUS FORTUNATUS. TR. BY J. ELLERTON.
[Sung by Jerome of Prague at the stake.]

COLMAN. C. M.

GEORGE KINGSLEY.

232 *Rejoicing in the risen Christ.*

1 AWAKE, glad soul! awake! awake!
Thy Lord has risen long,
Go to his grave, and with thee take
Both tuneful heart and song.

2 Where life is waking all around,
Where love's sweet voices sing,
The first bright blossom may be found
Of an eternal spring.

3 The shade and gloom of life are fled
This resurrection-day,
Henceforth in Christ are no more dead,
The grave hath no more prey.

4 In Christ we live, in Christ we sleep,
In Christ we wake and rise,
And the sad tears death makes us weep,
He wipes from all our eyes.

5 Then wake, glad heart! awake! awake!
And seek thy risen Lord,
Joy in his resurrection take,
And comfort in his word:

6 And let thy life, through all its ways,
One long thanksgiving be,
Its theme of joy, its song of praise—
Christ died, and rose for me.

JOHN S. B. MONSELL.

LOWRY. L. M.

JOSEPH E. SWEETSER.

233 *Majestic triumph over the grave.*

1 THE morning kindles all the sky,
The heavens resound with anthems high,
The shining angels as they speed,
Proclaim, "The Lord is risen indeed!"

2 Vainly with rocks his tomb was barred,
While Roman guards kept watch and ward;
Majestic from the spoiled tomb,
In pomp of triumph, he has come!

3 When the amazed disciples heard,
Their hearts with speechless joy were stirred;

Their Lord's beloved face to see,
Eager they haste to Galilee.

4 His piercéd hands to them he shows,
His face with love's own radiance glows:
They with the angels' message speed,
And shout, "The Lord is risen indeed!"

5 O Christ, thou King compassionate!
Our hearts possess, on thee we wait:
Help us to render praises due,
To thee the endless ages through!
AMBROSIAN. TR. BY MRS. E. CHARLES.

GRACE CHURCH. L. M.

IGNACE PLEYEL,

234 *Dying, rising, reigning.*

1 HE dies! the Friend of sinners dies!
Lo! Salem's daughters weep around;
A solemn darkness veils the skies,
A sudden trembling shakes the ground.

2 Come, saints, and drop a tear or two
For him who groaned beneath your load;
He shed a thousand drops for you,—
A thousand drops of richer blood.

3 Here's love and grief beyond degree:
The Lord of glory dies for man!
But lo! what sudden joys we see,
Jesus, the dead, revives again!

4 The rising God forsakes the tomb;
In vain the tomb forbids his rise;
Cherubic legions guard him home,
And shout him welcome to the skies.

5 Break off your tears, ye saints, and tell
How high your great Deliverer reigns;
Sing how he spoiled the hosts of hell,
And led the monster Death in chains:

6 Say, "Live forever, wondrous King!
Born to redeem, and strong to save;"
Then ask the monster, "Where's thy sting?"
And, "Where's thy victory, boasting
Grave?"
ISAAC WATTS, ALT. BY J. WESLEY.

RIALTO.   S. M.

GEORGE FREDERICK ROOT.

235   *Joy in His resurrection.*

1 THE Lord is risen indeed;
 The grave hath lost its prey;
With him shall rise the ransomed seed,
 To reign in endless day.

2 The Lord is risen indeed;
 He lives, to die no more;
He lives, his people's cause to plead,
 Whose curse and shame he bore.

3 The Lord is risen indeed;
 Attending angels, hear!
Up to the courts of heaven, with speed,
 The joyful tidings bear:

4 Then take your golden lyres,
 And strike each cheerful chord;
Join, all ye bright celestial choirs,
 To sing our risen Lord.

THOMAS KELLY.

236   *Gone into heaven.*

1 THOU art gone up on high
 To mansions in the skies;
And round thy throne unceasingly
 The songs of praise arise,

2 But we are lingering here,
 With sin and care oppressed;
Lord, send thy promised Comforter,
 And lead us to thy rest.

3 Thou art gone up on high:
 But thou didst first come down,
Through earth's most bitter agony
 To pass unto thy crown,

4 And girt with griefs and fears
 Our onward course must be;
But only let that path of tears
 Lead us at last to thee.

5 Thou art gone up on high:
 But thou shalt come again,
With all the bright ones of the sky
 Attendant in thy train,

6 O by thy saving power
 So make us live and die,
That we may stand, in that dread hour,
 At thy right hand on high.

EMMA TOKE.

[L. M. Tune, Ware   Page 91.]

237   *The King of glory.*

1 OUR Lord is risen from the dead;
 Our Jesus is gone up on high;
The powers of hell are captive led,
 Dragged to the portals of the sky:
There his triumphal chariot waits,
 And angels chant the solemn lay:
"Lift up your heads, ye heavenly gates·
 Ye everlasting doors, give way!

2 "Loose all your bars of massy light,
 And wide unfold the ethereal scene;
He claims these mansions as his right;
 Receive the King of glory in!"
"Who is the King of glory? Who?"
 "The Lord, that all our foes o'ercame;
The world, sin, death, and hell o'erthrew;
 And Jesus is the Conqueror's name."

3 Lo, his triumphal chariot waits,
 And angels chant the solemn lay:
"Lift up your heads, ye heavenly gates;
 Ye everlasting doors, give way!
"Who is the King of glory? Who?"
 "The Lord, of glorious power possessed;
The King of saints and angels too;
 God over all, forever blest!"

CHARLES WESLEY.

WARE. L. M. GEORGE KINGSLEY.

238 *Sufficiency of the atonement.*

1 JESUS, thy blood and righteousness
My beauty are, my glorious dress;
'Midst flaming worlds, in these arrayed,
With joy shall I lift up my head.

2 Bold shall I stand in thy great day,
For who aught to my charge shall lay?
Fully absolved through these I am,
From sin and fear, from guilt and shame.

3 The holy, meek, unspotted Lamb,
Who from the Father's bosom came,
Who died for me, e'en me to atone,
Now for my Lord and God I own.

4 Lord, I believe thy precious blood,
Which, at the mercy-seat of God,
Forever doth for sinners plead,
For me, e'en for my soul, was shed.

5 Lord, I believe were sinners more
Than sands upon the ocean shore,
Thou hast for all a ransom paid,
For all a full atonement made.
NICOLAUS L. ZINZENDORF. TR. BY J. WESLEY.

239 *An advocate with the Father.*—1 John 2 : 1.

1 JESUS, my Advocate above,
My Friend before the throne of love,
If now for me prevails thy prayer,
If now I find thee pleading there,—

2 If thou the secret wish convey,
And sweetly prompt my heart to pray,—
Hear, and my weak petitions join,
Almighty Advocate, to thine.

3 Jesus, my heart's desire obtain;
My earnest suit present, and gain:
My fullness of corruption show;
The knowledge of myself bestow.

4 O sovereign Love, to thee I cry,
Give me thyself, or else I die!
Save me from death, from hell set free;
Death, hell, are but the want of thee.
CHARLES WESLEY.

240 *Christ, King and Creator.*

1 O CHRIST, our King, Creator, Lord,
Saviour of all who trust thy word,
To them who seek thee ever near,
Now to our praises bend thine ear.

2 In thy dear cross a grace is found,
It flows from every streaming wound,
Whose power our inbred sin controls,
Breaks the firm bond and frees our souls.

3 Thou didst create the stars of night,
Yet thou hast veiled in flesh thy light;
Hast deigned a mortal form to wear,
A mortal's painful lot to bear.

4 When thou didst hang upon the tree,
The quaking earth acknowledged thee;
When thou didst there yield up thy breath,
The world grew dark as shades of death.

5 Now in the Father's glory high,
Great Conqueror, never more to die,
Us by thy mighty power defend,
And reign through ages without end.
GREGORY THE GREAT. TR. BY R. PALMER.

ORTONVILLE. C. M. Thomas Hastings.

241 *Majestic sweetness.*

1 MAJESTIC sweetness sits enthroned
Upon the Saviour's brow;
His head with radiant glories crowned,
His lips with grace o'erflow.

2 No mortal can with him compare,
Among the sons of men;
Fairer is he than all the fair
That fill the heavenly train.

3 He saw me plunged in deep distress,
He flew to my relief;
For me he bore the shameful cross,
And carried all my grief.

4 To him I owe my life and breath,
And all the joys I have;
He makes me triumph over death,
He saves me from the grave.

5 To heaven, the place of his abode,
He brings my weary feet;
Shows me the glories of my God,
And makes my joy complete.

6 Since from his bounty I receive
Such proofs of love divine,
Had I a thousand hearts to give,
Lord, they should all be thine.
SAMUEL STENNETT.

[L. M. Tune, Uxbridge. Page 109.]

242 *Life in Christ.*

1 I KNOW that my Redeemer lives;
What joy the blest assurance gives!
He lives, he lives, who once was dead;
He lives, my everlasting Head!

2 He lives, to bless me with his love;
He lives, to plead for me above;
He lives, my hungry soul to feed;
He lives, to help in time of need.

3 He lives, and grants me daily breath;
He lives, and I shall conquer death;
He lives, my mansion to prepare;
He lives, to bring me safely there.

4 He lives, all glory to his name;
He lives, my Saviour, still the same;
What joy the blest assurance gives,
I know that my Redeemer lives!
SAMUEL MEDLEY.

[H. M. Tune, Christ Church. Page 92.]

243 *Prophet, Priest, and King.*

1 JOIN all the glorious names
Of wisdom, love, and power,
That ever mortals knew,
Or angels ever bore;
All are too mean to speak his worth,
Too mean to set the Saviour forth.

2 Great Prophet of our God,
Our tongues shall bless thy name;
By thee the joyful news
Of our salvation came;
The joyful news of sins forgiven,
Of hell subdued, and peace with heaven.

3 Jesus, our great High Priest,
Has shed his blood and died;
The guilty conscience needs
No sacrifice beside:
His precious blood did once atone,
And now it pleads before the throne.

4 O thou almighty Lord,
Our Conqueror and King,
Thy scepter and thy sword,
Thy reigning grace, we sing:
Thine is the power; behold we sit
In willing bonds beneath thy feet.
ISAAC WATTS.

CHRIST CHURCH. H. M.

CHARLES STEGGALL.

244 *Rejoice evermore.*

1 REJOICE, the Lord is King!
　Your Lord and King adore;
Mortals, give thanks and sing,
　And triumph evermore;
Lift up your hearts, lift up your voice;
Rejoice, again I say, rejoice.

2 Jesus, the Saviour, reigns,
　The God of truth and love;
When he had purged our stains,
　He took his seat above;
Lift up your hearts, lift up your voice;
Rejoice, again I say, rejoice.

3 His kingdom cannot fail,
　He rules o'er earth and heaven;
The keys of death and hell
　Are to our Jesus given;
Lift up your hearts, lift up your voice;
Rejoice, again I say, rejoice.

4 He sits at God's right hand
　Till all his foes submit,
And bow to his command,
　And fall beneath his feet;
Lift up your hearts, lift up your voice;
Rejoice, again I say, rejoice.

5 He all his foes shall quell,
　And all our sins destroy;
Let every bosom swell
　With pure seraphic joy;
Lift up your hearts, lift up your voice;
Rejoice, again I say, rejoice.

6 Rejoice in glorious hope;
　Jesus the Judge shall come,
And take his servants up
　To their eternal home;
We soon shall hear the archangel's voice;
The trump of God shall sound,—Rejoice!
　　　　　　　　　CHARLES WESLEY.

245 *Glory to glory's King.*

1 GOD is gone up on high,
　With a triumphant noise;
The clarions of the sky
　Proclaim the angelic joys:
Join all on earth, rejoice and sing;
Glory ascribe to glory's King.

2 All power to our great Lord
　Is by the Father given;
By angel hosts adored,
　He reigns supreme in heaven:
Join all on earth, rejoice and sing;
Glory ascribe to glory's King.

3 High on his holy seat,
　He bears the righteous sway;
His foes beneath his feet
　Shall sink and die away:
Join all on earth, rejoice and sing;
Glory ascribe to glory's King.

4 Till all the earth, renewed
　In righteousness divine,
With all the hosts of God,
　In one great chorus join,
Join all on earth, rejoice and sing:
Glory ascribe to glory's King.
　　　　　　　　　CHARLES WESLEY.

AUTUMN. 8, 7. D.   SPANISH MELODY. FROM MARECHIO.

FINE.   D. S.

246   *Our Paschal Lamb.*

1 HAIL, thou once despiséd Jesus!
  Hail, thou Galilean King!
Thou didst suffer to release us;
  Thou didst free salvation bring.
Hail, thou agonizing Saviour,
  Bearer of our sin and shame!
By thy merits we find favor;
  Life is given through thy name.

2 Paschal Lamb, by God appointed,
  All our sins on thee were laid:
By almighty love anointed,
  Thou hast full atonement made.
All thy people are forgiven,
  Through the virtue of thy blood;
Opened is the gate of heaven;
  Peace is made 'twixt man and God.

3 Jesus, hail! enthroned in glory,
  There forever to abide;
All the heavenly hosts adore thee,
  Seated at thy Father's side:
There for sinners thou art pleading;
  There thou dost our place prepare:
Ever for us interceding,
  Till in glory we appear.

4 Worship, honor, power, and blessing,
  Thou art worthy to receive;
Loudest praises, without ceasing,
  Meet it is for us to give.
Help, ye bright angelic spirits;
  Bring your sweetest, noblest lays;
Help to sing our Saviour's merits;
  Help to chant Immanuel's praise!
                    JOHN BAKEWELL.

SCUDAMORE. 8, 7.   REV. RICHARD ROBERT CHOPE.

247 *Casting our crowns before Him.*

1 "WE shall see Him," in our nature,
  Seated on his lofty throne,
Loved, adored, by every creature,
  Owned as God, and God alone!

2 There the hosts of shining spirits
  Strike their harps, and loudly sing
To the praise of Jesus' merits,
  To the glory of their King.

3 When we pass o'er death's dark river,
  "We shall see him as he is,"
Resting in his love and favor,
  Owning all the glory his.

4 There to cast our crowns before him,
  O what bliss the thought affords!
There forever to adore him,
  King of kings, and Lord of lords!
                    UNKNOWN.

CORONATION.   C. M.

OLIVER HOLDEN.

248   *Crown Him Lord of all.*

1 ALL hail the power of Jesus' name!
  Let angels prostrate fall;
Bring forth the royal diadem,
  And crown him Lord of all.

2 Crown him, ye morning stars of light,
  Who fixed this earthly ball;
Now hail the strength of Israel's might,
  And crown him Lord of all.

3 Ye chosen seed of Israel's race,
  Ye ransomed from the fall,
Hail him who saves you by his grace,
  And crown him Lord of all.

4 Sinners, whose love can ne'er forget
  The wormwood and the gall;
Go, spread your trophies at his feet,
  And crown him Lord of all.

5 Let every kindred, every tribe,
  On this terrestrial ball,
To him all majesty ascribe,
  And crown him Lord of all.

6 O that with yonder sacred throng
  We at his feet may fall!
We'll join the everlasting song,
  And crown him Lord of all.
                    EDWARD PERRONET, ALT.

[8, 7, 4. Tune, Zion. Page 63.]

249   *Crown the Saviour.*

1 LOOK, ye saints, the sight is glorious,
  See the Man of sorrows now;
From the fight returned victorious,
  Every knee to him shall bow:
      Crown him, crown him;
  Crowns become the Victor's brow.

2 Crown the Saviour, angels, crown him:
  Rich the trophies Jesus brings:

In the seat of power enthrone him,
  While the vault of heaven rings:
      Crown him, crown him;
  Crown the Saviour King of kings.

3 Sinners in derision crowned him,
  Mocking thus the Saviour's claim;
Saints and angels crowd around him,
  Own his title, praise his name:
      Crown him, crown him;
  Spread abroad the Victor's fame.

4 Hark, those bursts of acclamation!
  Hark, those loud triumphant chords!
Jesus takes the highest station:
  O what joy the sight affords!
      Crown him, crown him,
  King of kings, and Lord of lords.
                    THOMAS KELLY.

[L. M. 6 l. Tune, Selena. Page 82.]

250   *Our everlasting Priest.*

1 O THOU eternal Victim, slain
A sacrifice for guilty man,
By the eternal Spirit made
An offering in the sinner's stead;
Our everlasting Priest art thou,
Pleading thy death for sinners now.

2 Thy offering still continues new;
Thy vesture keeps its crimson hue;
Thou art the ever-slaughtered Lamb,
Thy priesthood still remains the same.
Thy years, O Lord, can never fail;
Thy goodness is unchangeable.

3 O that our faith may never move,
But stand unshaken as thy love!
Sure evidence of things unseen,
Passing the years that intervene,
Now let it view upon the tree
The Lord, who bleeds and dies for me.
                    CHARLES WESLEY.

CARLISLE. S. M.

CHARLES LOCKHART.

251 *The victory of the cross.*

1 JESUS, the Conqueror, reigns,
In glorious strength arrayed;
His kingdom over all maintains,
And bids the earth be glad:

2 Ye sons of men, rejoice
In Jesus' mighty love;
Lift up your heart, lift up your voice,
To him who rules above.

3 Extol his kingly power;
Kiss the exalted Son,
Who died, and lives to die no more,
High on his Father's throne:

4 Our Advocate with God,
He undertakes our cause,
And spreads through all the earth abroad
The victory of his cross.

CHARLES WESLEY.

252 *Christ, our Intercessor.*

1 LORD, how shall sinners dare
Look up to thine abode,
Or offer their imperfect prayer
Before a holy God?

2 Bright terrors guard thy seat,
And glories veil thy face;
Yet mercy calls us to thy feet,
And to thy throne of grace.

3 My soul, with cheerful eye
See where thy Saviour stands,
The glorious Advocate on high,
With incense in his hands.

4 Teach my weak heart, O Lord,
With faith to call thee mine;
Bid me pronounce the blissful word—
Father, with joy divine.

ANNE STEELE.

LANGTON. S. M.

ADAPTED BY C. STREETFIELD.

253 *Jesus enthroned.*

1 ENTHRONED is Jesus now,
Upon his heavenly seat;
The kingly crown is on his brow,
The saints are at his feet.

2 In shining white they stand,
A great and countless throng;
A palmy scepter in each hand,
On every lip a song.

3 They sing the Lamb of God,
Once slain on earth for them;
The Lamb, through whose atoning blood
Each wears his diadem.

4 Thy grace, O Holy Ghost,
Thy blessed help supply,
That we may join that radiant host,
Triumphant in the sky.

THOMAS J. JUDKIN.

HEBER.   C. M.   GEORGE KINGSLEY.

254 *Our merciful High Priest.*

1 WITH joy we meditate the grace
Of our High Priest above;
His heart is made of tenderness,
His bowels melt with love.

2 Touched with a sympathy within,
He knows our feeble frame;
He knows what sore temptations mean,
For he hath felt the same.

3 He, in the days of feeble flesh,
Poured out strong cries and tears,
And in his measure feels afresh
What every member bears.

4 He'll never quench the smoking flax,
But raise it to a flame;
The bruiséd reed he never breaks,
Nor scorns the meanest name.

5 Then let our humble faith address
His mercy and his power;
We shall obtain delivering grace
In every trying hour.

                                    ISAAC WATTS.

255   *Christ, our guide.*

1 JESUS, the Lord of glory, died,
That we might never die;
And now he reigns supreme, to guide
His people to the sky.

2 Weak though we are, he still is near,
To lead, console, defend;
In all our sorrow, all our fear,
Our all-sufficient Friend.

3 From his high throne in bliss he deigns
Our every prayer to heed;

Bears with our folly, soothes our pains,
Supplies our every need.

4 And from his love's exhaustless spring,
Joys like a river come,
To make the desert bloom and sing,
O'er which.we travel home.

5 O Jesus, there is none like thee,
Our Saviour and our Lord;
Through earth and heaven exalted be,
Beloved, obeyed, adored.

                                    BAPTIST W. NOEL.

256   *King of kings, and Lord of lords.*

1 THE head that once was crowned with
thorns,
Is crowned with glory now;
A royal diadem adorns
The mighty Victor's brow.

2 The highest place that heaven affords,
Is to our Jesus given;
The King of kings, and Lord of lords,
He reigns o'er earth and heaven:

3 The joy of all who dwell above,
The joy of all below,
To whom he manifests his love,
And grants his name to know.

4 To them the cross, with all its shame,
With all its grace, is given;
Their name, an everlasting name,
Their joy, the joy of heaven.

5 They suffer with their Lord below,
They reign with him above;
Their everlasting joy to know
The mystery of his love.

                                    THOMAS KELLY.

DIADEMATA. S. M. D.

SIR GEORGE J. ELVEY.

257 *On his head were many crowns.*
Rev. 19:12.

1 CROWN him with many crowns,
  The Lamb upon his throne;
Hark, how the heavenly anthem drowns
  All music but its own!
Awake, my soul, and sing,
  Of him who died for thee,
And hail him as thy matchless King
  Through all eternity.

2 Crown him the Lord of love!
  Behold his hands and side,—
Rich wounds, yet visible above,
  In beauty glorified:
No angel in the sky
  Can fully bear that sight,
But downward bends his burning eye
  At mysteries so great.

3 Crown him the Lord of peace!
  Whose power a scepter sways
From pole to pole, that wars may cease,
  And all be prayer and praise:
His reign shall know no end,
  And round his piercèd feet
Fair flowers of paradise extend
  Their fragrance ever sweet.

4 Crown him the Lord of years,
  The Potentate of time,

Creator of the rolling spheres,
  Ineffably sublime!
All hail! Redeemer, hail!
  For thou hast died for me;
Thy praise shall never, never fail
  Throughout eternity.

MATTHEW BRIDGES.

[8, 7. Tune, Stockwell. Page 42.]

258 *His speaking blood.*

1 FATHER, hear the blood of Jesus;
  Speaking in thine ears above:
From impending wrath release us;
  Manifest thy pardoning love.

2 O receive us to thy favor,—
  For his only sake receive;
Give us to the bleeding Saviour,
  Let us by his dying live.

3 "To thy pardoning grace receive them,"
  Once he prayed upon the tree;
Still his blood cries out, "Forgive them;
  All their sins were laid on me."

4 Still our Advocate in heaven,
  Prays the prayer on earth begun,
"Father, show their sins forgiven;
  Father, glorify thy Son!"

CHARLES WESLEY.

ESSEX. 7.　　　　　　　　　　　　　　　THOMAS CLARK.

259　　*The Lord is risen.*

1 CHRIST, the Lord, is risen again,
Christ has broken every chain;
Hark! angelic voices cry,
Singing evermore on high,
　　　Hallelujah! Praise the Lord!

2 He who gave for us his life,
Who for us endured the strife,
Is our Paschal Lamb to-day!
We, too, sing for joy, and say,
　　　Hallelujah! Praise the Lord!

3 He who bore all pain and loss,
Comfortless, upon the cross,
Lives in glory now on high,
Pleads for us, and hears our cry;
　　　Hallelujah! Praise the Lord!

4 Now he bids us tell abroad
How the lost may be restored,
How the penitent forgiven,
How we, too, may enter heaven!
　　　Hallelujah! Praise the Lord!
MICHAEL WEISSE. TR. BY MISS C. WINKWORTH.

260　　*The Lord is risen.*

1 CHRIST, the Lord, is risen to-day,
Sons of men and angels say;
Raise your joys and triumphs high;
Sing, ye heavens,—and earth, reply.

2 Love's redeeming work is done;
Fought the fight, the battle won:
Lo! the sun's eclipse is o'er;
Lo! he sets in blood no more.

3 Vain the stone, the watch, the seal,
Christ has burst the gates of hell:
Death in vain forbids his rise;
Christ hath opened paradise.

4 Lives again our glorious King;
Where, O Death, is now thy sting?
Once he died our souls to save;
Where's thy victory, boasting Grave?

5 Soar we now where Christ has led,
Follow our exalted Head;
Made like him, like him we rise;
Ours the cross, the grave, the skies.
CHARLES WESLEY.

261　　*Ascension day.*

1 HAIL the day that sees Him rise;
Ravished from our wishful eyes!
Christ, awhile to mortals given,
Re-ascends his native heaven.

2 There the pompous triumph waits:
Lift your heads, eternal gates;
Wide unfold the radiant scene;
Take the King of glory in!

3 Circled round with angel powers,
Their triumphant Lord and ours,
Conqueror over death and sin,—
Take the King of glory in!

4 Him though highest heaven receives,
Still he loves the earth he leaves;
Though returning to his throne,
Still he calls mankind his own.

5 See, he lifts his hands above!
See, he shows the prints of love!
Hark, his gracious lips bestow
Blessings on his Church below!

6 Saviour, parted from our sight,
High above yon azure height,
Grant our hearts may thither rise,
Following thee beyond the skies.
CHARLES WESLEY.

THE HOLY SPIRIT.

FULTON. 7.

WILLIAM BATCHELDER BRADBURY.

262 *Earnest of endless rest.*

1 GRACIOUS Spirit, Love divine,
Let thy light within me shine!
All my guilty fears remove;
Fill me with thy heavenly love.

2 Speak thy pardoning grace to me;
Set the burdened sinner free;
Lead me to the Lamb of God;
Wash me in his precious blood.

3 Life and peace to me impart;
Seal salvation on my heart;
Breathe thyself into my breast,
Earnest of immortal rest.

4 Let me never from thee stray;
Keep me in the narrow way;
Fill my soul with joy divine;
Keep me, Lord, forever thine.

JOHN STOCKER.

263 *His grace entreated.*

1 HOLY SPIRIT, Truth divine!
Dawn upon this soul of mine;
Word of God, and inward Light!
Wake my spirit, clear my sight.

2 Holy Spirit, Love divine!
Glow within this heart of mine;
Kindle every high desire;
Perish self in thy pure fire!

3 Holy Spirit, Power divine!
Fill and nerve this will of mine;
By thee may I strongly live,
Bravely bear, and nobly strive.

4 Holy Spirit, Right divine!
King within my conscience reign;
Be my law, and I shall be
Firmly bound, forever free.

SAMUEL LONGFELLOW.

264 *The gracious Comforter.*

1 GRANTED is the Saviour's prayer,
Sent the gracious Comforter;
Promise of our parting Lord,
Jesus, to his heaven restored;

2 Christ, who now gone up on high,
Captive leads captivity,
While his foes from him receive
Grace, that God with man may live.

3 God, the everlasting God,
Makes with mortals his abode;
Whom the heavens cannot contain,
He vouchsafes to dwell in man.

4 Never will he thence depart,
Inmate of a humble heart;
Carrying on his work within,
Striving till he cast out sin.

5 There he helps our feeble moans,
Deepens our imperfect groans,
Intercedes in silence there,
Sighs the unutterable prayer.

6 Come, divine and peaceful Guest,
Enter our devoted breast:
Holy Ghost, our hearts inspire,
Kindle there the gospel fire.

7 Crown the agonizing strife,
Principle and Lord of life:
Life divine in us renew,
Thou the Gift and Giver too!

CHARLES WESLEY.

[8, 7. Tune, Stockwell. Page 42.]

265 *The Source of consolation.*

1 HOLY GHOST, dispel our sadness;
Pierce the clouds of nature's night;
Come, thou Source of joy and gladness,
Breathe thy life, and spread thy light.

2 From the height which knows no
measure,
As a gracious shower descend,
Bringing down the richest treasure
Man can wish, or God can send.

3 Author of the new creation,
Come with unction and with power;
Make our hearts thy habitation;
On our souls thy graces shower.

4 Hear, O hear our supplication,
Blessed Spirit, God of peace!
Rest upon this congregation,
With the fullness of thy grace.

PAUL GERHARDT. TR. BY J. C. JACOBI,
ALT. BY A. M. TOPLADY.

[8, 7. Tune, Love Divine. Page 182.]

266 *Guide and Comforter.*

1 HOLY SPIRIT, Fount of blessing,
Ever watchful, ever kind,
Thy celestial aid possessing,
Prisoned souls deliverance find.
Seal of truth, and Bond of union,
Source of light, and Flame of love,
Symbol of divine communion,
In the olive-bearing dove;

2 Heavenly Guide from paths of error,
Comforter of minds distressed,
When the billows fill with terror,
Pointing to an ark of rest;
Promised Pledge, eternal Spirit,
Greater than all gifts below,
May our hearts thy grace inherit;
May our lips thy glories show!

THOMAS J. JUDKIN.

[7. Tune, Fulton. Page 100.]

267 *The work of the Holy Spirit.*

1 HOLY GHOST, with light divine,
Shine upon this heart of mine;
Chase the shades of night away,
Turn my darkness into day.

2 Holy Ghost, with power divine,
Cleanse this guilty heart of mine;
Long hath sin, without control,
Held dominion o'er my soul.

3 Holy Ghost, with joy divine,
Cheer this saddened heart of mine;
Bid my many woes depart,
Heal my wounded, bleeding heart.

4 Holy Spirit, all divine,
Dwell within this heart of mine;
Cast down every idol-throne,
Reign supreme—and reign alone.

ANDREW REED.

[L. M. Tune, Ames. Page 75.]

268 *His universal effusion.*

1 ON all the earth Thy Spirit shower;
The earth in righteousness renew;
Thy kingdom come, and hell's o'erpower,
And to thy scepter all subdue.

2 Like mighty winds, or torrents fierce
Let him opposers all o'errun;
And every law of sin reverse,
That faith and love may make all one

3 Yea, let him, Lord, in every place
His richest energy declare;
While lovely tempers, fruits of grace,
The kingdom of thy Christ prepare.

4 Grant this, O holy God and true!
The ancient seers thou didst inspire,
To us perform the promise due;
Descend, and crown us now with fire.

HENRY MORE, ALT. BY J. WESLEY.

[L. M. Tune, Rose Hill. Page 147.]

269 *Come, Creator Spirit.*

1 O COME, Creator Spirit blest!
Within these souls of thine to rest;
Come, with thy grace and heavenly aid,
To fill the hearts which thou hast made.

2 Come, Holy Spirit, now descend!
Most blessed gift which God can send;
Thou Fire of love, and Fount of life!
Consume our sins, and calm our strife.

3 With patience firm and purpose high,
The weakness of our flesh supply;
Kindle our senses from above,
And make our hearts o'erflow with love.

4 Far from us drive the foe we dread,
And grant us thy true peace instead;
So shall we not, with thee to guide,
Turn from the paths of life aside.

GREGORY THE GREAT.

THE HOLY SPIRIT.

CHESTERFIELD.   C. M.

REV. THOMAS HAWEIS.

270   *Life, light, and love.*

1 ENTHRONED on high, almighty Lord,
   The Holy Ghost send down;
Fulfill in us thy faithful word,
   And all thy mercies crown.

2 Though on our heads no tongues of fire
   Their wondrous powers impart,
Grant, Saviour, what we more desire,—
   Thy Spirit in our heart.

3 Spirit of life, and light, and love,
   Thy heavenly influence give;
Quicken our souls, our guilt remove,
   That we in Christ may live.

4 To our benighted minds reveal
   The glories of his grace,
And bring us where no clouds conceal
   The brightness of his face.

5 His love within us shed abroad,
   Life's ever-springing well;
Till God in us, and we in God,
   In love eternal dwell.   THOMAS HAWEIS.

271   *Source of light and joy.*

1 GREAT Spirit, by whose mighty power
   All creatures live and move,
On us thy benediction shower;
   Inspire our souls with love.

2 Hail, Source of light! arise and shine;
   Darkness and doubt dispel;
Give peace and joy, for we are thine;
   In us forever dwell.

3 From death to life our spirits raise,
   And full redemption bring;
New tongues impart to speak the praise
   Of thee, our God and King.

4 Thine inward witness bear, unknown
   To all the world beside;
Exulting then we feel and own
   Our Saviour glorified.

   THOMAS HAWEIS.

272   *I worship Thee, O Holy Ghost.*

1 I WORSHIP thee, O Holy Ghost,
   I love to worship thee;
My risen Lord for aye were lost
   But for thy company.

2 I worship thee, O Holy Ghost,
   I love to worship thee;
I grieved thee long, alas! thou know'st
   It grieves me bitterly.

3 I worship thee, O Holy Ghost,
   I love to worship thee;
Thy patient love, at what a cost
   At last it conquered me!

4 I worship thee, O Holy Ghost,
   I love to worship thee;
With thee each day is Pentecost,
   Each night Nativity.

   W. F. WARREN.

[Not set to music.

273   *Receive ye the Holy Ghost.*—John 20 : 22

1 COME, Holy Ghost, our souls inspire,
And lighten with celestial fire;
Thou the anointing Spirit art,
Who dost thy sevenfold gifts impart.
Thy blessed unction from above
Is comfort, life, and fire of love.

2 Enable with perpetual light
The dullness of our blinded sight;
Anoint and cheer our soiled face
With the abundance of thy grace;
Keep far our foes, give peace at home;
Where thou art guide, no ill can come.

3 Teach us to know the Father, Son,
And thee, of both, to be but one;
That through the ages all along,
This may be our endless song:
Praise to thy eternal merit,
Father, Son, and Holy Spirit.

   GREGORY THE GREAT. TR. BY J. COSIN.

THE HOLY SPIRIT.

MELCOMBE. L. M.   SAMUEL WEBBE.

274   *The spirit of the ancient saints.*

1 O FOR that flame of living fire,
  Which shone so bright in saints of old!
Which bade their souls to heaven aspire,
  Calm in distress, in danger bold.

2 Where is that Spirit, Lord, which dwelt
  In Abrah'm's breast, and sealed him thine?
Which made Paul's heart with sorrow melt,
  And glow with energy divine?

3 That Spirit, which from age to age
  Proclaimed thy love, and taught thy ways?
Brightened Isaiah's vivid page,
  And breathed in David's hallowed lays?

4 Is not thy grace as mighty now
  As when Elijah felt its power;
When glory beamed from Moses' brow,
  Or Job endured the trying hour?

5 Remember, Lord, the ancient days;
  Renew thy work; thy grace restore;
And while to thee our hearts we raise,
  On us thy Holy Spirit pour.
                      WILLIAM H. BATHURST.

275   *Pentecostal gifts.*

1 COME, Holy Spirit, raise our songs
  To reach the wonders of that day,
When, with thy fiery cloven tongues
  Thou didst such glorious scenes display.

2 Lord, we believe to us and ours,
  The apostolic promise given;
We wait the pentecostal powers,
  The Holy Ghost sent down from heaven.

3 Assembled here with one accord,
  Calmly we wait the promised grace,
The purchase of our dying Lord;
  Come, Holy Ghost, and fill the place.

4 If every one that asks, may find,
  If still thou dost on sinners fall,
Come as a mighty rushing wind;
  Great grace be now upon us all.

5 O leave us not to mourn below,
  Or long for thy return to pine;
Now, Lord, the Comforter bestow,
  And fix in us the Guest divine.
                      CHARLES WESLEY.

276   *His power and unction.*

1 O SPIRIT of the living God,
  In all thy plenitude of grace,
Where'er the foot of man hath trod,
  Descend on our apostate race.

2 Give tongues of fire and hearts of love,
  To preach the reconciling word;
Give power and unction from above,
  Where'er the joyful sound is heard

3 Be darkness, at thy coming, light;
  Confusion—order, in thy path;
Souls without strength, inspire with might;
  Bid mercy triumph over wrath.

4 Baptize the nations; far and nigh
  The triumphs of the cross record:
The name of Jesus glorify,
  Till every kindred call him Lord.
                    JAMES MONTGOMERY.

THE HOLY SPIRIT.

ST. MARTIN'S.   C. M.   WILLIAM TANSUR.

277   *His quickening power.*

1 COME, Holy Spirit, heavenly Dove,
  With all thy quickening powers;
Kindle a flame of sacred love
  In these cold hearts of ours.

2 Look how we grovel here below,
  Fond of these earthly toys;
Our souls, how heavily they go,
  To reach eternal joys.

3 In vain we tune our formal songs,
  In vain we strive to rise;
Hosannas languish on our tongues,
  And our devotion dies.

4 Father, and shall we ever live
  At this poor dying rate,
Our love so faint, so cold to thee,
  And thine to us so great?

5 Come, Holy Spirit, heavenly Dove,
  With all thy quickening powers;
Come, shed abroad a Saviour's love,
  And that shall kindle ours.
                                ISAAC WATTS.

278   *Revelations of the Spirit.*

1 SPIRIT Divine, attend our prayer,
  And make our hearts thy home;
Descend with all thy gracious power:
  Come, Holy Spirit, come!

2 Come as the light: to us reveal
  Our sinfulness and woe;
And lead us in those paths of life
  Where all the righteous go.

3 Come as the fire, and purge our hearts,
  Like sacrificial flame:
Let our whole soul an offering be
  To our Redeemer's name.

4 Come as the wind, with rushing sound,
  With pentecostal grace;
And make the great salvation known
  Wide as the human race.

5 Spirit Divine, attend our prayer,
  And make our hearts thy home;
Descend with all thy gracious power:
  Come, Holy Spirit, come!
                                ANDREW REED.

279   *The enlightening Spirit.*

1 COME, Holy Ghost, our hearts inspire;
  Let us thine influence prove;
Source of the old prophetic fire,
  Fountain of life and love.

2 Come, Holy Ghost, for moved by thee
  The prophets wrote and spoke,
Unlock the truth, thyself the key;
  Unseal the sacred book.

3 Expand thy wings, celestial Dove,
  Brood o'er our nature's night;
On our disordered spirits move,
  And let there now be light.

4 God, through himself, we then shall know
  If thou within us shine;
And sound, with all thy saints below,
  The depths of love divine.
                                CHARLES WESLEY.

104

THE HOLY SPIRIT.

ELIZABETHTOWN.   C. M.   GEORGE KINGSLEY.

5 And every virtue we possess,
  And every virtue won,
And every thought of holiness
  Is his, and his alone.

6 Spirit of purity and grace,
  Our weakness pitying see;
O make our hearts thy dwelling-place,
  Purer and worthier thee!
                        HARRIET AUBER, ALT.

280 *The Source of every good gift.*

1 OUR blest Redeemer, ere he breathed
  His tender, last farewell,
A Guide, a Comforter, bequeathed,
  With us on earth to dwell.

2 He came in tongues of living flame,
  To teach, convince, subdue;
All-powerful as the wind he came,
  And all as viewless, too.

3 He came, sweet influence to impart,
  A gracious, willing Guest,
While he can find one humble heart
  Wherein to fix his rest.

4 And his that gentle voice we hear,
  Soft as the breath of even,
That checks each fault, calms every fear,
  And whispers us of heaven.

281 *The Spirit's witness.*

1 ETERNAL Spirit, God of truth,
  Our contrite hearts inspire;
Kindle a flame of heavenly love,
  The pure celestial fire.

2 'Tis thine to soothe the sorrowing,
  With guilt and fear oppressed;
'Tis thine to bid the dying live,
  And give the weary rest.

3 Subdue the power of every sin,
  Whate'er that sin may be;
That we, in singleness of heart,
  May worship only thee.

4 Then with our spirits witness bear,
  That we are sons of God;
Redeemed from sin, and death, and hell.
  Through Christ's atoning blood.
                        THOMAS COTTERILL.

ZEBULON.   H. M.   LOWELL MASON.

282 *Pleading the promise.*

1 O THOU that hearest prayer,
    Attend our humble cry,
  And let thy servants share
    Thy blessing from on high:
We plead the promise of thy word;
Grant us thy Holy Spirit, Lord!

2 If earthly parents hear
    Their children when they cry;

If they, with love sincere,
    Their children's wants supply;
Much more wilt thou thy love display,
And answer when thy children pray.

3 Our heavenly Father, thou;
    We, children of thy grace;
  O let thy Spirit now
    Descend and fill the place;
That all may feel the heavenly flame,
And all unite to praise thy name.
                        JOHN BURTON.

THE HOLY SPIRIT.

MARTH. 7, 5.

JOSEPH P. HOLBROOK.

283 *Prayer to the Holy Spirit.*

1 THOU who like the wind dost come,
　Come to me, but ne'er depart;
Blessed Spirit, make thy home
　In my thankful heart.

2 Answer not with tongues of light;
　Brood not o'er me like a dove;
Fall upon me in thy might;
　Fill me with thy love.

3 Sin has ruled me; set me free;
　Sin has scourged me; bring me rest:
Help my fainting soul to flee
　To my Saviour's breast.

4 Tell me much of cleansing blood;
　Show me sin, but sin forgiven:
Step by step, where Christ has trod,
　Help me home to heaven.

HERVEY D. GANSE.

NEW HAVEN. 6, 4.

THOMAS HASTINGS.

284 *Invocation of the Holy Spirit.*

1 COME, Holy Ghost, in love,
Shed on us from above
　Thine own bright ray!
Divinely good thou art;
Thy sacred gifts impart
To gladden each sad heart:
　O come to-day!

2 Come, tenderest Friend, and best,
Our most delightful Guest,
　With soothing power:
Rest, which the weary know,
Shade, 'mid the noontide glow,
Peace, when deep griefs o'erflow,
　Cheer us, this hour!

3 Come, Light serene, and still
Our inmost bosoms fill;
　Dwell in each breast;
We know no dawn but thine,
Send forth thy beams divine,
On our dark souls to shine,
　And make us blest!

4 Come, all the faithful bless;
Let all who Christ confess
　His praise employ;
Give virtue's rich reward;
Victorious death accord,
And, with our glorious Lord,
　Eternal joy!

ROBERT II., KING OF FRANCE.
TR. BY R. PALMER.

THE HOLY SPIRIT.

STATE STREET.   S. M.   JONATHAN CALL WOODMAN.

285 *For the Spirit's energy.*

1 COME, Holy Spirit, come,
   With energy divine,
And on this poor benighted soul
   With beams of mercy shine.

2 From the celestial hills
   Light, life, and joy dispense;
And may I daily, hourly, feel
   Thy quickening influence.

3 O melt this frozen heart,
   This stubborn will subdue;
Each evil passion overcome,
   And form me all anew.

4 The profit will be mine,
   But thine shall be the praise;
Cheerful to thee will I devote
   The remnant of my days.
                              BENJAMIN BEDDOME

286 *Renewal of Pentecost.*

1 LORD God, the Holy Ghost!
   In this accepted hour,
As on the day of Pentecost,
   Descend in all thy power.

2 We meet with one accord
   In our appointed place,
And wait the promise of our Lord,—
   The Spirit of all grace.

3 Like mighty rushing wind
   Upon the waves beneath,
Move with one impulse every mind;
   One soul, one feeling breathe.

4 The young, the old, inspire
   With wisdom from above;
And give us hearts and tongues of fire,
   To pray, and praise, and love.

5 Spirit of light! explore,
   And chase our gloom away,
With luster shining more and more,
   Unto the perfect day.
                              JAMES MONTGOMERY.

ONTARIO.   S. M.   LONDON TUNE BOOK.

287 *The Comforter.*

1 BLEST Comforter divine,
   Let rays of heavenly love
Amid our gloom and darkness shine,
   And point our souls above.

2 Turn us with gentle voice
   From every sinful way,
And bid the mourning saint rejoice,
   Though earthly joys decay.

3 By thine inspiring breath
   Make every cloud of care,
And e'en the gloomy vale of death,
   A smile of glory wear.

4 O fill thou every heart
   With love to all our race;
Great Comforter, to us impart
   These blessings of thy grace.
                              MRS. LYDIA H. SIGOURNEY.

THE SCRIPTURES.

DOVER.　S. M.

FROM AARON WILLIAMS.

288 *God's word, quick and powerful.*

1 THY word, almighty Lord,
　Where'er it enters in,
Is sharper than a two-edged sword,
　To slay the man of sin.

2 Thy word is power and life;
　It bids confusion cease,
And changes envy, hatred, strife,
　To love, and joy, and peace.

3 Then let our hearts obey
　The gospel's glorious sound;
And all its fruits, from day to day,
　Be in us and abound.
　　　　　　　　　JAMES MONTGOMERY.

289 *Spreading the Scriptures.*

1 JESUS, the word bestow,
　The true immortal seed;
Thy gospel then shall greatly grow,
　And all our land o'erspread;
Through earth extended wide
　Shall mightily prevail,
Destroy the works of self and pride,
　And shake the gates of hell.

2 Its energy exert
　In the believing soul;
Diffuse thy grace through every part,
　And sanctify the whole;
Its utmost virtue show
　In pure consummate love,
And fill with all thy life below,
　And give us thrones above.
　　　　　　　　　CHARLES WESLEY.

[L. M.　Tune, Missionary Chant.　P. 69.]
290 *The brightening glory of the Gospel.*

1 UPON the Gospel's sacred page
　The gathered beams of ages shine;
And, as it hastens, every age
　But makes its brightness more divine.

2 On mightier wing, in loftier flight,
　From year to year does knowledge soar;
And, as it soars, the Gospel light
　Becomes effulgent more and more.

3 More glorious still, as centuries roll,
　New regions blest, new powers unfurled,
Expanding with the expanding soul,
　Its radiance shall o'erflow the world,—

4 Flow to restore, but not destroy;
　As when the cloudless lamp of day
Pours out its floods of light and joy,
　And sweeps the lingering mists away.
　　　　　　　　　SIR JOHN BOWRING.

[L. M. 6 l.　Tune, Selena.　Page 82.]
291 *Delight in the Bible.*

1 WHEN quiet in my house I sit,
　Thy book be my companion still;
My joy thy sayings to repeat,
　Talk o'er the records of thy will,
And search the oracles divine,
Till every heart-felt word be mine.

2 O may the gracious words divine
　Subject of all my converse be;
So will the Lord his follower join,
　And walk and talk himself with me:
So shall my heart his presence prove,
And burn with everlasting love.

3 Oft as I lay me down to rest,
　O may the reconciling word
Sweetly compose my weary breast;
　While on the bosom of my Lord
I sink in blissful dreams away,
And visions of eternal day.

4 Rising to sing my Saviour's praise,
　Thee may I publish all day long;
And let thy precious word of grace
　Flow from my heart, and fill my tongue
Fill all my life with purest love,
And join me to the Church above.
　　　　　　　　　CHARLES WESLEY.

THE SCRIPTURES.

UXBRIDGE. L. M. LOWELL MASON.

292 *The two revelations.*

1 THE heavens declare thy glory, Lord;
  In every star thy wisdom shines;
But when our eyes behold thy word,
  We read thy name in fairer lines.

2 The rolling sun, the changing light,
  And nights and days, thy power confess,
But the blest volume thou hast writ,
  Reveals thy justice and thy grace.

3 Sun, moon, and stars, convey thy praise
  Round the whole earth, and never stand:
So when thy truth began its race,
  It touched and glanced on every land.

4 Nor shall thy spreading gospel rest,
  Till through the world thy truth has run:
Till Christ has all the nations blessed
  That see the light, or feel the sun.

5 Great Sun of righteousness, arise,
  Bless the dark world with heavenly light;
Thy gospel makes the simple wise,
  Thy laws are pure, thy judgments right.

6 Thy noblest wonders here we view,
  In souls renewed, and sins forgiven:
Lord, cleanse my sins, my soul renew,
  And make thy word my guide to heaven.
                                    ISAAC WATTS.

293 *The everlasting word.*

1 The starry firmament on high,
  And all the glories of the sky,
Yet shine not to thy praise, O Lord,
  So brightly as thy written word.

2 The hopes that holy word supplies,
  Its truths divine and precepts wise,

In each a heavenly beam I see,
And every beam conducts to thee.

3 Almighty Lord, the sun shall fail,
  The moon forget her nightly tale,
And deepest silence hush on high
  The radiant chorus of the sky;

4 But, fixed for everlasting years,
  Unmoved amid the wreck of spheres,
Thy word shall shine in cloudless day,
  When heaven and earth have passed
    away.
                              SIR ROBERT GRANT.

294 *The Saviour seen in the Scripture.*

1 Now let my soul, eternal King,
  To thee its grateful tribute bring;
My knee with humble homage bow;
  My tongue perform its solemn vow.

2 All nature sings thy boundless love,
  In worlds below and worlds above;
But in thy blessed word I trace
  Diviner wonders of thy grace.

3 There, what delightful truths I read!
  There, I behold the Saviour bleed:
His name salutes my listening ear,
  Revives my heart and checks my fear.

4 There Jesus bids my sorrows cease,
  And gives my laboring conscience peace.
He lifts my grateful thoughts on high,
  And points to mansions in the sky.

5 For love like this, O let my song,
  Through endless years, thy praise prolong,
Let distant climes thy name adore,
  Till time and nature are no more.
                          OTTIWELL HEGINBOTHAM.

8

THE SCRIPTURES.

BURLINGTON.   C. M.

JOHN FRECKLETON BURR₁ 1834.

295   *Riches of God's word.*

1 THE counsels of redeeming grace
    The sacred leaves unfold;
And here the Saviour's lovely face
    Our raptured eyes behold.

2 Here light descending from above
    Directs our doubtful feet;
Here promises of heavenly love
    Our ardent wishes meet.

3 Our numerous griefs are here redressed,
    And all our wants supplied:
Naught we can ask to make us blest
    Is in this book denied.

4 For these inestimable gains,
    That so enrich the mind,
O may we search with eager pains,
    Assured that we shall find.
                                SAMUEL STENNETT.

296   *Glory of the Scriptures.*

1 WHAT glory gilds the sacred page!
    Majestic, like the sun,
It gives a light to every age;
    It gives, but borrows none.

2 The power that gave it still supplies
    The gracious light and heat;
Its truths upon the nations rise:
    They rise, but never set.

3 Lord, everlasting thanks be thine
    For such a bright display,
As makes a world of darkness shine
    With beams of heavenly day.

4 My soul rejoices to pursue
    The steps of him I love,
Till glory breaks upon my view
    In brighter worlds above.
                                WILLIAM COWPER.

297   *Bible precious.*

1 How precious is the book divine,
    By inspiration given!
Bright as a lamp its doctrines shine,
    To guide our souls to heaven.

2 It sweetly cheers our drooping hearts,
    In this dark vale of tears;
Life, light, and joy it still imparts,
    And quells our rising fears.

3 This lamp, through all the tedious night
    Of life, shall guide our way;
Till we behold the clearer light
    Of an eternal day.
                                JOHN FAWCETT.

298   *Revelation disseminated.*

1 HAIL, sacred truth! whose piercing rays
    Dispel the shades of night;
Diffusing o'er a ruined world
    The healing beams of light.

2 Jesus, thy word, with friendly aid,
    Restores our wandering feet;
Converts the sorrows of the mind
    To joys divinely sweet.

3 O send thy light and truth abroad,
    In all their radiant blaze;
And bid the admiring world adore
    The glories of thy grace.
                                JOHN BUTTRESS. ALT.

110

MELODY.   C. M.   I. P. COLE.

299   *Excellence and sufficiency.*

1 FATHER of mercies, in thy word
  What endless glory shines!
Forever be thy name adored
  For these celestial lines.

2 Here may the wretched sons of want
  Exhaustless riches find;
Riches above what earth can grant,
  And lasting as the mind.

3 Here the fair tree of knowledge grows,
  And yields a free repast;
Sublimer sweets than nature knows
  Invite the longing taste.

4 Here the Redeemer's welcome voice
  Spreads heavenly peace around;
And life and everlasting joys
  Attend the blissful sound.

5 O may these heavenly pages be
  Our ever dear delight;
And still new beauties may we see,
  And still increasing light.

6 Divine instructor, gracious Lord,
  Be thou forever near;
Teach us to love thy sacred word,
  And view the Saviour there.
                          ANNE STEELE.

300   *Light from heaven.*

1 BRIGHT was the guiding star that led,
  With mild, benignant ray,
The Gentiles to the lowly bed
  Where the Redeemer lay.

2 But lo! a brighter, clearer light
  Now points to his abode;
It shines through sin and sorrow's night,
  To guide us to our God.

3 O gladly tread the narrow path,
  While light and grace are given;
Who meekly follow Christ on earth
  Shall reign with him in heaven.
                          HARRIET AUBER.

301   *God giveth the increase.—1 Cor. 3 : 1.*

1 ALMIGHTY God, thy word is cast
  Like seed upon the ground;
O let the dew of heaven descend,
  And shed its influence round.

2 Let not the foe of Christ and man
  This holy seed remove;
May it take root in every heart,
  And grow in faith and love.

3 Let not this life's deceitful cares,
  Nor worldly wealth and joy,
Nor scorching beam, nor stormy blast,
  The rising plant destroy.

4 Where'er the word of life is sown,
  A large increase bestow;
That all who hear thy message, Lord,
  Its saving power may know.
                  JOHN CAWOOD, ALT. BY W. F. HALL

111

THE SINNER—LOST CONDITION.

HAVEN.   C. M.   Thomas Hastings.

302   *Lord, help my unbelief.*

1 How sad our state by nature is!
  Our sin, how deep it stains!
And Satan binds our captive souls
  Fast in his slavish chains.

2 But there's a voice of sovereign grace
  Sounds from the sacred word:
"Ho! ye despairing sinners, come,
  And trust a faithful Lord."

3 My soul obeys the gracious call,
  And runs to this relief;
I would believe thy promise, Lord;
  O help my unbelief!

4 To the blest fountain of thy blood,
  Incarnate God, I fly;
Here let me wash my guilty soul
  From crimes of deepest dye.

5 A guilty, weak, and helpless worm,
  Into thine arms I fall;
Be thou my strength and righteousness,
  My Jesus, and my all.
                                        ISAAC WATTS.

303   *Without God in the world.*

1 GOD is in this and every place;
  But O, how dark and void
To me!—'tis one great wilderness,
  This earth without my God.

2 Empty of him who all things fills,
  Till he his light impart,
Till he his glorious self reveals,
  The veil is on my heart.

3 O thou who seest and know'st my grief,
  Thyself unseen, unknown,
Pity my helpless unbelief,
  And break my heart of stone.

4 Regard me with a gracious eye;
  The long-sought blessing give;
And bid me, at the point to die,
  Behold thy face and live.
                                        CHARLES WESLEY.

304   *His pitying love.*

1 PLUNGED in a gulf of dark despair,
  We wretched sinners lay,
Without one cheering beam of hope,
  Or spark of glimmering day.

2 With pitying eyes the Prince of grace
  Beheld our helpless grief:
He saw, and, O amazing love!
  He ran to our relief.

3 Down from the shining seats above,
  With joyful haste he sped,
Entered the grave in mortal flesh,
  And dwelt among the dead.

4 O for this love let rocks and hills
  Their lasting silence break;
And all harmonious human tongues,
  The Saviour's praises speak.

5 Angels, assist our mighty joys;
  Strike all your harps of gold;
But when you raise your highest notes,
  His love can ne'er be told.
                                        ISAAC WATTS.

112

LOUVAN. L. M.

VIRGIL CORYDON TAYLOR.

305 *Original corruption and actual sin.*

1 LORD, we are vile, conceived in sin,
And born unholy and unclean;
Sprung from the man whose guilty fall
Corrupts his race, and taints us all.

2 Soon as we draw our infant breath
The seeds of sin grow up for death;
Thy law demands a perfect heart,
But we 're defiled in every part.

3 Behold, we fall before thy face;
Our only refuge is thy grace:
No outward forms can make us clean:
The leprosy lies deep within.

4 Nor bleeding bird, nor bleeding beast,
Nor hyssop branch, nor sprinkling priest,
Nor running brook, nor flood, nor sea,
Can wash the dismal stain away.

5 Jesus, thy blood, thy blood alone,
Hath power sufficient to atone;
Thy blood can make us white as snow;
No Jewish types could cleanse us so.

6 While guilt disturbs and breaks our
peace,
Nor flesh nor soul hath rest or ease;
Lord, let us hear thy pardoning voice,
And make these broken hearts rejoice.
ISAAC WATTS.

306 *The great Physician.*

1 DEEP are the wounds which sin has
made;
Where shall the sinner find a cure?
In vain, alas! is nature's aid;
The work exceeds her utmost power.

2 But can no sovereign balm be found,
And is no kind physician nigh,
To ease the pain and heal the wound,
Ere life and hope forever fly?

3 There is a great Physician near;
Look up, O fainting soul, and live;
See, in his heavenly smiles, appear
Such help as nature cannot give.

4 See, in the Saviour's dying blood,
Life, health, and bliss abundant flow;
And in that sacrificial flood
A balm for all thy grief and woe.
ANNE STEELE.

307 *Inbred leprosy.*

1 JESUS, a word, a look from thee,
Can turn my heart and make it clean:
Purge out the inbred leprosy,
And save me from my bosom sin.

2 Lord, if thou wilt, I do believe
Thou canst the saving grace impart;
Thou canst this instant now forgive,
And stamp thine image on my heart.

3 My heart, which now to thee I raise,
I know thou canst this moment cleanse;
The deepest stains of sin efface,
And drive the evil spirit hence.

4 Be it according to thy word;
Accomplish now thy work in me;
And let my soul, to health restored,
Devote its deathless powers to thee.
CHARLES WESLEY.

THE SINNER—LOST CONDITION.

SHAWMUT.   S. M.

ARR. BY LOWELL MASON.

308   *In trespasses and sins.*

1 My former hopes are fled;
   My terror now begins:
I feel, alas! that I am dead
   In trespasses and sins.

2 When I review my ways,
   I dread impending doom:
But hark! a friendly whisper says,
   "Flee from the wrath to come."

3 With trembling hope I see
   A glimmering from afar;
A beam of day that shines for me,
   To save me from despair.

4 Forerunner of the sun,
   It marks the pilgrim's way;
I'll gaze upon it while I run,
   And watch the rising day.
            WILLIAM COWPER.

309   *Dependence on the Spirit.*

1 How helpless nature lies,
   Unconscious of her load!
The heart unchanged can never rise
   To happiness and God.

2 Can aught but power divine
   The stubborn will subdue?
'Tis thine, eternal Spirit, thine
   To form the heart anew;

3 The passions to recall,
   And upward bid them rise;
To make the scales of error fall
   From reason's darkened eyes.

4 O change these hearts of ours,
   And give them life divine;
Then shall our passions and our powers,
   Almighty Lord, be thine.
            ANNE STEELE.

310   *Helpless and guilty.*

1 Ah, how shall fallen man
   Be just before his God?
If he contend in righteousness,
   We sink beneath his rod.

2 If he our ways should mark
   With strict inquiring eyes,
Could we for one of thousand faults
   A just excuse devise?

3 The mountains, in thy wrath,
   Their ancient seats forsake;
The trembling earth deserts her place,
   Her rooted pillars shake.

4 Ah, how shall guilty man
   Contend with such a God?
None—none can meet him, and escape,
   But through the Saviour's blood.
            ISAAC WATTS.

311   *Obduracy bemoaned.*

1 O THAT I could repent!
   O that I could believe!
Thou, by thy voice, the marble rend,
   The rock in sunder cleave:
Thou, by thy two-edged sword,
   My soul and spirit part;
Strike with the hammer of thy word,
   And break my stubborn heart.

2 Saviour, and Prince of peace,
   The double grace bestow;
Unloose the bands of wickedness,
   And let the captive go:
Grant me my sins to feel,
   And then the load remove:
Wound, and pour in, my wounds to heal
   The balm of pardoning love.
            CHARLES WESLEY.

312   *Christ our ransom.*

1 OUR sins on Christ were laid;
   He bore the mighty load;
Our ransom-price he fully paid
   In groans, and tears, and blood.

2 To save a world, he dies;
   Sinners, behold the Lamb!
To him lift up your longing eyes;
   Seek mercy in his name.

3 Pardon and peace abound;
   He will your sins forgive;
Salvation in his name is found,—
   He bids the sinner live.

4 Jesus, we look to thee;
   Where else can sinners go?
Thy boundless love shall set us free
   From wretchedness and woe.
            JOHN FAWCETT.

THE SINNER—PROVISIONS OF THE GOSPEL.

STATE STREET. S. M. JONATHAN CALL WOODMAN.

313 *The only name.*

1 JESUS, thou Source divine,
　Whence hope and comfort flow!
Jesus, no other name than thine
　Can save from endless woe.

2 None else will Heaven approve:
　Thou art the only way,
Ordained by everlasting love,
　To realms of endless day.

3 Here let our feet abide,
　Nor from thy path depart:
Direct our steps, thou gracious Guide!
　And cheer the fainting heart.

4 Safe through this world of night,
　Lead to the blissful plains,
The regions of unclouded light,
　Where joy forever reigns.

ANNE STEELE.

314 *The precious blood.*

1 GOD'S holy law transgressed,
　Speaks nothing but despair;
Convinced of guilt, with grief oppressed
　We find no comfort there.

2 Not all our groans and tears,
　Nor works which we have done,
Nor vows, nor promises, nor prayers,
　Can e'er for sin atone.

3 Relief alone is found
　In Jesus' precious blood:
'Tis this that heals the mortal wound,
　And reconciles to God.

4 High lifted on the cross
　The spotless Victim dies;
This is salvation's only source;
　Hence all our hopes arise.

BENJAMIN BEDDOME.

AZMON. C. M. CARL GOTTHELF GLASER, ARR. BY LOWELL MASON.

315 *Wonders of redemption.*

1 How great the wisdom, power, and grace,
　Which in redemption shine!
The heavenly host with joy confess
　The work is all divine.

2 Before His feet they cast their crowns,—
　Those crowns which Jesus gave,—
And, with ten thousand thousand tongues,
　Proclaim his power to save.

3 They tell the triumphs of his cross,
　The sufferings which he bore;
How low he stooped, how high he rose,
　And rose to stoop no more.

4 With them let us our voices raise,
　And still the song renew;
Salvation well deserves the praise
　Of meL and angels too.

BENJAMIN BEDDOME.

ST. BERNARD.   C. M.   LONDON TUNE BOOK.

316   *The dearest name.*

1 How sweet the name of Jesus sounds
    In a believer's ear!
It soothes his sorrows, heals his wounds,
    And drives away his fear.

2 It makes the wounded spirit whole,
    And calms the troubled breast;
'Tis manna to the hungry soul,
    And to the weary, rest.

3 Dear name! the rock on which I build,
    My shield and hiding-place;
My never-failing treasure, filled
    With boundless stores of grace!

4 Jesus, my Shepherd, Saviour, Friend,
    My Prophet, Priest, and King,
My Lord, my Life, my Way, my End,
    Accept the praise I bring!

5 I would thy boundless love proclaim
    With every fleeting breath;
So shall the music of thy name
    Refresh my soul in death.
                        JOHN NEWTON.

317   *Ceaseless goodness.*

1 THY ceaseless, unexhausted love,
    Unmerited and free,
Delights our evil to remove,
    And help our misery.

2 Thou waitest to be gracious still;
    Thou dost with sinners bear;
That, saved, we may thy goodness feel,
    And all thy grace declare.

3 Thy goodness and thy truth to me,
    To every soul, abound:

A vast, unfathomable sea,
    Where all our thoughts are drowned.

4 Its streams the whole creation reach,
    So plenteous is the store;
Enough for all, enough for each,
    Enough for evermore.

5 Faithful, O Lord, thy mercies are,
    A rock that cannot move:
A thousand promises declare
    Thy constancy of love.

6 Throughout the universe it reigns,
    Unalterably sure;
And while the truth of God remains,
    His goodness must endure.
                        CHARLES WESLEY.

318   *The Way, the Truth, and the Life.*

1 THOU art the Way:—to thee alone
    From sin and death we flee;
And he who would the Father seek,
    Must seek him, Lord, by thee.

2 Thou art the Truth:—thy word alone
    True wisdom can impart;
Thou only canst inform the mind,
    And purify the heart.

3 Thou art the Life:—the rending tomb
    Proclaims thy conquering arm;
And those who put their trust in thee
    Nor death nor hell shall harm.

4 Thou art the Way, the Truth, the Life:
    Grant us that Way to know,
That Truth to keep, that Life to win,
    Whose joys eternal flow.
                        GEORGE W. DOANE.

THE SINNER—PROVISIONS OF THE GOSPEL.

COWPER. C. M.

LOWELL MASON.

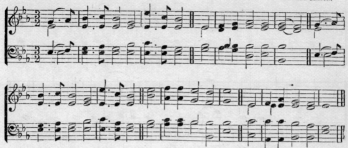

319 *The cleansing fountain.*

1 THERE is a fountain filled with blood
Drawn from Immanuel's veins;
And sinners, plunged beneath that flood,
Lose all their guilty stains.

2 The dying thief rejoiced to see
That fountain in his day;
And there may I, though vile as he,
Wash all my sins away.

3 Thou dying Lamb! thy precious blood
Shall never lose its power,
Till all the ransomed Church of God
Are saved, to sin no more.

4 E'er since, by faith, I saw the stream
Thy flowing wounds supply,
Redeeming love has been my theme,
And shall be till I die.

5 Then in a nobler, sweeter song,
I'll sing thy power to save,
When this poor lisping, stammering tongue
Lies silent in the grave.

6 Lord, I believe thou hast prepared,
Unworthy though I be,
For me a blood-bought, free reward,
A golden harp for me!

7 'Tis strung and tuned for endless years
And formed by power divine,
To sound in God the Father's ears,
No other name but thine.

WILLIAM COWPER.

320 *The pierced hand.*

1 WHEN wounded sore, the stricken soul
Lies bleeding and unbound,
One only hand, a pierced hand,
Can heal the sinner's wound.

2 When sorrow swells the laden breast,
And tears of anguish flow,
One only heart, a broken heart,
Can feel the sinner's woe.

3 When penitence has wept in vain
Over some foul, dark spot,
One only stream, a stream of blood,
Can wash away the blot.

4 'Tis Jesus' blood that washes white,
His hand that brings relief;
His heart that's touched with all our joys,
And feeleth for our grief.

5 Lift up thy bleeding hand, O Lord!
Unseal that cleansing tide:
We have no shelter from our sin
But in thy wounded side.

MRS. CECIL F. ALEXANDER.

CLEANSING FOUNTAIN. C. M.

WESTERN MELODY.

SILVER STREET. S. M.

ISAAC SMITH.

321 *Grace.*

1 GRACE! 'tis a charming sound,
  Harmonious to the ear;
Heaven with the echo shall resound,
  And all the earth shall hear.

2 Grace first contrived a way
  To save rebellious man;
And all the steps that grace display,
  Which drew the wondrous plan.

3 Grace taught my roving feet
  To tread the heavenly road;
And new supplies each hour I meet,
  While pressing on to God.

4 Grace all the work shall crown
  Through everlasting days;
It lays in heaven the topmost stone,
  And well deserves our praise.

PHILIP DODDRIDGE.

322 *Our debt paid upon the cross.*

1 WHAT majesty and grace
  Through all the gospel shine!

'Tis God that speaks, and we confess
  The doctrine most divine.

2 Down from his throne on high,
  The mighty Saviour comes;
Lays his bright robes of glory by,
  And feeble flesh assumes.

3 The debt that sinners owed,
  Upon the cross he pays;
Then through the clouds ascends to God,
  'Midst shouts of loftiest praise.

4 There our High Priest appears
  Before his Father's throne;
Mingles his merits with our tears,
  And pours salvation down.

5 Great Sovereign, we adore
  Thy justice and thy grace,
And on thy faithfulness and power
  Our firm dependence place.

SAMUEL STENNETT, ALT.

HUMMEL. C. M.

HEINRICH CHRISTOPHER ZEUNER.

323 *Full and free.*

1 O WHAT amazing words of grace
  Are in the gospel found!
Suited to every sinner's case,
  Who knows the joyful sound.

2 Poor, sinful, thirsty, fainting souls
  Are freely welcome here;

Salvation, like a river, rolls
  Abundant, free, and clear.

3 Come, then, with all your wants
      wounds;
  Your every burden bring;
Here love, unchanging love, abounds,
  A deep, celestial spring.

4 Whoever will—O gracious word!
  May of this stream partake:
Come, thirsty souls, and bless the Lord
  And drink, for Jesus' sake.

5 Millions of sinners, vile as you,
  Have here found life and peace;
Come, then, and prove its virtues too,
  And drink, adore, and bless.

SAMUEL MEDLEY, ALT.

CAMBRIDGE. C. M.

JOHN RANDALL.

324 *The joyful sound.*

1 SALVATION! O the joyful sound!
  What pleasure to our ears!
A sovereign balm for every wound,
  A cordial for our fears.

2 Salvation! let the echo fly
  The spacious earth around,
While all the armies of the sky
  Conspire to raise the sound.

3 Salvation! O thou bleeding Lamb!
  To thee the praise belongs:
Salvation shall inspire our hearts,
  And dwell upon our tongues.
                              ISAAC WATTS.

325 *The all-sufficient Saviour.*

1 THE Saviour! O what endless charms
  Dwell in that blissful sound!
Its influence every fear disarms,
  And spreads delight around.

2 Here pardon, life, and joy divine,
  In rich effusion flow,
For guilty rebels, lost in sin,
  And doomed to endless woe.

3 The almighty Former of the skies
  Stoops to our vile abode:
While angels view with wondering eyes,
  And hail the incarnate God.

4 How rich the depths of love divine!
  Of bliss a boundless store!
Redeemer, let me call thee mine,
  Thy fullness I implore.

5 On thee alone my hope relies;
  Beneath thy cross I fall;
My Lord, my Life, my Sacrifice,
  My Saviour, and my All!
                              ANNE STEELE.

326 *The gospel feast.*

1 LET every mortal ear attend,
  And every heart rejoice;
The trumpet of the gospel sounds
  With an inviting voice.

2 Ho! all ye hungry, starving souls,
  That feed upon the wind,
And vainly strive with earthly toys
  To fill an empty mind!

3 Eternal Wisdom hath prepared
  A soul-reviving feast,
And bids your longing appetites
  The rich provision taste.

4 Ho! ye that pant for living streams,
  And pine away and die,
Here you may quench your raging thirst
  With springs that never dry.

5 Rivers of love and mercy here
  In a rich ocean join;
Salvation in abundance flows,
  Like floods of milk and wine.

6 The happy gates of gospel grace
  Stand open night and day:
Lord, we are come to seek supplies,
  And drive our wants away.
                              ISAAC WATTS.

ROCKINGHAM. L. M. LOWELL MASON.

327 *Love which passeth knowledge.*

1 OF Him who did salvation bring,
I could forever think and sing;
Arise, ye needy,—he'll relieve;
Arise, ye guilty,—he'll forgive.

2 Ask but his grace, and lo, 'tis given;
Ask, and he turns your hell to heaven:
Though sin and sorrow wound my soul,
Jesus, thy balm will make it whole.

3 To shame our sins he blushed in blood;
He closed his eyes to show us God:
Let all the world fall down and know
That none but God such love can show.

4 'Tis thee I love, for thee alone
I shed my tears and make my moan;
Where'er I am, where'er I move,
I meet the object of my love.

5 Insatiate to this spring I fly;
I drink, and yet am ever dry:
Ah! who against thy charms is proof?
Ah! who that loves, can love enough?
BERNARD OF CLAIRVAUX. TR. BY A. W. BOEHM.

328 *The divine Teacher.*

1 How sweetly flowed the gospel's sound
From lips of gentleness and grace,
While listening thousands gathered round,
And joy and reverence filled the place!

2 From heaven He came, of heaven he
spoke,
To heaven he led his followers' way;

Dark clouds of gloomy night he broke,
Unveiling an immortal day.

3 "Come, wanderers, to my Father's
home;
Come, all ye weary ones, and rest."
Yes, sacred Teacher, we will come,
Obey, and be forever blest.

4 Decay, then, tenements of dust!
Pillars of earthly pride, decay!
A nobler mansion waits the just,
And Jesus has prepared the way.
SIR JOHN BOWRING.

329 *The gift unspeakable.*

1 HAPPY the man who finds the grace,
The blessing of God's chosen race,
The wisdom coming from above,
The faith that sweetly works by love.

2 Wisdom divine! who tells the price
Of wisdom's costly merchandise?
Wisdom to silver we prefer,
And gold is dross compared to her.

3 Her hands are filled with length of days,
True riches, and immortal praise;
Her ways are ways of pleasantness,
And all her flowery paths are peace.

4 Happy the man who wisdom gains;
Thrice happy, who his guest retains:
He owns, and shall forever own,
Wisdom, and Christ, and heaven, are one.
CHARLES WESLEY.

SCOTLAND. 12.

JOHN CLARKE.

330   *The voice of free grace.*

1 THE voice of free grace cries, "Escape
    to the mountain;
For Adam's lost race Christ hath opened a
    fountain :
For sin and uncleanness, and every trans-
    gression,
His blood flows most freely, in streams of
    salvation."
    Hallelujah to the Lamb, who has pur-
      chased our pardon!
    We will praise him again when we pass
      over Jordan.

2 Now glory to God in the highest is given;
Now glory to God is re-echoed in heaven;
Around the whole earth let us tell the glad
    story,
And sing of his love, his salvation and glory.

3 O Jesus, ride on,—thy kingdom is glo-
    rious;
O'er sin, death, and hell, thou wilt make us
    victorious:
Thy name shall be praised in the great
    congregation,
And saints shall ascribe unto thee their
    salvation.

4 When on Zion we stand, having gained
    the blest shore,
With our harps in our hands, we will praise
    evermore:
We'll range the blest fields on the banks of
    the river,
And sing of redemption forever and ever.

RICHARD BURDSALL.

LENOX. H. M.

LEWIS EDSON.

331 *The year of jubilee.*

1 BLOW ye the trumpet, blow,
  The gladly-solemn sound!
Let all the nations know,
  To earth's remotest bound,
The year of jubilee is come!
Return, ye ransomed sinners, home.

2 Jesus, our great High Priest,
  Hath full atonement made:
Ye weary spirits, rest;
  Ye mournful souls, be glad:
The year of jubilee is come!
Return, ye ransomed sinners, home.

3 Extol the Lamb of God,
  The all-atoning Lamb;
Redemption in his blood
  Throughout the world proclaim:
The year of jubilee is come!
Return, ye ransomed sinners, home.

4 Ye slaves of sin and hell,
  Your liberty receive,
And safe in Jesus dwell,
  And blest in Jesus live:
The year of jubilee is come!
Return, ye ransomed sinners, home.

5 Ye who have sold for naught
  Your heritage above,
Shall have it back unbought,
  The gift of Jesus' love:
The year of jubilee is come!
Return, ye ransomed sinners, home.

6 The gospel trumpet hear,
  The news of heavenly grace;
And, saved from earth, appear
  Before your Saviour's face:
The year of jubilee is come!
Return, ye ransomed sinners, home.
                              CHARLES WESLEY.

332 *Jesus, the all-atoning Lamb.*

1 LET earth and heaven agree,
  Angels and men be joined,
To celebrate with me
  The Saviour of mankind:
To adore the all-atoning Lamb,
And bless the sound of Jesus' name.

2 Jesus! transporting sound!
  The joy of earth and heaven!
No other help is found,
  No other name is given,
By which we can salvation have;
But Jesus came the world to save.

3 Jesus! harmonious name!
  It charms the hosts above;
They evermore proclaim
  And wonder at his love:
'Tis all their happiness to gaze,—
'Tis heaven to see our Jesus' face.

4 His name the sinner hears,
  And is from sin set free;
'Tis music in his ears;
  'Tis life and victory;
New songs do now his lips employ,
And dances his glad heart for joy.

5 O unexampled love!
  O all-redeeming grace!
How swiftly didst thou move
  To save a fallen race!
What shall I do to make it known,
What thou for all mankind hast done?

6 O for a trumpet voice,
  On all the world to call,
To bid their hearts rejoice
  In him who died for all!
For all my Lord was crucified;
For all, for all, my Saviour died.
                              CHARLES WESLEY.

RAKEM. L. M. 6l.   ISAAC BAKER WOODBURY.

FINE

333   *He died for me.*

1 WHEN time seems short and death is near,
And I am pressed by doubt and fear,
And sins, an overflowing tide,
Assail my peace on every side,
This thought my refuge still shall be,
I know the Saviour died for me.

2 His name is Jesus, and he died,
For guilty sinners crucified;

Content to die that he might win
Their ransom from the death of sin:
No sinner worse than I can be,
Therefore I know he died for me.

3 If grace were bought, I could not buy;
If grace were coined, no wealth have I;
By grace alone I draw my breath,
Held up from everlasting death;
Yet, since I know his grace is free,
I know the Saviour died for me.

GEORGE W. BETHUNE.

WILSON.   8, 7.   FROM FELIX MENDELSSOHN-BARTHOLDY.

334   *The Desire of nations.*

1 COME, thou long-expected Jesus,
Born to set thy people free:
From our fears and sins release us,
Let us find our rest in thee.

2 Israel's Strength and Consolation,
Hope of all the earth thou art;
Dear Desire of every nation,
Joy of every longing heart.

3 Born thy people to deliver,
Born a child, and yet a King,
Born to reign in us forever,
Now thy gracious kingdom bring.

4 By thine own eternal Spirit,
Rule in all our hearts alone;
By thine all-sufficient merit,
Raise us to thy glorious throne.

CHARLES WESLEY.

EXPOSTULATION. 11.

REV. JOSIAH HOPKINS.

335 *Turn ye.*

1 O TURN ye, O turn ye, for why will ye die,
　When God in great mercy is coming so nigh?
Now Jesus invites you, the Spirit says,
　"Come,"
And angels are waiting to welcome you
　home.

2 And now Christ is ready your souls to re-
　ceive,
O how can you question, if you will believe?
If sin is your burden, why will you not
　come?
'Tis you he bids welcome; he bids you come
　home.

3 In riches, in pleasures, what can you ob-
　tain,
To soothe your affliction, or banish your
　pain?
To bear up your spirit when summoned to
　die,
Or waft you to mansions of glory on high?

4 Why will you be starving, and feeding on
　air?
There's mercy in Jesus, enough and to
　spare;
If still you are doubting, make trial and see,
And prove that his mercy is boundless and
　free. JOSIAH HOPKINS.

336 *Delay not.*

1 DELAY not, delay not, O sinner, draw near,
　The waters of life are now flowing for
　thee:

No price is demanded, the Saviour is here,
　Redemption is purchased, salvation is
　free.

2 Delay not, delay not, why longer abuse
　The love and compassion of Jesus, thy
　God?
A fountain is open, how canst thou refuse
　To wash and be cleansed in his pardon-
　ing blood?

3 Delay not, delay not, O sinner, to come,
　For Mercy still lingers and calls thee to-
　day:
Her voice is not heard in the vale of the
　tomb;
　Her message, unheeded, will soon pass
　away.

4 Delay not, delay not, the Spirit of grace
　Long grieved and resisted, may take his
　sad flight,
And leave thee in darkness to finish thy
　race,
　To sink in the gloom of eternity's night.

5 Delay not, delay not, the hour is at
　hand,
　The earth shall dissolve, and the heavens
　shall fade,
The dead, small and great, in the judgment
　shall stand;
　What power then, O sinner, will lend thee
　its aid! THOMAS HASTINGS.

THE SINNER—WARNING AND INVITING.

ROSEFIELD.   7, 6 l.

REV. HENRI ABRAHAM CÆSAR MALAN.

337   *Fly to Jesus.*

1 WEARY souls, that wander wide
  From the central point of bliss,
Turn to Jesus crucified;
  Fly to those dear wounds of his:
Sink into the purple flood;
Rise into the life of God.

2 Find in Christ the way of peace,
  Peace unspeakable, unknown;
By his pain he gives you ease,
  Life by his expiring groan:
Rise exalted by his fall;
Find in Christ your all in all.

3 O believe the record true,
  God to you his Son hath given;
Ye may now be happy too,
  Find on earth the life of heaven:
Live the life of heaven above,
All the life of glorious love.

4 This the universal bliss,
  Bliss for every soul designed;
God's original promise this,
  God's great gift to all mankind:
Blest in Christ this moment be,
Blest to all eternity.
                    CHARLES WESLEY.

338   *Come, and welcome.*

1 FROM the cross uplifted high,
Where the Saviour deigns to die,
What melodious sounds we hear
Bursting on the ravished ear!
"Love's redeeming work is done,
Come and welcome, sinner, come!

2 "Sprinkled now with blood the throne,
Why beneath thy burdens groan?
On his pierced body laid,
Justice owns the ransom paid;
Bow the knee, embrace the Son,
Come and welcome, sinner, come!

3 "Spread for thee, the festal board
See with richest bounty stored;
To thy Father's bosom pressed,
Thou shalt be a child confessed,
Never from his house to roam;
Come and welcome, sinner, come!"
                    THOMAS HAWEIS.

339   *The work of sin.*

1 HEARTS of stone, relent, relent!
  Break, by Jesus' cross subdued;
See his body mangled, rent,
  Covered with his flowing blood!
Sinful soul, what hast thou done?
Crucified the Eternal Son!

2 Yes, thy sins have done the deed,
  Driven the nails that fixed him there,
Crowned with thorns his sacred head,
  Pierced him with a soldier's spear,
Made his soul a sacrifice;
For a sinful world he dies.

3 Wilt thou let him die in vain?
  Still to death pursue our God?
Open all his wounds again?
  Trample on his precious blood?
No; with all my sins I'll part;
Saviour, take my broken heart.
                    CHARLES WESLEY.

9   125

GREENVILLE. 8, 7, 4. JEAN JACQUES ROUSSEAU.

340 *Invitation hymn.*

1 COME, ye sinners, poor and needy,
    Weak and wounded, sick and sore;
Jesus ready stands to save you,
    Full of pity, love, and power:
        He is able,
    He is willing: doubt no more.

2 Now, ye needy, come and welcome;
    God's free bounty glorify;
True belief and true repentance,
    Every grace that brings you nigh,
        Without money,
    Come to Jesus Christ and buy.

3 Let not conscience make you linger,
    Nor of fitness fondly dream;
All the fitness he requireth
    Is to feel your need of him:
        This he gives you;
    'Tis the Spirit's glimmering beam.

4 Come, ye weary, heavy-laden,
    Bruised and mangled by the fall;

If you tarry till you 're better,
    You will never come at all;
        Not the righteous,—
    Sinners Jesus came to call.

5 Agonizing in the garden,
    Your Redeemer prostrate lies;
On the bloody tree behold him!
    Hear him cry, before he dies,
        "It is finished!"
    Sinners, will not this suffice?

6 Lo! the incarnate God, ascending,
    Pleads the merit of his blood:
Venture on him, venture freely;
    Let no other trust intrude:
        None but Jesus
    Can do helpless sinners good.

7 Saints and angels, joined in concert,
    Sing the praises of the Lamb;
While the blissful seats of heaven
    Sweetly echo with his name:
        Hallelujah!
    Sinners here may do the same.

JOSEPH HART.

ALBYN. 8, 7, 4. REV. JOHN BLACK.

THE SINNER—WARNING AND INVITING.

NEANDER. 8, 7, 7, or 8, 7, 4. Rev. Joachim Neander.

341 *The healing fountain.*

1 COME to Calvary's holy mountain,
  Sinners ruined by the fall;
Here a pure and healing fountain
  Flows to you, to me, to all,
In a full perpetual tide,
Opened when our Saviour died.

2 Come, in sorrow and contrition,
  Wounded, impotent, and blind;
Here the guilty, free remission,
  Here the lost a refuge find.
Health this fountain will restore;
He that drinks need thirst no more.

3 Come, ye dying, live forever;
  'Tis a soul-reviving flood;
God is faithful; he will never
  Break his covenant sealed in blood;
Signed when our Redeemer died,
Sealed when he was glorified.
  JAMES MONTGOMERY.

342 *Hear, and live.*

1 SINNERS, will you scorn the message
  Sent in mercy from above?
Every sentence, O how tender!
  Every line is full of love:
  Listen to it;
Every line is full of love.

2 Hear the heralds of the gospel
  News from Zion's King proclaim;

"Pardon to each rebel sinner,
  Free forgiveness in his name:"
  How important!
"Free forgiveness in his name."

3 Tempted souls, they bring you succor;
  Fearful hearts, they quell your fears,
And, with news of consolation,
  Chase away the falling tears:
  Tender heralds!
Chase away the falling tears.

4 O ye angels, hovering round us,
  Waiting spirits, speed your way;
Haste ye to the court of heaven,
  Tidings bear without delay.
  Rebel sinners
Glad the message will obey.
  JONATHAN ALLEN.

343 *The last call.*

1 HEAR, O sinner, mercy hails you,
  Now with sweetest voice she calls;
Bids you haste to seek the Saviour,
  Ere the hand of justice falls;
  Hear, O sinner!
'Tis the voice of mercy calls.

2 Haste, O sinner, to the Saviour!
  Seek his mercy while you may;
Soon the day of grace is over;
  Soon your life will pass away:
  Haste, O sinner!
You must perish if you stay.
  ANDREW REED.

HORTON. 7.   XAVIER SCHNYDER VON WARTENSEE.

344   *The gracious call.*

1 COME, said Jesus' sacred voice,
Come, and make my path your choice;
I will guide you to your home;
Weary pilgrim, hither come.

2 Thou who, houseless, sole, forlorn,
Long hast borne the proud world's scorn,
Long hast roamed the barren waste,
Weary pilgrim, hither haste.

3 Ye who, tossed on beds of pain,
Seek for ease, but seek in vain;
Ye, by fiercer anguish torn,
In remorse for guilt who mourn;

4 Hither come, for here is found
Balm that flows for every wound,
Peace that ever shall endure,
Rest eternal, sacred, sure.
                          MRS. ANNA L. BARBAULD.

345   *Delay dangerous.*

1 HASTEN, sinner, to be wise!
   Stay not for the morrow's sun:
Wisdom if you still despise,
   Harder is it to be won.

2 Hasten, mercy to implore!
   Stay not for the morrow's sun,
Lest thy season should be o'er
   Ere this evening's stage be run.

3 Hasten, sinner, to return!
Stay not for the morrow's sun,

Lest thy lamp should fail to burn
   Ere salvation's work is done.

4 Hasten, sinner, to be blest!
   Stay not for the morrow's sun,
Lest perdition thee arrest
   Ere the morrow is begun.
                          THOMAS SCOTT

346   *At Zion's gate.*

1 PILGRIM, burdened with thy sin,
   Come the way to Zion's gate:
There, till mercy lets thee in,
   Knock, and weep, and watch, and wait
Knock—He knows the sinner's cry;
   Weep—he loves the mourner's tears;
Watch, for saving grace is nigh;
   Wait, till heavenly light appears.

2 Hark, it is the Bridegroom's voice:
   "Welcome, pilgrim, to thy rest!"
Now within the gate rejoice,
   Safe, and sealed, and bought, and blest
Safe, from all the lures of vice;
   Sealed, by signs the chosen know;
Bought by love, and life the price;
   Blest, the mighty debt to owe.

3 Holy pilgrim, what for thee
   In a world like this remain?
From thy guarded breast shall flee
   Fear, and shame, and doubt, and pain;
Fear, the hope of heaven shall fly;
   Shame, from glory's view retire;
Doubt, in certain rapture die;
   Pain, in endless bliss expire.
                          GEORGE CRABBE.

HOLLINGSIDE.   7. D.   Rev. John Bacchus Dykes.

FIRST PART

347   *Why will ye die?*

1 SINNERS, turn; why will ye die?
God, your Maker, asks you why;
God, who did your being give,
Made you with himself to live;
He the fatal cause demands;
Asks the work of his own hands,
Why, ye thankless creatures, why
Will ye cross his love, and die?

2 Sinners, turn; why will ye die?
God, your Saviour, asks you why;
He, who did your souls retrieve,
Died himself, that ye might live.
Will ye let him die in vain?
Crucify your Lord again?
Why, ye ransomed sinners, why
Will ye slight his grace, and die?

3 Sinners, turn; why will ye die?
God, the Spirit, asks you why;
He, who all your lives hath strove,
Wooed you to embrace his love.
Will ye not his grace receive?
Will ye still refuse to live?
Why, ye long-sought sinners, why
Will ye grieve your God, and die?

4 Dead, already dead within,—
Spiritually dead in sin;
Dead to God while here you breathe,
Pant ye after second death?

Will ye still in sin remain,
Greedy of eternal pain?
O ye dying sinners, why,
Why will ye forever die?
                              CHARLES WESLEY.

SECOND PART

348   *Tender expostulation.*

1 WHAT could your Redeemer do,
More than he hath done for you?
To procure your peace with God,
Could he more than shed his blood?
After all his flow of love,
All his drawings from above,
Why will ye your Lord deny?
Why will ye resolve to die?

2 "Turn," he cries, "ye sinners, turn;"
By his life, your God hath sworn,
He would have you turn and live;
He would all the world receive.
If your death were his delight,
Would he you to life invite?
Would he ask, beseech, and cry,
"Why will ye resolve to die?"

3 Sinners, turn, while God is near;
Dare not think him insincere:
Now, e'en now, your Saviour stands;
All day long he spreads his hands;
Cries, "Ye will not happy be;
No, ye will not come to me—
Me, who life to none deny:
Why will ye resolve to die?"
                              CHARLES WESLEY.

THE SINNER—WARNING AND INVITING.

WELLS. L. M. ARR. BY ISRAEL HOLROYD.

349 *The accepted time.*

1 WHILE life prolongs its precious light,
  Mercy is found, and peace is given;
But soon, ah, soon, approaching night
  Shall blot out every hope of heaven.

2 While God invites, how blest the day!
  How sweet the gospel's charming sound!
Come, sinners, haste, O haste away,
  While yet a pardoning God is found.

3 Soon, borne on time's most rapid wing,
  Shall death command you to the grave,
Before his bar your spirits bring,
  And none be found to hear or save.

4 In that lone land of deep despair,
  No Sabbath's heavenly light shall rise,
No God regard your bitter prayer,
  No Saviour call you to the skies.

5 Now God invites; how blest the day!
  How sweet the gospel's charming sound!
Come, sinners, haste, O haste away,
  While yet a pardoning God is found.
                    TIMOTHY DWIGHT.

FIRST PART.
350 *All things are ready.*

1 SINNERS, obey the gospel word;
Haste to the supper of my Lord;
Be wise to know your gracious day;
All things are ready,—come away.

2 Ready the Father is to own
And kiss his late-returning son;
Ready your loving Saviour stands,
And spreads for you his bleeding hands.

3 Ready the Spirit of his love,
Just now the stony to remove;

To apply and witness with the blood,
And wash and seal the sons of God.

4 Ready for you the angels wait,
To triumph in your blest estate;
Tuning their harps, they long to praise
The wonders of redeeming grace.

5 The Father, Son, and Holy Ghost,
Are ready, with their shining host:
All heaven is ready to resound,
"The dead's alive! the lost is found!"
                    CHARLES WESLEY.

SECOND PART.
351 *The bliss of penitence.*

1 COME, O ye sinners, to the Lord,
In Christ to paradise restored:
His proffered benefits embrace,
The plenitude of gospel grace:

2 A pardon written with his blood;
The favor and the peace of God;
The seeing eye, the feeling sense,
The mystic joys of penitence:

3 The godly fear, the pleasing smart,
The meltings of a broken heart;
The tears that tell your sins forgiven;
The sighs that waft your souls to heaven.

4 The guiltless shame, the sweet distress,
The unutterable tenderness,
The genuine, meek humility;
The wonder, "Why such love to me?"

5 The o'erwhelming power of saving grace,
The sight that veils the seraph's face;
The speechless awe that dares not move,
And all the silent heaven of love.
                    CHARLES WESLEY.

INGHAM. L. M. LOWELL MASON.

352 *God calling yet.*

1 GOD calling yet! shall I not hear?
Earth's pleasures shall I still hold dear?
Shall life's swift passing years all fly,
And still my soul in slumber lie?

2 God calling yet! shall I not rise?
Can I his loving voice despise,
And basely his kind care repay?
He calls me still; can I delay?

3 God calling yet! and shall he knock,
And I my heart the closer lock?
He still is waiting to receive,
And shall I dare his Spirit grieve?

4 God calling yet! and shall I give
No heed, but still in bondage live?
I wait, but he does not forsake;
He calls me still; my heart, awake!

5 God calling yet! I cannot stay;
My heart I yield without delay:
Vain world, farewell, from thee I part;
The voice of God hath reached my heart.
GERHARD TERSTEEGEN.
TR. BY MISS J. BORTHWICK.

353 *Quench not the Spirit.*—1 Thess. 5:19.

1 SAY, sinner, hath a voice within
Oft whispered to thy secret soul,
Urged thee to leave the ways of sin,
And yield thy heart to God's control?

2 Sinner, it was a heavenly voice,
It was the Spirit's gracious call;
't bade thee make the better choice,
And haste to seek in Christ thine all.

3 Spurn not the call to life and light;
Regard in time the warning kind;
That call thou mayst not always slight,
And yet the gate of mercy find.

4 God's Spirit will not always strive
With hardened, self-destroying man;
Ye, who persist his love to grieve,
May never hear his voice again.

5 Sinner, perhaps this very day
Thy last accepted time may be;
O shouldst thou grieve him now away,
Then hope may never beam on thee.
MRS. ANN B. HYDE.

354 *Haste, traveler, haste!*

1 HASTE, traveler, haste! the night comes
on,
And many a shining hour is gone;
The storm is gathering in the west,
And thou art far from home and rest.

2 O far from home thy footsteps stray;
Christ is the Life, and Christ the Way.
And Christ the Light; thy setting sun
Sinks ere thy morning is begun.

3 The rising tempest sweeps the sky;
The rains descend, the winds are high;
The waters swell, and death and fear
Beset thy path, nor refuge near.

4 Then linger not in all the plain,
Flee for thy life, the mountain gain;
Look not behind, make no delay,
O speed thee, speed thee on thy way.
WILLIAM B. COLLYER.

OLNEY. S. M.   LOWELL MASON.

355 *Whosoever will.—Rev. 22: 17.*

1 THE Spirit, in our hearts,
   Is whispering, "Sinner, come:"
The bride, the Church of Christ, proclaims
   To all his children, "Come!"

2 Let him that heareth say
   To all about him, "Come!"
Let him that thirsts for righteousness,
   To Christ, the fountain, come!

3 Yea, whosoever will,
   O let him freely come,
And freely drink the stream of life:
   'Tis Jesus bids him come.

4 Lo! Jesus, who invites,
   Declares, "I quickly come;"
Lord, even so! we wait thine hour;
   O blest Redeemer, come!
                                   H. U. ONDERDONK.

356 *The guardianship of angels.*

1 YE simple souls that stray
   Far from the path of peace,
That lonely, unfrequented way
   To life and happiness,
Why will ye folly love,
   And throng the downward road,
And hate the wisdom from above,
   And mock the sons of God?

2 So wretched and obscure,
   The men whom ye despise,
So foolish, impotent, and poor,—
   Above your scorn we rise:
We through the Holy Ghost,
   Can witness better things;
For he whose blood is all our boast,
   Hath made us priests and kings.

3 Riches unsearchable
   In Jesus' love we know;
And pleasures springing from the well
   Of life, our souls o'erflow:
The Spirit we receive
   Of wisdom, grace, and power;
And always sorrowful we live,
   Rejoicing evermore.

4 Angels our servants are,
   And keep in all our ways,
And in their watchful hands they bear
   The sacred sons of grace:
Unto that heavenly bliss
   They all our steps attend;
And God himself our Father is,
   And Jesus is our friend.
                                   JOHN WESLEY.

357 *All things are ready.—Matt. 22: 4.*

1 "ALL things are ready," come,
   Come to the supper spread;
Come, rich and poor, come, old and young,
   Come, and be richly fed.

2 "All things are ready," come,
   The invitation's given,
Through Him who now in glory sits
   At God's right hand in heaven.

3 "All things are ready," come,
   The door is open wide;
O feast upon the love of God,
   For Christ, his Son, has died.

4 "All things are ready," come,
   To-morrow may not be;
O sinner, come, the Saviour waits
   This hour to welcome thee.
                                   ALBERT MIDLANE.

CAPELLO.   S. M.   LOWELL MASON.

358   *The second death.*

1 O WHERE shall rest be found,
    Rest for the weary soul?
'Twere vain the ocean's depths to sound,
    Or pierce to either pole.

2 The world can never give
    The bliss for which we sigh;
'Tis not the whole of life to live,
    Nor all of death to die.

3 Beyond this vale of tears
    There is a life above,
Unmeasured by the flight of years;
    And all that life is love.

4 There is a death, whose pang
    Outlasts the fleeting breath:
O what eternal horrors hang
    Around the second death!

5 Thou God of truth and grace,
    Teach us that death to shun;
Lest we be banished from thy face,
    For evermore undone.
                        JAMES MONTGOMERY.

359   *Accepting the invitation.*

1 COME, weary sinners, come,
    Groaning beneath your load;
The Saviour calls his wanderers home;
    Haste to your pardoning God.

2 Come, all by guilt oppressed,
    Answer the Saviour's call,
"O come, and I will give you rest,
    And I will save you all."

3 Redeemer, full of love,
    We would thy word obey,
And all thy faithful mercies prove:
    O take our guilt away.

4 We would on thee rely,
    On thee would cast our care;
Now to thine arms of mercy fly,
    And find salvation there.
                        CHARLES WESLEY, ALT.

360   *Seek Him while he may be found.*

1 MY son, know thou the Lord,
    Thy father's God obey;
Seek his protecting care by night,
    His guardian hand by day.

2 Call, while he may be found;
    Seek him while he is near;
Serve him with all thy heart and mind,
    And worship him with fear.

3 If thou wilt seek his face,
    His ear will hear thy cry;
Then shalt thou find his mercy sure,
    His grace forever nigh.

4 But if thou leave thy God,
    Nor choose the path to heaven,
Then shalt thou perish in thy sins,
    And never be forgiven.
                        ROBERT C. BRACKENBURY.

361   *The day of grace.*

1 NOW is the accepted time,
    Now is the day of grace;
Now, sinners, come without delay,
    And seek the Saviour's face.

2 Now is the accepted time,
    The Saviour calls to-day;
To-morrow it may be too late—
    Then why should you delay?

3 Now is the accepted time,
    The gospel bids you come;
And every promise in his word
    Declares there yet is room.
                        JOHN DOBELL.

HAMBURG.   L. M.   ARR. FROM A GREGORIAN CHANT, BY LOWELL MASON.

362   *The abundance of His grace.*

1 Ho! every one that thirsts draw nigh:
'Tis God invites the fallen race:
Mercy and free salvation buy;
    Buy wine, and milk, and gospel grace.

2 Come to the living waters, come!
Sinners, obey your Maker's call;
Return, ye weary wanderers, home,
    And find his grace is free for all.

3 See from the Rock a fountain rise;
For you in healing streams it rolls;
Money ye need not bring, nor price,
    Ye laboring, burdened, sin-sick souls.

4 Nothing ye in exchange shall give;
Leave all you have and are behind;
Frankly the gift of God receive;
    Pardon and peace in Jesus find.
                            JOHN WESLEY.

363   *Come to Me.*

1 WITH tearful eyes I look around;
Life seems a dark and stormy sea;
Yet 'midst the gloom I hear a sound,
    A heavenly whisper, "Come to me!"

2 It tells me of a place of rest,
It tells me where my soul may flee:
O to the weary, faint, oppressed,
    How sweet the bidding, "Come to me!"

3 When against sin I strive in vain,
And cannot from its yoke get free,
Sinking beneath the heavy chain,
    The words arrest me, "Come to me!"

4 When nature shudders, loath to part
From all I love, enjoy, and see;
When a faint chill steals o'er my heart,
    A sweet voice utters, "Come to me!"

5 "Come, for all else must fail and die,
Earth is no resting-place for thee;
Heavenward direct thy weeping eye;
    I am thy portion; come to me!"
                            CHARLOTTE ELLIOTT.

364   *The gospel feast.*

1 COME, sinners, to the gospel feast;
Let every soul be Jesus' guest:
Ye need not one be left behind,
    For God hath bidden all mankind.

2 Sent by my Lord, on you I call;
The invitation is to all:
Come all the world! come, sinner, thou:
    All things in Christ are ready now.

3 Come, all ye souls by sin oppressed,
Ye restless wanderers after rest;
Ye poor, and maimed, and halt, and blind,
    In Christ a hearty welcome find.

4 My message as from God receive;
Ye all may come to Christ and live:
O let his love your hearts constrain,
    Nor suffer him to die in vain.

5 See him set forth before your eyes,
That precious, bleeding sacrifice:
His offered benefits embrace,
    And freely now be saved by grace.
                            CHARLES WESLEY.

THE SINNER—WARNING AND INVITING.

MEAR. C. M.

WELSH AIR. AARON WILLIAMS.

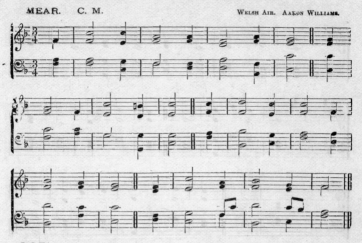

365 *Sin kills beyond the tomb.*

1 VAIN man, thy fond pursuits forbear;
  Repent, thine end is nigh;
Death, at the farthest, can't be far:
  O think before thou die.

2 Reflect, thou hast a soul to save;
  Thy sins, how high they mount!
What are thy hopes beyond the grave?
  How stands that dark account?

3 Death enters, and there's no defense;
  His time there's none can tell;
He'll in a moment call thee hence,
  To heaven, or down to hell.

4 Thy flesh, perhaps thy greatest care,
  Shall into dust consume;
But, ah! destruction stops not there;
  Sin kills beyond the tomb.

JOSEPH HART.

366 *Boast not thyself of to-morrow.*
Prov. 27: 1.

1 WHY should we boast of time to come,
  Though but a single day?
This hour may fix our final doom,
  Though strong, and young, and gay.

2 The present we should now redeem;
  This only is our own;
The past, alas! is all a dream;
  The future is unknown.

3 O think what vast concerns depend
  Upon a moment's space,
When life and all its cares shall end
  In vengeance or in grace.

4 O for that power which melts the heart,
  And lifts the soul on high!
There sin and grief and death depart,
  And pleasures never die.

M. WILKS.

367 *The Justifier of the ungodly.*

1 LOVERS of pleasure more than God,
  For you he suffered pain;
For you the Saviour spilt his blood:
  And shall he bleed in vain?

2 Sinners, his life for you he paid;
  Your basest crimes he bore;
Your sins were all on Jesus laid,
  That you might sin no more.

3 To earth the great Redeemer came,
  That you might come to heaven;
Believe, believe in Jesus' name,
  And all your sin's forgiven.

4 Believe in him who died for thee,
  And, sure as he hath died,
Thy debt is paid, thy soul is free,
  And thou art justified.

CHARLES WESLEY.

368 *The hammer of His word.*

1 COME, O thou all-victorious Lord,
  Thy power to us make known;
Strike with the hammer of thy word,
  And break these hearts of stone.

2 O that we all might now begin
  Our foolishness to mourn;
And turn at once from every sin,
  And to the Saviour turn!

3 Give us ourselves and thee to know
  In this our gracious day;
Repentance unto life bestow,
  And take our sins away.

4 Convince us first of unbelief,
  And freely then release;
Fill every soul with sacred grief,
  And then with sacred peace.

CHARLES WESLEY.

THE SINNER—WARNING AND INVITING.

BALERMA. C. M.

ADAPTED BY R. SIMPSON.

369 *Desperate resolution.*

1 COME, humble sinner, in whose breast
  A thousand thoughts revolve,
Come, with your guilt and fear oppressed,
  And make this last resolve:—

2 I'll go to Jesus, though my sin
  Like mountains round me close;
I know his courts, I'll enter in,
  Whatever may oppose.

3 Prostrate I'll lie before his throne,
  And there my guilt confess;
I'll tell him, I'm a wretch undone
  Without his sovereign grace.

4 Perhaps he will admit my plea,
  Perhaps will hear my prayer;
But, if I perish, I will pray,
  And perish only there.

5 I can but perish if I go;
  I am resolved to try;
For if I stay away, I know
  I must forever die.

EDMUND JONES.

370 *The wanderer recalled.*

1 RETURN, O wanderer, return,
  And seek thy Father's face;
Those new desires which in thee burn
  Were kindled by his grace.

2 Return, O wanderer, return;
  He hears thy humble sigh:
He sees thy softened spirit mourn,
  When no one else is nigh.

3 Return, O wanderer, return,
  Thy Saviour bids thee live:
Come to his cross, and, grateful, learn
  How freely he'll forgive.

4 Return, O wanderer, return,
  And wipe the falling tear:
Thy Father calls,—no longer mourn;
  'Tis love invites thee near.

5 Return, O wanderer, return;
  Regain thy long-sought rest:
The Saviour's melting mercies yearn
  To clasp thee to his breast,

WILLIAM B. COLLYER, ALT.

371 *No peace to the wicked.*

1 SINNERS, the voice of God regard;
  'Tis mercy speaks to-day;
He calls you by his sacred word
  From sin's destructive way.

2 Like the rough sea, that cannot rest,
  You live, devoid of peace;
A thousand stings within your breast
  Deprive your souls of ease.

3 Your way is dark, and leads to hell:
  Why will you persevere?
Can you in endless torments dwell,
  Shut up in black despair?

4 Why will you in the crooked ways
  Of sin and folly go?
In pain you travel all your days,
  To reach eternal woe.

5 But he that turns to God shall live,
  Through his abounding grace:
His mercy will the guilt forgive
  Of those that seek his face.

6 Bow to the scepter of his word,
  Renouncing every sin;
Submit to him, your sovereign Lord,
  And learn his will divine.

JOHN FAWCETT.

FAITHFUL. C. M. SAMUEL PARKMAN TUCKERMAN.

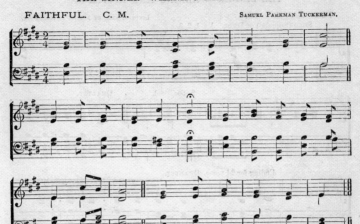

372 *The voice that wakes the dead.*

1 THOU Son of God, whose flaming eyes
  Our inmost thoughts perceive,
Accept the grateful sacrifice
  Which now to thee we give.

2 We bow before thy gracious throne,
  And think ourselves sincere:
But show us, Lord, is every one
  Thy real worshiper?

3 Is here a soul that knows thee not,
  Nor feels his need of thee,—
A stranger to the blood which bought
  His pardon on the tree?

4 Convince him now of unbelief;
  His desperate state explain;
And fill his heart with sacred grief,
  And penitential pain.

5 Speak with that voice that wakes the dead,
  And bid the sleeper rise;
And bid his guilty conscience dread
  The death that never dies.
                              CHARLES WESLEY.

373 *Warnings multiplied.*

1 BENEATH our feet, and o'er our head,
  Is equal warning given;
Beneath us lie the countless dead,
  Above us is the heaven.

2 Death rides on every passing breeze,
  And lurks in every flower;
Each season has its own disease,
  Its peril every hour.

3 Our eyes have seen the rosy light
  Of youth's soft cheek decay,
And fate descend in sudden night
  On manhood's middle day.

4 Our eyes have seen the steps of age
  Halt feebly to the tomb;
And shall earth still our hearts engage,
  And dreams of days to come?

5 Turn, mortal, turn; thy danger know:
  Where'er thy foot can tread,
The earth rings hollow from below,
  And warns thee by her dead.

6 Turn, mortal, turn; thy soul apply
  To truths divinely given:
The dead, who underneath thee lie,
  Shall live for hell or heaven.
                              REGINALD HEBER.

374 *Waiting to be gracious.*

1 JESUS, Redeemer of mankind,
  Display thy saving power;
Thy mercy let the sinner find,
  And know his gracious hour.

2 Who thee beneath their feet have trod,
  And crucified afresh,
Touch with thine all-victorious blood,
  And turn the stone to flesh.

3 Open their eyes thy cross to see,
  Their ears, to hear thy cries:
Sinner, thy Saviour weeps for thee;
  For thee he weeps and dies.

4 All the day long he meekly stands,
  His rebels to receive;
And shows his wounds and spreads his
    hands,
  And bids you turn and live.

5 Turn, and your sins of deepest dye
  He will with blood efface;
E'en now he waits the blood to apply;
  Be saved, be saved by grace.
                              CHARLES WESLEY.

TOO LATE. 10.

LINDSAY, ARR. BY JOSEPH P. HOLBROOK.

SOLO (Soprano) or DUET. Vs. 1, 2, 3.

SOLO (Base). QUARTET.

Ending for 2d verse. QUARTET.

375 *Too late!*

1 LATE, late, so late! and dark the night, and chill!
Late, late, so late! But we can enter still.
"Too late, too late! ye cannot enter now."

2 No light had we;—for that we do repent,
And learning this, the Bridegroom will re-lent.
"Too late, too late! ye cannot enter now."

3 No light! so late! and dark and chill the night—
O let us in, that we may find the light.
"Too late, too late! ye cannot enter now!"

4 Have we not heard the Bridegroom is so sweet!
O let us in, though late, to kiss his feet.
O let us in, O let us in,
O let us in, though late, to kiss his feet.
"No! no! too late! too late! ye cannot enter now!"

ALFRED TENNYSON.

FOURTH VERSE.

DUET. QUARTET.

SOLO (Base or Contralto). *pp* QUARTET.

138

THE SINNER—WARNING AND INVITING.

IN THE SILENT MIDNIGHT WATCHES. 8, 5.
Hubert P. Main.

376   *Mercy, death, doom.*

1 In the silent midnight watches,
  List,—thy bosom door!
How it knocketh, knocketh, knocketh,
  Knocketh evermore!
Say not 'tis thy pulse is beating:
  'Tis thy heart of sin;
'Tis thy Saviour knocks, and crieth,
  Rise, and let me in!

2 Death comes down with reckless footstep,
  To the hall and hut:
Think you death will stand a-knocking
  Where the door is shut?

Jesus waiteth, waiteth, waiteth;
  But thy door is fast!
Grieved, away thy Saviour goeth:
  Death breaks in at last.

3 Then 'tis thine to stand entreating
  Christ to let thee in;
At the gate of heaven beating,
  Wailing for thy sin.
Nay, alas! thou foolish virgin,
  Hast thou then forgot?
Jesus waited long to know thee,
  But he knows thee not.

              A. Cleveland Coxe.

WOOD END. 8, 5.
G. P. Merrick.

AUBURNDALE.   C. P. M.   O. L. CARTER.

377   *The gift of faith.*

1 AUTHOR of faith, to thee I cry,
To thee, who wouldst not have me die,
  But know the truth and live:
Open mine eyes to see thy face;
Work in my heart the saving grace;
  The life eternal give.

2 Shut up in unbelief, I groan,
And blindly serve a God unknown,
  Till thou the veil remove;
The gift unspeakable impart,
And write thy name upon my heart,
  And manifest thy love.

3 I know the work is only thine,
The gift of faith is all divine;
  But, if on thee we call,
Thou wilt that gracious gift bestow,
And cause our hearts to feel and know
  That thou hast died for all.

4 Thou bidd'st us knock and enter in,
Come unto thee, and rest from sin,
  The blessing seek and find:
Thou bidd'st us ask thy grace, and have;
Thou canst, thou wouldst, this moment save
  Both me and all mankind.

5 Be it according to thy word;
Now let me find my pardoning Lord:
  Let what I ask be given:
The bar of unbelief remove;
Open the door of faith and love,
  And take me into heaven.
                              CHARLES WESLEY

378   *Pleading the sacrifice of Christ.*

1 O LAMB of God, for sinners slain,
I plead with thee, my suit to gain,—
  I plead what thou hast done:
Didst thou not die the death for me?
Jesus, remember Calvary,
  And break my heart of stone.

2 Take the dear purchase of thy blood.
My Friend and Advocate with God,
  My Ransom and my Peace,
Surety, who all my debt hast paid,
For all my sins atonement made,
  The Lord my Righteousness.

3 O let thy Spirit shed abroad
The love, the perfect love of God,
  In this cold heart of mine!
O might he now descend, and rest,
And dwell forever in my breast,
  And make it all divine!
                              CHARLES WESLEY.

PLEYEL'S HYMN.   7.

IGNACE PLEYEL.

379   *Depth of mercy.*

1 DEPTH of mercy! can there be
Mercy still reserved for me?
Can my God his wrath forbear,—
Me, the chief of sinners, spare?

2 I have long withstood his grace,
Long provoked him to his face;
Would not hearken to his calls;
Grieved him by a thousand falls.

3 Now incline me to repent;
Let me now my sins lament;
Now my foul revolt deplore,
Weep, believe, and sin no more.

4 Kindled his relentings are;
Me he now delights to spare;
Cries, "How shall I give thee up?"
Lets the lifted thunder drop.

5 There for me the Saviour stands,
Shows his wounds and spreads his hands;
God is love! I know, I feel;
Jesus weeps, and loves me still.
                        CHARLES WESLEY.

380   *With Thee is mercy.*

1 SOVEREIGN Ruler, Lord of all,
Prostrate at thy feet I fall;
Hear, O hear my ardent cry,
Frown not, lest I faint and die.

2 Vilest of the sons of men,
Worst of rebels I have been;
Oft abused thee to thy face,
Trampled on thy richest grace.

3 Justly might thy vengeful dart
Pierce this bleeding, broken heart;

Justly might thy kindled ire
Send me to eternal fire.

4 But with thee is mercy found,
Balm to heal my every wound;
Soothe, O soothe this troubled breast,
Give the weary wanderer rest.
                        THOMAS RAFFLES.

[C. P. M. Tune, Auburndale. Page 140.]

381   *The Man on Calvary.*

1 O THOU who hast our sorrows borne,
Help us to look on thee and mourn,
   On thee whom we have slain,—
Have pierced a thousand, thousand times,
And by reiterated crimes
   Renewed thy sacred pain.

2 O give us eyes of faith to see
The Man transfixed on Calvary,—
   To know thee who thou art,
The one eternal God and true;
And let the sight affect, subdue,
   And break my stubborn heart.

3 Lover of souls! to rescue mine,
Reveal the charity divine,
   That suffered in my stead;
That made thy soul a sacrifice,
And quenched in death those flaming eyes,
   And bowed that sacred head.

4 The veil of unbelief remove,
And by thy manifested love,
   And by thy sprinkled blood,
Destroy the love of sin in me,
And get thyself the victory,
   And bring me back to God.
                        CHARLES WESLEY.

10   141

THE SINNER—REPENTANCE.

PERRINA. 7, 6, 8.

JOSEPH P. HOLBROOK.

382 *Looking unto Jesus.*

1 LAMB of God, for sinners slain,
   To thee I humbly pray;
Heal me of my grief and pain,
   O take my sins away.
From this bondage, Lord, release,
   No longer let me be oppressed:
Jesus, Master, seal my peace,
   And take me to thy breast.

2 Wilt thou cast a sinner out
   Who humbly comes to thee?
No, my God, I cannot doubt
   Thy mercy is for me:
Let me then obtain the grace,
   And be of paradise possessed:
Jesus, Master, seal my peace,
   And take me to thy breast.

3 Worldly good I do not want,
   Be that to others given:
Only for thy love I pant,
   My all in earth and heaven:
This the crown I fain would seize,
   The good wherewith I would be blest:
Jesus, Master, seal my peace,
   And take me to thy breast.

CHARLES WESLEY.

383 *Remember Calvary.*

1 LAMB of God, whose dying love
   We now recall to mind,
Send the answer from above,
   And let us mercy find:
Think on us who think on thee,
   And every struggling soul release;
O remember Calvary,
   And bid us go in peace!

2 By thine agonizing pain,
   And bloody sweat, we pray,
By thy dying love to man,
   Take all our sins away:
Burst our bonds, and set us free;
   From all iniquity release;
O remember Calvary,
   And bid us go in peace!

3 Let thy blood, by faith applied,
   The sinner's pardon seal;
Speak us freely justified,
   And all our sickness heal:
By thy passion on the tree,
   Let all our griefs and troubles cease:
O remember Calvary,
   And bid us go in peace!

CHARLES WESLEY.

THE SINNER—REPENTANCE.

EVEN ME. 8, 7, 3. WILLIAM BATCHELDER BRADBURY.

384 *Even me.*

1 LORD, I hear of showers of blessing
   Thou art scattering full and free;
Showers, the thirsty land refreshing;
   Let some drops now fall on me,
      Even me.

2 Pass me not, O God, my Father,
   Sinful though my heart may be;
Thou mightst leave me, but the rather
   Let thy mercy light on me,
      Even me.

3 Pass me not, O gracious Saviour,
   Let me live and cling to thee;
I am longing for thy favor;
   Whilst thou 'rt calling, O call me,
      Even me.

4 Pass me not, O mighty Spirit,
   Thou canst make the blind to see;
Witnesser of Jesus' merit,
   Speak the word of power to me,
      Even me.

5 Love of God, so pure and changeless,
   Blood of Christ, so rich, so free,
Grace of God, so strong and boundless,
   Magnify them all in me,
      Even me.
             MRS. ELIZABETH CODNER.

[7, 6, 8. Tune, Perrina. Page 142.]

385 *Saved by grace.*

1 LET the world their virtue boast,
   Their works of righteousness;
I, a wretch undone and lost,
   Am freely saved by grace;
Other title I disclaim,
   This, only this, is all my plea,
I the chief of sinners am,
   But Jesus died for me.

2 Happy they whose joys abound
   Like Jordan's swelling stream;

Who their heaven in Chr'st have found
   And give the praise to him.
Meanest follower of the Lamb,
   His steps I at a distance see;
I the chief of sinners am,
   But Jesus died for me.

3 Jesus, thou for me hast died,
   And thou in me wilt live;
I shall feel thy death applied;
   I shall thy life receive:
Yet, when melted in the flame
   Of love, this shall be all my plea,
I the chief of sinners am,
   But Jesus died for me.
             CHARLES WESLEY.

[7, 6, 8. Tune, Perrina. Page 142.]

386 *Refuge in the blood of the Lamb.*

1 GOD of my salvation, hear,
   And help me to believe;
Simply do I now draw near,
   Thy blessing to receive.
Full of guilt, alas! I am,
   But to thy wounds for refuge flee:
Friend of sinners, spotless Lamb,
   Thy blood was shed for me.

2 Standing now as newly slain,
   To thee I lift mine eye;
Balm of all my grief and pain
   Thy blood is always nigh;
Now as yesterday the same
   Thou art, and wilt forever be:
Friend of sinners, spotless Lamb,
   Thy blood was shed for me.

3 No good word, or work, or thought,
   Bring I to buy thy grace;
Pardon I accept unbought,
   Thy proffer I embrace,
Coming, as at first I came,
   To take, and not bestow on thee:
Friend of sinners, spotless Lamb,
   Thy blood was shed for me.
             CHARLES WESLEY.

THE SINNER—REPENTANCE.

GREY. 7, 5.   REV. F. R. GREY.

387 *Hear, and save.*

1 LORD of mercy and of might,
Of mankind the life and light,
Maker, Teacher, Infinite—
    Jesus! hear and save.

2 Strong Creator, Saviour mild,
Humbled to a little child,
Captive, beaten, bound, reviled—
    Jesus! hear and save.

3 Borne aloft on angels' wings,
Throned above celestial things,
Lord of lords, and King of kings—
    Jesus! hear and save.

4 Soon to come to earth again,
Judge of angels and of men,
Hear us now, and hear us then—
    Jesus! hear and save.
                                REGINALD HEBER.

[S. M. Tune, Dennis. Page 65.]

388 *The soul's home.*

1 LIKE Noah's weary dove,
    That soared the earth around,
But not a resting-place above
    The cheerless waters found:

2 O cease, my wandering soul,
    On restless wing to roam;
All the wide world, to either pole,
    Has not for thee a home.

3 Behold the ark of God!
    Behold the open door!
Hasten to gain that dear abode,
    And rove, my soul, no more.

4 There, safe thou shalt abide,
    There, sweet shall be thy rest,
And every longing satisfied,
    With full salvation blest.
                        WILLIAM A. MUHLENBERG.

ASHWELL. L. M.   LOWELL MASON.

389 *The sinner's only plea.*

1 WHEREWITH, O Lord, shall I draw near,
    And bow myself before thy face?
How in thy purer eyes appear?
    What shall I bring to gain thy grace?

2 Will gifts delight the Lord most high?
    Will multiplied oblations please?
Thousands of rams his favor buy,
    Or slaughtered hecatombs appease?

3 Can these avert the wrath of God?
    Can these wash out my guilty stain?
Rivers of oil, and seas of blood,
    Alas! they all must flow in vain.

4 Who would himself to thee approve,
    Must take the path thyself hast showed:
Justice pursue, and mercy love,
    And humbly walk by faith with God.

5 But though my life henceforth be thine,
    Present for past can ne'er atone:
Though I to thee the whole resign,
    I only give thee back thine own.

6 Guilty I stand before thy face;
    On me I feel thy wrath abide;
'Tis just the sentence should take place;
    'Tis just,—but O, thy Son hath died!
                                CHARLES WESLEY.

WINDHAM. L. M.

DANIEL READ.

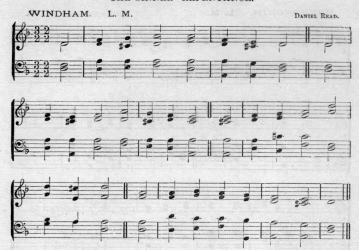

390 *The withdrawal of the Spirit deprecated.*

1 STAY, thou insulted Spirit, stay,
  Though I have done thee such despite;
Nor cast the sinner quite away,
  Nor take thine everlasting flight.

2 Though I have steeled my stubborn heart,
  And shaken off my guilty fears;
And vexed, and urged thee to depart,
  For many long rebellious years:

3 Though I have most unfaithful been,
  Of all who e'er thy grace received;
Ten thousand times thy goodness seen;
  Ten thousand times thy goodness grieved:

4 Yet, O, the chief of sinners spare,
  In honor of my great High Priest;
Nor in thy righteous anger swear
  To exclude me from thy people's rest.
    CHARLES WESLEY.

391 *Pleading for pity.*

1 SHOW pity, Lord, O Lord, forgive;
Let a repenting rebel live;
Are not thy mercies large and free?
May not a sinner trust in thee?

2 My crimes are great, but don't surpass
The power and glory of thy grace:
Great God, thy nature hath no bound,
So let thy pardoning love be found.

3 O wash my soul from every sin,
And make my guilty conscience clean;
Here on my heart the burden lies,
And past offenses pain my eyes.

4 My lips with shame my sins confess,
Against thy law, against thy grace;
Lord, should thy judgments grow severe,
I am condemned, but thou art clear.

5 Should sudden vengeance seize my
    breath,
I must pronounce thee just, in death,
And if my soul were sent to hell,
Thy righteous law approves it well.

6 Yet save a trembling sinner, Lord,
Whose hope, still hovering round thy word,
Would light on some sweet promise there,
Some sure support against despair.
    ISAAC WATTS.

392 *The sinner's only hope.*

1 JESUS, the sinner's Friend, to thee,
Lost and undone, for aid I flee,
Weary of earth, myself, and sin:
Open thine arms, and take me in.

2 Pity and heal my sin-sick soul;
'Tis thou alone canst make me whole;
Dark, till in me thine image shine,
And lost, I am, till thou art mine.

3 At last I own it cannot be
That I should fit myself for thee:
Here, then, to thee I all resign;
Thine is the work, and only thine.

4 What shall I say thy grace to move?
Lord, I am sin—but thou art love:
I give up every plea beside—
Lord, I am lost—but thou hast died.
    CHARLES WESLEY.

WOODWORTH.   L. M.   WILLIAM BATCHELDER BRADBURY.

393   *Just as I am.*

1 JUST as I am, without one plea,
But that thy blood was shed for me,
And that thou bidd'st me come to thee,
O Lamb of God, I come! I come!

2 Just as I am, and waiting not
To rid my soul of one dark blot,
To thee whose blood can cleanse each spot,
O Lamb of God, I come! I come!

3 Just as I am, though tossed about
With many a conflict, many a doubt,
Fightings within, and fears without,
O Lamb of God, I come! I come!

4 Just as I am—poor, wretched, blind;
Sight, riches, healing of the mind,
Yea, all I need, in thee to find,
O Lamb of God, I come! I come!

5 Just as I am—thou wilt receive,
Wilt welcome, pardon, cleanse, relieve;
Because thy promise I believe,
O Lamb of God, I come! I come!

6 Just as I am—thy love unknown
Hath broken every barrier down;
Now, to be thine, yea, thine alone,
O Lamb of God, I come! I come!
                        CHARLOTTE ELLIOTT.

394   *Dawning hope.*

1 MY soul before Thee prostrate lies;
To thee, her Source, my spirit flies;
My wants I mourn, my chains I see;
O let thy presence set me free.

2 Jesus, vouchsafe my heart and will
With thy meek lowliness to fill;
No more her power let nature boast,
But in thy will may mine be lost.

3 Already springing hope I feel,
God will destroy the power of hell,
And, from a land of wars and pain,
Lead me where peace and safety reign.

4 One only care my soul shall know,
Father, all thy commands to do;
And feel, what endless years shall prove,
That thou, my Lord, my God, art love.
          C. F. RICHTER.   TR. BY J. WESLEY.

395   *Only Jesus.*

1 WHEN, gracious Lord, when shall it be
That I shall find my all in thee?
The fullness of thy promise prove,
The seal of thine eternal love?

2 A poor blind child I wander here,
If haply I may feel thee near:
O dark! dark! dark! I still must say,
Amidst the blaze of gospel day.

3 Thee, only thee, I fain would find,
And cast the world and flesh behind;
Thou, only thou, to me be given,
Of all thou hast in earth or heaven.

4 When from the arm of flesh set free,
Jesus, my soul shall fly to thee;
Jesus, when I have lost my all,
I shall upon thy bosom fall.
                           CHARLES WESLEY.

ROSE HILL.   L. M.

JOSEPH E. SWEETSER.

396   *Stubbornness of heart.*

1 O FOR a glance of heavenly day,
To take this stubborn heart away,
And thaw, with beams of love divine,
This heart, this frozen heart of mine!

2 The rocks can rend; the earth can quake;
The seas can roar; the mountains shake:
Of feeling, all things show some sign,
But this unfeeling heart of mine.

3 To hear the sorrows thou hast felt,
O Lord, an adamant would melt:
But I can read each moving line,
And nothing moves this heart of mine.

4 Thy judgments, too, which devils fear—
Amazing thought!—unmoved I hear;
Goodness and wrath in vain combine
To stir this stupid heart of mine.

5 But power divine can do the deed;
And, Lord, that power I greatly need:
Thy Spirit can from dross refine,
And melt and change this heart of mine.
JOSEPH HART.

397   *Only by faith.*

1 LORD, I despair myself to heal;
I see my sin, but cannot feel;
I cannot, till thy Spirit blow,
And bid the obedient waters flow.

2 'Tis thine a heart of flesh to give;
Thy gifts I only can receive;
Here, then, to thee I all resign;
To draw, redeem, and seal, are thine.

3 With simple faith, on thee I call,
My Light, my Life, my Lord, my All:
I wait the moving of the pool;
I wait the word that speaks me whole.

4 Speak, gracious Lord, my sickness cure,
Make my infected nature pure;
Peace, righteousness, and joy impart,
And pour thyself into my heart.
CHARLES WESLEY.

398   *The kind Physician.*

1 JESUS, thy far-extended fame
My drooping soul exults to hear;
Thy name, thy all-restoring name,
Is music in a sinner's ear.

2 Sinners of old thou didst receive
With comfortable words, and kind;
Their sorrows cheer, their wants relieve,
Heal the diseased, and cure the blind.

3 And art thou not the Saviour still,
In every place and age the same?
Hast thou forgot thy gracious skill,
Or lost the virtue of thy name?

4 Faith in thy changeless name I have:
The good, the kind Physician, thou
Art able now our souls to save,
Art willing to restore them now.

5 All my disease, my every sin,
To thee, O Jesus, I confess:
In pardon, Lord, my cure begin,
And perfect it in holiness.
CHARLES WESLEY.

147

THE SINNER—REPENTANCE.

BOYLSTON.   S. M.   LOWELL MASON.

FIRST PART

399   *Restore my peace.*

1 AND wilt Thou yet be found,
  And may I still draw near?
Then listen to the plaintive sound
  Of a poor sinner's prayer.

2 Jesus, thine aid afford,
  If still the same thou art:
To thee I look, to thee, my Lord,
  I lift my helpless heart.

3 Thou seest my troubled breast,
  The strugglings of my will,
The foes that interrupt my rest,
  The agonies I feel.

4 O my offended Lord,
  Restore my inward peace;
I know thou canst; pronounce the word,
  And bid the tempest cease.

5 I long to see thy face;
  Thy Spirit I implore—
The living water of thy grace,
  That I may thirst no more.
                        CHARLES WESLEY.

SECOND PART.

400   *Yearning for deliverance.*

1 WHEN shall Thy love constrain,
  And force me to thy breast?
When shall my soul return again
  To her eternal rest?

2 Ah! what avails my strife,
  My wandering to and fro?
Thou hast the words of endless life:
  Ah! whither should I go?

3 Thy condescending grace
  To me did freely move;
It calls me still to seek thy face,
  And stoops to ask my love.

4 Lord, at thy feet I fall;
  I groan to be set free;
I fain would now obey the call,
  And give up all for thee.
                        CHARLES WESLEY.

THIRD PART.

401   *The surrender.*

1 AND can I yet delay
  My little all to give?
To tear my soul from earth away
  For Jesus to receive?

2 Nay, but I yield, I yield;
  I can hold out no more:
I sink, by dying love compelled,
  And own thee conqueror.

3 Though late, I all forsake;
  My friends, my all, resign:
Gracious Redeemer, take, O take,
  And seal me ever thine.

4 Come, and possess me whole,
  Nor hence again remove;
Settle and fix my wavering soul
  With all thy weight of love.

5 My one desire be this,
  Thy only love to know;
To seek and taste no other bliss,
  No other good below.

6 My life, my portion thou;
  Thou all-sufficient art:
My hope, my heavenly treasure, now
  Enter, and keep my heart.
                        CHARLES WESLEY

THE SINNER—REPENTANCE.

OWEN.   S. M.

JOSEPH E. SWEETSER.

402   *To whom shall I go?*

1 Ah! whither should I go,
  Burdened, and sick, and faint?
To whom should I my trouble show,
  And pour out my complaint?

2 My Saviour bids me come;
  Ah! why do I delay?
He calls the weary sinner home,
  And yet from him I stay.

3 What is it keeps me back,
  From which I cannot part,
Which will not let the Saviour take
  Possession of my heart?

4 Searcher of hearts, in mine
  Thy trying power display;
Into its darkest corners shine,
  And take the veil away.
                        CHARLES WESLEY.

403   *Out of the depths.*

1 OUT of the depths of woe,
  To thee, O Lord, I cry;
Darkness surrounds me, but I know
  That thou art ever nigh.

2 Humbly on thee I wait,
  Confessing all my sin;
Lord, I am knocking at the gate;
  Open, and take me in.

3 O hearken to my voice,
  Give ear to my complaint;
Thou bidd'st the mourning soul rejoice,
  Thou comfortest the faint.

4 Glory to God above,
  The waters soon will cease!
For, lo! the swift-returning dove
  Brings home the sign of peace.

5 Though storms his face obscure,
  And dangers threaten loud,
Jehovah's covenant is sure,
  His bow is in the cloud.
                        JAMES MONTGOMERY.

404   *For a broken heart.*

1 O THAT I could repent,
  With all my idols part,
And to thy gracious eye present
  A humble, contrite heart!

2 A heart with grief oppressed,
  For having grieved my God;
A troubled heart, that cannot rest
  Till sprinkled with thy blood.

3 Jesus, on me bestow
  The penitent desire;
With true sincerity of woe
  My aching breast inspire.

4 With softening pity look,
  And melt my hardness down:
Strike with thy love's resistless stroke,
  And break this heart of stone.
                        CHARLES WESLEY.

405   *The Son of God in tears.*

1 DID Christ o'er sinners weep,
  And shall our cheeks be dry?
Let floods of penitential grief
  Burst forth from every eye.

2 The Son of God in tears
  The wondering angels see!
Be thou astonished, O my soul;
  He shed those tears for thee.

3 He wept that we might weep;
  Each sin demands a tear:
In heaven alone no sin is found,
  And there's no weeping there.
                        BENJAMIN BEDDOME.

149

THE SINNER—REPENTANCE.

PARSONS. C. M. *ARR. FROM S. HUBBARD.

406 *Unwearied earnestness.*

1 FATHER, I stretch my hands to thee;
    No other help I know:
If thou withdraw thyself from me,
    Ah! whither shall I go?

2 What did thine only Son endure,
    Before I drew my breath!
What pain, what labor, to secure
    My soul from endless death!

3 O Jesus, could I this believe,
    I now should feel thy power;
And all my wants thou wouldst relieve,
    In this accepted hour.

4 Author of faith! to thee I lift
    My weary, longing eyes;
O let me now receive that gift;
    My soul without it dies.

5 Surely thou canst not let me die;
    O speak, and I shall live;
And here I will unwearied lie,
    Till thou thy Spirit give.

6 How would my fainting soul rejoice
    Could I but see thy face!
Now let me hear thy quickening voice,
    And taste thy pardoning grace.
                                CHARLES WESLEY.

407 *Earnest desire for pardon.*

1 O THAT I could my Lord receive,
    Who did the world redeem;
Who gave his life that I might live
    A life concealed in him!

2 O that I could the blessing prove,
    My heart's extreme desire;
Live happy in my Saviour's love,
    And in his arms expire!

3 Mercy I ask to seal my peace,
    That, kept by mercy's power,
I may from every evil cease,
    And never grieve thee more.

4 Now, if thy gracious will it be.
    E'en now my sins remove,
And set my soul at liberty
    By thy victorious love.

5 In answer to a thousand prayers,
    Thou pardoning God, descend;
Number me with salvation's heirs,
    My sins and troubles end.

6 Nothing I ask or want beside,
    Of all in earth or heaven,
But let me feel thy blood applied,
    And live and die forgiven.
                                CHARLES WESLEY.

408 *Reposing on Christ.*

1 WE sinners, Lord, with earnest heart,
    With sighs and prayers and tears,
To thee our inmost cares impart,
    Our burdens and our fears.

2 Thy sovereign grace can give relief,
    Thou Source of peace and light!
Dispel the gloomy cloud of grief,
    And make our darkness bright.

3 Around thy Father's throne on high,
    All heaven thy glory sings;
And earth, for which thou cam'st to die.
    Loud with thy praises rings.

4 Dear Lord, to thee our prayers ascend;
    Our eyes thy face would see:
O let our weary wanderings end,
    Our spirits rest in thee!
                                BERNARD OF CLAIRVAUX.

150

THE SINNER—REPENTANCE.

BEMERTON.   C. M.   HENRY WELLINGTON GREATOREX.

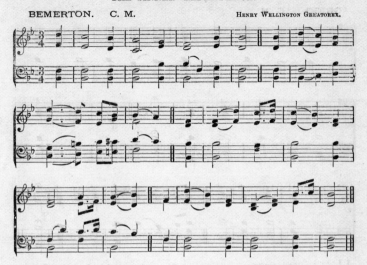

409   *I would be Thine.*

1 I WOULD be thine: O take my heart
    And fill it with thy love;
Thy sacred image, Lord, impart,
    And seal it from above.

2 I would be thine; but while I strive
    To give myself away,
I feel rebellion still alive,
    And wander while I pray.

3 I would be thine; but, Lord, I feel
    Evil still lurks within:
Do thou thy majesty reveal,
    And banish all my sin.

4 I would be thine; I would embrace
    The Saviour, and adore;
Inspire with faith, infuse thy grace,
    And now my soul restore.
                        ANDREW REED.

410   *Sincere contrition.*

1 O FOR that tenderness of heart
    Which bows before the Lord,
Acknowledging how just thou art,
    And trembling at thy word!
O for those humble, contrite tears,
    Which from repentance flow;
That consciousness of guilt, which fears
    The long-suspended blow!

2 Saviour, to me, in pity, give
    The sensible distress;
The pledge thou wilt at last receive,
    And bid me die in peace;

Wilt from the dreadful day remove,
    Before the evil come;
My spirit hide with saints above,
    My body in the tomb.
                        CHARLES WESLEY.

411   *The Sun of righteousness.*

1 O SUN of righteousness, arise
    With healing in thy wing;
To my diseased, my fainting soul,
    Life and salvation bring.

2 These clouds of pride and sin dispel,
    By thy all-piercing beam:
Lighten mine eyes with faith; my heart
    With holy hope inflame.

3 My mind, by thy all-quickening power,
    From low desires set free;
Unite my scattered thoughts, and fix
    My love entire on thee.

4 Father, thy long-lost son receive;
    Saviour, thy purchase own;
Blest Comforter, with peace and joy
    Thy new-made creature crown.

5 Eternal, undivided Lord,
    Co-equal One in Three,
On thee all faith, all hope be placed;
    All love be paid to thee.
                        JOHN WESLEY.

Doxology.

To Father, Son, and Holy Ghost,
    The God whom we adore,
Be glory, as it was, is now,
    And shall be evermore!
                        TATE AND BRADY.

THE SINNER—REPENTANCE.

GRIGG.　　C. M.

JOSEPH GRIGG.

412　*Timely penitence.*

1 WHEN rising from the bed of death,
　O'erwhelmed with guilt and fear,
I view my Maker face to face,
　O how shall I appear?

2 If yet, while pardon may be found,
　And mercy may be sought,
My soul with inward horror shrinks,
　And trembles at the thought,—

3 When thou, O Lord, shalt stand disclosed
　In majesty severe,
And sit in judgment on my soul,
　O how shall I appear?

4 O may my broken, contrite heart,
　Timely my sins lament;
And early, with repentant tears,
　Eternal woe prevent.

5 Behold the sorrows of my heart,
　Ere yet it be too late;
And hear my Saviour's dying groan,
　To give those sorrows weight.

6 For never shall my soul despair
　Her pardon to secure,
Who knows thine only Son hath died
　To make that pardon sure.
　　　　　　　　　　JOSEPH ADDISON.

413　*All things possible to God.*

1 O THAT Thou wouldst the heavens rend,
　In majesty come down,
Stretch out thine arm omnipotent,
　And seize me for thine own!

2 Thou my impetuous spirit guide,
　And curb my headstrong will;

Thou only canst drive back the tide,
　And bid the sun stand still.

3 What though I cannot break my chain,
　Or e'er throw off my load?
The things impossible to men
　Are possible to God.

4 Thou canst o'ercome this heart of mine,
　Thou wilt victorious prove;
For everlasting strength is thine,
　And everlasting love.
　　　　　　　　　　CHARLES WESLEY.

414　*The prodigal's return.*

1 THE prodigal, with streaming eyes,
　From folly just awake,
Reviews his wanderings with surprise;
　His heart begins to break.

2 "I starve," he cries, "nor can I bear
The famine in this land,
While servants of my Father share
　The bounty of his hand.

3 "With deep repentance I'll return,
　And seek my Father's face;
Unworthy to be called a son,
　I'll ask a servant's place."

4 Far off the Father saw him move,
　In pensive silence mourn,
And quickly ran, with arms of love,
　To welcome his return.

5 Through all the courts the tidings flew,
　And spread the joy around;
The angels tuned their harps anew,—
　The long-lost son is found!
　　　　　　　　MRS. LYDIA H. SIGOURNEY.

TOPLADY. 7, 6l.

Thomas Hastings.

FINE.

D. C.

415 *Rock of ages.*

1 ROCK of ages, cleft for me,
Let me hide myself in thee;
Let the water and the blood,
From thy wounded side which flowed,
Be of sin the double cure,
Save from wrath and make me pure.

2 Could my tears forever flow,
Could my zeal no languor know,
These for sin could not atone;
Thou must save, and thou alone:
In my hand no price I bring;
Simply to thy cross I cling.

3 While I draw this fleeting breath,
When my eyes shall close in death,
When I rise to worlds unknown,
And behold thee on thy throne,
Rock of ages, cleft for me,
Let me hide myself in thee.
AUGUSTUS M. TOPLADY, ALT.

416 *The true Light.*

1 CHRIST, whose glory fills the skies,
Christ, the true, the only Light,
Sun of righteousness, arise,
Triumph o'er the shades of night:
Dayspring from on high, be near,
Day-star, in my heart appear.

2 Dark and cheerless is the morn,
Unaccompanied by thee;
Joyless is the day's return,
Till thy mercy's beams I see;
Till thou inward life impart,
Glad my eyes, and warm my heart.

3 Visit then this soul of mine;
Pierce the gloom of sin and grief;
Fill me, Radiancy divine;
Scatter all my unbelief:
More and more thyself display,
Shining to the perfect day.
CHARLES WESLEY.

417 *The Litany.*

1 By thy birth, and by thy tears;
By thy human griefs and fears;
By thy conflict in the hour
Of the subtle tempter's power,—
Saviour, look with pitying eye;
Saviour, help me, or I die.

2 By the tenderness that wept
O'er the grave where Lazarus slept;
By the bitter tears that flowed
Over Salem's lost abode,—
Saviour, look with pitying eye;
Saviour, help me, or I die.

3 By thy lonely hour of prayer;
By the fearful conflict there;
By thy cross and dying cries;
By thy one great sacrifice,—
Saviour, look with pitying eye;
Saviour, help me, or I die.

4 By thy triumph o'er the grave;
By thy power the lost to save;
By thy high, majestic throne;
By the empire all thine own,—
Saviour, look with pitying eye;
Saviour, help me, or I die.
SIR ROBERT GRANT.

WIMBORNE.   L. M.   JOHN WHITAKER.

418   *Peace and hope of the righteous.*

1 LORD, how secure and blest are they
    Who feel the joys of pardoned sin!
Should storms of wrath shake earth and sea,
    Their minds have heaven and peace within.

2 The day glides sweetly o'er their heads,
    Made up of innocence and love;
And soft and silent as the shades,
    Their nightly minutes gently move.

3 Quick as their thoughts their joys come on,
    But fly not half so swift away;
Their souls are ever bright as noon,
    And calm as summer evenings be.

4 How oft they look to the heavenly hills,
    Where groves of living pleasure grow;
And longing hopes and cheerful smiles,
    Sit undisturbed upon their brow!

5 They scorn to seek earth's golden toys,
    But spend the day, and share the night,
In numbering o'er the richer joys
    That Heaven prepares for their delight.
                                    ISAAC WATTS.

419   *Filial love and longing.*

1 GREAT God, indulge my humble claim;
    Be thou my hope, my joy, my rest;
The glories that compose thy name
    Stand all engaged to make me blest.

2 Thou great and good, thou just and wise,
    Thou art my Father and my God;
And I am thine by sacred ties,
    Thy son, thy servant bought with blood.

3 With heart and eyes, and lifted hands,
    For thee I long, to thee I look,
As travelers in thirsty lands
    Pant for the cooling water-brook.

4 E'en life itself, without thy love,
    No lasting pleasure can afford;
Yea, 'twould a tiresome burden prove,
    If I were banished from thee, Lord.

5 I'll lift my hands, I'll raise my voice,
    While I have breath to pray or praise;
This work shall make my heart rejoice,
    And fill the remnant of my days
                                    ISAAC WATTS.

[L. M. 6 l.   Tune, Evanston.   Page 195.]

420   *The soul's anchorage.*

1 Now I have found the ground whereon
    Sure my soul's anchor may remain,
The wounds of Jesus, for my sin
    Before the world's foundation slain;
Whose mercy shall unshaken stay,
When heaven and earth are fled away.

2 Father, thine everlasting grace
    Our scanty thought surpasses far;
Thy heart still melts with tenderness,
    Thine arms of love still open are,
Returning sinners to receive,
That mercy they may taste, and live.

3 O Love, thou bottomless abyss,
    My sins are swallowed up in thee!
Covered is my unrighteousness,
    Nor spot of guilt remains on me,
While Jesus' blood, through earth and skies
Mercy, free, boundless mercy, cries.

4 By faith I plunge me in this sea;
    Here is my hope, my joy, my rest;
Hither, when hell assails, I flee;
    I look into my Saviour's breast:
Away, sad doubt and anxious fear!
Mercy is all that's written there.
                        JOHANN A. ROTHE. TR. BY J. WESLEY.

EVANSTON. L. M. 61.

JOSEPH P. HOLBROOK.

421 *Christ, the solid rock.*

1 MY hope is built on nothing less
Than Jesus' blood and righteousness;
I dare not trust the sweetest frame,
But wholly lean on Jesus' name:
On Christ, the solid rock, I stand;
All other ground is sinking sand.

2 When darkness seems to veil his face,
I rest on his unchanging grace;
In every high and stormy gale,
My anchor holds within the veil:
On Christ, the solid rock, I stand;
All other ground is sinking sand.

3 His oath, his covenant, and blood,
Support me in the whelming flood:
When all around my soul gives way,
He then is all my hope and stay:
On Christ, the solid rock, I stand;
All other ground is sinking sand.

EDWARD MOTE.

422 *Alive in Christ.*

1 AND can it be that I should gain
An interest in the Saviour's blood?
Died he for me, who caused his pain?
For me, who him to death pursued?
Amazing love! how can it be
That thou, my Lord, shouldst die for me?

2 'Tis mystery all! the Immortal dies!
Who can explore his strange design?
In vain the first-born seraph tries
To sound the depths of love divine;
'Tis mercy all! let earth adore;
Let angel minds inquire no more.

3 He left his Father's throne above,—
So free, so infinite his grace!—
Emptied himself of all but love,
And bled for Adam's helpless race:
'Tis mercy all, immense and free,
For, O my God, it found out me!

4 Long my imprisoned spirit lay,
Fast bound in sin and nature's night;
Thine eye diffused a quickening ray,
I woke, the dungeon flamed with light,
My chains fell off, my heart was free,
I rose, went forth, and followed thee.

5 No condemnation now I dread,
Jesus, with all in him, is mine;
Alive in him, my living Head,
And clothed in righteousness divine,
Bold I approach the eternal throne,
And claim the crown, through Christ, my
own.

CHARLES WESLEY.

THE CHRISTIAN—JUSTIFICATION AND ADOPTION.

EVAN. C. M.

REV. WM. HENRY HAVERGAL.

423 *Convicted,—pardoned.*

1 IN evil long I took delight,
  Unawed by shame or fear,
Till a new object struck my sight,
  And stopped my wild career.

2 I saw One hanging on a tree,
  In agonies and blood,
Who fixed his languid eyes on me,
  As near his cross I stood.

3 Sure never till my latest breath
  Can I forget that look:
It seemed to charge me with his death,
  Though not a word he spoke.

4 My conscience felt and owned the guilt,
  And plunged me in despair;
I saw my sins his blood had spilt,
  And helped to nail him there.

5 Alas! I knew not what I did!
  But now my tears are vain:
Where shall my trembling soul be hid?
  For I the Lord have slain!

6 A second look he gave, which said,
  "I freely all forgive;
This blood is for thy ransom paid;
  I die that thou mayst live."

7 Thus, while his death my sin displays
  In all its blackest hue,
Such is the mystery of grace,
  It seals my pardon too.
                              JOHN NEWTON.

424 *The earnest of redemption.*

1 WHY should the children of a King
  Go mourning all their days?

Great Comforter, descend and bring
  The tokens of thy grace.

2 Dost thou not dwell in all thy saints,
  And seal the heirs of heaven?
When wilt thou banish my complaints,
  And show my sins forgiven?

3 Assure my conscience of her part
  In the Redeemer's blood;
And bear thy witness with my heart,
  That I am born of God.

4 Thou art the earnest of his love,
  The pledge of joys to come;
May thy blest wings, celestial Dove,
  Safely convey me home.
                              ISAAC WATTS.

425 *The blood of sprinkling.*

1 MY God, my God, to thee I cry;
  Thee only would I know;
Thy purifying blood apply,
  And wash me white as snow.

2 Touch me, and make the leper clear:
  Purge my iniquity:
Unless thou wash my soul from sin,
  I have no part in thee.

3 But art thou not already mine?
  Answer, if mine thou art;
Whisper within, thou Love divine,
  And cheer my drooping heart.

4 Behold, for me the Victim bleeds,
  His wounds are open wide;
For me the blood of sprinkling pleads,
  And speaks me justified.
                              CHARLES WESLEY.

TRUMAN. C. M. D.

JOSEPH P. HOLBROOK.

426   *The voice of Jesus.*

1 I HEARD the voice of Jesus say,
  "Come unto me and rest;
Lay down, thou weary one, lay down
  Thy head upon my breast!"
I came to Jesus as I was,
  Weary, and worn, and sad;
I found in him a resting-place,
  And he hath made me glad.

2 I heard the voice of Jesus say,
  "Behold, I freely give
The living water; thirsty one,
  Stoop down, and drink, and live!"
I came to Jesus, and I drank
  Of that life-giving stream;
My thirst was quenched, my soul revived,
  And now I live in him.

3 I heard the voice of Jesus say,
  "I am this dark world's Light;
Look unto me, thy morn shall rise
  And all thy day be bright!"
I looked to Jesus, and I found
  In him my Star, my Sun;
And in that light of life I'll walk,
  Till all my journey's done.

HORATIUS BONAR.

427   *Amazing grace.*

1 AMAZING grace! how sweet the sound,
  That saved a wretch like me!
I once was lost, but now am found,
  Was blind, but now I see.
'Twas grace that taught my heart to fear,
  And grace my fears relieved;
How precious did that grace appear
  The hour I first believed!

2 Through many dangers, toils, and snares,
  I have already come;
'Tis grace hath brought me safe thus far,
  And grace will lead me home.
The Lord has promised good to me,
  His word my hope secures;
He will my shield and portion be
  As long as life endures.

3 Yes, when this flesh and heart shall fail
  And mortal life shall cease,
I shall possess, within the veil,
  A life of joy and peace.
The earth shall soon dissolve like snow,
  The sun forbear to shine;
But God, who called me here below,
  Will be forever mine.

JOHN NEWTON.

BURLINGTON. C. M. JOHN FRECKLETON BURROWES.

428 *Reconciliation with God.*

1 ETERNAL Sun of righteousness,
Display thy beams divine,
And cause the glories of thy face
Upon my heart to shine.

2 Light in thy light O may I see,
Thy grace and mercy prove;
Revived, and cheered, and blest by thee,
The God of pardoning love.

3 Lift up thy countenance serene,
And let thy happy child
Behold, without a cloud between,
The Godhead reconciled.

4 That all-comprising peace bestow
On me, through grace forgiven;
The joys of holiness below,
And then the joys of heaven.
CHARLES WESLEY.

429 *Delightful assurance.*

1 SOVEREIGN of all the worlds on high,
Allow my humble claim;
Nor while, unworthy, I draw nigh,
Disdain a Father's name.

2 My Father, God! that gracious word
Dispels my guilty fear;
Not all the notes by angels heard
Could so delight my ear.

3 Come, Holy Ghost, thyself impress
On my expanding heart;
And show that in the Father's grace
I share a filial part.

4 Cheered by that witness from on high,
Unwavering I believe;
And, "Abba, Father," humbly cry;
Nor can the sign deceive.
PHILIP DODDRIDGE.

DOWNS. C. M. LOWELL MASON.

430 *Peace in believing.*

1 JESUS, to thee I now can fly,
On whom my help is laid:
Oppressed by sins, I lift mine eye,
And see the shadows fade.

2 Believing on my Lord, I find
A sure and present aid;
On thee alone my constant mind
Be every moment stayed.

3 Whate'er in me seems wise, or good,
Or strong, I here disclaim;
I wash my garments in the blood
Of the atoning Lamb.

4 Jesus, my strength, my life, my rest,
On thee will I depend,
Till summoned to the marriage-feast,
When faith in sight shall end.
CHARLES WESLEY.

WOODLAND.   C. M.   NATHANIEL D. GOULD.

431   *The well of life.*

1 FOUNTAIN of life, to all below
    Let thy salvation roll;
Water, replenish, and o'erflow
    Every believing soul.

2 Into that happy number, Lord,
    Us weary sinners take;
Jesus, fulfill thy gracious word,
    For thine own mercy's sake.

3 Turn back our nature's rapid tide,
    And we shall flow to thee,
While down the stream of time we glide
    To our eternity.

4 The well of life to us thou art,
    Of joy the swelling flood;
Wafted by thee, with willing heart,
    We swift return to God.

5 We soon shall reach the boundless sea;
    Into thy fulness fall;
Be lost and swallowed up in thee,
    Our God, our all in all.
                              CHARLES WESLEY.

432   *Victorious faith.*

1 FATHER of Jesus Christ, my Lord,
    My Saviour, and my Head,
I trust in thee, whose powerful word
    Hath raised him from the dead.

2 In hope, against all human hope,
    Self-desperate, I believe;
Thy quickening word shall raise me up,
    Thou wilt thy Spirit give.

3 Faith, mighty faith, the promise sees,
    And looks to that alone;

Laughs at impossibilities,
    And cries, "It shall be done!"

4 To thee the glory of thy power
    And faithfulness I give;
I shall in Christ, at that glad hour,
    And Christ in me shall live.

5 Obedient faith, that waits on thee,
    Thou never wilt reprove;
But thou wilt form thy Son in me,
    And perfect me in love.
                              CHARLES WESLEY

433   *His boundless grace.*

1 WHAT shall I do my God to love?
    My loving God to praise?
The length and breadth, and height to
        prove,
    And depth of sovereign grace?

2 Thy sovereign grace to all extends,
    Immense and unconfined;
From age to age it never ends;
    It reaches all mankind.

3 Throughout the world its breadth is
        known,
    Wide as infinity:
So wide it never passed by one,
    Or it had passed by me.

4 My trespass was grown up to heaven;
    But, far above the skies,
Through Christ abundantly forgiven,
    I see thy mercies rise.

5 The depth of all-redeeming love,
    What angel tongue can tell?
O may I to the utmost prove
    The gift unspeakable!
                              CHARLES WESLEY.

MORRIS. S. M. D.

*REV. JOHN BLACK.

434 *No more a wandering sheep.*

1 I WAS a wandering sheep,
I did not love the fold,
I did not love my Shepherd's voice,
I would not be controlled;
I was a wayward child,
I did not love my home,
I did not love my Father's voice,
I loved afar to roam.

2 The Shepherd sought his sheep,
The Father sought his child;
He followed me o'er vale and hill,
O'er deserts waste and wild:
He found me nigh to death,
Famished, and faint, and lone;
He bound me with the bands of love,
He saved the wandering one.

3 Jesus my Shepherd is;
'Twas he that loved my soul,
'Twas he that washed me in his blood,
'Twas he that made me whole:
'Twas he that sought the lost,
That found the wandering sheep;
'Twas he that brought me to the fold,
'Tis he that still doth keep.

4 No more a wandering sheep,
I love to be controlled,
I love my tender Shepherd's voice,
I love the peaceful fold;

No more a wayward child,
I seek no more to roam;
I love my heavenly Father's voice,
I love, I love his home!
HORATIUS BONAR.

435 *The revealing Spirit.*

1 SPIRIT of faith, come down,
Reveal the things of God;
And make to us the Godhead known,
And witness with the blood:
'Tis thine the blood to apply,
And give us eyes to see,
That he who did for sinners die.
Hath surely died for me.

2 No man can truly say
That Jesus is the Lord,
Unless thou take the veil away,
And breathe the living word;
Then, only then, we feel
Our interest in his blood;
And cry, with joy unspeakable,
"Thou art my Lord, my God!"

3 O that the world might know
The all-atoning Lamb!
Spirit of faith, descend and show
The virtue of his name:
The grace which all may find,
The saving power, impart;
And testify to all mankind,
And speak in every heart.
CHARLES WESLEY.

THE CHRISTIAN—JUSTIFICATION AND ADOPTION.

SHIRLAND. S. M. Samuel Stanley

436 *God, my Father.*

1 HERE I can firmly rest;
  I dare to boast of this,
That God, the highest and the best,
  My Friend and Father is.

2 Naught have I of my own,
  Naught in the life I lead;
What Christ hath given, that alone
  I dare in faith to plead.

3 I rest upon the ground
  Of Jesus and his blood;
It is through him that I have found
  My soul's eternal good.

4 At cost of all I have,
  At cost of life and limb,
I cling to God who yet shall save;
  I will not turn from him.

5 His Spirit in me dwells,
  O'er all my mind he reigns;
My care and sadness he dispels,
  And soothes away my pains.

6 He prospers day by day
  His work within my heart,
Till I have strength and faith to say,
  "Thou, God, my Father art!"
  PAUL GERHARDT. TR. BY MISS C. WINKWORTH

BADEA. S. M. German Melody.

437 *Knowledge of forgiveness.*

1 How can a sinner know
  His sins on earth forgiven?
How can my gracious Saviour show
  My name inscribed in heaven?

2 What we have felt and seen
  With confidence we tell;
And publish to the sons of men
  The signs infallible.

3 We who in Christ believe
  That he for us hath died,
We all his unknown peace receive,
  And feel his blood applied.

4 Exults our rising soul,
  Disburdened of her load,
And swells unutterably full
  Of glory and of God.

5 His love, surpassing far
  The love of all beneath,
We find within our hearts, and dare
  The pointless darts of death.

6 Stronger than death or hell
  The sacred power we prove;
And, conquerors of the world, we dwell
  In heaven, who dwell in love.
  CHARLES WESLEY.

LENOX.   H. M.

Lewis Edson.

438 *Abba, Father.*—Rom. 8: 15.

1 ARISE, my soul, arise;
  Shake off thy guilty fears;
  The bleeding Sacrifice
    In my behalf appears:
Before the throne my Surety stands,
My name is written on his hands.

2 He ever lives above,
  For me to intercede;
  His all-redeeming love,
    His precious blood to plead;
His blood atoned for all our race,
And sprinkles now the throne of grace.

3 Five bleeding wounds he bears,
  Received on Calvary;
  They pour effectual prayers,
    They strongly plead for me:
"Forgive him, O forgive," they cry,
"Nor let that ransomed sinner die."

4 The Father hears him pray,
  His dear anointed One:
  He cannot turn away
    The presence of his Son:
His Spirit answers to the blood,
And tells me I am born of God.

5 My God is reconciled;
  His pardoning voice I hear:
  He owns me for his child;
    I can no longer fear:
With confidence I now draw nigh,
And, "Father, Abba, Father," cry.

CHARLES WESLEY.

[C. P. M. Tune, Meribah. Page 358.]

439   *The inward witness.*

1 THOU great mysterious God unknown,
  Whose love hath gently led me on
    E'en from my infant days;
  Mine inmost soul expose to view,
  And tell me if I ever knew
    Thy justifying grace.

2 If I have only known thy fear,
  And followed, with a heart sincere,
    Thy drawings from above;
  Now, now the further grace bestow,
  And let my sprinkled conscience know
    Thy sweet forgiving love.

3 Short of thy love I would not stop,
  A stranger to the gospel hope,
    The sense of sin forgiven;
  I would not, Lord, my soul deceive,
  Without the inward witness live,
    That antepast of heaven.

4 If now the witness were in me,
  Would he not testify of thee,
    In Jesus reconciled?
  And should I not with faith draw nigh,
  And boldly, "Abba, Father," cry,
    And know myself thy child?

5 Father, in me reveal thy Son,
  And to my inmost soul make known
    How merciful thou art;
  The secret of thy love reveal,
  And by thy hallowing Spirit dwell
    Forever in my heart.

CHARLES WESLEY.

VIOLA. 7, 6l.

WILLIAM BATCHELDER BRADBURY.

440 *The indwelling Spirit.*

1 ABBA, Father, hear thy child,
Late in Jesus reconciled;
Hear, and all the graces shower,
All the joy, and peace, and power;
All my Saviour asks above,
All the life and heaven of love.

2 Lord, I will not let thee go
Till the blessing thou bestow:
Hear my Advocate divine;
Lo! to his my suit I join;
Joined to his, it cannot fail;
Bless me; for I will prevail.

3 Heavenly Father, Life divine,
Change my nature into thine;
Move, and spread throughout my soul,
Actuate, and fill the whole:
Be it I no longer now
Living in the flesh, but thou.

4 Holy Ghost, no more delay;
Come, and in thy temple stay:
Now thine inward witness bear,
Strong, and permanent, and clear:
Spring of life, thyself impart;
Rise eternal in my heart.

CHARLES WESLEY.

REPOSE. 7, 6l.

ARR. BY JOSEPH P. HOLBROOK.

441 *Chief of sinners.*

1 CHIEF of sinners though I be,
Jesus shed his blood for me;
Died that I might live on high,
Died that I might never die;
As the branch is to the vine,
I am his and he is mine.

2 O the height of Jesus' love!
Higher than the heavens above,
Deeper than the depths of sea,
Lasting as eternity;
Love that found me,—wondrous thought!—
Found me when I sought him not!

3 Chief of sinners though I be,
Christ is all in all to me;
All my wants to him are known,
All my sorrows are his own;
Safe with him from earthly strife,
He sustains the hidden life.

MC COMB.

RAPTURE. 12, 9.

R. D. HUMPHREYS.

442 *The joys of conversion.*

1 O HOW happy are they,
Who the Saviour obey,
And have laid up their treasure above!
Tongue can never express
The sweet comfort and peace
Of a soul in its earliest love.

2 That sweet comfort was mine,
When the favor divine
I received through the blood of the Lamb;
When my heart first believed,
What a joy I received,
What a heaven in Jesus's name!

3 'Twas a heaven below
My Redeemer to know,
And the angels could do nothing more,
Than to fall at his feet,
And the story repeat,
And the Lover of sinners adore.

4 Jesus all the day long
Was my joy and my song:
O that all his salvation might see!
"He hath loved me," I cried,
"He hath suffered and died,
To redeem even rebels like me."

5 O the rapturous height
Of that holy delight
Which I felt in the life-giving blood!

Of my Saviour possessed,
I was perfectly blessed,
As if filled with the fullness of God.
CHARLES WESLEY.

[7, 6, 7. Tune, Amsterdam. Page 401.]

443 *The righteousness of faith.*

1 OFT I in my heart have said,—
Who shall ascend on high,
Mount to Christ, my glorious Head,
And bring him from the sky?
Borne on contemplation's wing,
Surely I shall find him there,
Where the angels praise their King,
And gain the Morning Star.

2 Oft I in my heart have said,—
Who to the deep shall stoop,
Sink with Christ among the dead,
From thence to bring him up?
Could I but my heart prepare,
By unfeigned humility,
Christ would quickly enter there,
And ever dwell in me.

3 But the righteousness of faith
Hath taught me better things:
"Inward turn thine eyes," it saith,
While Christ to me it brings:
"Christ is ready to impart
Life to all, for life who sigh:
In thy mouth and in thy heart
The word is ever nigh."
CHARLES WESLEY.

164

SAMSON. L. M.

GEORGE FREDERICK HANDEL.

444 *The new joy.*

1 TREMBLING before thine awful throne,
O Lord, in dust my sins I own;
Justice and mercy for my life
Contend; O smile, and heal the strife.

2 The Saviour smiles; upon my soul
New tides of hope tumultuous roll;
His voice proclaims my pardon found,
Seraphic transport wings the sound.

3 Earth has a joy unknown to heaven,
The newborn peace of sins forgiven;
Tears of such pure and deep delight,
Ye angels, never dimmed your sight.

4 Bright heralds of the eternal Will,
Abroad his errands ye fulfill;
Or, throned in floods of beamy day,
Symphonious in his presence play.

5 Loud is the song, the heavenly plain
Is shaken with the choral strain;
And dying echoes, floating far,
Draw music from each chiming star.

6 But I amid your choirs shall shine,
And all your knowledge shall be mine:
Ye on your harps must lean to hear
A secret chord that mine will bear.
AUGUSTUS L. HILLHOUSE.

445 *The realizing light of faith.*

1 AUTHOR of faith, eternal Word,
Whose Spirit breathes the active flame,
Faith, like its finisher and Lord,
To-day as yesterday the same;

2 To thee our humble hearts aspire,
And ask the gift unspeakable;
Increase in us the kindled fire,
In us the work of faith fulfill.

3 By faith we know thee strong to save:
Save us, a present Saviour thou:
Whate'er we hope, by faith we have;
Future and past subsisting now.

4 To him that in thy name believes,
Eternal life with thee is given;
Into himself he all receives,
Pardon, and holiness, and heaven.

5 The things unknown to feeble sense,
Unseen by reason's glimmering ray,
With strong, commanding evidence,
Their heavenly origin display.

6 Faith lends its realizing light;
The clouds disperse, the shadows fly;
The Invisible appears in sight,
And God is seen by mortal eye.
CHARLES WESLEY.

446 *Salvation by grace.*

1 WE have no outward righteousness,
No merits or good works to plead;
We only can be saved by grace:
Thy grace, O Lord, is free indeed.

2 Save us by grace, through faith alone,
A faith thou must thyself impart;
A faith that would by works be shown,
A faith that purifies the heart:

3 A faith that doth the mountains move,
A faith that shows our sins forgiven,
A faith that sweetly works by love,
And ascertains our claim to heaven.

4 This is the faith we humbly seek,
The faith in thy all-cleansing blood,
That blood which doth for sinners speak;
O let it speak us up to God!
CHARLES WESLEY.

ROCKINGHAM.   L. M.

LOWELL MASON.

447   *O happy day!*

1 O HAPPY day that fixed my choice
   On thee, my Saviour and my God!
Well may this glowing heart rejoice,
   And tell its raptures all abroad.

2 O happy bond, that seals my vows
   To him who merits all my love!
Let cheerful anthems fill his house,
   While to that sacred shrine I move.

3 'Tis done, the great transaction's done;
   I am my Lord's, and he is mine;
He drew me, and I followed on,
   Charmed to confess the voice divine.

4 Now rest, my long-divided heart;
   Fixed on this blissful center, rest;
Nor ever from thy Lord depart,
   With him of every good possessed.

5 High Heaven, that heard the solemn vow,
   That vow renewed shall daily hear,
Till in life's latest hour I bow,
   And bless in death a bond so dear.
      PHILIP DODDRIDGE.

448   *Salvation by faith.*

1 INTO thy gracious hands I fall,
   And with the arms of faith embrace;
O King of glory, hear my call;
   O raise me, heal me by thy grace.
Now righteous through thy grace I am;
   No condemnation now I dread;
I taste salvation in thy name,
   Alive in thee, my living Head.

2 Still let thy wisdom be my guide,
   Nor take thy flight from me away;
Still with me let thy grace abide,
   That I from thee may never stray:
Let thy word richly in me dwell,
   Thy peace and love my portion be;
My joy to endure and do thy will,
   Till perfect I am found in thee.

3 Arm me with thy whole armor, Lord,
   Support my weakness with thy might;
Gird on thy thigh thy conquering sword,
   And shield me in the threatening fight;
From faith to faith, from grace to grace,
   So in thy strength shall I go on,
Till heaven and earth flee from thy face,
   And glory end what grace begun.
      WOLFGANG C. DESSLER, TR. BY J. WESLEY.

449   *Forgiving love.*

1 My soul, with humble fervor raise
To God the voice of grateful praise,
And all my ransomed powers combine,
To bless his attributes divine.

2 Deep on my heart let memory trace
His acts of mercy and of grace,
Who, with a Father's tender care,
Saved me when sinking in despair;

3 Gave my repentant soul to prove
The joy of his forgiving love;
Poured balm into my bleeding breast,
And led my weary feet to rest.
      JOHN H. LIVINGSTONE.

166

DARLEY. L. M.   W. H. W. DARLEY.

450 *The highway of holiness.*

1 JESUS, my all, to heaven is gone,
He whom I fix my hopes upon;
His track I see, and I'll pursue
The narrow way, till him I view.

2 The way the holy prophets went,
The road that leads from banishment,
The King's highway of holiness,
I'll go, for all his paths are peace.

3 This is the way I long have sought,
And mourned because I found it not;
My grief a burden long has been,
Because I was not saved from sin.

4 The more I strove against its power,
I felt its weight and guilt the more;
Till late I heard my Saviour say,
"Come hither, soul, I am the way."

5 Lo! glad I come; and thou, blest Lamb,
Shalt take me to thee, as I am;
Nothing but sin have I to give;
Nothing but love shall I receive.

6 Then will I tell to sinners round,
What a dear Saviour I have found;
I'll point to thy redeeming blood,
And say, "Behold the way to God."
                                        JOHN CENNICK.

451 *His sovereign grace.*

1 GLORY to God, whose sovereign grace
Hath animated senseless stones,
Called us to stand before his face,
And raised us into Abrah'm's sons.

2 The people that in darkness lay,
In sin and error's deadly shade,

Have seen a glorious gospel-day
In Jesus' lovely face displayed.

3 Thou only, Lord, the work hast done,
And bared thine arm in all our sight;
Hast made the reprobates thine own,
And claimed the outcasts as thy right.

4 Thy single arm, almighty Lord,
To us the great salvation brought;
Thy Word, thy all-creating Word,
That spake at first the world from naught.

5 For this the saints lift up their voice,
And ceaseless praise to thee is given;
For this the hosts above rejoice,
And praise thee in the highest heaven.
                                        CHARLES WESLEY.

452 *The Lord our righteousness.*

1 LET not the wise their wisdom boast,
The mighty glory in their might,
The rich in flattering riches trust,
Which take their everlasting flight.

2 The rush of numerous years bears down
The most gigantic strength of man;
And where is all his wisdom gone,
When, dust, he turns to dust again?

3 One only gift can justify
The boasting soul that knows his God;
When Jesus doth his blood apply,
I glory in his sprinkled blood.

4 The Lord my Righteousness I praise,
I triumph in the love divine;
The wisdom, wealth, and strength of grace,
In Christ to endless ages mine.
                                        CHARLES WESLEY.

HOUGHTON. 10, 11. WILLIAM GARDINER.

453 *His plenteous grace.*

1 O WHAT shall I do my Saviour to praise,
So faithful and true, so plenteous in grace,
So strong to deliver, so good to redeem
The weakest believer that hangs upon him!

2 How happy the man whose heart is set free,
The people that can be joyful in thee!
Their joy is to walk in the light of thy face,
And still they are talking of Jesus's grace:

3 For thou art their boast, their glory, and
power,
And I also trust to see the glad hour,
My soul's new creation, a life from the dead,
The day of salvation that lifts up my head.

4 For Jesus, my Lord, is now my defense;
I trust in his word; none plucks me from
thence;
Since I have found favor, he all things
will do;
My King and my Saviour shall make me
anew.

5 Yes, Lord, I shall see the bliss of thine
own;
Thy secret to me shall soon be made
known;
For sorrow and sadness I joy shall receive,
And share in the gladness of all that believe.

CHARLES WESLEY.

LYONS. 10, 11. FRANCIS JOSEPH HAYDN.

454 *Accepted in the Beloved.*

1 ALL praise to the Lamb! accepted I am,
Through faith in the Saviour's adorable
name:
In him I confide, his blood is applied;
For me he hath suffered, for me he hath died.

2 Not a cloud doth arise, to darken my
skies,
Or hide for a moment my Lord from mine
eyes:
In him I am blest, I lean on his breast,
And lo! in his wounds I continue to rest.

CHARLES WESLEY.

THE CHRISTIAN—CONSECRATION.

ROCKPORT. 7, 6, 8. ISAAC BAKER WOODBURY.

FINE.

D. C.

455 *Tears of joy.*

1 LORD, and is thine anger gone,
  And art thou pacified?
After all that I have done,
  Dost thou no longer chide?
Let thy love my heart constrain,
  And all my restless passions sway:
Keep me, lest I turn again
  Out of the narrow way.

2 See my utter helplessness,
  And leave me not alone;
O preserve in perfect peace,
  And seal me for thine own:
More and more thyself reveal,
  Thy presence let me always find;
Comfort, and confirm, and heal
  My feeble, sin-sick mind.

3 As the apple of thine eye,
  Thy weakest servant keep;
Help me at thy feet to lie,
  And there forever weep:
Tears of joy mine eyes o'erflow,
  That I have any hope of heaven;
Much of love I ought to know,
  For I have much forgiven.
                        CHARLES WESLEY.

456 *Nothing but Christ crucified.*

1 VAIN, delusive world, adieu,
  With all of creature good!
Only Jesus I pursue,
  Who bought me with his blood:
All thy pleasures I forego;
  I trample on thy wealth and pride;

Only Jesus will I know,
  And Jesus crucified.

2 Other knowledge I disdain;
  'Tis all but vanity:
Christ, the Lamb of God, was slain,
  He tasted death for me.
Me to save from endless woe
  The sin-atoning Victim died:
Only Jesus will I know,
  And Jesus crucified.

3 Here will I set up my rest;
  My fluctuating heart
From the haven of his breast
  Shall never more depart:
Whither should a sinner go?
  His wounds for me stand open wide;
Only Jesus will I know,
  And Jesus crucified.

4 Him to know is life and peace,
  And pleasure without end;
This is all my happiness,
  On Jesus to depend;
Daily in his grace to grow,
  And ever in his faith abide;
Only Jesus will I know,
  And Jesus crucified.

5 O that I could all invite,
  This saving truth to prove!
Show the length, the breadth, the height,
  And depth of Jesus' love!
Fain I would to sinners show
  The blood by faith alone applied;
Only Jesus will I know,
  And Jesus crucified.
                        CHARLES WESLEY.

169

THE CHRISTIAN—CONSECRATION.

PERCY. L. M.

H. Percy Smith.

457 *Renouncing all for Christ.*

1 COME, Saviour, Jesus, from above,
  Assist me with thy heavenly grace;
Empty my heart of earthly love,
  And for thyself prepare the place.

2 O let thy sacred presence fill,
  And set my longing spirit free;
Which pants to have no other will,
  But night and day to feast on thee.

3 While in this region here below,
  No other good will I pursue:
I'll bid this world of noise and show,
  With all its glittering snares, adieu.

4 That path with humble speed I'll seek,
  In which my Saviour's footsteps shine;
Nor will I hear, nor will I speak,
  Of any other love but thine.

5 Henceforth may no profane delight
  Divide this consecrated soul;
Possess it thou, who hast the right,
  As Lord and Master of the whole.

6 Nothing on earth do I desire,
  But thy pure love within my breast;
This, only this, will I require,
  And freely give up all the rest.
  MAD. A. BOURIGNON. TR. BY J. WESLEY.

458 *Personal consecration.*

1 GOD of my life, what just return
  Can sinful dust and ashes give?
I only live my sin to mourn:
  To love my God I only live.

2 To thee, benign and saving Power,
  I consecrate my lengthened days;

While, marked with blessings, every hour
  Shall speak thy co-extended praise.

3 Be all my added life employed
  Thine image in my soul to see:
Fill with thyself the mighty void;
  Enlarge my heart to compass thee.

4 The blessing of thy love bestow;
  For this my cries shall never fail;
Wrestling, I will not let thee go,—
  I will not, till my suit prevail.

5 Come, then, my Hope, my Life, my Lord,
  And fix in me thy lasting home;
Be mindful of thy gracious word,—
  Thou, with thy promised Father, come
  CHARLES WESLEY.

459 *Living to God.*

1 O THOU, who hast at thy command
  The hearts of all men in thy hand,
Our wayward, erring hearts incline
  To have no other will but thine.

2 Our wishes, our desires, control;
  Mold every purpose of the soul;
O'er all may we victorious prove
  That stands between us and thy love.

3 Thrice blest will all our blessings be,
  When we can look through them to thee
When each glad heart its tribute pays
  Of love, and gratitude, and praise.

4 And while we to thy glory live,
  May we to thee all glory give,
Until the final summons come,
  That calls thy willing servants home.
  MRS. M. J. COTTERILL.

SESSIONS.   L. M.

LUTHER ORLANDO EMERSON.

460   *The vow sealed at the cross.*

1 LORD, I am thine, entirely thine,
Purchased and saved by blood divine;
With full consent thine I would be,
And own thy sovereign right in me.

2 Grant one poor sinner more a place
Among the children of thy grace;
A wretched sinner, lost to God,
But ransomed by Immanuel's blood.

3 Thine would I live, thine would I die,
Be thine through all eternity;
The vow is past beyond repeal,
And now I set the solemn seal.

4 Here, at that cross where flows the blood
That bought my guilty soul for God,
Thee, my new Master, now I call,
And consecrate to thee my all.

5 Do thou assist a feeble worm
The great engagement to perform;
Thy grace can full assistance lend,
And on that grace I dare depend.
SAMUEL DAVIES.

461   *Thirsting for perfect love.*

1 I THIRST, thou wounded Lamb of God,
To wash me in thy cleansing blood;
To dwell within thy wounds; then pain
Is sweet, and life or death is gain.

2 Take my poor heart, and let it be
Forever closed to all but thee:
Seal thou my breast, and let me wear
That pledge of love forever there.

3 How blest are they who still abide
Close sheltered in thy bleeding side!
Who thence their life and strength derive,
And by thee move, and in thee live.

4 What are our works but sin and death,
Till thou thy quickening Spirit breathe?
Thou giv'st the power thy grace to move;
O wondrous grace! O boundless love!

5 How can it be, thou heavenly King,
That thou shouldst us to glory bring?
Make slaves the partners of thy throne,
Decked with a never-fading crown?

6 Hence our hearts melt, our eyes o'erflow,
Our words are lost, nor will we know,
Nor will we think of aught beside,
"My Lord, my Love is crucified."
NICOLAUS L. ZINZENDORF.
TR. BY J. WESLEY.

462   *The Lord is my portion.*—Lam. 3: 24.

1 O LOVE, thy sovereign aid impart,
And guard the gift thyself hast given:
My portion thou, my treasure art,
My life, and happiness, and heaven.

2 Would aught on earth my wishes share?
Though dear as life the idol be,
The idol from my breast I'd tear,
Resolved to seek my all in thee.

3 Whate'er I fondly counted mine,
To thee, my Lord, I here restore;
Gladly I all for thee resign;
Give me thyself, I ask no more.
CHARLES WESLEY.

THE CHRISTIAN—CONSECRATION.

ALETTA. 7. WILLIAM BATCHELDER BRADBURY.

4 Saviour, at thy feet I fall;
Thou my Life, my God, my All!
Let thy happy servant be
One for evermore with thee!
MARY A. S. BARBER.

464 *The mind of Jesus*

1 FATHER of eternal grace,
  Glorify thyself in me;
Sweetly beaming in my face
  May the world thine image see.

2 Happy only in thy love,
  Poor, unfriended, or unknown:
Fix my thoughts on things above,
  Stay my heart on thee alone.

3 To thy gracious will resigned,
  All thy will by me be done;
Give me, Lord, the perfect mind
  Of thy well-belovéd Son.

4 Counting gain and glory loss,
  May I tread the path he trod;
Die with Jesus on the cross,
  Rise with him to live with God.
JAMES MONTGOMERY.

463 *Perfect peace.*

1 PRINCE of peace, control my will;
Bid this struggling heart be still;
Bid my fears and doubtings cease,
Hush my spirit into peace.

2 Thou hast bought me with thy blood,
Opened wide the gate to God:
Peace I ask—but peace must be,
Lord, in being one with thee.

3 May thy will, not mine, be done;
May thy will and mine be one:
Chase these doubtings from my heart;
Now thy perfect peace impart.

FISK. 7. ✠

465 *Thine forever.*

1 THINE forever!—God of love,
Hear us from thy throne above;
Thine forever may we be,
Here and in eternity.

2 Thine forever!—Lord of life,
Shield us through our earthly strife;
Thou, the Life, the Truth, the Way,
Guide us to the realms of day.

3 Thine forever!—Saviour, keep
These thy frail and trembling sheep;
Safe alone beneath thy care,
Let us all thy goodness share.

4 Thine forever!—thou our Guide,
All our wants by thee supplied,
All our sins by thee forgiven,
Lead us, Lord, from earth to heaven.
MRS. MARY F. MAUDE.

BARBY.   C. M.

WILLIAM TANSUR.

466   *The solemn vow.*

1 WITNESS, ye men and angels, now,
  Before the Lord we speak;
To him we make our solemn vow,
  A vow we dare not break:

2 That long as life itself shall last,
  Ourselves to Christ we yield;
Nor from his cause will we depart,
  Or ever quit the field.

3 We trust not in our native strength,
  But on his grace rely,
That, with returning wants, the Lord
  Will all our need supply.

4 Lord, guide our doubtful feet aright,
  And keep us in thy ways;
And, while we turn our vows to prayers,
  Turn thou our prayers to praise.
                        BENJAMIN BEDDOME.

467   *I will take the cup of salvation.*
          Psa. 116 : 13.

1 WHAT shall I render to my God
  For all his mercy's store?
I'll take the gifts he hath bestowed,
  And humbly ask for more.

2 My vows I will to his great name
  Before his people pay,
And all I have, and all I am,
  Upon his altar lay.

3 Thy lawful servant, Lord, I owe
  To thee whate'er is mine,
Born in thy family below,
  And by redemption thine.

4 The God of all-redeeming grace
  My God I will proclaim,
Offer the sacrifice of praise,
  And call upon his name.

5 Praise him, ye saints, the God of love,
  Who hath my sins forgiven,
Till, gathered to the Church above,
  We sing the songs of heaven.
                        SAMUEL WESLEY.

468   *Accept my heart.*

1 MY God, accept my heart this day,
  And make it always thine;
That I from thee no more may stray,
  No more from thee decline.

2 Before the cross of him who died,
  Behold, I prostrate fall;
Let every sin be crucified,
  Let Christ be all in all.

3 Let every thought, and work, and word,
  To thee be ever given;
Then life shall be thy service, Lord,
  And death the gate of heaven!
                        MATTHEW BRIDGES.

469   *Soul and body dedicated to the Lord.*

1 LET Him to whom we now belong,
  His sovereign right assert;
And take up every thankful song,
  And every loving heart.

2 He justly claims us for his own,
  Who bought us with a price:
The Christian lives to Christ alone;
  To Christ alone he dies.

3 Jesus, thine own at last receive;
  Fulfill our hearts' desire;
And let us to thy glory live,
  And in thy cause expire.

4 Our souls and bodies we resign;
  With joy we render thee
Our all,—no longer ours, but thine
  To all eternity.
                        CHARLES WESLEY.

DURBIN. 7, 6l. Rev. W. D. Maclagan.

All my actions sanctify,
  All my words and thoughts receive;
Claim me for thy service, claim
  All I have, and all I am.

3 Take my soul and body's powers:
  Take my memory, mind, and will;
All my goods, and all my hours;
  All I know, and all I feel:
All I think, or speak, or do;
  Take my heart, but make it new.

470 *Entire consecration.*

1 FATHER, Son, and Holy Ghost,
  One in Three, and Three in One,
As by the celestial host,
  Let thy will on earth be done;
Praise by all to thee be given,
  Glorious Lord of earth and heaven.

2 If so poor a worm as I
  May to thy great glory live,

4 Now, O God, thine own I am,
  Now I give thee back thine own:
Freedom, friends, and health, and fame,
  Consecrate to thee alone:
Thine I live, thrice happy I;
  Happier still if thine I die.

CHARLES WESLEY.

SAXBY. L. M. Rev. T. R. Matthews.

3 O for a faith like his, that we
  The bright example may pursue!
May gladly give up all to thee,
  To whom our more than all is due.

471 *The trial of Abraham.*

1 ABRAHAM, when severely tried,
  His faith by his obedience showed;
He with the harsh command complied,
  And gave his Isaac back to God.

2 His son the father offered up,—
  Son of his age, his only son;
Object of all his joy and hope,
  And less beloved than God alone.

4 Is there a thing than life more dear?
  A thing from which we cannot part?
We can; we now rejoice to tear
  The idol from our bleeding heart.

5 Jesus, accept our sacrifice:
  All things for thee we count but loss
Lo! at thy word our idol dies,—
  Dies on the altar of thy cross.

6 For what to thee, O Lord, we give,
  A hundred-fold we here obtain;
And soon with thee shall all receive,
  And loss shall be eternal gain.

CHARLES WESLEY.

174

THE CHRISTIAN—CONSECRATION.

WARSAW. H. M. THOMAS CLARK.

472 *Dedication to God.*

1 My soul and all its powers
  Thine, wholly thine, shall be;
All, all my happy hours
  I consecrate to thee:
Me to thine image now restore,
And I shall praise thee evermore.

2 Long as I live beneath,
  To thee O let me live;

To thee my every breath
  In thanks and praises give:
Whate'er I have, whate'er I am,
Shall magnify my Maker's name.

3 I wait thy will to do,
  As angels do in heaven;
In Christ a creature new,
  Most graciously forgiven;
I wait thy perfect will to prove,
All sanctified by spotless love.

CHARLES WESLEY.

MARSHALL. S. M. REV. GEORGE JARVIS GEER.

473 *Self-consecration.*

1 Lord, in the strength of grace,
  With a glad heart and free,
Myself, my residue of days,
  I consecrate to thee.

2 Thy ransomed servant, I
  Restore to thee thine own;
And from this moment live or die
  To serve my God alone.

CHARLES WESLEY.

YOAKLEY. L. M. 61. REV. WILLIAM YOAKLEY.

474 *A living sacrifice.*

1 O GOD, what offering shall I give
  To thee, the Lord of earth and skies?
My spirit, soul, and flesh receive,
  A holy, living sacrifice:
Small as it is, 'tis all my store;
More shouldst thou have, if I had more.

2 Now then, my God, thou hast my soul:
  No longer mine, but thine I am:
Guard thou thine own, possess it whole;
  Cheer it with hope, with love inflame.
Thou hast my spirit; there display
Thy glory to the perfect day.

3 Thou hast my flesh, thy hallowed shrine,
  Devoted solely to thy will:
Here let thy light forever shine:
  This house still let thy presence fill:
O Source of life! live, dwell, and move
In me, till all my life be love.
                    JOACHIM LANGE. TR. BY J. WESLEY.

475 *The single eye.*

1 BEHOLD the servant of the Lord!
  I wait thy guiding hand to feel;
To hear and keep thy every word,
  To prove and do thy perfect will:
Joyful from my own works to cease,
Glad to fulfill all righteousness.

2 My every weak, though good design,
  O'errule or change, as seems thee meet;
Jesus, let all my work be thine!
  Thy work, O Lord, is all complete,
And pleasing in thy Father's sight;
Thou only hast done all things right.

3 Here, then, to thee thine own I leave;
  Mold as thou wilt thy passive clay;
But let me all thy stamp receive,
  But let me all thy words obey;
Serve with a single heart and eye,
And to thy glory live and die.
                    CHARLES WESLEY.

476 *The prize of our high calling.*

1 JESUS, thy boundless love to me
  No thought can reach, no tongue declare;
O knit my thankful heart to thee,
  And reign without a rival there:
Thine wholly, thine alone, I am;
Be thou alone my constant flame.

2 O grant that nothing in my soul
  May dwell, but thy pure love alone:
O may thy love possess me whole,
  My joy, my treasure, and my crown:
Strange flames far from my heart remove
My every act, word, thought, oe love.

3 Unwearied may I this pursue;
  Dauntless to the high prize aspire
Hourly within my soul renew
  This holy flame, this heavenly fire:
And day and night, be all my care
To guard the sacred treasure there.

4 In suffering be thy love my peace;
  In weakness be thy love my power;
And when the storms of life shall cease,
  Jesus, in that important hour,
In death as life be thou my guide,
And save me, who for me hast died.
                    PAUL GERHARDT, TR. BY J. WESLEY.

ST. MATTHIAS.   L. M. 6l.

WILLIAM HENRY MONK.

477 *Christ in you, the hope of glory.*

1 THOU hidden love of God, whose height,
  Whose depth unfathomed, no man knows!
I see from far thy beauteous light,
  Inly I sigh for thy repose:
My heart is pained, nor can it be
At rest, till it finds rest in thee.

2 Is there a thing beneath the sun,
  That strives with thee my heart to share?
Ah, tear it thence, and reign alone,
  The Lord of every motion there;
Then shall my heart from earth be free,
When it hath found repose in thee.

3 O hide this self from me, that I
  No more, but Christ in me, may live;
My vile affections crucify,
  Nor let one darling lust survive!
In all things nothing may I see,
Nothing desire or seek, but thee.

4 O Love, thy sovereign aid impart,
  To save me from low-thoughted care;
Chase this self-will through all my heart,
  Through all its latent mazes there;
Make me thy duteous child, that I
Ceaseless may, "Abba, Father," cry.

5 Each moment draw from earth away
  My heart, that lowly waits thy call;
Speak to my inmost soul, and say,
  "I am thy Love, thy God, thy All!"
To feel thy power, to hear thy voice,
To taste thy love, be all my choice.

  GERHARD TERSTEEGEN. TR. BY J. WESLEY.

478 *Pressing toward the mark.*

1 I THANK thee, uncreated Sun,
  That thy bright beams on me have shined;

I thank thee, who hast overthrown
  My foes, and healed my wounded mind;
I thank thee, whose enlivening voice
Bids my freed heart in thee rejoice.

2 Uphold me in the doubtful race,
  Nor suffer me again to stray;
Strengthen my feet, with steady pace
  Still to press forward in thy way;
My soul and flesh, O Lord of might,
Fill, satiate, with thy heavenly light.

3 Give to mine eyes refreshing tears;
  Give to my heart chaste, hallowed fires;
Give to my soul, with filial fears,
  The love that all heaven's host inspires;
That all my powers, with all their might,
In thy sole glory may unite.

4 Thee will I love, my joy, my crown;
  Thee will I love, my Lord, my God;
Thee will I love, beneath thy frown
  Or smile, thy scepter or thy rod.
What though my flesh and heart decay?
Thee shall I love in endless day!

  JOHANN A. SCHEFFLER. TR. BY J. WESLEY.

479 *His blood cleanseth from all sin.*

1 PRISONERS of hope, lift up your heads,
  The day of liberty draws near!
Jesus, who on the serpent treads,
  Shall soon in your behalf appear:
The Lord will to his temple come;
Prepare your hearts to make him room.

2 Ye all shall find, whom in his word
  Himself hath caused to put your trust,
The Father of our dying Lord
  Is ever to his promise just;
Faithful, if we our sins confess,
To cleanse from all unrighteousness.

3 O ye of fearful hearts, be strong!
  Your downcast eyes and hands lift up!
Ye shall not be forgotten long;
  Hope to the end, in Jesus hope!
Tell him ye wait his grace to prove;
And cannot fail, if God is love.

  CHARLES WESLEY.

THE CHRISTIAN—SANCTIFICATION AND GROWTH.

NASHVILLE.   L. P. M.   ADAPTED BY LOWELL MASON,

480   *The sealing and sanctifying Spirit.*

1 FATHER of everlasting grace,
Thy goodness and thy truth we praise,
    Thy goodness and thy truth we prove;
Thou hast, in honor of thy Son,
The gift unspeakable sent down,—
    Spirit of life, and power, and love.

2 Send us the Spirit of thy Son,
To make the depths of Godhead known,
    To make us share the life divine:
Send him the sprinkled blood to apply;
Send him our souls to sanctify,
    And show and seal us ever thine.

3 So shall we pray, and never cease;
So shall we thankfully confess
    Thy wisdom, truth, and power, and love;
With joy unspeakable adore,
And bless and praise thee evermore,
    And serve thee as thy hosts above:

4 Till, added to that heavenly choir,
We raise our songs of triumph higher,
    And praise thee in a bolder strain;
Outsoar the first-born seraph's flight,
And sing, with all the saints in light,
Thy everlasting love to man.

                                    CHARLES WESLEY.

481   *Crucified with Christ.*

1 COME, Holy Ghost, all-quickening fire,
My consecrated heart inspire,
    Sprinkled with the atoning blood:
Still to my soul thyself reveal:
Thy mighty working may I feel,
    And know that I am one with God.

2 Humble, and teachable, and mild,
O may I, as a little child,
    My lowly Master's steps pursue!
Be anger to my soul unknown;
Hate, envy, jealousy, be gone;
    In love create thou all things new.

3 Let earth no more my heart divide;
With Christ may I be crucified;
    To thee with my whole heart aspire;
Dead to the world and all its toys,
Its idle pomp, and fading joys,
    Be thou alone my one desire.

4 My will be swallowed up in thee;
Light in thy light still may I see,
    Beholding thee with open face:
Called the full power of faith to prove,
Let all my hallowed heart be love,
    And all my spotless life be praise.

                                    CHARLES WESLEY.

MORNINGTON.   S. M.   EARL OF MORNINGTON, AD. BY LOWELL MASON.

482   *The law of love.*

1 THE thing my God doth hate
    That I no more may do,
Thy creature, Lord, again create,
    And all my soul renew:

2 My soul shall then, like thine,
    Abhor the thing unclean,
And, sanctified by love divine,
    Forever cease from sin.

3 That blessed law of thine,
    Jesus, to me impart;
The Spirit's law of life divine,
    O write it on my heart!

4 Implant it deep within,
    Whence it may ne'er remove,
The law of liberty from sin,
    The perfect law of love.

5 Thy nature be my law,
    Thy spotless sanctity;
And sweetly every moment draw
    My happy soul to thee.

6 Soul of my soul, remain!
    Who didst for all fulfill,
In me, O Lord, fulfill again
    Thy heavenly Father's will.
                    CHARLES WESLEY.

483   *The Guide and Counselor.*

1 JESUS, my Truth, my Way,
    My sure, unerring Light,
On thee my feeble steps I stay,
    Which thou wilt guide aright.

2 My Wisdom and my Guide,
    My Counselor thou art:
O never let me leave thy side,
    Or from thy paths depart.

3 I lift mine eyes to thee,
    Thou gracious, bleeding Lamb,
That I may now enlightened be,
    And never put to shame.

4 Never will I remove
    Out of thy hands my cause;
But rest in thy redeeming love,
    And hang upon thy cross.

5 O make me all like thee,
    Before I hence remove;
Settle, confirm, and 'stablish me,
    And build me up in love.

6 Let me thy witness live,
    When sin is all destroyed;
And then my spotless soul receive,
    And take me home to God.
                    CHARLES WESLEY.

484   *Christian aspiration.*

1 GOD of almighty love,
    By whose sufficient grace
I lift my heart to things above,
    And humbly seek thy face;

2 Through Jesus Christ the Just,
    My faint desires receive,
And let me in thy goodness trust,
    And to thy glory live.

3 Whate'er I say or do,
    Thy glory be my aim;
My offerings all be offered through
    The ever-blessed name.

4 Jesus, my single eye
    Be fixed on thee alone:
Thy name be praised on earth, on high,
    Thy will by all be done.
                    CHARLES WESLEY.

179

HORTON. 7.

XAVIER SCHNYDER VON WARTENSEE.

485 *Loyalty to Christ.*

1 KING of kings, and wilt thou deign
O'er this wayward heart to reign?
Henceforth take it for thy throne,
Rule here, Lord, and rule alone.

2 Then, like heaven's angelic bands,
Waiting for thine high commands,
All my powers shall wait on thee,
Captive, yet divinely free.

3 At thy word my will shall bow,
Judgment, reason, bending low;
Hope, desire, and every thought,
Into glad obedience brought.

4 Zeal shall haste on eager wing,
Hourly some new gift to bring;
Wisdom, humbly casting down
At thy feet her golden crown.

5 Tuned by thee in sweet accord,
All shall sing their gracious Lord;
Love, the leader of the choir,
Breathing round her seraph fire.
WILLIAM A. MUHLENBERG.

486 *Cut short the work in righteousness.*

1 SAVIOUR of the sin-sick soul,
Give me faith to make me whole;
Finish thy great work of grace;
Cut it short in righteousness.

2 Speak the second time, "Be clean!"
Take away my inbred sin;
Every stumbling-block remove;
Cast it out by perfect love.

3 Nothing less will I require;
Nothing more can I desire:

None but Christ to me be given;
None but Christ in earth or heaven.

4 O that I might now decrease!
O that all I am might cease!
Let me into nothing fall;
Let my Lord be all in all!
CHARLES WESLEY.

487 *Christ comforting mourners.*

1 GRACIOUS soul, to whom are given
Holy hungerings after heaven,
Restless breathings, earnest moans,
Deep, unutterable groans,
Agonies of strong desire,
Love's suppressed, unconscious fire;

2 Turn again to God, thy rest,
Jesus hath pronounced thee blest:
Humbly to thy Jesus turn,
Comforter of all that mourn:
Happy mourner, hear, and see,
Claim the promise made to thee.

3 Gently will he lead the weak,
Bruised reeds he ne'er will break;
Touched with sympathizing care,
Thee he in his arms shall bear,
Bless with late but lasting peace,
Fill with all his righteousness.

4 Lift to him thy weeping eye,
Heaven behind the cloud descry:
If with Christ thou suffer here,
When his glory shall appear,
Christ his suffering son shall own;
Thine the cross, and thine the crown.
CHARLES WESLEY.

ONIDO. 7. D.

IGNACE PLEYEL.

488   *Ineffable love.*

1 JESUS, full of love divine,
I am thine and thou art mine;
Let me live and die to prove
Thine unutterable love.
More and more of love I claim,
Glowing still with quenchless flame;
All my heart to thee aspires,
Yearns with infinite desires.

2 Every thought, design, and word,
Burns with love to thee, my Lord;
Body, soul, and spirit joined,
All in love to thee combined.
Ever since I saw thy face,
Proved thy plenitude of grace,
Chose thee as the better part—
Love has filled and fired my heart.

3 Jesus, Saviour, thou art mine;
Jesus, all I have is thine;
Never shall the altar-fire,
Kindled on my heart, expire.
Love my darkness shall illume,
Love shall all my sins consume:
Sweetly then I die to prove
An eternity of love!

BENJAMIN GOUGH.

489   *For reviving grace.*

1 LIGHT of life, seraphic fire,
Love divine, thyself impart:
Every fainting soul inspire,
Shine in every drooping heart;
Every mournful sinner cheer,
Scatter all our guilty gloom;
Son of God, appear, appear!
To thy human temples come.

2 Come in this accepted hour;
Bring thy heavenly kingdom in;
Fill us with thy glorious power,
Rooting out the seeds of sin:
Nothing more can we require,
We will covet nothing less;
Be thou all our heart's desire,
All our joy, and all our peace.

CHARLES WESLEY.

490   *Panting for purity.*

1 HOLY Lamb, who thee receive,
Who in thee begin to live,
Day and night they cry to thee,
"As thou art, so let us be!"

2 Jesus, see my panting breast;
See, I pant in thee to rest;
Gladly would I now be clean;
Cleanse me now from every sin.

3 Fix, O fix my wavering mind;
To thy cross my spirit bind;
Earthly passions far remove;
Swallow up my soul in love.

4 Dust and ashes though we be,
Full of sin and misery,
Thine we are, thou Son of God;
Take the purchase of thy blood!

MRS. ANNA S. DOBEE. TR. BY J. WESLEY.

181

LOVE DIVINE.　8, 7. D.

JOHN ZUNDEL.

491　*The new creation.*

1 LOVE divine, all love excelling,
　Joy of heaven, to earth come down!
Fix in us thy humble dwelling;
　All thy faithful mercies crown.
Jesus, thou art all compassion,
　Pure unbounded love thou art;
Visit us with thy salvation;
　Enter every trembling heart.

2 Breathe, O breathe thy loving Spirit
　Into every troubled breast!
Let us all in thee inherit,
　Let us find that second rest.
Take away our bent to sinning;
　Alpha and Omega be;
End of faith, as its beginning,
　Set our hearts at liberty.

3 Come, almighty to deliver,
　Let us all thy life receive;
Suddenly return, and never,
　Never more thy temples leave:
Thee we would be always blessing,
　Serve thee as thy hosts above,
Pray, and praise thee without ceasing,
　Glory in thy perfect love.

4 Finish then thy new creation;
　Pure and spotless let us be;
Let us see thy great salvation,
　Perfectly restored in thee:

Changed from glory into glory,
　Till in heaven we take our place,
Till we cast our crowns before thee,
　Lost in wonder, love, and praise.
CHARLES WESLEY.

492　*The one thing needful.*

1 WELL for him who all things losing,
　E'en himself doth count as naught,
Still the one thing needful choosing,
　That with all true bliss is fraught!

2 Well for him who nothing knoweth
　But his God, whose boundless love
Makes the heart wherein it gloweth
　Calm and pure as saints above!

3 Well for him who all forsaking,
　Walketh not in shadows vain,
But the path of peace is taking
　Through this vale of tears and pain!

4 O that we our hearts might sever
　From earth's tempting vanities,
Fixing them on him forever
　In whom all our fullness lies!

5 Thou, abyss of love and goodness,
　Draw us by thy cross to thee,
That our senses, soul, and spirit,
　Ever one with Christ may be!
GOTTFRIED ARNOLD. TR. BY MISS C. WINKWORTH.

PEYTON.   H. M.

WALTER BOND GILBERT.

493 *Rejoicing in hope.*

1 YE ransomed sinners, hear,
   The prisoners of the Lord;
And wait till Christ appear,
   According to his word:
Rejoice in hope, rejoice with me,
We shall from all our sins be free.

2 In God we put our trust;
   If we our sins confess,
Faithful is he and just,
   From all unrighteousness
To cleanse us all, both you and me:
We shall from all our sins be free.

3 Who Jesus' sufferings share,
   My fellow-prisoners now,
Ye soon the crown shall wear
   On your triumphant brow:
Rejoice in hope, rejoice with me,
We shall from all our sins be free.

4 The word of God is sure,
   And never can remove;
We shall in heart be pure,
   And perfected in love:
Rejoice in hope, rejoice with me,
We shall from all our sins be free.

5 Then let us gladly bring
   Our sacrifice of praise:
Let us give thanks and sing,
   And glory in his grace:
Rejoice in hope, rejoice with me,
We shall from all our sins be free.

CHARLES WESLEY.

[7, 6, 8. Tune, Penitence. Page 204.]

494   *Speak the word.*

1 EVER fainting with desire,
   For thee, O Christ, I call;
Thee I restlessly require;
   I want my God, my all.
Jesus, dear redeeming Lord,
   I wait thy coming from above;
Help me, Saviour, speak the word,
   And perfect me in love.

2 Thou my life, my treasure be,
   My portion here below;
Nothing would I seek but thee,
   Thee only would I know;
My exceeding great reward,
   My heaven on earth, my heaven above:
Help me, Saviour, speak the word,
   And perfect me in love.

3 Grant me now the bliss to feel
   Of those that are in thee:
Son of God, thyself reveal;
   Engrave thy name on me.
As in heaven, be here adored,
   And let me now the promise prove:
Help me, Saviour, speak the word,
   And perfect me in love.

CHARLES WESLEY

Doxology.

To God the Father's throne
   Your highest honors raise;
Glory to God the Son,
   To God the Spirit, praise:
With all our powers, eternal King,
Thy everlasting praise we sing.

ISAAC WATTS, ALT.

187

WOODWORTH. L. M.   WILLIAM BATCHELDER BRADBURY.

495 *The yoke easy and the burden light.*

1 O THAT my load of sin were gone!
    O that I could at last submit
At Jesus' feet to lay it down—
    To lay my soul at Jesus' feet!

2 Rest for my soul I long to find:
    Saviour of all, if mine thou art,
Give me thy meek and lowly mind,
    And stamp thine image on my heart.

3 Break off the yoke of inbred sin,
    And fully set my spirit free;
I cannot rest till pure within,
    Till I am wholly lost in thee.

4 Fain would I learn of thee, my God,
    Thy light and easy burden prove,
The cross all stained with hallowed blood,
    The labor of thy dying love.

5 I would, but thou must give the power;
    My heart from every sin release;
Bring near, bring near the joyful hour,
    And fill me with thy perfect peace.
                              CHARLES WESLEY.

496   *Following the Saviour.*

1 O THOU, to whose all-searching sight
    The darkness shineth as the light,
Search, prove my heart, it pants for thee;
    O burst these bonds, and set it free.

2 Wash out its stains, refine its dross,
    Nail my affections to the cross;
Hallow each thought; let all within
    Be clean, as thou, my Lord, art clean.

3 If in this darksome wild I stray,
    Be thou my light, be thou my way;

No foes, no violence I fear,
    No fraud, while thou, my God, art near.

4 When rising floods my soul o'erflow,
    When sinks my heart in waves of woe,
Jesus, thy timely aid impart,
    And raise my head, and cheer my heart.

5 Saviour, where'er thy steps I see,
    Dauntless, untired, I follow thee;
O let thy hand support me still,
    And lead me to thy holy hill.

6 If rough and thorny be the way,
    My strength proportion to my day;
Till toil, and grief, and pain shall cease,
    Where all is calm, and joy, and peace.
        GERHARD TERSTEEGEN. TR. BY J. WESLEY.

497   *For constant devotedness.*

1 LORD, fill me with a humble fear;
    My utter helplessness reveal;
Satan and sin are always near,
    Thee may I always nearer feel.

2 O that to thee my constant mind
    Might with an even flame aspire,
Pride in its earliest motions find,
    And mark the risings of desire!

3 O that my tender soul might fly
    The first abhorred approach of ill,
Quick as the apple of an eye,
    The slightest touch of sin to feel!

4 Till thou anew my soul create,
    Still may I strive, and watch, and pray,
Humbly and confidently wait,
    And long to see the perfect day.
                              CHARLES WESLEY.

THE CHRISTIAN—SANCTIFICATION AND GROWTH.

GREENWOOD. S. M.

JOSEPH E. SWEETSER.

498 *The throne of grace.*

1 BEHOLD the throne of grace;
   The promise calls us near;
There Jesus shows a smiling face,
   And waits to answer prayer.

2 My soul, ask what thou wilt,
   Thou canst not be too bold;
Since his own blood for thee he spilt,
   What else can he withhold?

3 Thine image, Lord, bestow,
   Thy presence and thy love,
That we may serve thee here below,
   And reign with thee above.

4 Teach us to live by faith,
   Conform our wills to thine;
Let us victorious be in death,
   And then in glory shine.

JOHN NEWTON.

499 *Living temples.*

1 AND will the mighty God,
   Whom heaven cannot contain,
Make me his temple and abode,
   And in me live and reign?

2 Come, Spirit of the Lord,
   Teacher and heavenly Guide!
Be it according to thy word,
   And in my heart reside.

3 O Holy, Holy Ghost!
   Pervade this soul of mine:
In me renew thy Pentecost,
   Reveal thy power divine!

4 Make it my highest bliss
   Thy blessed fruits to know:
Thy joy, and peace, and gentleness,
   Goodness and faith to show.

5 Be it my greatest fear
   Thy holiness to grieve;
Walk in the Spirit even here,
   And in the Spirit live.

GEORGE RAWSON.

500 *Thine, living or dying.*

1 JESUS, I live to thee,
   The loveliest and best;
My life in thee, thy life in me,
   In thy blest love I rest.

2 Jesus, I die to thee,
   Whenever death shall come;
To die in thee is life to me,
   In my eternal home.

3 Whether to live or die,
   I know not which is best;
To live in thee is bliss to me,
   To die is endless rest.

4 Living or dying, Lord,
   I ask but to be thine;
My life in thee, thy life in me,
   Makes heaven forever mine.

HENRY HARBAUGH.

501 *Purity of heart.*

1 BLEST are the pure in heart,
   For they shall see our God;
The secret of the Lord is theirs;
   Their soul is his abode.

2 Still to the lowly soul
   He doth himself impart,
And for his temple and his throne
   Selects the pure in heart.

3 Lord, we thy presence seek,
   May ours this blessing be;
O give the pure and lowly heart,—
   A temple meet for thee.

JOHN KEBLE.

ST. THOMAS. S. M. GEORGE FREDERICK HANDEL.

502 *Glorious liberty.*

1 O COME, and dwell in me,
  Spirit of power within,
And bring the glorious liberty
  From sorrow, fear, and sin!

2 The seed of sin's disease,
  Spirit of health, remove,
Spirit of finished holiness,
  Spirit of perfect love.

3 Hasten the joyful day
  Which shall my sins consume;
When old things shall be done away,
  And all things new become.

4 I want the witness, Lord,
  That all I do is right,
According to thy will and word,
  Well pleasing in thy sight.

5 I ask no higher state;
  Indulge me but in this,
And soon or later then translate
  To my eternal bliss.
                        CHARLES WESLEY.

503 *Waiting at the cross.*

1 FATHER, I dare believe
  Thee merciful and true;
Thou wilt my guilty soul forgive,
  My fallen soul renew.

2 Come, then, for Jesus' sake,
  And bid my heart be clean;
An end of all my troubles make,
  An end of all my sin.

3 I cannot wash my heart,
  But by believing thee,
And waiting for thy blood to impart
  The spotless purity.

4 While at thy cross I lie,
  Jesus, the grace bestow;
Now thy all-cleansing blood apply,
  And I am white as snow.
                        CHARLES WESLEY.

504 *Charity supreme.*

1 HAD I the gift of tongues,
  Great God, without thy grace,
My loudest words, my loftiest songs,
  Would be but sounding brass.

2 Though thou shouldst give me skill
  Each mystery to explain,
Without a heart to do thy will,
  My knowledge would be vain.

3 Had I such faith in God
  As mountains to remove,
No faith could work effectual good,
  That did not work by love.

4 Grant, then, this one request,
  Whatever be denied,—
That love divine may rule my breast,
  And all my actions guide.
                        SAMUEL STENNETT, ALT.

Doxology.

To God, the Father, Son,
  And Spirit, One in Three,
Be glory, as it was, is now,
  And shall forever be.
                        JOHN WESLEY.

HOPE. S. M. D.

HENRY STEPHEN CUTLER.

FIRST PART.

505 *For entire consecration.*

1 JESUS, my strength, my hope,
  On thee I cast my care;
With humble confidence look up,
  And know thou hear'st my prayer.
Give me on thee to wait,
  Till I can all things do;
On thee, almighty to create,
  Almighty to renew.

2 I want a sober mind,
  A self-renouncing will,
That tramples down, and casts behind,
  The baits of pleasing ill:
A soul inured to pain,
  To hardship, grief, and loss;
Bold to take up, firm to sustain,
  The consecrated cross.

3 I want a godly fear,
  A quick discerning eye,
That looks to thee when sin is near,
  And sees the tempter fly:
A spirit still prepared,
  And armed with jealous care;
Forever standing on its guard,
  And watching unto prayer.

CHARLES WESLEY.

SECOND PART.

506 *For perfect submission*

1 I WANT a heart to pray,
  To pray, and never cease;
Never to murmur at thy stay,
  Or wish my sufferings less.
This blessing, above all,
  Always to pray, I want;
Out of the deep on thee to call,
  And never, never faint.

2 I want a true regard,
  A single, steady aim,
Unmoved by threatening or reward
  To thee and thy great name;
A jealous, just concern
  For thine immortal praise;
A pure desire that all may learn
  And glorify thy grace.

3 I rest upon thy word;
  The promise is for me;
My succor and salvation, Lord,
  Shall surely come from thee:
But let me still abide,
  Nor from my hope remove,
Till thou my patient spirit guide
  Into thy perfect love.

CHARLES WESLEY.

MANOAH.   C. M.

FROM MEHUL AND HAYDN.

507 *Walk in the light.*

1 WALK in the light! so shalt thou know
   That fellowship of love,
His Spirit only can bestow
   Who reigns in light above.

2 Walk in the light! and thou shalt find
   Thy heart made truly his,
Who dwells in cloudless light enshrined,
   In whom no darkness is.

3 Walk in the light! and thou shalt own
   Thy darkness passed away,
Because that light hath on thee shone
   In which is perfect day.

4 Walk in the light! and e'en the tomb
   No fearful shade shall wear;
Glory shall chase away its gloom,
   For Christ hath conquered there.

5 Walk in the light! thy path shall be
   Peaceful, serene, and bright:
For God, by grace, shall dwell in thee,
   And God himself is light.
                              BERNARD BARTON.

508 *The fullness of God.*

1 BEING of beings, God of love,
   To thee our hearts we raise;
Thy all-sustaining power we prove,
   And gladly sing thy praise.

2 Thine, wholly thine, we pant to be;
   Our sacrifice receive:
Made, and preserved, and saved by thee,
   To thee ourselves we give.

3 Heavenward our every wish aspires,
   For all thy mercy's store;

The sole return thy love requires,
   Is that we ask for more.

4 For more we ask; we open then
   Our hearts to embrace thy will;
Turn, and revive us, Lord, again;
   With all thy fullness fill.

5 Come, Holy Ghost, the Saviour's love
   Shed in our hearts abroad;
So shall we ever live, and move,
   And be, with Christ in God.
                              CHARLES WESLEY.

509 *The thought of God.*

1 O HOW the thought of God attracts
   And draws the heart from earth,
And sickens it of passing shows
   And dissipating mirth!

2 'Tis not enough to save our souls,
   To shun the eternal fires;
The thought of God will rouse the heart
   To more sublime desires.

3 God only is the creature's home,
   Though rough and strait the road;
Yet nothing less can satisfy
   The love that longs for God.

4 O utter but the name of God
   Down in your heart of hearts,
And see how from the world at once
   All tempting light departs!

5 A trusting heart, a yearning eye,
   Can win their way above;
If mountains can be moved by faith,
   Is there less power in love?
                              FREDERICK W. FABER.

SPOHR.   C. M. D.   ARR. FROM LOUIS SPOHR.

510 *For full redemption.*

1 MY Saviour, on the word of truth
    In earnest hope I live;
I ask for all the precious things
    Thy boundless love can give.
I look for many a lesser light
    About my path to shine;
But chiefly long to walk with thee,
    And only trust in thine.

2 Thou knowest that I am not blest
    As thou wouldst have me be,
Till all the peace and joy of faith
    Possess my soul in thee;
And still I seek, 'mid many fears,
    With yearnings unexpressed,
The comfort of thy strengthening love,
    Thy soothing, settling rest.

3 It is not as thou wilt with me,
    Till, humbled in the dust,
I know no place in all my heart
    Wherein to put my trust:
Until I find, O Lord, in thee,
    The Lowly and the Meek,
The fullness which thy own redeemed
    Go nowhere else to seek.
                    ANNA L. WARING.

511 *For a tender conscience.*

1 I WANT a principle within,
    Of jealous, godly fear;
A sensibility of sin,
    A pain to feel it near:
I want the first approach to feel
    Of pride, or fond desire;
To catch the wandering of my will,
    And quench the kindling fire.

2 From Thee that I no more may part,
    No more thy goodness grieve,
The filial awe, the fleshly heart,
    The tender conscience give.
Quick as the apple of an eye,
    O God, my conscience make;
Awake my soul when sin is nigh,
    And keep it still awake.

3 If to the right or left I stray,
    That moment, Lord, reprove;
And let me weep my life away,
    For having grieved thy love.
O may the least omission pain
    My well-instructed soul,
And drive me to the blood again,
    Which makes the wounded whole.
                    CHARLES WESLEY.

EVAN.   C. M.   REV. WILLIAM HENRY HAVERGAL.

512   *The counsel of His grace.*

1 I KNOW that my Redeemer lives,
  And ever prays for me:
A token of his love he gives,
  A pledge of liberty.

2 I find him lifting up my head;
  He brings salvation near;
His presence makes me free indeed,
  And he will soon appear.

3 He wills that I should holy be;
  What can withstand his will?
The counsel of his grace in me
  He surely shall fulfill.

4 Jesus, I hang upon thy word;
  I steadfastly believe
Thou wilt return, and claim me, Lord,
  And to thyself receive.

5 When God is mine, and I am his,
  Of paradise possessed,
I taste unutterable bliss,
  And everlasting rest.
                    CHARLES WESLEY.

513   *The rest of faith.*

1 LORD, I believe a rest remains
  To all thy people known;
A rest where pure enjoyment reigns,
  And thou art loved alone:

2 A rest where all our soul's desire
  Is fixed on things above;
Where fear, and sin, and grief expire,
  Cast out by perfect love.

3 O that I now the rest might know,
  Believe, and enter in!

Now, Saviour, now the power bestow,
  And let me cease from sin.

4 Remove this hardness from my heart;
  This unbelief remove:
To me the rest of faith impart,
  The Sabbath of thy love.
                    CHARLES WESLEY.

514   *Come, Lord Jesus.*

1 O JESUS, at thy feet we wait,
  Till thou shalt bid us rise,
Restored to our unsinning state,
  To love's sweet paradise.

2 Saviour from sin, we thee receive,
  From all indwelling sin:
Thy blood, we steadfastly believe,
  Shall make us throughly clean.

3 Since thou wouldst have us free from sin,
  And pure as those above,
Make haste to bring thy nature in,
  And perfect us in love.

4 The counsel of thy love fulfil:
  Come quickly, gracious Lord!
Be it according to thy will,
  According to thy word.

5 O that the perfect grace were given,
  Thy love diffused abroad!
O that our hearts were all a heaven,
  Forever filled with God!
                    CHARLES WESLEY.

Doxology.

To Father, Son, and Holy Ghost,
  The God whom we adore,
Be glory, as it was, is now,
  And shall be evermore.
                    TATE AND BRADY.

BRIDGMAN.   C. M.   BEETHOVEN, ARR. BY GEORGE KINGSLEY.

515   *A present paradise.*

1 O JOYFUL sound of gospel grace!
   Christ shall in me appear;
I, even I, shall see his face,
   I shall be holy here.

2 The glorious crown of righteousness
   To me reached out I view:
Conqueror through him, I soon shall seize,
   And wear it as my due.

3 The promised land, from Pisgah's top,
   I now exult to see:
My hope is full, O glorious hope!
   Of immortality.

4 With me, I know, I feel, thou art;
   But this cannot suffice,
Unless thou plantest in my heart
   A constant paradise.

5 Come. O my God, thyself reveal,
   Fill all this mighty void:
Thou only canst my spirit fill;
   Come, O my God, my God!
                        CHARLES WESLEY.

516   *The world overcome.*

1 LET worldly minds the world pursue;
   It has no charms for me:
Once I admired its trifles too,
   But grace hath set me free.

2 Its pleasures can no longer please,
   Nor happiness afford:
Far from my heart be joys like these,
   Now I have seen the Lord.

3 As by the light of opening day
   The stars are all concealed,
So earthly pleasures fade away,
   When Jesus is revealed.

4 Creatures no more divide my choice;
   I bid them all depart:
His name, his love, his gracious voice,
   Have fixed my roving heart.
                        JOHN NEWTON

517   *In earth as it is in heaven.*
            Matt. 6: 10.

1 JESUS, the Life, the Truth, the Way
   In whom I now believe,
As taught by thee, in faith I pray,
   Expecting to receive.

2 Thy will by me on earth be done,
   As by the powers above,
Who always see thee on thy throne,
   And glory in thy love.

3 I ask in confidence the grace,
   That I may do thy will,
As angels who behold thy face,
   And all thy words fulfill.

4 Surely I shall, the sinner I,
   Shall serve thee without fear,
If thou my nature sanctify
   In answer to my prayer.
                        CHARLES WESLEY

Doxology.

To Father, Son, and Holy Ghost,
   The God whom we adore,
Be glory, as it was, is now,
   And shall be evermore.
                        TATE AND BRADY.

THE CHRISTIAN—SANCTIFICATION AND GROWTH.

AZMON.   C. M.   CARL GOTTHELF GLASER, ARR. BY LOWELL MASON.

518   *The refining fire.*

1 JESUS, thine all-victorious love
  Shed in my heart abroad:
Then shall my feet no longer rove,
  Rooted and fixed in God.

2 O that in me the sacred fire
  Might now begin to glow,
Burn up the dross of base desire
  And make the mountains flow!

3 O that it now from heaven might fall,
  And all my sins consume!
Come, Holy Ghost, for thee I call;
  Spirit of burning, come!

4 Refining fire, go through my heart;
  Illuminate my soul;
Scatter thy life through every part,
  And sanctify the whole.

5 My steadfast soul, from falling free,
  Shall then no longer move,
While Christ is all the world to me,
  And all my heart is love.
                          CHARLES WESLEY.

519   *The affections crucified.*

1 JESUS, my Life, thyself apply;
  Thy Holy Spirit breathe:
My vile affections crucify;
  Conform me to thy death.

2 Conqueror of hell, and earth, and sin,
  Still with the rebel strive:
Enter my soul, and work within,
  And kill, and make alive.

3 More of thy life, and more I have,
  As the old Adam dies:

Bury me, Saviour, in thy grave,
  That I with thee may rise.

4 Reign in me, Lord: thy foes control,
  Who would not own thy sway;
Diffuse thine image through my soul;
  Shine to the perfect day.

5 Scatter the last remains of sin,
  And seal me thine abode:
O make me glorious all within,
  A temple built by God!
                          CHARLES WESLEY.

520   *Give me Thyself.*

1 JESUS hath died that I might live,
  Might live to God alone;
In him eternal life receive,
  And be in spirit one.

2 Saviour, I thank thee for the grace,
  The gift unspeakable;
And wait with arms of faith to embrace,
  And all thy love to feel.

3 My soul breaks out in strong desire
  The perfect bliss to prove;
My longing heart is all on fire
  To be dissolved in love.

4 Give me thyself; from every boast,
  From every wish set free;
Let all I am in thee be lost,
  But give thyself to me.

5 Thy gifts, alas! cannot suffice,
  Unless thyself be given;
Thy presence makes my paradise,
  And where thou art is heaven.
                          CHARLES WESLEY.

SIMPSON. C. M.   FROM LOUIS SPOHR.

521   *A perfect heart.*

1 O FOR a heart to praise my God,
  A heart from sin set free!
A heart that always feels thy blood,
  So freely spilt for me!

2 A heart resigned, submissive, meek,
  My great Redeemer's throne;
Where only Christ is heard to speak,
  Where Jesus reigns alone.

3 O for a lowly, contrite heart,
  Believing, true, and clean,
Which neither life nor death can part
  From him that dwells within!

4 A heart in every thought renewed,
  And full of love divine;
Perfect, and right, and pure, and good,
  A copy, Lord, of thine.

5 Thy nature, gracious Lord, impart;
  Come quickly from above;
Write thy new name upon my heart,
  Thy new, best name of Love.
                          CHARLES WESLEY.

522   *The work wrought.*

1 COME, O my God, the promise seal,
  This mountain, sin, remove;
Now in my waiting soul reveal
  The virtue of thy love.

2 I want thy life, thy purity,
  Thy righteousness, brought in:
I ask, desire, and trust in thee
  To be redeemed from sin.

3 Saviour, to thee my soul looks up,
  My present Saviour thou!
In all the confidence of hope,
  I claim the blessing now.

4 'Tis done! thou dost this moment save,
  With full salvation bless;
Redemption through thy blood I have,
  And spotless love and peace.
                          CHARLES WESLEY.

523   *Faith omnipotent.*

1 GOD of eternal truth and grace,
  Thy faithful promise seal;
Thy word, thy oath, to Abrah'm's race.
  In me, O Lord, fulfill.

2 That mighty faith on me bestow,
  Which cannot ask in vain,
Which holds, and will not let thee go,
  Till I my suit obtain:

3 Till thou into my soul inspire
  The perfect love unknown;
And tell my infinite desire,
  "Whate'er thou wilt, be done."

4 But is it possible that I
  Should live, and sin no more?
Lord, if on thee I dare rely,
  The faith shall bring the power.

5 On me the faith divine bestow
  Which doth the mountain move;
And all my spotless life shall show
  The omnipotence of love.
                          CHARLES WESLEY.

JANES. L. M.

JOHANN C. W. AMADEUS MOZART.

524 *There remaineth therefore a rest to the people of God.—Heb. 4: 9.*

1 COME, O Thou greater than our heart,
And make thy faithful mercies known;
The mind which was in thee impart;
Thy constant mind in us be shown.

2 O let us by thy cross abide,
Thee, only thee, resolved to know,
The Lamb for sinners crucified,
A world to save from endless woe.

3 Take us into thy people's rest,
And we from our own works shall cease;
With thy meek Spirit arm our breast,
And keep our minds in perfect peace.

4 Jesus, for this we calmly wait;
O let our eyes behold thee near!
Hasten to make our heaven complete;
Appear, our glorious God, appear!
CHARLES WESLEY.

525 *Christ all in all.*

1 HOLY, and true, and righteous Lord,
I wait to prove thy perfect will;
Be mindful of thy gracious word,
And stamp me with thy Spirit's seal.

2 Open my faith's interior eye;
Display thy glory from above;
And all I am shall sink and die,
Lost in astonishment and love.

3 Confound, o'erpower me by thy grace;
I would be by myself abhorred;
All might, all majesty, all praise,
All glory, be to Christ my Lord.

4 Now let me gain perfection's height;
Now let me into nothing fall,
As less than nothing in thy sight,
And feel that Christ is all in all.
CHARLES WESLEY.

526 *Waiting for the promise.*

1 O JESUS, full of truth and grace,
O all-atoning Lamb of God,
I wait to see thy glorious face;
I seek redemption through thy blood.

2 Thou art the anchor of my hope;
The faithful promise I receive:
Surely thy death shall raise me up,
For thou hast died that I might live.

3 Satan, with all his arts, no more
Me from the gospel hope can move;
I shall receive the gracious power,
And find the pearl of perfect love.

4 My flesh, which cries, "It cannot be,"
Shall silence keep before the Lord;
And earth, and hell, and sin shall flee
At Jesus' everlasting word.
CHARLES WESLEY.

527 *For lowliness and purity.*

1 JESUS, in whom the Godhead's rays
Beam forth with mildest majesty;
I see thee full of truth and grace,
And come for all I want to thee.

2 Save me from pride—the plague expel
Jesus, thine humble self impart:
O let thy mind within me dwell;
O give me lowliness of heart.

3 Enter thyself, and cast out sin;
Thy spotless purity bestow;
Touch me, and make the leper clean;
Wash me, and I am white as snow.

4 Sprinkle me, Saviour, with thy blood,
And all thy gentleness is mine;
And plunge me in the purple flood,
Till all I am is lost in thine.
CHARLES WESLEY.

528 *The Canaan of perfect love.*

1 GOD of all power, and truth, and grace,
  Which shall from age to age endure,
Whose word, when heaven and earth shall pass,
  Remains, and stands forever sure;

2 That I thy mercy may proclaim,
  That all mankind thy truth may see,
Hallow thy great and glorious name,
  And perfect holiness in me.

3 Give me a new, a perfect heart,
  From doubt, and fear, and sorrow free;
The mind which was in Christ impart,
  And let my spirit cleave to thee.

4 O that I now, from sin released,
  Thy word may to the utmost prove;
Enter into the promised rest,
  The Canaan of thy perfect love!
                           CHARLES WESLEY.

529 *The will of God.*

1 HE wills that I should holy be:
  That holiness I long to feel;
That full divine conformity
  To all my Saviour's righteous will.

2 See, Lord, the travail of thy soul
  Accomplished in the change of mine;
And plunge me, every whit made whole,
  In all the depths of love divine.

3 On thee, O God, my soul is stayed,
  And waits to prove thine utmost will;
The promise by thy mercy made,
  Thou canst, thou wilt, in me fulfill.

4 No more I stagger at thy power,
  Or doubt thy truth, which cannot move:
Hasten the long-expected hour,
  And bless me with thy perfect love.
                           CHARLES WESLEY.

530 *Heavenly bliss in prospect.*

1 ARISE, my soul, on wings sublime,
  Above the vanities of time;
Let faith now pierce the veil, and see
  The glories of eternity.

2 Born by a new, celestial birth,
  Why should I grovel here on earth?
Why grasp at vain and fleeting toys,
  So near to heaven's eternal joys?

3 Shall aught beguile me on the road,
  The narrow road that leads to God?
Or can I love this earth so well,
  As not to long with God to dwell?

4 To dwell with God, to taste his love,
  Is the full heaven enjoyed above:
The glorious expectation now
  Is heavenly bliss begun below.
                           THOMAS GIBBONS.

531 *The new covenant.*

1 O GOD, most merciful and true,
  Thy nature to my soul impart;
'Stablish with me the covenant new,
  And stamp thine image on my heart.

2 To real holiness restored,
  O let me gain my Saviour's mind;
And in the knowledge of my Lord,
  Fullness of life eternal find.

3 Remember, Lord, my sins no more,
  That them I may no more forget;
But, sunk in guiltless shame, adore,
  With speechless wonder, at thy feet.

4 O'erwhelmed with thy stupendous grace,
  I shall not in thy presence move;
But breathe unutterable praise,
  And rapturous awe, and silent love.

5 Then every murmuring thought, and vain,
  Expires, in sweet confusion lost:
I cannot of my cross complain,
  I cannot of my goodness boast.

6 Pardoned for all that I have done,
  My mouth as in the dust I hide;
And glory give to God alone,
  My God in Jesus pacified.
                           CHARLES WESLEY.

532 *True perfection.*

1 WHAT! never speak one evil word,
  Or rash, or idle, or unkind!
O how shall I, most gracious Lord,
  This mark of true perfection find?

2 Thy sinless mind in me reveal;
  Thy Spirit's plenitude impart;
And all my spotless life shall tell
  The abundance of a loving heart.

3 Saviour, I long to testify
  The fullness of thy saving grace;
O may thy power the blood apply,
  Which bought for me the sacred peace.

4 Forgive, and make my nature whole,
  My inbred malady remove;
To perfect health restore my soul,
  To perfect holiness and love.
                           CHARLES WESLEY.

AVON.   C. M.

Hugh Wilson.

533   *Entire purification.*

1 FOREVER here my rest shall be,
  Close to thy bleeding side;
  This all my hope, and all my plea,
  "For me the Saviour died."

2 My dying Saviour, and my God,
  Fountain for guilt and sin,
  Sprinkle me ever with thy blood,
  And cleanse and keep me clean.

3 Wash me, and make me thus thine own;
  Wash me, and mine thou art;
  Wash me, but not my feet alone,
  My hands, my head, my heart.

4 The atonement of thy blood apply,
  Till faith to sight improve;
  Till hope in full fruition die,
  And all my soul be love.

CHARLES WESLEY.

534   *Perfect rest from sin.*

1 JESUS, the sinner's rest thou art,
  From guilt, and fear, and pain;
  While thou art absent from the heart
  We look for rest in vain.

2 O when wilt thou my Saviour be?
  O when shall I be clean?
  The true eternal Sabbath see,—
  A perfect rest from sin?

3 The consolations of thy word
  My soul have long upheld;
  The faithful promise of the Lord
  Shall surely be fulfilled.

4 I look to my incarnate God
  Till he his work begin;
  And wait till his redeeming blood
  Shall cleanse me from all sin.

AUGUSTUS M. TOPLADY.

535   *The gift of righteousness.*

1 I ASK the gift of righteousness,
  The sin-subduing power;
  Power to believe, and go in peace,
  And never grieve Thee more.

2 I ask the blood-bought pardon sealed,
  The liberty from sin,
  The grace infused, the love revealed,
  The kingdom fixed within.

3 Thou hear'st me for salvation pray;
  Thou seest my heart's desire;
  Made ready in thy powerful day,
  Thy fullness I require.

4 My restless soul cries out, oppressed,
  Impatient to be freed;
  Nor can I, Lord, nor will I rest,
  Till I am saved indeed.

5 Thou canst, thou wilt, I dare believe,
  So arm me with thy power,
  That I to sin may never cleave,
  May never feel it more.

CHARLES WESLEY.

Doxology.

To Father, Son, and Holy Ghost,
  The God whom we adore,
Be glory, as it was, is now,
  And shall be evermore!

TATE AND BRADY.

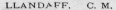

LLANDAFF.   C. M.

EDWIN MOSS.

536   *Steadfast faith.*

1 My God, I know, I feel thee mine,
    And will not quit my claim,
Till all I have is lost in thine,
    And all renewed I am.

2 I hold thee with a trembling hand,
    And will not let thee go,
Till steadfastly by faith I stand,
    And all thy goodness know.

3 Love only can the conquest win,
    The strength of sin subdue:
Come, O my Saviour, cast out sin,
    And form my soul anew.

4 No longer then my heart shall mourn,
    While, sanctified by grace,
I only for thy glory burn,
    And always see thy face.
                    CHARLES WESLEY.

537   *Thy will be done.*—Matt. 6 : 10.

1 Thy presence, Lord, the place shall fill;
    My heart shall be thy throne;
Thy holy, just, and perfect will,
    Shall in my flesh be done.

2 I thank thee for the present grace,
    And now in hope rejoice,
In confidence to see thy face,
    And always hear thy voice.

3 I have the things I ask of thee;
    What more shall I require?
That still my soul may restless be,
    And only thee desire.

4 Thy only will be done, not mine,
    But make me, Lord, thy home;
Come as thou wilt, I that resign,
    But O, my Jesus, come!
                    CHARLES WESLEY.

538   *For patience and sanctity.*

1 Deepen the wound Thy hands have made
    In this weak, helpless soul,
Till mercy, with its balmy aid,
    Descend to make me whole.

2 The sharpness of thy two-edged sword
    Enable me to endure,
Till bold to say, "My hallowing Lord
    Hath wrought a perfect cure."

3 I see the exceeding broad command,
    Which all contains in one:
Enlarge my heart to understand
    The mystery unknown.

4 O that, with all thy saints, I might
    By sweet experience prove
What is the length, and breadth, and
        height,
    And depth, of perfect love!
                    CHARLES WESLEY.

539   *The hope of our calling.*

1 What is our calling's glorious hope,
    But inward holiness?
For this to Jesus I look up;
    I calmly wait for this.

2 I wait till he shall touch me clean,
    Shall life and power impart,
Give me the faith that casts out sin,
    And purifies the heart.

3 When Jesus makes my heart his home,
    My sin shall all depart;
And, lo! he saith, "I quickly come,
    To fill and rule thy heart."

4 Be it according to thy word;
    Redeem me from all sin;
My heart would now receive thee, Lord;
    Come in, my Lord, come in!
                    CHARLES WESLEY.

HABAKKUK.   C. P. M.   EDWARD HODGES.

5 O that I could, with favored John,
Recline my weary head upon
    The dear Redeemer's breast!
From care, and sin, and sorrow free,
Give me, O Lord, to find in thee
    My everlasting rest.
                              CHARLES WESLEY.

540 *Panting for fullness of love.*

1 O LOVE divine, how sweet thou art!
When shall I find my willing heart
    All taken up by thee?
I thirst, I faint, I die to prove
The greatness of redeeming love,
    The love of Christ to me.

2 Stronger his love than death or hell;
Its riches are unsearchable;
    The first-born sons of light
Desire in vain its depths to see;
They cannot reach the mystery,
    The length, the breadth, the height.

3 God only knows the love of God;
O that it now were shed abroad
    In this poor stony heart!
For love I sigh, for love I pine;
This only portion, Lord, be mine;
    Be mine this better part.

4 O that I could forever sit
With Mary at the Master's feet!
    Be this my happy choice;
My only care, delight, and bliss,
My joy, my heaven on earth, be this,
    To hear the Bridegroom's voice.

541 *The blessed hope.*

1 BUT can it be that I should prove
Forever faithful to thy love,
    From sin forever cease?
I thank thee for the blessed hope;
It lifts my drooping spirits up;
    It gives me back my peace.

2 In thee, O Lord, I put my trust,
Mighty, and merciful, and just;
    Thy sacred word is passed;
And I, who dare thy word believe,
Without committing sin shall live,
    Shall live to God at last.

3 I rest in thine almighty power;
The name of Jesus is my tower
    That hides my life above;
Thou canst, thou wilt, my helper be;
My confidence is all in thee,
    The faithful God of love.

4 Wherefore, in never-ceasing prayer.
My soul to thy continual care
    I faithfully commend;
Assured that thou through life wilt save.
And show thyself beyond the grave
    My everlasting Friend.
                              CHARLES WESLEY.

542 [C. P. M. Tune, Ariel. Page 11.]
The glorious hope.

1 O GLORIOUS hope of perfect love!
It lifts me up to things above;
  It bears on eagles' wings;
It gives my ravished soul a taste,
And makes me for some moments feast
  With Jesus' priests and kings.

2 Rejoicing now in earnest hope,
)stand, and from the mountain top
  See all the land below:
Rivers of milk and honey rise,
And all the fruits of paradise
  In endless plenty grow.

3 A land of corn, and wine, and oil,
Favored with God's peculiar smile,
  With every blessing blest;
There dwells the Lord our Righteousness,
And keeps his own in perfect peace,
  And everlasting rest.

4 O that I might at once go up;
No more on this side Jordan stop,
  But now the land possess;
This moment end my legal years,
Sorrows and sins, and doubts and fears,
  A howling wilderness!

CHARLES WESLEY.

543 [C. P. M. Tune, Meribah. Page 358.]
Power over temptation.

1 HELP, Lord, to whom for help I fly,
And still my tempted soul stand by
  Throughout the evil day;
The sacred watchfulness impart,
And keep the issues of my heart,
  And stir me up to pray.

2 My soul with thy whole armor arm;
In each approach of sin alarm,
  And show the danger near:
Surround, sustain, and strengthen me,
And fill with godly jealousy
  And sanctifying fear.

3 Whene'er my careless hands hang down,
O let me see thy gathering frown,
  And feel thy warning eye;
And, starting, cry from ruin's brink,
"Save, Jesus, or I yield, I sink;
  O save me, or I die."

4 If near the pit I rashly stray,
Before I wholly fall away,
  The keen conviction dart;
Recall me by that pitying look,
That kind, upbraiding glance, which broke
  Unfaithful Peter's heart.

5 In me thine utmost mercy show,
And make me like thyself below,
  Unblamable in grace;
Ready prepared and fitted here,
By perfect holiness, to appear
  Before thy glorious face.

CHARLES WESLEY.

544 [C. P. M. Tune, Meribah. Page 358.]
A present help in trouble.

1 O GOD, thy faithfulness I plead,
My present help in time of need,
  My great Deliverer thou!
Haste to mine aid, thine ear incline,
And rescue this poor soul of mine:
  I claim the promise now.

2 One only way the erring mind
Of man, short-sighted man, can find,
  From inbred sin to fly:
Stronger than love, I fondly thought
Death, only death, can cut the knot,
  Which love cannot untie.

3 But thou, O Lord, art full of grace;
Thy love can find a thousand ways
  To foolish man unknown:
My soul upon thy love I cast;
I rest me, till the storm be past,
  Upon thy love alone.

4 Thy faithful, wise, almighty love
Shall every stumbling-block remove,
  And make an open way:
Thy love shall burst the shades of death,
And bear me from the gulf beneath,
  To everlasting day.

CHARLES WESLEY.

545 [C. P. M. Tune, Meribah. Page 358.]
The pure in heart shall see God.

1 SAVIOUR, on me the grace bestow,
That, with thy children, I may know
  My sins on earth forgiven;
Give me to prove the kingdom mine,
And taste, in holiness divine,
  The happiness of heaven.

2 Me with that restless thirst inspire,
That sacred, infinite desire,
  And feast my hungry heart;
Less than thyself cannot suffice;
My soul for all thy fullness cries,
  For all thou hast and art.

3 Jesus, the crowning grace impart;
Bless me with purity of heart,
  That, now beholding thee,
I soon may view thy open face,
On all thy glorious beauties gaze,
  And God forever see.

CHARLES WESLEY.

THE CHRISTIAN—UNFAITHFULNESS LAMENTED.

DEDHAM. C. M.

WILLIAM GARDINER.

546 *Mourning departed joys.*

1 SWEET was the time when first I felt
　The Saviour's pardoning blood
Applied to cleanse my soul from guilt,
　And bring me home to God.

2 Soon as the morn the light revealed,
　His praises tuned my tongue;
And when the evening shades prevailed,
　His love was all my song.

3 In prayer my soul drew near the Lord,
　And saw his glory shine;
And when I read his holy word,
　I called each promise mine.

4 But now, when evening shade prevails,
　My soul in darkness mourns;
And when the morn the light reveals,
　No light to me returns.

5 Rise, Lord, and help me to prevail;
　O make my soul thy care;
I know thy mercy cannot fail;
　Let me that mercy share.
　　　　　　　　　　JOHN NEWTON.

547 *Sad reflections on spiritual sloth.*

1 MY drowsy powers, why sleep ye so?
　Awake, my sluggish soul!
Nothing hath half thy work to do,
　Yet nothing's half so dull.

2 Go to the ants! for one poor grain
　See how they toil and strive;
Yet we, who have a heaven to obtain,
　How negligent we live!

3 We, for whose sake all nature stands,
　And stars their courses move;

We, for whose guard the angel bands
　Come flying from above;

4 We, for whom God the Son came down,
　And labored for our good;
How careless to secure that crown
　He purchased with his blood!

5 Lord, shall we live so sluggish still,
　And never act our parts?
Come, holy Dove, from the heavenly hill,
　And warm our frozen hearts!

6 Give us with active warmth to move,
　With vigorous souls to rise;
With hands of faith, and wings of love,
　To fly and take the prize.
　　　　　　　　　　ISAAC WATTS.

548 *Returning to Christ.*

1 MY head is low, my heart is sad,
　My feet with travel torn,
Yet, O my Saviour, thou art glad
　To see thy child return!

2 It was thy love that homeward led,
　Thine arm that upward stayed;
It is thy hand which on my head
　Is now in mercy laid.

3 O Saviour, in this broken heart
　Confirm the trembling will,
Which longs to reach thee where thou art,
　Rest in thee and be still.

4 Within that bosom which hath shed
　Both tears and blood for me,
O let me hide this aching head,
　Once pressed and blessed by thee.
　　　　　　　　　　JOHN S. B. MONSELL.

THE CHRISTIAN—UNFAITHFULNESS LAMENTED.

CHURCH. C. M.

JOSEPH P. HOLBROOK.

549 *For the return of the Spirit.*

1 O FOR a closer walk with God,
  A calm and heavenly frame;
A light to shine upon the road
  That leads me to the Lamb!

2 Where is the blessedness I knew,
  When first I saw the Lord?
Where is the soul-refreshing view
  Of Jesus and his word?

3 What peaceful hours I once enjoyed!
  How sweet their memory still!
But they have left an aching void
  The world can never fill.

4 Return, O holy Dove, return,
  Sweet messenger of rest!
I hate the sins that made thee mourn,
  And drove thee from my breast.

5 The dearest idol I have known,
  Whate'er that idol be,
Help me to tear it from thy throne,
  And worship only thee.

6 So shall my walk be close with God,
  Calm and serene my frame;
So purer light shall mark the road
  That leads me to the Lamb.
                    WILLIAM COWPER.

550 *Faint, yet pursuing.*

1 As pants the hart for cooling streams,
  When heated in the chase,
So longs my soul, O God, for thee,
  And thy refreshing grace.

2 For thee my God, the living God,
  My thirsty soul doth pine;

O when shall I behold thy face,
  Thou Majesty divine?

3 I sigh to think of happier days,
  When thou, O Lord, wast nigh;
When every heart was tuned to praise,
  And none more blest than I.

4 Why restless, why cast down, my soul?
  Hope still, and thou shalt sing
The praise of him who is thy God,
  Thy Saviour, and thy King.
                    TATE AND BRADY.

551 *God gracious to the contrite.*

1 COME, let us to the Lord our God
  With contrite hearts return;
Our God is gracious, nor will leave
  The desolate to mourn.

2 His voice commands the tempest forth,
  And stills the stormy wave;
His arm, though it be strong to smite,
  Is also strong to save.

3 Our hearts, if God we seek to know,
  Shall know him and rejoice;
His coming like the morn shall be,
  Like morning songs his voice.

4 As dew upon the tender herb,
  Diffusing fragrance round;
As showers that usher in the spring,
  And cheer the thirsty ground;

5 So shall his presence bless our souls,
  And shed a joyful light;
That hallowed morn shall chase away
  The sorrows of the night.
                    JOHN MORRISON.

THE CHRISTIAN—UNFAITHFULNESS LAMENTED.

HALL. 7.

WURTEMBURG MELODY.

552 *Love to the Saviour.*

1 HARK, my soul! it is the Lord;
'Tis thy Saviour,—hear his word:
Jesus speaks, he speaks to thee:
"Say, poor sinner, lov'st thou me?"

2 "I delivered thee when bound,
And, when bleeding, healed thy wound;
Sought thee wandering, set thee right,
Turned thy darkness into light.

3 "Can a mother's tender care
Cease toward the child she bare?
Yes, she may forgetful be,
Yet will I remember thee.

4 "Mine is an unchanging love,
Higher than the heights above;
Deeper than the depths beneath,
Free and faithful, strong as death.

5 "Thou shalt see my glory soon,
When the work of faith is done;
Partner of my throne shalt be:
Say, poor sinner, lov'st thou me?"

6 Lord, it is my chief complaint
That my love is weak and faint,
Yet I love thee and adore:
O for grace to love thee more!

WILLIAM COWPER.

[S. M. Tune, Ozrem. Page 203.]

553 *God's absence deprecated.*

1 O THOU, whose mercy hears
Contrition's humble sigh:
Whose hand, indulgent, wipes the tears
From sorrow's weeping eye;

2 See, at thy throne of grace,
A wretched wanderer mourn:
Hast thou not bid me seek thy face?
Hast thou not said, "Return?"

3 Shall guilty fears prevail
To drive me from thy feet?
O let not this last refuge fail,
This only safe retreat.

4 Absent from thee, my Light,
Without one cheering ray,
Through dangers, fears, and gloomy night,
How desolate my way!

5 On this benighted heart
With beams of mercy shine;
And let thy voice again impart
A taste of joy divine.

ANNE STEELE.

[S. M. Tune, Ozrem. Page 203.]

554 *The wanderer returning.*

1 How oft this wretched heart
Has wandered from the Lord!
How oft my roving thoughts depart,
Forgetful of his word!

2 Yet mercy calls, "Return;"
Saviour, to thee I come:
My vile ingratitude I mourn;
O take the wanderer home.

3 Thy love so free, so sweet,
Blest Saviour, I adore;
O keep me at thy sacred feet,
And let me rove no more.

ANNE STEELE.

202

OZREM. S. M.   ISAAC BAKER WOODBURY.

FIRST PART.

555 *The warning voice of Jesus.*

1 GRACIOUS Redeemer, shake
  This slumber from my soul!
Say to me now, "Awake, awake!
  And Christ shall make thee whole."

2 Lay to thy mighty hand;
  Alarm me in this hour;
And make me fully understand
  The thunder of thy power.

3 Give me on thee to call,
  Always to watch and pray,
Lest I into temptation fall,
  And cast my shield away.

4 For each assault prepared,
  And ready may I be;
Forever standing on my guard,
  And looking up to thee.

5 O do thou always warn
  My soul of evil near;
When to the right or left I turn,
  Thy voice still let me hear:

6 "Come back! this is the way;
  Come back, and walk therein;"
O may I hearken and obey,
  And shun the paths of sin.
                        CHARLES WESLEY.

SECOND PART.

556 *Commending the soul to God.*

1 THOU seest my feebleness;
  Jesus, be thou my power,
My help and refuge in distress,
  My fortress and my tower.

2 Give me to trust in thee;
  Be thou my sure abode:

My horn, and rock, and buckler be,
  My Saviour and my God.

3 Myself I cannot save,
  Myself I cannot keep,
But strength in thee I surely have,
  Whose eyelids never sleep.

4 My soul to thee alone,
  Now therefore I commend:
Thou, Jesus, love me as thine own,
  And love me to the end.
                        CHARLES WESLEY.

557 *Restore my peace.*

1 O JESUS, full of grace,
  To thee I make my moan:
Let me again behold thy face,
  Call home thy banished one.

2 Again my pardon seal,
  Again my soul restore,
And freely my backslidings heal,
  And bid me sin no more.

3 Wilt thou not bid me rise?
  Speak, and my soul shall live;
"Forgive," my stricken spirit cries,
  "Abundantly forgive."

4 Thine utmost mercy show;
  Say to my drooping soul,
"In peace and full assurance go;
  Thy faith hath made thee whole."
                        CHARLES WESLEY.

Doxology.

To God, the Father, Son,
  And Spirit, One in Three,
Be glory, as it was, is now,
  And shall forever be.
                        JOHN WESLEY.

PENITENCE.   7, 6, 8.

WILLIAM HENRY OAKLEY.

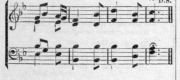

4 Look, as when thy languid eye
    Was closed that we might live;
"Father," at the point to die
    My Saviour prayed, "forgive!"
Surely, with that dying word,
    He turns, and looks, and cries, "'Tis
        done!"
O my bleeding, loving Lord,
    Thou break'st my heart of stone!

CHARLES WESLEY.

558   *Humility and contrition.*

1 JESUS, let thy pitying eye
    Call back a wandering sheep;
False to thee, like Peter, I
    Would fain, like Peter, weep.
Let me be by grace restored;
    On me be all long-suffering shown;
Turn, and look upon me, Lord,
    And break my heart of stone.

2 Saviour, Prince, enthroned above,
    Repentance to impart,
Give me, through thy dying love,
    The humble, contrite heart;
Give what I have long implored,
    A portion of thy grief unknown;
Turn, and look upon me, Lord,
    And break my heart of stone.

3 See me, Saviour, from above,
    Nor suffer me to die;
Life, and happiness, and love
    Drop from thy gracious eye:
Speak the reconciling word,
    And let thy mercy melt me down;
Turn, and look upon me, Lord,
    And break my heart of stone.

559   *The deceitfulness of sin.*

1 JESUS, Friend of sinners, hear
    Yet once again, I pray;
From my debt of sin set clear,
    For I have naught to pay:
Speak, O speak the kind release;
    A poor backsliding soul restore;
Love me freely, seal my peace,
    And bid me sin no more.

2 For my selfishness and pride
    Thou hast withdrawn thy grace;
Left me long to wander wide,
    An outcast from thy face;
But I now my sins confess,
    And mercy, mercy, I implore;
Love me freely, seal my peace,
    And bid me sin no more.

3 Sin's deceitfulness hath spread
    A hardness o'er my heart;
But if thou thy Spirit shed,
    The stony shall depart:
Shed thy love, thy tenderness,
    And let me feel thy softening power,
Love me freely, seal my peace,
    And bid me sin no more.

CHARLES WESLEY.

THE CHRISTIAN—UNFAITHFULNESS LAMENTED.

WARREN. L. M.

VIRGIL CORYDON TAYLOR.

560 *Zeal implored.*

1 O THOU who all things canst control,
Chase this dread slumber from my soul;
With joy and fear, with love and awe,
Give me to keep thy perfect law.

2 O may one beam of thy blest light
Pierce through, dispel the shade of night;
Touch my cold breast with heavenly fire;
With holy, conquering zeal inspire.

3 For zeal I sigh, for zeal I pant;
Yet heavy is my soul, and faint:
With steps unwavering, undismayed,
Give me in all thy paths to tread.

4 With outstretched hands, and streaming eyes,
Oft I begin to grasp the prize;
I groan, I strive, I watch, I pray;
But ah! my zeal soon dies away.

5 The deadly slumber then I feel
Afresh upon my spirit steal:
Rise, Lord, stir up thy quickening power,
And wake me that I sleep no more.

FROM THE GERMAN. TR. BY J. WESLEY.

561 *Peace in the favor of God.*

1 O WHERE is now that glowing love
That marked our union with the Lord?
Our hearts were fixed on things above,
Nor could the world a joy afford.

2 Where is the zeal that led us then
To make our Saviour's glory known?
That freed us from the fear of men,
And kept our eye on him alone?

3 Where are the happy seasons, spent
In fellowship with him we loved?
The sacred joy, the sweet content,
The blessedness that then we proved?

4 Behold, again we turn to thee;
O cast us not away, though vile:
No peace we have, no joy we see,
O Lord our God, but in thy smile.

THOMAS KELLY.

GALILEE. L. M.

RICHARD LANGDON.

562 *For the fire of divine love.*

1 O THOU who camest from above,
The pure celestial fire to impart,
Kindle a flame of sacred love
On the mean altar of my heart.

2 There let it for thy glory burn,
With inextinguishable blaze;
And trembling to its source return,
In humble prayer and fervent praise.

3 Jesus, confirm my heart's desire
To work, and speak, and think for thee;
Still let me guard the holy fire,
And still stir up thy gift in me.

4 Ready for all thy perfect will,
My acts of faith and love repeat,
Till death thy endless mercies seal,
And make the sacrifice complete.

CHARLES WESLEY.

14

205

THE CHRISTIAN—ACTIVITY.

ONWARD (Christus Victor.) 6, 5.   Sir Arthur Seymour Sullivan.

563 *Onward, Christian soldiers.*

1 ONWARD, Christian soldiers!
    Marching as to war,
With the cross of Jesus
    Going on before.
Christ, the royal Master,
    Leads against the foe;
Forward into battle,
    See, his banners go!
        Onward, Christian soldiers!
            Marching as to war,
        With the cross of Jesus
            Going on before.

2 At the sign of triumph
    Satan's host doth flee;
On, then, Christian soldiers,
    On to victory!
Hell's foundations quiver
    At the shout of praise;
Brothers, lift your voices,
    Loud your anthems raise.

3 Like a mighty army
    Moves the Church of God;

Brothers, we are treading
    Where the saints have trod;
We are not divided,
    All one body we,
One in hope and doctrine,
    One in charity.

4 Crowns and thrones may perish,
    Kingdoms rise and wane,
But the Church of Jesus
    Constant will remain;
Gates of hell can never
    'Gainst that Church prevail;
We have Christ's own promise,
    And that cannot fail.

5 Onward, then, ye people!
    Join our happy throng,
Blend with ours your voices
    In the triumph-song;
Glory, laud, and honor
    Unto Christ the King,
This through countless ages
    Men and angels sing.
                    SABINE BARING-GOULD.

ELAH. 6, 5. From Francis Joseph Haydn.

564 *Forward into light*

1 FORWARD! be our watchword,
   Steps and voices joined;
Seek the things before us,
   Not a look behind:
Burns the fiery pillar
   At our army's head:
Who shall dream of shrinking,
   By our Captain led?
Forward through the desert,
   Through the toil and fight:
Jordan flows before us,
   Zion beams with light!

2 Forward! flock of Jesus,
   Salt of all the earth,
Till each yearning purpose
   Spring to glorious birth:
Sick, they ask for healing;
   Blind, they grope for day;
Pour upon the nations
   Wisdom's loving ray.
Forward, out of error,
   Leave behind the night;
Forward through the darkness,
   Forward into light!

3 Glories upon glories
   Hath our God prepared,
By the souls that love him
   One day to be shared:
Eye hath not beheld them,
   Ear hath never heard;
Nor of these hath uttered
   Thought or speech a word:
Forward, marching eastward
   Where the heaven is bright,
Till the veil be lifted,
   Till our faith be sight!

4 Far o'er yon horizon
   Rise the city towers,
Where our God abideth;
   That fair home is ours:
Flash the streets with jasper,
   Shine the gates with gold;
Flows the gladdening river
   Shedding joys untold;
Thither, onward thither,
   In the Spirit's might:
Pilgrims to your country,
   Forward into light!

HENRY ALFORD.

THE CHRISTIAN—ACTIVITY.

WORK SONG. 7, 6, 5.   Lowell Mason.

565 *Work, while it is day.*

1 WORK, for the night is coming,
  Work through the morning hours;
Work, while the dew is sparkling,
  Work 'mid springing flowers;
Work, when the day grows brighter,
  Work in the glowing sun;
Work, for the night is coming,
  When man's work is done.

2 Work, for the night is coming,
  Work through the sunny noon;
Fill brightest hours with labor,
  Rest comes sure and soon.
Give every flying minute
  Something to keep in store:
Work, for the night is coming,
  When man works no more.

3 Work, for the night is coming,
  Under the sunset skies;
While their bright tints are glowing,
  Work, for daylight flies.
Work till the last beam fadeth,
  Fadeth to shine no more;
Work while the night is darkening,
  When man's work is o'er.

                              SIDNEY DYER.

CALEDONIA. 7, 7, 7, 6.   Scotch.

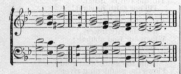

566 *The spiritual warfare.*

1 SOLDIERS of the cross, arise!
Lo! your Leader from the skies
Waves before you glory's prize,
  The prize of victory.

Seize your armor, gird it on;
Now the battle will be won;
See, the strife will soon be done
  Then struggle manfully.

2 Now the fight of faith begin,
Be no more the slaves of sin,
Strive the victor's palm to win,
  Trusting in the Lord:
Gird ye on the armor bright,
Warriors of the King of light,
Never yield, nor lose by flight
  Your divine reward.

3 Jesus conquered when he fell,
Met and vanquished earth and hell;
Now he leads you on to swell
   The triumphs of his cross.
Though all earth and hell appear,
Who will doubt, or who can fear?
God, our strength and shield, is near;
   We cannot lose our cause.

4 Onward, then, ye hosts of God!
Jesus points the victor's rod;
Follow where your Leader trod;
   You soon shall see his face.
Soon, your enemies all slain,
Crowns of glory you shall gain,
Soon you'll join that glorious train
   Who shout their Saviour's praise.

JARED B. WATERBURY.

WEBB. 7, 6.

GEORGE JAMES WEBB.

567 *Stand up for Jesus.*

1 STAND up, stand up for Jesus,
   Ye soldiers of the cross;
Lift high his royal banner,
   It must not suffer loss:
From victory unto victory
   His army shall he lead,
Till every foe is vanquished
   And Christ is Lord indeed.

2 Stand up, stand up for Jesus,
   The trumpet call obey;
Forth to the mighty conflict,
   In this his glorious day:
"Ye that are men, now serve him,"
   Against unnumbered foes;
Your courage rise with danger,
   And strength to strength oppose.

3 Stand up, stand up for Jesus,
   Stand in his strength alone;
The arm of flesh will fail you;
   Ye dare not trust your own:
Put on the gospel armor,
   Each piece put on with prayer;
Where duty calls, or danger,
   Be never wanting there.

4 Stand up, stand up for Jesus,
   The strife will not be long;
This day the noise of battle,
   The next the victor's song:

To him that overcometh,
   A crown of life shall be;
He with the King of glory
   Shall reign eternally.

GEORGE DUFFIELD, JR.

568 *Enduring hardness as good
   soldiers.*

1 Go forward, Christian soldier,
   Beneath His banner true:
The Lord himself, thy Leader,
   Shall all thy foes subdue.
His love foretells thy trials,
   He knows thine hourly need;
He can, with bread of heaven,
   Thy fainting spirit feed.

2 Go forward, Christian soldier,
   Fear not the secret foe;
Far more are o'er thee watching
   Than human eyes can know.
Trust only Christ, thy Captain,
   Cease not to watch and pray;
Heed not the treacherous voices,
   That lure thy soul astray.

3 Go forward, Christian soldier,
   Nor dream of peaceful rest,
Till Satan's host is vanquished,
   And heaven is all possessed;
Till Christ himself shall call thee
   To lay thine armor by,
And wear, in endless glory,
   The crown of victory.

LAURENCE TUTTIETT.

THE CHRISTIAN—ACTIVITY.

MENDELSSOHN.   C. P. M.   ⸭OTTO NICOLAI.

569   *Battle-hymn of the Reformation.*

1 FEAR not, O little flock, the foe
Who madly seeks your overthrow;
   Dread not his rage and power;
What though your courage sometimes
      faints?
This seeming triumph o'er God's saints
   Lasts but a little hour.

2 Fear not, be strong! your cause belongs
To him who can avenge your wrongs;
   Leave all to him, your Lord:
Though hidden yet from mortal eyes,
Salvation shall for you arise;
   He girdeth on his sword!

3 As true as God's own promise stands,
Not earth nor hell with all their bands
   Against us shall prevail;
The Lord shall mock them from his throne;
God is with us; we are his own;
   Our victory cannot fail!

4 Amen, Lord Jesus, grant our prayer!
Great Captain, now thine arm make bare,
   Thy Church with strength defend;
So shall thy saints and martyrs raise
A joyful chorus to thy praise,
   Through ages without end.
        GUSTAVUS ADOLPHUS, IN PROSE. JACOB FABRICIUS.
                TR. BY MISS C. WINKWORTH.

570   *Looking unto Jesus.*

1 ARE there not in the laborer's day
Twelve hours, in which he safely may
   His calling's work pursue?

Though sin and Satan still are near,
Nor sin nor Satan can I fear,
   With Jesus in my view.

2 Light of the world! thy beams I bless;
On thee, bright Sun of righteousness,
   My faith hath fixed its eye:
Guided by thee, through all I go,
Nor fear the ruin spread below,
   For thou art always nigh.

3 Ten thousand snares my paths beset,
Yet will I, Lord, the work complete,
   Which thou to me hast given;
Regardless of the pains I feel,
Close by the gates of death and hell,
   I urge my way to heaven.
                        CHARLES WESLEY.

571   *Loving gratitude.*

1 BE it my only wisdom here,
To serve the Lord with filial fear,
   With loving gratitude:
Superior sense may I display,
By shunning every evil way,
   And walking in the good.

2 O may I still from sin depart;
A wise and understanding heart,
   Jesus, to me be given:
And let me through thy Spirit know
To glorify my God below,
   And find my way to heaven.
                        CHARLES WESLEY.

EDINBURGH.   7, 6, 5, 4.   REV. ROBERT LOWRY.

CHORUS.

[C. P. M. Tune, Meribah. Page 358.]

572 *One more day's work for Jesus.*

1 ONE more day's work for Jesus,
    One less of life for me!
      But heaven is nearer,
      And Christ is dearer
    Than yesterday, to me;
      His love and light
    Fill all my soul to-night.
  One more day's work for Jesus, etc.

2 One more day's work for Jesus!
    How sweet the work has been,
      To tell the story,
      To show the glory,
    Where Christ's flock enter in!
      How it did shine
    In this poor heart of mine!

3 One more day's work for Jesus!
    O yes, a weary day;
      But heaven shines clearer
      And rest comes nearer,
    At each step of the way;
      And Christ in all,
    Before his face I fall.

4 O blessed work for Jesus!
    O rest at Jesus' feet!
      There toil seems pleasure,
      My wants are treasure,
    And pain for him is sweet.
      Lord, if I may,
    I'll serve another day!

                    ANNA S. WARNER.

573 *For the head of a family.*

1 I AND my house will serve the Lord;
  But first, obedient to his word
      I must myself appear;
  By actions, words, and tempers, show
  That I my heavenly Master know,
      And serve with heart sincere.

2 I must the fair example set;
  From those that on my pleasure wait
      The stumbling-block remove;
  Their duty by my life explain,
  And still in all my works maintain
      The dignity of love.

3 Easy to be entreated, mild,
  Quickly appeased and reconciled,
      A follower of my God,
  A saint indeed, I long to be,
  And lead my faithful family
      In the celestial road.

4 Lord, if thou didst the wish infuse,
  A vessel fitted for thy use
      Into thy hands receive:
  Work in me both to will and do;
  And show them how believers true,
      And real Christians, live.

                    CHARLES WESLEY

211

THE CHRISTIAN—ACTIVITY.

BOYLSTON. S. M. LOWELL MASON.

574 *For watchfulness.*

1 A CHARGE to keep I have,
  A God to glorify;
A never-dying soul to save,
  And fit it for the sky.
To serve the present age,
  My calling to fulfill,—
O may it all my powers engage,
  To do my Master's will.

2 Arm me with jealous care,
  As in thy sight to live;
And O, thy servant, Lord, prepare,
  A strict account to give.
Help me to watch and pray,
  And on thyself rely,
Assured, if I my trust betray,
  I shall forever die.
  CHARLES WESLEY.

575 *Sow beside all waters.*

1 Sow in the morn thy seed;
  At eve hold not thy hand;
To doubt and fear give thou no heed,
  Broadcast it o'er the land.

2 Thou know'st not which shall thrive,
  The late or early sown;
Grace keeps the precious germ alive,
  When and wherever strown:

3 And duly shall appear,
  In verdure, beauty, strength,
The tender blade, the stalk, the ear,
  And the full corn at length.

4 Thou canst not toil in vain:
  Cold, heat, and moist, and dry,
Shall foster and mature the grain
  For garners in the sky.

5 Then, when the glorious end,
  The day of God, shall come,
The angel reapers shall descend,
  And heaven shout, "Harvest home!"
  JAMES MONTGOMERY.

576 *Make haste to live.*

1 MAKE haste, O man, to live,
  For thou so soon must die;
Time hurries past thee like the breeze;
  How swift its moments fly!

2 Make haste, O man, to do
  Whatever must be done;
Thou hast no time to lose in sloth,
  Thy day will soon be gone.

3 Up, then, with speed, and work;
  Fling ease and self away;
This is no time for thee to sleep,
  Up, watch, and work, and pray!

4 Make haste, O man, to live,
  Thy time is almost o'er;
O sleep not, dream not, but arise,
  The Judge is at the door.
  HORATIUS BONAR.

Doxology.

To God, the Father, Son,
  And Spirit, One in Three,
Be glory, as it was, is now,
  And shall forever be.
  JOHN WESLEY.

LEIGHTON.   S. M.

HENRY WELLINGTON GREATOREX.

577   *Victory on the Lord's side.*

1 ARISE, ye saints, arise!
  The Lord our Leader is;
The foe before his banner flies,
  And victory is his.

2 We follow thee, our Guide,
  Our Saviour, and our King;
We follow thee, through grace supplied
  From heaven's eternal spring.

3 We soon shall see the day
  When all our toils shall cease;
When we shall cast our arms away,
  And dwell in endless peace.

4 This hope supports us here;
  It makes our burdens light;
'Twill serve our drooping hearts to cheer,
  Till faith shall end in sight:

5 Till, of the prize possessed,
  We hear of war no more;
And ever with our Leader rest,
  On yonder peaceful shore.

                                THOMAS KELLY.

578   *Recompense of toil.*

1 LABORERS of Christ, arise,
  And gird you for the toil!
The dew of promise from the skies
  Already cheers the soil.

2 Go where the sick recline,
  Where mourning hearts deplore;
And where the sons of sorrow pine,
  Dispense your hallowed store.

3 Be faith, which looks above,
  With prayer, your constant guest;
And wrap the Saviour's changeless love
  A mantle round your breast.

4 So shall you share the wealth
  That earth may ne'er despoil,
And the blest gospel's saving health
  Repay your arduous toil.

                        MRS. LYDIA H. SIGOURNEY.

579   *Sowing in tears, reaping in joy.*

1 THE harvest dawn is near,
  The year delays not long;
And he who sows with many a tear,
  Shall reap with many a song.

2 Sad to his toil he goes,
  His seed with weeping leaves;
But he shall come at twilight's close,
  And bring his golden sheaves.

                            GEORGE BURGESS.

580   *On guard.*

1 LET us keep steadfast guard
  With lighted hearts all night,
That when Christ comes, we stand pre-
        pared,
  And meet him with delight.

2 At midnight's season chill
  Lay Paul and Silas bound,—
Bound, and in prison sang they still,
  And singing, freedom found.

3 Our prison is this earth,
  And yet we sing to thee:
Break sin's strong fetters, lead us forth,
  Set us, believing, free!

4 Meet for thy realm in heaven,
  Make us, O holy King!
That through the ages it be given
  To us thy praise to sing.

                                BREVIARY.

LABAN.   S. M.   LOWELL MASON.

581 *Perseverance.*

1 My soul, be on thy guard;
    Ten thousand foes arise;
The hosts of sin are pressing hard
    To draw thee from the skies.

2 O watch, and fight, and pray;
    The battle ne'er give o'er;
Renew it boldly every day,
    And help divine implore.

3 Ne'er think the victory won,
    Nor lay thine armor down:
The work of faith will not be done,
    Till thou obtain the crown.

4 Fight on, my soul, til death
    Shall bring thee to thy God;
He 'll take thee, at thy parting breath,
    To his divine abode.
                            GEORGE HEATH.

582 *The standard of the cross.*

1 HARK, how the watchmen cry!
    Attend the trumpet's sound;
Stand to your arms, the foe is nigh,
    The powers of hell surround.
Who bow to Christ's command,
    Your arms and hearts prepare;
The day of battle is at hand—
    Go forth to glorious war.

2 See on the mountain-top
    The standard of your God;
In Jesus' name I lift it up,
    All stained with hallowed blood.
His standard-bearer, I
    To all the nations call:
Let all to Jesus' cross draw nigh;
    He bore the cross for all.

3 Go up with Christ your Head;
    Your Captain's footsteps see;
Follow your Captain, and be led
    To certain victory.
All power to him is given;
    He ever reigns the same:
Salvation, happiness, and heaven,
    Are all in Jesus' name.
                            CHARLES WESLEY.

583 *Courage—victory.*

1 URGE on your rapid course,
    Ye blood-besprinkled bands;
The heavenly kingdom suffers force;
    'Tis seized by violent hands:
See there the starry crown
    That glitters through the skies;
Satan, the world, and sin, tread down,
    And take the glorious prize.

2 Through much distress and pain,
    Through many a conflict here,
Through blood, ye must the entrance gain,
    Yet, O disdain to fear:
"Courage!" your Captain cries,
    Who all your toil foreknew;
"Toil ye shall have, yet all despise;
    I have o'ercome for you."

3 The world cannot withstand
    Its ancient Conqueror;
The world must sink beneath the hand
    Which arms us for the war:
This is the victory,—
    Before our faith they fall;
Jesus hath died for you and me;
    Believe, and conquer all.
                            CHARLES WESLEY.

CLAPTON. S. M.

REV. WILLIAM JONES.

584 *Weigh not thy life.*

1 My soul, weigh not thy life
  Against thy heavenly crown;
Nor suffer Satan's deadliest strife
  To beat thy courage down.

2 With prayer and crying strong,
  Hold on the fearful fight,
And let the breaking day prolong
  The wrestling of the night.

3 The battle soon will yield,
  If thou thy part fulfill;
For strong as is the hostile shield,
  Thy sword is stronger still.

4 Thine armor is divine,
  Thy feet with victory shod;
And on thy head shall quickly shine
  The diadem of God.
UNKNOWN.

585 *Victory.*

1 "I THE good fight have fought,"
  O when shall I declare?
The victory by my Saviour got,
  I long with Paul to share.

2 O may I triumph so,
  When all my warfare 's past;
And, dying, find my latest foe
  Under my feet at last!

3 This blessed word be mine,
  Just as the port is gained,
"Kept by the power of grace divine,
  I have the faith maintained."

4 The apostles of my Lord,
  To whom it first was given,
They could not speak a greater word,
  Nor all the saints in heaven.
CHARLES WESLEY.

586 *The mind that was in Christ.*

1 EQUIP me for the war,
  And teach my hands to fight;
My simple, upright heart prepare,
  And guide my words aright.

2 Control my every thought,
  My whole of sin remove;
Let all my works in thee be wrought,
  Let all be wrought in love.

3 O arm me with the mind,
  Meek Lamb, that was in thee;
And let my knowing zeal be joined
  With perfect charity.

4 With calm and tempered zeal
  Let me enforce thy call;
And vindicate thy gracious will,
  Which offers life to all.

5 O may I love like thee;
  In all thy footsteps tread;
Thou hatest all iniquity,
  But nothing thou hast made.

6 O may I learn the art,
  With meekness to reprove;
To hate the sin with all my heart,
  But still the sinner love.
CHARLES WESLEY.

BENJAMIN. S. M.

Francis Joseph Haydn.

FIRST PART.

587 *The whole armor of God.*

1 SOLDIERS of Christ, arise,
  And put your armor on,
Strong in the strength which God supplies
  Through his eternal Son;
Strong in the Lord of hosts,
  And in his mighty power,
Who in the strength of Jesus trusts
  Is more than conqueror.

2 Stand, then, in his great might,
  With all his strength endued;
But take, to arm you for the fight,
  The panoply of God:
That, having all things done,
  And all your conflicts passed,
Ye may o'ercome through Christ alone,
  And stand entire at last.

3 Leave no unguarded place,
  No weakness of the soul;
Take every virtue, every grace,
  And fortify the whole:
Indissolubly joined,
  To battle all proceed;
But arm yourselves with all the mind
  That was in Christ, your Head.
      CHARLES WESLEY.

SECOND PART.

588 *The shield of faith.*

1 SOLDIERS of Christ, lay hold
  On faith's victorious shield;
Armed with that adamant and gold,
  Be sure to win the field:
If faith surround your heart,
  Satan shall be subdued;
Repelled his every fiery dart,
  And quenched with Jesus' blood.

2 Jesus hath died for you!
  What can his love withstand?
Believe, hold fast your shield, and who
  Shall pluck you from his hand?
Believe that Jesus reigns;
  All power to him is given:
Believe, till freed from sin's remains;
  Believe yourselves to heaven.
      CHARLES WESLEY.

THIRD PART.

589 *The well-fought day.*

1 PRAY, without ceasing pray,
  Your Captain gives the word;
His summons cheerfully obey,
  And call upon the Lord:
To God your every want
  In instant prayer display;
Pray always: pray, and never faint;
  Pray, without ceasing pray.

2 In fellowship, alone,
  To God with faith draw near;
Approach his courts, besiege his throne
  With all the power of prayer:
His mercy now implore,
  And now show forth his praise;
In shouts, or silent awe, adore
  His miracles of grace.

3 From strength to strength go on;
  Wrestle, and fight, and pray;
Tread all the powers of darkness down,
  And win the well-fought day:
Still let the Spirit cry
  In all his soldiers, "Come!"
Till Christ the Lord descend from high,
  And take the conquerors home.
      CHARLES WESLEY.

WINCHESTER OLD.   C. M.   THOMAS ESTE'S PSALTER.

590   *Bearing the cross.*

1 LORD, as to thy dear cross we flee,
  And pray to be forgiven,
So let thy life our pattern be,
  And form our souls for heaven.

2 Help us, through good report and ill,
  Our daily cross to bear;
Like thee, to do our Father's will,
  Our brother's griefs to share.

3 Let grace our selfishness expel,
  Our earthliness refine;
And kindness in our bosoms dwell
  As free and true as thine.

4 If joy shall at thy bidding fly,
  And grief's dark day come on,
We, in our turn, would meekly cry,
  "Father, thy will be done!"

5 Kept peaceful in the midst of strife,
  Forgiving and forgiven,
O may we lead the pilgrim's life,
  And follow thee to heaven!
                        JOHN H. GURNEY.

591   *Christian courage.*

1 WORKMAN of God! O lose not heart,
  But learn what God is like;
And in the darkest battle-field
  Thou shalt know where to strike.

2 Thrice blest is he to whom is given
  The instinct that can tell
That God is on the field, when he
  Is most invisible.

3 Blest too is he who can divine
  Where real right doth lie,
And dares to take the side that seems
  Wrong to man's blindfold eye.

4 Then learn to scorn the praise of men,
  And learn to lose with God;
For Jesus won the world through shame
  And beckons thee his road.
                        FREDERICK W. FABER.

592   *Toil sanctified.*

1 SON of the carpenter, receive
  This humble work of mine;
Worth to my meanest labor give,
  By joining it to thine.

2 Servant, at once, and Lord of all,
  While dwelling here below,
Thou didst not scorn our earthly toil
  And weariness to know.

3 Thy bright example I pursue,
  To thee in all things rise,
And all I think, or speak, or do,
  Is one great sacrifice.

4 Careless through outward cares I go,
  From all distraction free;
My hands are but engaged below,
  My heart is still with thee.

5 O when wilt thou, my life, appear?
  Then gladly will I cry,
"'Tis done, the work thou gav'st me here,
  'Tis finished, Lord," and die!
                        CHARLES WESLEY.

THE CHRISTIAN—ACTIVITY.

ARLINGTON.   C. M.   THOMAS AUGUSTINE ARNE.

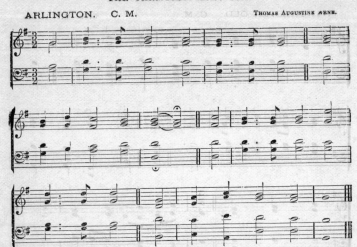

593 *Faith sees the final triumph.*

1 AM I a soldier of the cross,
  A follower of the Lamb,
And shall I fear to own his cause,
  Or blush to speak his name?

2 Must I be carried to the skies
  On flowery beds of ease,
While others fought to win the prize,
  And sailed through bloody seas?

3 Are there no foes for me to face?
  Must I not stem the flood?
Is this vile world a friend to grace,
  To help me on to God?

4 Sure I must fight, if I would reign;
  Increase my courage, Lord;
I'll bear the toil, endure the pain,
  Supported by thy word.

5 Thy saints in all this glorious war
  Shall conquer, though they die:
They see the triumph from afar,
  By faith they bring it nigh.

6 When that illustrious day shall rise
  And all thy armies shine
In robes of victory through the skies,
  The glory shall be thine.
                              ISAAC WATTS.

594 *The race for glory.*

1 AWAKE, my soul, stretch every nerve,
  And press with vigor on;
A heavenly race demands thy zeal,
  And an immortal crown.

2 A cloud of witnesses around
  Hold thee in full survey;

Forget the steps already trod,
  And onward urge thy way.

3 'Tis God's all-animating voice
  That calls thee from on high;
'Tis his own hand presents the prize
  To thine aspiring eye:—

4 That prize, with peerless glories bright,
  Which shall new luster boast,
When victors' wreaths and monarchs
    gems
  Shall blend in common dust.

5 Blest Saviour, introduced by thee,
  Have I my race begun;
And, crowned with victory, at thy feet
  I'll lay my honors down.
                         PHILIP DODDRIDGE.

595 *Not ashamed of the Gospel.*

1 I'M not ashamed to own my Lord,
  Or to defend his cause;
Maintain the honor of his word,
  The glory of his cross.

2 Jesus, my God! I know his name;
  His name is all my trust;
Nor will he put my soul to shame,
  Nor let my hope be lost.

3 Firm as his throne his promise stands,
  And he can well secure
What I've committed to his hands,
  Till the decisive hour.

4 Then will he own my worthless name
  Before his Father's face,
And in the New Jerusalem
  Appoint my soul a place.
                            ISAAC WATTS.

ST. AGNES.   C. M.

REV. JOHN BACCHUS DYKES.

596   *To doubt, disloyal.*

1 O IT is hard to work for God,
   To rise and take his part
Upon this battle-field of earth,
   And not sometimes lose heart!

2 He hides himself so wondrously,
   As though there were no God;
He is least seen when all the powers
   Of ill are most abroad;

3 Or he deserts us in the hour
   The fight is all but lost;
And seems to leave us to ourselves
   Just when we need him most.

4 It is not so, but so it looks;
   And we lose courage then:
And doubts will come if God hath kept
   His promises to men.

5 But right is right, since God is God;
   And right the day must win;
To doubt would be disloyalty,
   To falter would be sin!
                    FREDERICK W. FABER.

597   *Week-day worship.*

1 BEHOLD us, Lord, a little space
   From daily tasks set free,
And met within thy holy place
   To rest awhile with thee.

2 Around us rolls the ceaseless tide
   Of business, toil, and care,
And scarely can we turn aside
   For one brief hour of prayer.

3 Yet these are not the only walls
   Wherein thou mayst be sought;
On homeliest work thy blessing falls
   In truth and patience wrought.

4 Thine is the loom, the forge, the mart,
   The wealth of land and sea;
The worlds of science and of art,
   Revealed and ruled by thee.

5 Then let us prove our heavenly birth
   In all we do and know;
And claim the kingdom of the earth
   For thee, and not thy foe.

6 Work shall be prayer, if all be wrought
   As thou wouldst have it done;
And prayer, by thee inspired and taught,
   Itself with work be one.
                    JOHN ELLERTON.

598   *More reapers.*

1 O STILL in accents sweet and strong
   Sounds forth the ancient word,
"More reapers for white harvest fields.
   More laborers for the Lord!"

2 We hear the call; in dreams no more
   In selfish ease we lie,
But girded for our Father's work,
   Go forth beneath his sky.

3 Where prophets' word, and martyrs'
      blood,
   And prayers of saints were sown,
We, to their labors entering in,
   Would reap where they have strown.
                    SAMUEL LONGFELLOW.

MISSIONARY CHANT. L. M. HEINRICH CHRISTOPHER ZEUNER.

599 *The Christian warrior.*

1 BEHOLD the Christian warrior stand
In all the armor of his God;
The Spirit's sword is in his hand,
His feet are with the gospel shod;

2 In panoply of truth complete,
Salvation's helmet on his head;
With righteousness a breast-plate meet,
And faith's broad shield before him spread.

3 Undaunted to the field he goes;
Yet vain were skill and valor there,
Unless, to foil his legion foes,
He takes the trustiest weapon, prayer.

4 Thus, strong in his Redeemer's strength,
Sin, death, and hell, he tramples down;
Fights the good fight, and wins at length,
Through mercy, an immortal crown.
JAMES MONTGOMERY.

BISHOP. L. M. JOSEPH P. HOLBROOK.

600 *Your life is hid with Christ in God.*

1 YE faithful souls who Jesus know,
If risen indeed with him ye are,
Superior to the joys below,
His resurrection's power declare.

2 Your faith by holy tempers prove,
By actions show your sins forgiven,
And seek the glorious things above,
And follow Christ, your Head, to heaven.

3 There your exalted Saviour see,
Seated at God's right hand again,
In all his Father's majesty,
In everlasting pomp to reign.

4 To him continually aspire,
Contending for your native place;
And emulate the angel choir,
And only live to love and praise.

5 For who by faith your Lord receive,
Ye nothing seek or want beside;
Dead to the world and sin ye live,
Your creature-love is crucified.

6 Your real life, with Christ concealed,
Deep in the Father's bosom lies;
And glorious as your Head revealed,
Ye soon shall meet him in the skies.
CHARLES WESLEY.

ILLINOIS. L. M.   Rev. Jonathan Spilman arr. by Thomas Hastings.

601   *Take up thy cross.*

1 "Take up thy cross," the Saviour said,
  "If thou wouldst my disciple be;
Deny thyself, the world forsake,
  And humbly follow after me."

2 Take up thy cross; let not its weight
  Fill thy weak spirit with alarm;
His strength shall bear thy spirit up,
  And brace thy heart and nerve thine arm.

3 Take up thy cross, nor heed the shame;
  Nor let thy foolish pride rebel;
Thy Lord for thee the cross endured,
  To save thy soul from death and hell.

4 Take up thy cross, then, in his strength,
  And calmly every danger brave;
'Twill guide thee to a better home,
  And lead to victory o'er the grave.

5 Take up thy cross, and follow Christ;
  Nor think till death to lay it down;
For only he who bears the cross
  May hope to wear the glorious crown.
             CHARLES W. EVEREST.

602   *The sure reward.*

1 It may not be our lot to wield
The sickle in the ripened field;
Nor ours to hear, on summer eves,
The reaper's song among the sheaves.

2 Yet where our duty's task is wrought
In unison with God's great thought,
The near and future blend in one,
And whatsoe'er is willed, is done.

3 And ours the grateful service whence
Comes, day by day, the recompense;

The hope, the trust, the purpose stayed,
The fountain, and the noonday shade.

4 And were this life the utmost span,
The only end and aim of man,
Better the toil of fields like these
Than waking dream and slothful ease.

5 But life, though falling like our grain,
Like that revives and springs again;
And, early called, how blest are they
Who wait in heaven, their harvest day!
            JOHN G. WHITTIER.

603   *Zeal in labor.*

1 Go, labor on; spend and be spent,
  Thy joy to do the Father's will;
It is the way the Master went;
  Should not the servant tread it still?

2 Go, labor on; 'tis not for naught;
  Thine earthly loss is heavenly gain;
Men heed thee, love thee, praise thee not:
  The Master praises,—what are men?

3 Go, labor on; your hands are weak;
  Your knees are faint, your soul cast
    down;
Yet falter not; the prize you seek
  Is near,—a kingdom and a crown!

4 Toil on, faint not; keep watch, and pray
  Be wise the erring soul to win;
Go forth into the world's highway;
  Compel the wanderer to come in.

5 Toil on, and in thy toil rejoice;
  For toil comes rest, for exile home;
Soon shalt thou hear the Bridegroom's
    voice,
  The midnight peal, "Behold, I come!"
            HORATIUS BONAR.

FEDERAL STREET. L. M.   HENRY KEMBLE OLIVER.

604. *Not ashamed of Jesus.*

1 JESUS, and shall it ever be,
A mortal man ashamed of thee?
Ashamed of thee, whom angels praise,
Whose glories shine through endless days?

2 Ashamed of Jesus! sooner far
Let evening blush to own a star;
He sheds the beams of light divine
O'er this benighted soul of mine.

3 Ashamed of Jesus just as soon
Let midnight be ashamed of noon;
'Tis midnight with my soul till he,
Bright Morning Star, bid darkness flee.

4 Ashamed of Jesus! that dear Friend
On whom my hopes of heaven depend!
No; when I blush, be this my shame,
That I no more revere his name.

5 Ashamed of Jesus! yes, I may,
When I've no guilt to wash away;
No tear to wipe, no good to crave,
No fears to quell, no soul to save.

6 Till then—nor is my boasting vain—
Till then I boast a Saviour slain;
And O, may this my glory be,
That Christ is not ashamed of me!
                          JOSEPH GRIGG, ALT. BY B. FRANCIS.

605. *Living to Christ.*

1 My gracious Lord, I own thy right
To every service I can pay,
And call it my supreme delight
To hear thy dictates, and obey.

2 What is my being but for thee,
Its sure support, its noblest end?

'Tis my delight thy face to see,
And serve the cause of such a Friend.

3 I would not sigh for worldly joy,
Or to increase my worldly good;
Nor future days nor power employ
To spread a sounding name abroad.

4 'Tis to my Saviour I would live,
To him who for my ransom died;
Nor could all worldly honor give
Such bliss as crowns me at his side.

5 His work my hoary age shall bless,
When youthful vigor is no more;
And my last hour of life confess
His dying love, his saving power.
                              PHILIP DODDRIDGE.

606. *Beginning the labors of the day.*

1 FORTH in thy name, O Lord, I go,
My daily labors to pursue;
Thee, only thee, resolved to know,
In all I think, or speak, or do.

2 Thee will I set at my right hand,
Whose eyes mine inmost substance see,
And labor on at thy command,
And offer all my works to thee.

3 Give me to bear thy easy yoke,
And every moment watch and pray;
And still to things eternal look,
And hasten to thy glorious day.

4 For thee delightfully employ
Whate'er thy bounteous grace hath
        given;
And run my course with even joy,
And closely walk with thee to heaven.
                              CHARLES WESLEY.

[8, 7. Tune, Autumn. Page 94.]

607 *The Master calling.*

1 HARK, the voice of Jesus calling,
  "Who will go and work to-day?
Fields are white, and harvests waiting,
  Who will bear the sheaves away?"
Loud and long the Master calleth,
  Rich reward he offers free;
Who will answer, gladly saying,
  "Here am I, send me, send me?"

2 Let none hear you idly saying,
  "There is nothing I can do,"
While the souls of men are dying,
  And the Master calls for you:
Take the task he gives you gladly;
  Let his work your pleasure be;
Answer quickly when he calleth,
  "Here am I, send me, send me."
                                    DANIEL MARCH.

ST. CATHERINE   L. M. 6l.   ADAPTED BY J. G. WALTON.

608 *Faith of our fathers.*

1 FAITH of our fathers! living still
  In spite of dungeon, fire, and sword:
O how our hearts beat high with joy
  Whene'er we hear that glorious word:
Faith of our fathers! holy faith!
We will be true to thee till death!

2 Our fathers, chained in prisons dark,
  Were still in heart and conscience free:
How sweet would be their children's fate,
  If they, like them, could die for thee!
Faith of our fathers! holy faith!
We will be true to thee till death!

3 Faith of our fathers! we will love
  Both friend and foe in all our strife:
And preach thee, too, as love knows how,
  By kindly words and virtuous life:
Faith of our fathers! holy faith!
We will be true to thee till death!
                              FREDERICK W. FABER.

[7, 6, 8. Tune, Penitence. Page 204.]

609 *Thy service is perfect freedom.*

1 LO! I come with joy to do
  The Master's blessed will;

Him in outward works pursue,
  And serve his pleasure still.
Faithful to my Lord's commands,
  I still would choose the better part,
Serve with careful Martha's hands,
  And loving Mary's heart.

2 Careful, without care I am,
  Nor feel my happy toil,
Kept in peace by Jesus' name,
  Supported by his smile:
Joyful thus my faith to show,
  I find his service my reward:
Every work I do below,
  I do it to the Lord.

3 O that all the art might know
  Of living thus to thee,
Find their heaven begun below,
  And here thy glory see!
Walk in all the works prepared
  By thee, to exercise their grace
Till they gain their full reward,
  And see thy glorious face!
                              CHARLES WESLEY.

NAOMI.   C. M.   Hans George Naegeli, arr. by Lowell Mason.

610 *A calm and thankful heart.*

1 Father, whate'er of earthly bliss
   Thy sovereign will denies,
Accepted at thy throne of grace,
   Let this petition rise :

2 Give me a calm, a thankful heart,
   From every murmur free ;
The blessings of thy grace impart,
   And make me live to thee.

3 Let the sweet hope that thou art mine
   My life and death attend ;
Thy presence through my journey shine,
   And crown my journey's end.
                        ANNE STEELE.

611 *The only solace in sorrow.*

1 O Thou who driest the mourner's tear,
   How dark this world would be,
If, when deceived and wounded here,
   We could not fly to thee !

2 The friends who in our sunshine live,
   When winter comes, are flown ;
And he who has but tears to give,
   Must weep those tears alone.

3 But thou wilt heal that broken heart,
   Which, like the plants that throw
Their fragrance from the wounded part,
   Breathes sweetness out of woe.

4 O who could bear life's stormy doom,
   Did not thy wing of love
Come brightly wafting through the
       gloom,
   Our peace-branch from above?

5 Then sorrow, touched by thee, grows
       bright
   With more than rapture's ray ;
As darkness shows us worlds of light
   We never saw by day.
                        THOMAS MOORE.

612 *Consolation in sickness.*

1 When languor and disease invade
   This trembling house of clay,
'Tis sweet to look beyond my pains,
   And long to fly away ;

2 Sweet to look inward, and attend
   The whispers of His love ;
Sweet to look upward, to the place
   Where Jesus pleads above ;

3 Sweet to look back, and see my name
   In life's fair book set down ;
Sweet to look forward, and behold
   Eternal joys my own ;

4 Sweet to reflect how grace divine
   My sins on Jesus laid ;
Sweet to remember that his blood
   My debt of suffering paid ;

5 Sweet to rejoice in lively hope,
   That, when my change shall come,
Angels shall hover round my bed,
   And waft my spirit home.

6 If such the sweetness of the stream,
   What must the fountain be,
Where saints and angels draw their bliss
   Directly, Lord, from thee !
                        AUGUSTUS M. TOPLADY.

ST. AUGUSTINE.   C. M.   * REV. JOHN BLACK.

613   *Friend of souls.*

1 O FRIEND of souls! how blest the time
  When in thy love I rest,
When from my weariness I climb
  E'en to thy tender breast!

2 The night of sorrow endeth there,
  Thy rays outshine the sun,
And in thy pardon and thy care
  The heaven of heavens is won.

3 The world may call itself my foe,
  Or flatter and allure;
I care not for the world; I go
  To this tried Friend and sure.

4 And when life's fiercest storms are sent
  Upon life's wildest sea,
My little bark is confident,
  Because it holdeth thee.

5 To others, death seems dark and grim,
  But not, O Lord, to me:
I know thou ne'er forsakest him
  Who puts his trust in thee.

6 Nay, rather, with a joyful heart
  I welcome the release
From this dark desert, and depart
  To thy eternal peace.
          WOLFGANG C. DESSLER.

614   *Unfaltering trust.*

1 FATHER of love, our Guide and Friend,
  O lead us gently on,
Until life's trial-time shall end,
  And heavenly peace be won.

2 We know not what the path may be
  As yet by us untrod;

But we can trust our all to thee,
  Our Father and our God.

3 If called, like Abraham's child, to climb
  The hill of sacrifice,
Some angel may be there in time;
  Deliverance shall arise:

4 Or, if some darker lot be good,
  O teach us to endure
The sorrow, pain, or solitude,
  That makes the spirit pure.

5 Christ by no flowery pathway came;
  And we, his followers here,
Must do thy will and praise thy name,
  In hope, and love, and fear.

6 And, till in heaven we sinless bow,
  And faultless anthems raise,
O Father, Son, and Spirit, now
  Accept our feeble praise.
          WILLIAM J. IRONS.

615   *Crosses and blessings.*

1 SINCE all the varying scenes of time
  God's watchful eye surveys,
O who so wise to choose our lot,
  Or to appoint our ways?

2 Good, when he gives—supremely good,
  Nor less when he denies;
E'en crosses, from his sovereign hand,
  Are blessings in disguise.

3 Why should we doubt a Father's love,
  So constant and so kind?
To his unerring, gracious will
  Be every wish resigned.
          JAMES HERVEY.

CADDO.   C. M.   WILLIAM BATCHELDER BRADBURY.

616   *Habitual devotion.*

1 WHILE thee I seek, protecting Power,
    Be my vain wishes stilled;
And may this consecrated hour
    With better hopes be filled.

2 Thy love the power of thought bestowed;
    To thee my thoughts would soar:
Thy mercy o'er my life has flowed;
    That mercy I adore.

3 In each event of life, how clear
    Thy ruling hand I see!
Each blessing to my soul more dear,
    Because conferred by thee.

4 In every joy that crowns my days,
    In every pain I bear,
My heart shall find delight in praise,
    Or seek relief in prayer.

5 When gladness wings my favored hour,
    Thy love my thoughts shall fill;
Resigned, when storms of sorrow lower,
    My soul shall meet thy will.

6 My lifted eye, without a tear,
    The gathering storm shall see;
My steadfast heart shall know no fear;
    That heart will rest on thee.
                        HELEN M. WILLIAMS.

617   *Acquiescence in the Divine will.*

1 AUTHOR of good, we rest on thee:
    Thine ever watchful eye
Alone our real wants can see,
    Thy hand alone supply.

2 In thine all-gracious providence
    Our cheerful hopes confide;
O let thy power be our defense,
    Thy love our footsteps guide.

3 And since, by passion's force subdued,
    Too oft, with stubborn will,
We blindly shun the latent good,
    And grasp the specious ill,—

4 Not what we wish, but what we want,
    Let mercy still supply:
The good we ask not, Father, grant;
    The ill we ask, deny.
                        JAMES MERRICK.

618   *Overwhelming grief.*

1 O THOU, who in the olive shade,
    When the dark hour came on,
Didst, with a breath of heavenly aid,
    Strengthen thy suffering Son,—

2 O by the anguish of that night,
    Send us down blest relief;
Or, to the chastened, let thy might
    Hallow this whelming grief.

3 And thou, that, when the starry sky
    Saw the dread strife begun,
Didst teach adoring faith to cry,
    "Father, thy will be done,"—

4 By thy meek Spirit, thou, of all
    That e'er have mourned the chief,
Blest Saviour, if the stroke must fall,
    Hallow this whelming grief.
                        MRS. FELICIA D. HEMANS.

GOULD.　C. M.　　　　　　　　　　　　　JOHN EDGAR GOULD.

619　　*Remember me!*

1 O THOU from whom all goodness flows,
　I lift my soul to thee;
In all my sorrows, conflicts, woes,
　Dear Lord, remember me.

2 If, for thy sake, upon my name
　Reproach and shame shall be,
I'll hail reproach, and welcome shame,
　If thou remember me.

3 When worn with pain, disease, and grief,
　This feeble body see;
Grant patience, rest, and kind relief;
　Hear, and remember me.

4 When, in the solemn hour of death,
　I wait thy just decree,
Saviour, with my last parting breath,
　I'll cry, "Remember me."

5 And when before thy throne I stand,
　And lift my soul to thee,
Then, with the saints at thy right hand,
　O Lord, remember me.
　　　　　　　　　　　　　THOMAS HAWEIS.

620　　*Light at evening*

1 WE journey through a vale of tears,
　By many a cloud o'ercast;
And worldly cares and worldly fears,
　Go with us to the last.

2 Not to the last! Thy word hath said
　Could we but read aright,
"Poor pilgrim, lift in hope thy head,
　At eve it shall be light!"

3 Though earthborn shadows now may
　　　　shroud
　Thy thorny path awhile,
God's blessed word can part each cloud,
　And bid the sunshine smile.

4 Only believe, in living faith,
　His love and power divine;
And ere thy sun shall set in death,
　His light shall round thee shine.

5 When tempest clouds are dark on high
　His bow of love and peace
Shines sweetly in the vaulted sky,
　A pledge that storms shall cease.

6 Hold on thy way, with hope unchilled
　By faith and not by sight,
And thou shalt own his word fulfilled,
　"At eve it shall be light."
　　　　　　　　　　　　　BERNARD BARTON.

621　　*Grateful acknowledgment.*

1 I LOVE the Lord: he heard my cries,
　And pitied every groan;
Long as I live, when troubles rise,
　I'll hasten to his throne.

2 I love the Lord: he bowed his ear,
　And chased my grief away;
O let my heart no more despair,
　While I have breath to pray.

3 The Lord beheld me sore distressed;
　He bade my pains remove;
Return, my soul, to God, thy rest,
　For thou hast known his love.
　　　　　　　　　　　　　ISAAC WATTS.

HE LEADETH ME. L. M.

WILLIAM BATCHELDER BRADBURY.

622 *He leadeth me.*

1 HE leadeth me! O blessed thought!
O words with heavenly comfort fraught!
Whate'er I do, where'er I be,
Still 'tis God's hand that leadeth me.
  He leadeth me, he leadeth me,
  By his own hand he leadeth me:
  His faithful follower I would be,
  For by his hand he leadeth me.

2 Sometimes 'mid scenes of deepest gloom,
Sometimes where Eden's bowers bloom,
By waters still, o'er troubled sea,—
Still 'tis his hand that leadeth me!

3 Lord, I would clasp thy hand in mine,
Nor ever murmur nor repine,
Content, whatever lot I see,
Since 'tis my God that leadeth me!

4 And when my task on earth is done,
When, by thy grace, the victory's won,
E'en death's cold wave I will not flee,
Since God through Jordan leadeth me.
                                J. H. GILMORE.

623 *Patient thankfulness and trust.*

1 ETERNAL Beam of light divine,
Fountain of unexhausted love,

In whom the Father's glories shine,
  Through earth beneath, and heaven
    above;

2 Jesus, the weary wanderer's rest,
Give me thy easy yoke to bear;
With steadfast patience arm my breast,
  With spotless love and lowly fear.

3 Thankful I take the cup from thee,
Prepared and mingled by thy skill;
Though bitter to the taste it be,
  Powerful the wounded soul to heal.

4 Be thou, O Rock of ages, nigh!
So shall each murmuring thought be
    gone,
And grief, and fear, and care shall fly,
  As clouds before the midday sun.

5 Speak to my warring passions, "Peace;"
Say to my trembling heart, "Be still;"
Thy power my strength and fortress is,
  For all things serve thy sovereign will.

6 O Death! where is thy sting? Where
    now
Thy boasted victory, O Grave?
Who shall contend with God? or who
  Can hurt whom God delights to save?
                                CHARLES WESLEY.

FILLMORE. L. M. D. * JEREMIAH INGALLS.

624 *For sustaining grace.*

1 MY hope, my all, my Saviour thou,
To thee, lo, now my soul I bow!
I feel the bliss thy wounds impart,
I find thee, Saviour, in my heart.

2 Be thou my strength, be thou my way:
Protect me through my life's short day:
In all my acts may wisdom guide,
And keep me, Saviour, near thy side.

3 In fierce temptation's darkest hour,
Save me from sin and Satan's power;
Tear every idol from thy throne,
And reign, my Saviour, reign alone.

4 My suffering time shall soon be o'er;
Then shall I sigh and weep no more:
My ransomed soul shall soar away,
To sing thy praise in endless day.
THOMAS COKE.

625 *Friend of the friendless.*

1 GOD of my life, to thee I call;
Afflicted, at thy feet I fall;
When the great water-floods prevail
Leave not my trembling heart to fail.

2 Friend of the friendless and the faint,
Where should I lodge my deep complaint?
Where, but with thee, whose open door
Invites the helpless and the poor?

3 Did ever mourner plead with thee,
And thou refuse that mourner's plea?
Does not the promise still remain,
That none shall seek thy face in vain?

4 Poor I may be, despised, forgot,
Yet God, my God, forgets me not;
And he is safe, and must succeed,
For whom the Saviour deigns to plead.
WILLIAM COWPER.

626 *In hope, believing against hope.*

1 AWAY, my unbelieving fear!
Fear shall in me no more have place,
My Saviour doth not yet appear,
He hides the brightness of his face;
But shall I therefore let him go,
And basely to the tempter yield?
No, in the strength of Jesus, no,
I never will give up my shield.

2 Although the vine its fruit deny,
Although the olive yield no oil,
The withering fig-trees droop and die,
The fields elude the tiller's toil,
The empty stall no herd afford,
And perish all the bleating race,
Yet will I triumph in the Lord,—
The God of my salvation praise.
CHARLES WESLEY.

DWIGHT. L. M.

ARR. BY JOSEPH P. HOLBROOK

627 *Blessing for mourners.*

1 DEEM not that they are blest alone
 Whose days a peaceful tenor keep;
The anointed Son of God makes known
 A blessing for the eyes that weep.

2 The light of smiles shall fill again
 The lids that overflow with tears;
And weary hours of woe and pain
 Are promises of happier years.

3 There is a day of sunny rest
 For every dark and troubled night;
And grief may bide an evening guest,
 But joy shall come with early light.

4 Nor let the good man's trust depart,
 Though life its common gifts deny,
Though with a pierced and broken heart,
 And spurned of men, he goes to die.

5 For God has marked each sorrowing day,
 And numbered every secret tear;
And heaven's long age of bliss shall pay
 For all his children suffer here.
 WILLIAM C. BRYANT.

628 *Resignation.*

1 THY will be done! I will not fear
 The fate provided by thy love;
Though clouds and darkness shroud me here,
 I know that all is bright above.

2 The stars of heaven are shining on,
 Though these frail eyes are dimmed with
  tears;
The hopes of earth indeed are gone,
 But are not ours the immortal years?

3 Father, forgive the heart that clings,
 Thus trembling, to the things of time;
And bid my soul, on angel wings,
 Ascend into a purer clime.

4 There shall no doubts disturb its trust,
 No sorrows dim celestial love;
But these afflictions of the dust,
 Like shadows of the night, remove.

5 E'en now, above, there's radiant day,
 While clouds and darkness brood below;
Then, Father, joyful on my way
 To drink the bitter cup I go.
 J. ROSCOE.

629 *Sympathetic love.*

1 O LOVE divine, that stooped to share
 Our sharpest pang, our bitterest tear!
On thee we cast each earthborn care;
 We smile at pain while thou art near.

2 Though long the weary way we tread,
 And sorrow crown each lingering year,
No path we shun, no darkness dread,
 Our hearts still whispering, "Thou art
  near!"

3 When drooping pleasure turns to grief,
 And trembling faith is changed to fear,
The murmuring wind, the quivering leaf,
 Shall softly tell us, "Thou art near!"

4 On thee we fling our burdening woe,
 O Love divine, forever dear,
Content to suffer while we know,
 Living and dying, thou art near!
 OLIVER W. HOLMES.

ZEPHYR.   L. M.

WILLIAM BATCHELDER BRADBURY.

630 *It is I; be not afraid.*—Matt. 14 : 27.

1 WHEN Power divine, in mortal form,
Hushed with a word the raging storm,
In soothing accents Jesus said,
"Lo! it is I; be not afraid."

2 So when in silence nature sleeps,
And lonely watch the mourner keeps,
One thought shall every pang remove,—
Trust, feeble man, thy Maker's love.

3 God calms the tumult and the storm;
He rules the seraph and the worm:
No creature is by him forgot
Of those who know, or know him not.

4 And when the last dread hour is come,
And shuddering nature waits her doom,
This voice shall wake the pious dead,
"Lo! it is I; be not afraid."

SIR J. E. SMITH.

631   *Meekness and patience.*

1 THOU Lamb of God, thou Prince of peace,
: For thee my thirsty soul doth pine;
My longing heart implores thy grace;
O make me in thy likeness shine.

2 When pain o'er my weak flesh prevails,
With lamb-like patience arm my breast;
When grief my wounded soul assails,
In lowly meekness may I rest.

3 Close by thy side still may I keep,
Howe'er life's various currents flow;
With steadfast eye mark every step,
And follow thee where'er thou go.

4 Thou, Lord, the dreadful fight hast won;
Alone thou hast the wine-press trod;
In me thy strengthening grace be shown:
O may I conquer through thy blood.

5 So, when on Zion thou shalt stand,
And all heaven's host adore their King,
Shall I be found at thy right hand,
And, free from pain, thy glories sing.

C. F. RICHTER. TR. BY J. WESLEY.

632   *Comfort in the promises.*

1 O GOD, to thee we raise our eyes;
Calm resignation we implore;
O let no murmuring thought arise,
But humbly let us still adore.

2 With meek submission may we bear
Each needful cross thou shalt ordain;
Nor think our trials too severe,
Nor dare thy justice to arraign.

3 For though mysterious now thy ways
To erring mortals may appear,
Hereafter we thy name shall praise,
For all our keenest sufferings here.

4 Thy needful help, O God, afford,
Nor let us sink in deep despair;
Aid us to trust thy sacred word,
And find our sweetest comfort there.

CHARLOTTE RICHARDSON.

Doxology.

PRAISE God, from whom all blessings flow,
Praise him, all creatures here below;
Praise him above, ye heavenly host;
Praise Father, Son, and Holy Ghost.

THOMAS KEN.

OLMUTZ.   S. M.

GREGORIAN CHANT, ARR. BY LOWELL MASON.

633   *Believers encouraged.*

1 YOUR harps, ye trembling saints,
  Down from the willows take;
Loud to the praise of love divine
  Bid every string awake.

2 Though in a foreign land,
  We are not far from home;
And nearer to our house above
  We every moment come.

3 His grace will to the end
  Stronger and brighter shine;
Nor present things, nor things to come
  Shall quench the spark divine.

4 When we in darkness walk,
  Nor feel the heavenly flame,
Then is the time to trust our God,
  And rest upon his name.

5 Soon shall our doubts and fears
  Subside at his control;
His loving-kindness shall break through
  The midnight of the soul.

6 Blest is the man, O God,
  That stays himself on thee;
Who wait for thy salvation, Lord,
  Shall thy salvation see.
          AUGUSTUS M. TOPLADY, ALT. BY B. W. NOEL.

634   *With Christ.*

1 JESUS, one word from thee
  Fills my sad soul with peace:
My griefs are like a tossing sea;
  They hear thy voice and cease.

2 Soon as thy pitying face
  Shone through my stormy fears,

The storm swept by, nor left a trace,
  Save the sweet dew of tears.

3 And when thou call'st me, Lord,
  Where thickest dangers be,
Even the waves a path afford;
  I walk the waves with thee.

4 With thee within my bark
  I'll dare death's threatening tide,
Nor count the passage strange or dark
  With Jesus by my side.

5 Dear Lord, thy faithful grace
  I know and I adore:
What shall it be to see thy face
  In heaven, for evermore!
                    HERVEY D. GANSE.

635   *In the Saviour's care.*

1 MY spirit, on thy care,
  Blest Saviour, I recline;
Thou wilt not leave me to despair,
  For thou art Love divine.

2 In thee I place my trust,
  On thee I calmly rest;
I know thee good, I know thee just,
  And count thy choice the best.

3 Whate'er events betide,
  Thy will they all perform;
Safe in thy breast my head I hide,
  Nor fear the coming storm.

4 Let good or ill befall,
  It must be good for me;
Secure of having thee in all,
  Of having all in thee.
                      HENRY F. LYTE.

SELVIN.   S. M.   GERMAN, ARR. BY LOWELL MASON.

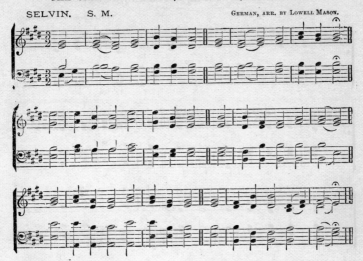

636   *Walking by faith.*

1 IF, on a quiet sea,
  Toward heaven we calmly sail,
With grateful hearts, O God, to thee,
  We'll own the favoring gale.

2 But should the surges rise,
  And rest delay to come,
Blest be the tempest, kind the storm,
  Which drives us nearer home.

3 Soon shall our doubts and fears
  All yield to thy control;
Thy tender mercies shall illume
  The midnight of the soul.

4 Teach us, in every state,
  To make thy will our own;
And when the joys of sense depart,
  To live by faith alone.
                    AUGUSTUS M. TOPLADY.

637   *My times are in Thy hand.*—Ps. 31 : 15.

1 "My times are in thy hand:"
  My God, I wish them there;
My life, my friends, my soul, I leave
  Entirely to thy care.

2 "My times are in thy hand,"
  Whatever they may be;
Pleasing or painful, dark or bright,
  As best may seem to thee.

3 "My times are in thy hand:"
  Why should I doubt or fear?
My Father's hand will never cause
  His child a needless tear.

4 "My times are in thy hand,"
  Jesus, the crucified!
The hand my cruel sins had pierced
  Is now my guard and guide.

5 "My times are in thy hand;"
  I'll always trust in thee;
And, after death, at thy right hand
  I shall forever be.
                    WILLIAM F. LLOYD.

638   *Through death to life.*

1 O WHAT, if we are Christ's,
  Is earthly shame or loss?
Bright shall the crown of glory be,
  When we have borne the cross.

2 Keen was the trial once,
  Bitter the cup of woe,
When martyred saints, baptized in blood,
  Christ's sufferings shared below.

3 Bright is their glory now,
  Boundless their joy above,
Where, on the bosom of their God,
  They rest in perfect love.

4 Lord, may that grace be ours,
  Like them in faith to bear
All that of sorrow, grief, or pain,
  May be our portion here.

5 Enough, if thou at last
  The word of blessing give,
And let us rest before thy throne,
  Where saints and angels live.
                    SIR HENRY W. BAKER.

AURELIA. 7, 6.

SAMUEL SEBASTIAN WESLEY.

639 *No cause for fear.*

1 GOD is my strong salvation;
  What foe have I to fear?
In darkness and temptation,
  My light, my help, is near:
Though hosts encamp around me,
  Firm in the fight I stand;
What terror can confound me,
  With God at my right hand?

2 Place on the Lord reliance;
  My soul, with courage wait;
His truth be thine affiance,
  When faint and desolate:
His might thy heart shall strengthen,
  His love thy joy increase;
Mercy thy days shall lengthen;
  The Lord will give thee peace.
JAMES MONTGOMERY.

640 *The pilgrims of Jesus.*

1 O HAPPY band of pilgrims,
  If onward ye will tread,
With Jesus as your Fellow,
  To Jesus as your Head!
O happy, if ye labor
  As Jesus did for men;

O happy, if ye hunger
  As Jesus hungered then!

2 The cross that Jesus carried
  He carried as your due:
The crown that Jesus weareth
  He weareth it for you.
The faith by which ye see him,
  The hope in which ye yearn,
The love that through all trouble
  To him alone will turn,—

3 What are they but forerunners
  To lead you to his sight?
What are they save the effluence
  Of uncreated Light?
The trials that beset you,
  The sorrows ye endure,
The manifold temptations
  That death alone can cure,—

4 What are they but his jewels
  Of right celestial worth?
What are they but the ladder,
  Set up to heaven on earth?
O happy band of pilgrims,
  Look upward to the skies,
Where such a light affliction
  Shall win so great a prize.
JOSEPH OF THE STUDIUM. TR. BY J. M. NEALE.

ENDSLEIGH.   7, 6.

S. SALVATORI.

641   *Peace and joy.*

1 SOMETIMES a light surprises
  The Christian while he sings;
It is the Lord who rises
  With healing on his wings;
When comforts are declining,
  He grants the soul again
A season of clear shining,
  To cheer it after rain.

2 In holy contemplation,
  We sweetly then pursue
The theme of God's salvation,
  And find it ever new:
Set free from present sorrow,
  We cheerfully can say,
Let the unknown to-morrow
  Bring with it what it may.

3 It can bring with it nothing
  But he will bear us through;
Who gives the lilies clothing,
  Will clothe his people too:
Beneath the spreading heavens
  No creature but is fed;
And he who feeds the ravens
  Will give his children bread.

4 Though vine nor fig-tree neither
  Their wonted fruit should bear,
Though all the fields should wither,
  Nor flocks nor herds be there;
Yet God the same abiding,
  His praise shall tune my voice;
For while in him confiding,
  I cannot but rejoice.

WILLIAM COWPER.

642   *I will fear no change.*

1 IN heavenly love abiding,
  No change my heart shall fear;
And safe is such confiding,
  For nothing changes here.
The storm may roar without me,
  My heart may low be laid,
But God is round about me,
  And can I be dismayed?

2 Wherever he may guide me,
  No want shall turn me back;
My Shepherd is beside me,
  And nothing can I lack.
His wisdom ever waketh,
  His sight is never dim,
He knows the way he taketh,
  And I will walk with him.

3 Green pastures are before me,
  Which yet I have not seen;
Bright skies will soon be o'er me,
  Where darkest clouds have been.
My hope I cannot measure,
  My path to life is free,
My Saviour has my treasure,
  And he will walk with me.

ANNA L. WARING.

ELLESDIE. 8, 7. D. ARR. FROM JOHANN C. W. A. MOZART.

643 *The cross accepted.*

1 JESUS, I my cross have taken,
　All to leave, and follow thee;
Naked, poor, despised, forsaken,
　Thou, from hence, my all shalt be:
Perish every fond ambition,
　All I 've sought, and hoped, and known;
Yet how rich is my condition,
　God and heaven are still my own!

2 Let the world despise and leave me,
　They have left my Saviour, too;
Human hearts and looks deceive me;
　Thou art not, like man, untrue;
And, while thou shalt smile upon me,
　God of wisdom, love, and might,
Foes may hate, and friends may shun me;
　Show thy face, and all is bright.

3 Go, then, earthly fame and treasure!
　Come, disaster, scorn, and pain!
In thy service, pain is pleasure;
　With thy favor, loss is gain.
I have called thee, "Abba, Father;"
　I have stayed my heart on thee:
Storms may howl, and clouds may gather,
　All must work for good to me.

4 Man may trouble and distress me,
　'Twill but drive me to thy breast;
Life with trials hard may press me,
　Heaven will bring me sweeter rest.
O 'tis not in grief to harm me,
　While thy love is left to me;
O 'twere not in joy to charm me,
　Were that joy unmixed with thee.

5 Know, my soul, thy full salvation
　Rise o'er sin, and fear, and care;
Joy to find in every station
　Something still to do or bear.
Think what Spirit dwells within thee;
　What a Father's smile is thine;
What a Saviour died to win thee:
　Child of heaven, shouldst thou repine

6 Haste thee on from grace to glory,
　Armed by faith, and winged by prayer;
Heaven's eternal day 's before thee,
　God's own hand shall guide thee there.
Soon shall close thy earthly mission,
　Swift shall pass thy pilgrim days,
Hope shall change to glad fruition,
　Faith to sight, and prayer to praise.
　　　　　　　　　HENRY F. LYTE.

[8, 7. Tune, Autumn. Page 94.]

644 *Only waiting.*

1 ONLY waiting, till the shadows
 Are a little longer grown;
Only waiting, till the glimmer
 Of the day's last beam is flown;
Till the light of earth is faded
 From the hearts once full of day;
Till the stars of heaven are breaking
 Through the twilight soft and gray.

2 Only waiting, till the reapers
 Have the last sheaf gathered home;
For the summer-time is faded,
 And the autumn winds have come.
Quickly, reapers, gather quickly
 These last ripe hours of my heart,
For the bloom of life is withered,
 And I hasten to depart.

3 Only waiting, till the shadows
 Are a little longer grown;
Only waiting, till the glimmer
 Of the day's last beam is flown.
Then, from out the gathered darkness
 Holy, deathless stars shall rise,
By whose light my soul shall gladly
 Tread its pathway to the skies.

FRANCES L. MACE.

[8, 7. Tune, Stockwell. Page 42.]

645 *In deep affliction.*

1 FULL of trembling expectation,
 Feeling much, and fearing more,
Mighty God of my salvation,
 I thy timely aid implore.

2 Suffering Son of man, be near me,
 In my sufferings to sustain;
By thy sorer griefs to cheer me,
 By thy more than mortal pain.

3 By thy most severe temptation
 In that dark Satanic hour,
By thy last mysterious passion,
 Screen me from the adverse power.

4 By thy fainting in the garden,
 By thy dreadful death, I pray,
Write upon my heart the pardon;
 Take my sins and fears away.

CHARLES WESLEY.

[8, 7, 4. Tune, Greenville. Page 126.]

646 *Gently lead us.*

1 GENTLY, Lord, O gently lead us
 Through this gloomy vale of tears;
And, O Lord, in mercy give us
 Thy rich grace in all our fears.
 O refresh us,
Traveling through this wilderness.

2 When temptation's darts assail us,
 When in devious paths we stray,
Let thy goodness never fail us,
 Lead us in thy perfect way.

3 In the hour of pain and anguish,
 In the hour when death draws near,
Suffer not our hearts to languish,
 Suffer not our souls to fear.

4 When this mortal life is ended,
 Bid us in thine arms to rest,
Till, by angel-bands attended,
 We awake among the blest.

THOMAS HASTINGS.

[8, 7. Tune, Ellerdie. Page 236.]

647 *Worldly pleasures renounced.*

1 VAIN are all terrestrial pleasures,
 Mixed with dross the purest gold;
Seek we, then, for heavenly treasures
 Treasures never waxing old.
Let our best affections center
 On the things around the throne:
There no thief can ever enter;
 Moth and rust are there unknown

2 Earthly joys no longer please us;
 Here would we renounce them all
Seek our only rest in Jesus,
 Him our Lord and Master call.
Faith, our languid spirits cheering,
 Points to brighter worlds above,
Bids us look for his appearing;
 Bids us triumph in his love.

3 May our light be always burning,
 And our loins be girded round,
Waiting for our Lord's returning,
 Longing for the welcome sound.
Thus the Christian life adorning,
 Never need we be afraid,
Should he come at night or morning,
 Early dawn, or evening shade.

DAVID E. FORD.

ADMAH. L. M. 6l.   LOWELL MASON.

648 *The pilgrim's Guide.*

1 LEADER of faithful souls, and Guide
  Of all that travel to the sky,
Come and with us, e'en us, abide,
  Who would on thee alone rely;
On thee alone our spirits stay,
While held in life's uneven way.

2 Strangers and pilgrims here below,
  This earth, we know, is not our place;
But hasten through the vale of woe,
  And, restless to behold thy face,
Swift to our heavenly country move,
Our everlasting home above.

3 We've no abiding city here,
  But seek a city out of sight;
Thither our steady course we steer,
  Aspiring to the plains of light,
Jerusalem, the saints' abode,
Whose founder is the living God.

4 Patient the appointed race to run,
  This weary world we cast behind:
From strength to strength we travel on,
  The New Jerusalem to find:
Our labor this, our only aim,
To find the New Jerusalem.

5 Through thee, who all our sins hast borne,
  Freely and graciously forgiven,

With songs to Zion we return,
  Contending for our native heaven;
That palace of our glorious King,—
We find it nearer while we sing.

6 Raised by the breath of love divine,
  We urge our way with strength renewed
The church of the first-born to join,
  We travel to the mount of God;
With joy upon our heads arise,
And meet our Saviour in the skies.
                                CHARLES WESLEY.

649   *Steadfast reliance.*

1 THOUGH waves and storms go o'er my
      head,
  Though strength, and health, and friends
      be gone;
Though joys be withered all, and dead,
  Though every comfort be withdrawn;
On this my steadfast soul relies,—
Father, thy mercy never dies.

2 Fixed on this ground will I remain,
  Though my heart fail, and flesh decay:
This anchor shall my soul sustain,
  When earth's foundations melt away:
Mercy's full power I then shall prove,
Loved with an everlasting love.
        JOHANN A. ROTHE. TR. BY J. WESLEY.

EATON. L. M. 6l.

ZERUBBABEL WYVILL.

650 *The ever-present Saviour.*

1 JESUS, to thee our hearts we lift,—
  Our hearts with love to thee o'erflow,—
With thanks for thy continued gift,
  That still thy gracious name we know,
Retain our sense of sin forgiven,
And wait for all our inward heaven.

2 What mighty troubles hast thou shown
  Thy feeble, tempted followers here!
We have through fire and water gone,
  But saw thee on the floods appear,
And felt thee present in the flame,
And shouted our Deliverer's name.

3 Thou who hast kept us to this hour,
  O keep us faithful to the end,
When, robed in majesty and power,
  Our Jesus shall from heaven descend,
His friends and witnesses to own,
And seat us on his glorious throne!
               CHARLES WESLEY.

651 *I will fear no evil.*—Ps. 23 : 4.

1 PEACE, doubting heart! my God's I am;
  Who formed me man forbids my fear;

The Lord hath called me by my name;
  The Lord protects, forever near:
His blood for me did once atone,
And still he loves and guards his own.

2 When, passing through the watery deep,
  I ask in faith his promised aid,
The waves an awful distance keep,
  And shrink from my devoted head:
Fearless, their violence I dare;
They cannot harm, for God is there!

3 To him mine eye of faith I turn,
  And through the fire pursue my way;
The fire forgets its power to burn,
  The lambent flames around me play:
I own his power, accept the sign,
And shout to prove the Saviour mine.

4 Still nigh me, O my Saviour, stand,
  And guard in fierce temptation's hour
Hide in the hollow of thy hand;
  Show forth in me thy saving power;
Still be thy arms my sure defense,
Nor earth, nor hell, shall pluck me thence.
               CHARLES WESLEY.

HENLEY.   11, 10.   LOWELL MASON.

652   *Rest for the weary.*

1 COME unto me, when shadows darkly gather,
  When the sad heart is weary and distressed,
Seeking for comfort from your heavenly Father,
  Come unto me, and I will give you rest.

2 Large are the mansions in thy Father's dwelling,
  Glad are the homes that sorrows never dim;
Sweet are the harps in holy music swelling,
  Soft are the tones which raise the heavenly hymn.

3 There, like an Eden blossoming in gladness,
  Bloom the fair flowers the earth too rudely pressed;
Come unto me, all ye who droop in sadness,
  Come unto me, and I will give you rest.

UNKNOWN.

PRECIOUS NAME.   8, 7.   WILLIAM HOWARD DOANE.

CHORUS.

653   *The precious name.*

1 TAKE the name of Jesus with you,
  Child of sorrow and of woe;
It will joy and comfort give you;
  Take it, then, where'er you go.
‖: Precious name, O how sweet!
  Hope of earth and joy of heaven. :‖

2 Take the name of Jesus ever,
  As a shield from every snare;

If temptations round you gather,
  Breathe that holy name in prayer.

3 O the precious name of Jesus!
  How it thrills our souls with joy,
When his loving arms receive us,
  And his songs our tongues employ!

4 At the name of Jesus bowing,
  Falling prostrate at his feet,
King of kings in heaven we'll crown him,
  When our journey is complete.

MRS. LYDIA BAXTER.

JEWETT. 6.   ARR. FROM CARL MARIA VON WEBER, BY JOSEPH P. HOLBROOK.

654 *Jesus, as thou wilt.*

1 MY Jesus, as thou wilt:
    O may thy will be mine;
Into thy hand of love
    I would my all resign.
Through sorrow or through joy,
    Conduct me as thine own,
And help me still to say,
    "My Lord, thy will be done."

2 My Jesus, as thou wilt:
    Though seen through many a tear,
Let not my star of hope
    Grow dim or disappear.
Since thou on earth hast wept
    And sorrowed oft alone,
If I must weep with thee,
    My Lord, thy will be done.

3 My Jesus, as thou wilt:
    All shall be well for me;
Each changing future scene
    I gladly trust with thee.
Straight to my home above,
    I travel calmly on,
And sing in life or death,
    "My Lord, thy will be done."
                        BENJAMIN SCHMOLKE.
                   TR. BY MISS J. BORTHWICK.

655 *Christian trial, suffering, and submission.*

1 THY way, not mine, O Lord,
    However dark it be!
Lead me by thine own hand;
    Choose out the path for me.
I dare not choose my lot;
    I would not if I might;
Choose thou for me, my God,
    So shall I walk aright.

2 The kingdom that I seek
    Is thine; so let the way
That leads to it be thine,
    Else I must surely stray.
Take thou my cup, and it
    With joy or sorrow fill,
As best to thee may seem;
    Choose thou my good and ill.

3 Choose thou for me my friends,
    My sickness or my health;
Choose thou my cares for me,
    My poverty or wealth.
Not mine, not mine the choice,
    In things or great or small;
Be thou my guide, my strength,
    My wisdom, and my all.
                        HORATIUS BONAR.

REFUGE. 7. D.

JOSEPH P. HOLBROOK.

656 *The only refuge.*

1 JESUS, Lover of my soul,
  Let me to thy bosom fly,
While the nearer waters roll,
  While the tempest still is high!
Hide me, O my Saviour, hide,
  Till the storm of life is past;
Safe into the haven guide,
  O receive my soul at last!

2 Other refuge have I none;
  Hangs my helpless soul on thee:
Leave, O leave me not alone,
  Still support and comfort me:
All my trust on thee is stayed,
  All my help from thee I bring;
Cover my defenseless head
  With the shadow of thy wing!

3 Thou, O Christ, art all I want;
  More than all in thee I find;
Raise the fallen, cheer the faint,
  Heal the sick, and lead the blind.
Just and holy is thy name,
  I am all unrighteousness:
False and full of sin I am,
  Thou art full of truth and grace.

4 Plenteous grace with thee is found,
  Grace to cover all my sin:
Let the healing streams abound;
  Make and keep me pure within.
Thou of life the fountain art,
  Freely let me take of thee:
Spring thou up within my heart,
  Rise to all eternity.

CHARLES WESLEY.

MARTYN. 7. D.

SIMEON BUTLER MARSH.

GANGES.   C. P. M.

S. CHANDLER.

657 *Bliss-inspiring hope.*

1 COME on, my partners in distress,
My comrades through the wilderness,
   Who still your bodies feel;
Awhile forget your griefs and fears,
And look beyond this vale of tears,
   To that celestial hill.

2 Beyond the bounds of time and space,
Look forward to that heavenly place,
   The saints' secure abode;
On faith's strong eagle pinions rise,
And force your passage to the skies,
   And scale the mount of God.

3 Who suffer with our Master here,
We shall before his face appear
   And by his side sit down;
To patient faith the prize is sure,
And all that to the end endure
   The cross, shall wear the crown.

4 Thrice blessed, bliss-inspiring hope!
It lifts the fainting spirits up,
   It brings to life the dead:
Our conflicts here shall soon be past,
And you and I ascend at last,
   Triumphant with our Head.

5 That great mysterious Deity
We soon with open face shall see;
   The beatific sight
Shall fill the heavenly courts with praise,
And wide diffuse the golden blaze
   Of everlasting light.

CHARLES WESLEY.

658 *The aged pilgrim.*

1 THY mercy heard my infant prayer;
Thy love, with all a mother's care,
   Sustained my childish days:
Thy goodness watched my ripening youth,
And formed my heart to love thy truth,
   And filled my lips with praise.

2 And now, in age and grief, thy name
Doth still my languid heart inflame,
   And bow my faltering knee:
O yet this bosom feels the fire;
This trembling hand and drooping lyre
   Have yet a strain for thee!

3 Yes; broken, tuneless, still, O Lord,
This voice, transported, shall record
   Thy goodness, tried so long;
Till, sinking slow, with calm decay,
Its feeble murmurs melt away
   Into a seraph's song.

SIR ROBERT GRANT.

CLINTON.   C. M.   JOSEPH P. HOLBROOK.

659 *Heavenly rest anticipated.*

1 WHEN I can read my title clear
  To mansions in the skies,
I bid farewell to every fear,
  And wipe my weeping eyes.

2 Should earth against my soul engage,
  And fiery darts be hurled,
Then I can smile at Satan's rage,
  And face a frowning world.

3 Let cares like a wild deluge come,
  Let storms of sorrow fall,
So I but safely reach my home,
  My God, my heaven, my all.

4 There I shall bathe my weary soul
  In seas of heavenly rest,
And not a wave of trouble roll
  Across my peaceful breast.
                            ISAAC WATTS.

660 *God's pavilion.*

1 GRANT me within thy courts a place,
  Among thy saints a seat,
Forever to behold thy face,
  And worship at thy feet;—

2 In thy pavilion to abide,
  When storms of trouble blow,
And in thy tabernacle hide,
  Secure from every foe.

3 "Seek ye my face!" Without delay,
  When thus I hear thee speak,
My heart would leap for joy, and say,
  "Thy face, Lord, will I seek."

4 Then leave me not when griefs assail,
  And earthly comforts flee;
When father, mother, kindred fail,
  My God, remember me!
                      JAMES MONTGOMERY.

661 *Fullness of joy in His presence.*

1 THY gracious presence, O my God,
  All that I wish contains;
With this, beneath affliction's load,
  My heart no more complains.

2 This can my every care control,
  Gild each dark scene with light:
This is the sunshine of the soul;
  Without it all is night.

3 O happy scenes above the sky,
  Where thy full beams impart
Unclouded beauty to the eye,
  And rapture to the heart!

4 Her portion in those realms of bliss,
  My spirit longs to know;
My wishes terminate in this,
  Nor can they rest below.

5 Lord, shall the breathings of my heart
  Aspire in vain to thee?
Confirm my hope, that where thou art
  I shall forever be.

6 Then shall my cheerful spirit sing
  The darksome hours away,
And rise, on faith's expanded wing,
  To everlasting day.
                            ANNE STEELE.

Doxology.

To Father, Son, and Holy Ghost,
  The God whom we adore,
Be glory, as it was, is now,
  And shall be evermore.
                        TATE AND BRADY.

HEBER.   C. M.   GEORGE KINGSLEY.

662 *Vanity of earthly enjoyments.*

1 How vain are all things here below!
  How false, and yet how fair!
Each pleasure hath its poison too,
  And every sweet a snare.

2 The brightest things below the sky
  Give but a flattering light;
We should suspect some danger nigh,
  Where we possess delight.

3 Our dearest joys, and nearest friends,
  The partners of our blood,—
How they divide our wavering minds,
  And leave but half for God!

4 The fondness of a creature's love,—
  How strong it strikes the sense!
Thither the warm affections move,
  Nor can we call them thence.

5 My Saviour, let thy beauties be
  My soul's eternal food;
And grace command my heart away
  From all created good.

ISAAC WATTS.

663   *Radiant hope.*

1 O who, in such a world as this,
  Could bear his lot of pain,
Did not one radiant hope of bliss
  Unclouded yet remain?

2 That hope the sovereign Lord has given
  Who reigns above the skies;
Hope that unites the soul to heaven
  By faith's endearing ties.

3 Each care, each ill of mortal birth,
  Is sent in pitying love,
To lift the lingering heart from earth,
  And speed its flight above.

4 And every pang that wrings the breast,
  And every joy that dies,
Bid us to seek a purer rest,
  And trust to holier ties.

JAMES MONTGOMERY.

664   *Deliverance at hand.*

1 My span of life will soon be done,
  The passing moments say;

As lengthening shadows o'er the mead
  Proclaim the close of day.

2 O that my heart might dwell aloof
  From all created things,
And learn that wisdom from above,
  Whence true contentment springs!

3 Courage, my soul! thy bitter cross,
  In every trial here,
Shall bear thee to thy heaven above,
  But shall not enter there.

4 The sighing ones, that humbly seek
  In sorrowing paths below,
Shall in eternity rejoice,
  Where endless comforts flow.

5 Soon will the toilsome strife be o'er
  Of sublunary care,
And life's dull vanities no more
  This anxious breast ensnare.

6 Courage, my soul! on God rely;
  Deliverance soon will come;
A thousand ways has Providence
  To bring believers home.

FRANCES M. COWPER.

665   *De profundis.*

1 Out of the depths to thee I cry,
  Whose fainting footsteps trod
The paths of our humanity,
  Incarnate Son of God!

2 Thou Man of grief, who once apart
  Didst all our sorrows bear,—
The trembling hand, the fainting heart,
  The agony, and prayer!

3 Is this the consecrated dower,
  Thy chosen ones obtain,
To know thy resurrection power
  Through fellowship of pain?

4 Then, O my soul, in silence wait;
  Faint not, O faltering feet;
Press onward to that blest estate,
  In righteousness complete.

5 Let faith transcend the passing hour,
  The transient pain and strife,
Upraised by an immortal power,—
  The power of endless life.

MRS. E. E. MARCY.

MAITLAND.　　C. M.　　　　　　　　　　　　GEORGE N. ALLEN.

666　　*No cross, no crown.*

1 MUST Jesus bear the cross alone,
　　And all the world go free?
No, there's a cross for every one,
　　And there's a cross for me.

2 How happy are the saints above,
　　Who once went sorrowing here!
But now they taste unmingled love,
　　And joy without a tear.

3 The consecrated cross I'll bear,
　　Till death shall set me free;
And then go home my crown to wear,
　　For there's a crown for me.
　　　　　　　　　THOMAS SHEPHERD, ALT.

667　　　*For victorious faith.*

1 O FOR a faith that will not shrink,
　　Though pressed by every foe,
That will not tremble on the brink
　　Of any earthly woe!

2 That will not murmur nor complain
　　Beneath the chastening rod,
But, in the hour of grief or pain,
　　Will lean upon its God;

3 A faith that shines more bright and clear
　　When tempests rage without;
That when in danger knows no fear,
　　In darkness feels no doubt;

4 That bears, unmoved, the world's dread
　　　frown,
　　Nor heeds its scornful smile;
That seas of trouble cannot drown,
　　Nor Satan's arts beguile;

5 A faith that keeps the narrow way
　　Till life's last hour is fled,
And with a pure and heavenly ray
　　Illumes a dying bed.

6 Lord, give us such a faith as this,
　　And then, whate'er may come,
We'll taste, e'en here, the hallowed bliss
　　Of an eternal home.
　　　　　　　　　WILLIAM H. BATHURST.

668　　*Strength renewed in waiting upon*
　　　　　　the Lord.

1 LORD, I believe thy every word,
　　Thy every promise true;
And lo! I wait on thee, my Lord,
　　Till I my strength renew.

2 If in this feeble flesh I may
　　Awhile show forth thy praise,
Jesus, support the tottering clay,
　　And lengthen out my days.

3 If such a worm as I can spread
　　The common Saviour's name,
Let him who raised thee from the dead
　　Quicken my mortal frame.

4 Still let me live thy blood to show,
　　Which purges every stain;
And gladly linger out below
　　A few more years in pain.
　　　　　　　　　CHARLES WESLEY.

Doxology.

To Father, Son, and Holy Ghost,
　　The God whom we adore,
Be glory, as it was, is now,
　　And shall be evermore.
　　　　　　　　　TATE AND BRADY.

COOLING. C. M.

ALONZO J. ABBEY. FROM THE TRIAD.

669 *To live is Christ, and to die is gain.*—Phil. 1. 21.

1 LORD, it belongs not to my care
Whether I die or live;
To love and serve thee is my share,
And this thy grace must give.

2 If life be long, I will be glad
That I may long obey;
If short, yet why should I be sad
To soar to endless day?

3 Christ leads me through no darker rooms
Than he went through before;
He that unto God's kingdom comes
Must enter by his door.

4 Come, Lord, when grace hath made me meet
Thy blessed face to see;
For, if thy work on earth be sweet,
What will thy glory be?

5 Then I shall end my sad complaints,
And weary, sinful days,
And join with the triumphant saints
Who sing Jehovah's praise.

6 My knowledge of that life is small;
The eye of faith is dim;
But 'tis enough that Christ knows all,
And I shall be with him.

RICHARD BAXTER.

670 *Christ strengthening the weak.*

1 O THOU, whose filmed and failing eye,
Ere yet it closed in death,
Beheld thy mother's agony,
The shameful cross beneath!

2 Remember them, like her, through whom
The sword of grief is driven,

And O, to cheer their cheerless gloom,
Be thy dear mercy given.

3 Let thine own word of tenderness
Drop on them from above;
Its music shall the lone heart bless,
Its touch shall heal with love.

4 O Son of Mary, Son of God,
The way of mortal ill,
By thy blest feet in triumph trod,
Our feet are treading still.

5 But not with strength like thine, we go
This dark and dreadful way;
As thou wert strengthened in thy woe,
So strengthen us, we pray.

ALEXANDER R. THOMPSON.

671 *Blessed are they that mourn.*
Matt. 5 : 4.

1 FROM lips divine, like healing balm
To hearts oppressed and torn,
The heavenly consolation fell,
"Blessed are they that mourn."

2 Unto the hopes by sorrow crushed
A noble faith succeeds;
And life, by trials furrowed, bears
The fruit of loving deeds.

3 How rich, how sweet, how **full of
strength**
Our human spirits are,
Baptized into the sanctities
Of suffering and of prayer!

4 Yes, heavenly wisdom, love divine,
Breathed through the lips which said
"O blessed are the hearts that mourn;
They shall be comforted."

WILLIAM H. BURLEIGH.

SCHUMANN.   S. M.   ROBERT SCHUMANN.

1 COMMIT thou all thy griefs
  And ways into His hands,
To his sure trust and tender care
  Who earth and heaven commands.

2 Who points the clouds their course,
  Whom winds and seas obey,
He shall direct thy wandering feet,
  He shall prepare thy way.

3 Thou on the Lord rely,
  So, safe, shalt thou go on;
Fix on his work thy steadfast eye,
  So shall thy work be done.

4 No profit canst thou gain
  By self-consuming care;
To him commend thy cause; his ear
  Attends the softest prayer.

5 Thy everlasting truth,
  Father, thy ceaseless love,
Sees all thy children's wants, and knows
  What best for each will prove.

6 Thou every-where hast sway,
  And all things serve thy might;
Thy every act pure blessing is,
  Thy path unsullied light.
    PAUL GERHARDT. TR. BY J. WESLEY.

1 GIVE to the winds thy fears;
  Hope, and be undismayed;
God hears thy sighs and counts thy tears;
  God shall lift up thy head.

2 Through waves, and clouds, and storms,
  He gently clears thy way;

Wait thou his time, so shall this night
  Soon end in joyous day.

3 Still heavy is thy heart?
  Still sink thy spirits down?
Cast off the weight, let fear depart,
  And every care be gone.

4 What though thou rulest not?
  Yet heaven, and earth, and hell
Proclaim, "God sitteth on the throne,
  And ruleth all things well."

5 Leave to his sovereign sway
  To choose and to command:
So shalt thou, wondering, own his way,
  How wise, how strong his hand!

6 Far, far above thy thought
  His counsel shall appear,
When fully he the work hath wrought
  That caused thy needless fear.
    PAUL GERHARDT. TR. BY J. WESLEY.

1 THOU Refuge of my soul,
  On thee, when sorrows rise,
On thee, when waves of trouble roll,
  My fainting hope relies.

2 To thee I tell my grief,
  For thou alone canst heal;
Thy word can bring a sweet relief
  For every pain I feel.

3 But O when doubts prevail,
  I fear to call thee mine;
The springs of comfort seem to fail,
  And all my hopes decline.

4 Yet, Lord, where shall I flee?
  Thou art my only trust;
And still my soul would cleave to thee,
  Though prostrate in the dust.
    ANNE STEELE. ALT.

WARING.　8, 6.

FROM LOUIS SPOHR.

675 *Contented piety.*

1 FATHER, I know that all my life
　Is portioned out for me;
And the changes that are sure to come
　I do not fear to see;
But I ask thee for a present mind
　Intent on pleasing thee.

2 I ask thee for a thoughtful love,
　Through constant watching wise,
To meet the glad with joyful smiles,
　And wipe the weeping eyes;
And a heart at leisure from itself,
　To soothe and sympathize.

3 I would not have the restless will
　That hurries to and fro,
Seeking for some great thing to do,
　Or secret thing to know;
I would be treated as a child,
　And guided where I go.

4 Wherever in the world I am,
　In whatsoe'er estate,
I have a fellowship with hearts,
　To keep and cultivate;
And a work of lowly love to do
　For the Lord on whom I wait.

5 So I ask thee for the daily strength,
　To none that ask denied,
And a mind to blend with outward life,
　While keeping at thy side;
Content to fill a little space,
　If thou be glorified.

6 And if some things I do not ask
　In my cup of blessing be,
I would have my spirit filled the more
　With grateful love to thee;
More careful, not to serve thee much,
　But to please thee perfectly.
ANNA L. WARING.

676 *Go not far from me, O my Strength.*

1 GO not far from me, O my Strength,
　Whom all my times obey;
Take from me any thing thou wilt,
　But go not thou away;
And let the storm that does thy work
　Deal with me as it may.

2 No suffering, while it lasts, is joy,
　How blest soe'er it be;
Yet may the chastened child be glad
　His Father's face to see;
And O, it is not hard to bear
　What must be borne in thee.

3 Safe in thy sanctifying grace,
　Almighty to restore;
Borne onward, sin and death behind,
　And love and life before,
O let my soul abound in hope,
　And praise thee more and more!

4 Deep unto deep may call, but I
　With peaceful heart will say,
"Thy loving-kindness hath a charge
　No waves can take away;"
And let the storm that speeds me home,
　Deal with me as it may.
ANNA L. WARING.

JESHURUN. 7, 6, 7. HENRY JOHN GAUNTLETT.

677 *Fearless in the furnace of affliction.*

1 GOD of Israel's faithful three,
  Who braved a tyrant's ire,
Nobly scorned to bow the knee,
  And walked, unhurt, in fire;
Breathe their faith into my breast,
  Arm me in this fiery hour;
Stand, O Son of man, confessed
  In all thy saving power!

2 For while thou, my Lord, art nigh,
  My soul disdains to fear;
Sin and Satan I defy,
  Still impotently near;
Earth and hell their wars may wage;
  Calm I mark their vain design,
Smile to see them idly rage
  Against a child of thine.

  CHARLES WESLEY.

678 *The shadow of a great Rock.*

1 To the haven of thy breast,
  O Son of man, I fly;
Be my refuge and my rest,
  For O the storm is high!
Save me from the furious blast;
  A covert from the tempest be;
Hide me, Jesus, till o'erpast
  The storm of sin I see.

2 Welcome as the water-spring
  To a dry, barren place,
O descend on me, and bring
  Thy sweet, refreshing grace;
O'er a parched and weary land,
  As a great rock extends its shade,
Hide me, Saviour, with thy hand,
  And screen my naked head.

3 In the time of my distress
  Thou hast my succor been;
In my utter helplessness,
  Restraining me from sin;
O how swiftly didst thou move
  To save me in the trying hour!
Still protect me with thy love,
  And shield me with thy power.

  CHARLES WESLEY.

Doxology.

FATHER, Son, and Holy Ghost,
  Thy Godhead we adore,
Join we with the heavenly host,
  To praise thee evermore!
Live, by earth and heaven adored,
  The Three in One, the One in Three
Holy, holy, holy Lord,
  All glory be to thee!

  CHARLES WESLEY.

PORTUGUESE HYMN.   11.

UNKNOWN.

679   *The firm foundation.*

1 How firm a foundation, ye saints of the Lord,
Is laid for your faith in his excellent word!
What more can he say, than to you he hath said,
To you, who for refuge to Jesus have fled?

2 "Fear not, I am with thee, O be not dismayed,
For I am thy God, I will still give thee aid;
I'll strengthen thee, help thee, and cause thee to stand,
Upheld by my gracious, omnipotent hand.

3 "When through the deep waters I call thee to go,
The rivers of sorrow shall not overflow;
For I will be with thee thy trials to bless,
And sanctify to thee thy deepest distress.

4 "When through fiery trials thy pathway shall lie,
My grace, all-sufficient, shall be thy supply,
The flame shall not hurt thee; I only design
Thy dross to consume, and thy gold to refine.

5 "E'en down to old age all my people shall prove
My sovereign, eternal, unchangeable love;
And when hoary hairs shall their temples adorn,
Like lambs they shall still in my bosom be borne.

6 "The soul that on Jesus hath leaned for repose,
I will not, I will not desert to his foes;
That soul, though all hell should endeavor to shake,
I'll never, no never, no never forsake!"
GEORGE KEITH.

GRASMERE. 7, 8, 7. Edwin Moss.

680 *Fearless in tribulation.*

1 HEAD of the Church triumphant,
  We joyfully adore thee;
Till thou appear, thy members here
  Shall sing like those in glory:
We lift our hearts and voices
  With blest anticipation;
And cry aloud, and give to God
  The praise of our salvation.

2 Thou dost conduct thy people
  Through torrents of temptation:
Nor will we fear, while thou art near,
  The fire of tribulation:
The world, with sin and Satan,
  In vain our march opposes;
By thee we shall break through them all,
  And sing the song of Moses.

3 By faith we see the glory
  To which thou shalt restore us:
The cross despise for that high prize
  Which thou hast set before us:
And if thou count us worthy,
  We each, as dying Stephen,
Shall see thee stand at God's right hand,
  To take us up to heaven.
                              CHARLES WESLEY.

[8. Tune, Vernon. Page 375.]

681 *Passionate longing for heaven.*

1 STILL out of the deepest abyss
  Of trouble, I mournfully cry;
And pine to recover my peace,
  And see my Redeemer, and die.
I cannot, I cannot forbear,
  These passionate longings for home
O when shall my spirit be there?
  O when will the messenger come?

2 Thy nature I long to put on,
  Thine image on earth to regain:
And then in the grave to lay down
  This burden of body and pain.
O Jesus, in pity draw near,
  And lull me to sleep on thy breast,
Appear, to my rescue appear,
  And gather me into thy rest!

3 To take a poor fugitive in,
  The arms of thy mercy display,
And give me to rest from all sin,
  And bear me triumphant away;
Away from a world of distress,
  Away to the mansions above;
The heaven of seeing thy face,
  The heaven of feeling thy love.
                              CHARLES WESLEY.

LUX BENIGNA.　10, 4, 10.　　　Rev. John Bacchus Dykes.

682　*Lead, kindly Light.*

1 LEAD, kindly Light, amid the encircling
　　gloom,
　　Lead thou me on!
The night is dark, and I am far from home;
　　Lead thou me on!
Keep thou my feet; I do not ask to see
The distant scene; one step enough for me.

2 I was not ever thus, nor prayed that thou
　　Shouldst lead me on;
I loved to choose and see my path; but now
　　Lead thou me on!

I loved the garish day, and, spite of fears,
Pride ruled my will. Remember not past
　　years!

3 So long thy power hath blest me, sure it
　　still
　　Will lead me on
O'er moor and fen, o'er crag and torrent, till
　　The night is gone,
And with the morn those angel faces smile
Which I have loved long since, and lost
　　awhile!

　　　　　　　　　　　JOHN H. NEWMAN.

COME, YE DISCONSOLATE.　11, 10.　　　Samuel Webbe.

683　*Come, ye disconsolate.*

1 COME, ye disconsolate, where'er ye lan-
　　guish;
　　Come to the mercy-seat, fervently kneel;
Here bring your wounded hearts, here tell
　　your anguish;
　　Earth has no sorrow that Heaven cannot
　　heal.

2 Joy of the desolate, light of the straying,
　　Hope of the penitent, fadeless and pure,

Here speaks the Comforter, tenderly saying,
　　"Earth has no sorrow that Heaven can-
　　not cure."

3 Here see the bread of life; see waters
　　flowing
　　Forth from the throne of God, pure from
　　above;
Come to the feast of love; come, ever
　　knowing
　　Earth has no sorrow but Heaven can re-
　　move.

　　　　　　　　　　　THOMAS MOORE.

RETREAT. L. M.   Thomas Hastings.

684   *The mercy-seat.*

1 FROM every stormy wind that blows,
From every swelling tide of woes,
There is a calm, a sure retreat:
'Tis found beneath the mercy-seat.

2 There is a place where Jesus sheds
The oil of gladness on our heads;
A place than all besides more sweet:
It is the blood-bought mercy-seat.

3 There is a scene where spirits blend,
Where friend holds fellowship with friend;
Though sundered far, by faith they meet
Around one common mercy-seat.

4 Ah! whither could we flee for aid,
When tempted, desolate, dismayed;
Or how the hosts of hell defeat,
Had suffering saints no mercy-seat?

5 There, there on eagle wings we soar,
And sin and sense molest no more;
And heaven comes down our souls to
    greet,
While glory crowns the mercy-seat.
                                   HUGH STOWELL.

685   *Dedication to the Lord.*

1 O LORD, thy heavenly grace impart,
And fix my frail, inconstant heart;
Henceforth my chief desire shall be
To dedicate myself to thee.

2 Whate'er pursuits my time employ,
One thought shall fill my soul with joy:
That silent, secret thought shall be,
That all my hopes are fixed on thee.

3 Thy glorious eye pervadeth space;
Thy presence, Lord, fills every place;
And wheresoe'er my lot may be,
Still shall my spirit cleave to thee.

4 Renouncing every worldly thing,
And safe beneath thy spreading wing,
My sweetest thought henceforth shall be.
That all I want I find in thee.
          JEAN F. OBERLIN.   TR. BY MRS. D. WILSON.

686   *The Spirit's guidance.*

1 JESUS, my Saviour, Brother, Friend,
  On whom I cast my every care,
On whom for all things I depend,
  Inspire, and then accept, my prayer.

2 If I have tasted of thy grace,
  The grace that sure salvation brings;
If with me now thy Spirit stays,
  And, hovering, hides me in his wings:

3 Still let him with my weakness stay,
  Nor for a moment's space depart;
Evil and danger turn away,
  And keep till he renews my heart.

4 If to the right or left I stray,
  His voice behind me may I hear,
"Return, and walk in Christ, thy Way;
  Fly back to Christ, for sin is near!"
                                 CHARLES WESLEY.

687   *The pure Light of souls.*

1 O THOU pure Light of souls that love,
  True Joy of every human breast,
Sower of life's immortal seed,
  Our Saviour and Redeemer blest!

2 Be thou our guide, be thou our goal;
  Be thou our pathway to the skies;
Our joy, when sorrow fills the soul;
  In death our everlasting prize.
                                     BREVIARY.

SWEET HOUR OF PRAYER. L. M. ⬧ WILLIAM BATCHELDER.

688 *Sweet hour of prayer.*

1 SWEET hour of prayer, sweet hour of
    prayer,
That calls me from a world of care,
And bids me, at my Father's throne,
Make all my wants and wishes known
In seasons of distress and grief,
My soul has often found relief,
And oft escaped the tempter's snare,
By thy return, sweet hour of prayer.

2 Sweet hour of prayer, sweet hour of
    prayer,
Thy wings shall my petition bear
To Him, whose truth and faithfulness
Engage the waiting soul to bless:
And since he bids me seek his face,
Believe his word, and trust his grace,
I 'll cast on him my every care,
And wait for thee, sweet hour of prayer.

3 Sweet hour of prayer, sweet hour of
    prayer,
May I thy consolation share,
Till, from Mount Pisgah's lofty height,
I view my home, and take my flight:
This robe of flesh I'll drop, and rise,
To seize the everlasting prize;
And shout, while passing through the air,
Farewell, farewell, sweet hour of prayer!
                    WILLIAM W. WALFORD.

689 *Design of prayer.*

1 PRAYER is appointed to convey
    The blessings God designs to give:
Long as they live should Christians pray;
    They learn to pray when first they live.

2 If pain afflict, or wrongs oppress;
    If cares distract, or fears dismay;
If guilt deject, if sin distress;
    In every case, still watch and pray.

3 'Tis prayer supports the soul that 's weak,
    Though thought be broken, language
        lame;
Pray, if thou canst or canst not speak;
    But pray with faith in Jesus' name.

4 Depend on him ; thou canst not fail;
    Make all thy wants and wishes known ;
Fear not ; his merits must prevail:
    Ask but in faith, it shall be done.
                    JOSEPH HART.

690 *Blessings of prayer.*

1 WHAT various hindrances we meet
In coming to a mercy-seat !
Yet who that knows the worth of prayer.
But wishes to be often there ?

2 Prayer makes the darkened cloud with
    draw ;
Prayer climbs the ladder Jacob saw ;
Gives exercise to faith and love ;
Brings every blessing from above.

3 Restraining prayer, we cease to fight :
Prayer keeps the Christian's armor brigh : ,
And Satan trembles when he sees
The weakest saint upon his knees.

4 Were half the breath that 's vainly spent.
To heaven in supplication sent,
Our cheerful song would oftener be,
" Hear what the Lord has done for me."
                    WILLIAM COWPER.

WELTON. L. M. FROM REV. HENRI ABRAHAM CÆSAR MALAN.

691 *The joy of loving hearts.*

1 JESUS, thou Joy of loving hearts!
Thou Fount of life! thou Light of men!
From the best bliss that earth imparts,
We turn unfilled to thee again.

2 Thy truth unchanged hath ever stood;
Thou savest those that on thee call;
To them that seek thee, thou art good,
To them that find thee, all in all.

3 We taste thee, O thou Living Bread,
And long to feast upon thee still;
We drink of thee, the Fountain Head,
And thirst our souls from thee to fill!

4 Our restless spirits yearn for thee,
Where'er our changeful lot is cast;
Glad, when thy gracious smile we see,
Blest, when our faith can hold thee fast.

5 O Jesus, ever with us stay;
Make all our moments calm and bright;
Chase the dark night of sin away,
Shed o'er the world thy holy light!
BERNARD OF CLAIRVAUX. TR. BY R. PALMER.

692 *God's praises crown eternity.*

1 GOD of my life, through all my days
My grateful powers shall sound thy praise;
The song shall wake with opening light,
And warble to the silent night.

2 When anxious cares would break my rest,
And griefs would tear my throbbing breast,
Thy tuneful praises, raised on high,
Shall check the murmur and the sigh.

3 When death o'er nature shall prevail,
And all my powers of language fail,

Joy through my swimming eyes shall break,
And mean the thanks I cannot speak.

4 But O, when that last conflict's o'er,
And I am chained to earth no more,
With what glad accents shall I rise
To join the music of the skies!

5 Soon shall I learn the exalted strains
Which echo o'er the heavenly plains;
And emulate, with joy unknown,
The glowing seraphs round thy throne.

6 The cheerful tribute will I give,
Long as a deathless soul can live:
A work so sweet, a theme so high,
Demands and crowns eternity!
PHILIP DODDRIDGE.

693 *His loving kindness better than life.*

1 O GOD, thou art my God alone;
Early to thee my soul shall cry;
A pilgrim in a land unknown,
A thirsty land, whose springs are dry.

2 Thee, in the watches of the night,
When I remember on my bed,
Thy presence makes the darkness light;
Thy guardian wings are round my head

3 Better than life itself, thy love;
Dearer than all beside to me;
For whom have I in heaven above,
Or what on earth, compared with thee?

4 Praise with my heart, my mind, my voice,
For all thy mercy I will give;
My soul shall still in God rejoice,
My tongue shall bless thee while I live.
JAMES MONTGOMERY.

ROLLAND. L. M.

WILLIAM BATCHELDER BRADBURY.

694 *I shall be satisfied, when I awake, with Thy likeness.*

1 LORD Jesus Christ, my Life, my Light,
My strength by day, my trust by night,
On earth I'm but a passing guest,
And sorely by my sins oppressed.

2 O let thy sufferings give me power
To meet the last and darkest hour,
Thy cross, the staff whereon I lean,
My couch, the grave where thou hast been.

3 Since thou hast died, the pure, the just,
I take my homeward way in trust;
The gates of heaven, Lord, open wide,
When here I may no more abide.

4 And when the last great day is come,
And thou, our Judge, shalt speak the doom,
Let me with joy behold the light,
And set me then upon thy right.

5 Renew this wasted flesh of mine,
That like the sun it there may shine
Among the angels pure and bright,
Yea, like thyself, in glorious light.

6 Ah, then I have my heart's desire,
When, singing with the angels' choir,
Among the ransomed of thy grace,
Forever I behold thy face.

M. BEHEMB. TR. BY MISS C. WINKWORTH.

695 *The fairest of the fair.*

1 THOUGH all the world my choice deride,
Yet Jesus shall my portion be;
For I am pleased with none beside;
The fairest of the fair is he.

2 Sweet is the vision of thy face,
And kindness o'er thy lips is shed;
Lovely art thou, and full of grace,
And glory beams around thy head.

3 Thy sufferings I embrace with thee,
Thy poverty and shameful cross;
The pleasures of the world I flee,
And deem its treasures only dross.

4 Be daily dearer to my heart,
And ever let me feel thee near;
Then willingly with all I'd part,
Nor count it worthy of a tear.

GERHARD TERSTEEGEN.

696 *At home with God anywhere.*

1 MY Lord, how full of sweet content,
I pass my years of banishment!
Where'er I dwell, I dwell with thee,
In heaven, in earth, or on the sea.
To me remains nor place nor time;
My country is in every clime:
I can be calm and free from care
On any shore, since God is there.

2 While place we seek, or place we shun,
The soul finds happiness in none;
But with a God to guide our way,
'Tis equal joy, to go or stay.
Could I be cast where thou art not,
That were indeed a dreadful lot;
But regions none remote I call,
Secure of finding God in all.

MAD. J. M. B. DE LA MOTTE GUYON.
TR. BY WM. COWPER.

EMMONS.   C. M.

ARR. FROM FRIEDRICH BURGMÜLLER.

697   *Thou dear Redeemer.*

1 THOU dear Redeemer, dying Lamb,
   I love to hear of thee;
No music's like thy charming name,
   Nor half so sweet can be.

2 O let me ever hear thy voice
   In mercy to me speak;
In thee, my Priest, will I rejoice,
   And thy salvation seek.

3 My Jesus shall be still my theme,
   While in this world I stay;
I'll sing my Jesus' lovely name
   When all things else decay.

4 When I appear in yonder cloud,
   With all thy favored throng,
Then will I sing more sweet, more loud,
   And Christ shall be my song.
                        JOHN CENNICK.

698   *God, my sufficient Portion.*

1 MY God, my Portion, and my Love,
   My everlasting All,
I've none but thee in heaven above,
   Or on this earthly ball.

2 What empty things are all the skies,
   And this inferior clod!
There's nothing here deserves my joys,
   There's nothing like my God.

3 To thee I owe my wealth, and friends,
   And health, and safe abode;
Thanks to thy name for meaner things;
   But they are not my God.

4 How vain a toy is glittering wealth,
   If once compared to thee!

Or what's my safety, or my health,
   Or all my friends to me?

5 Were I possessor of the earth,
   And called the stars my own,
Without thy graces and thyself,
   I were a wretch undone.

6 Let others stretch their arms like seas,
   And grasp in all the shore;
Grant me the visits of thy grace,
   And I desire no more.
                        ISAAC WATTS.

699   *Praise delightful.*

1 MY Saviour, my almighty Friend,
   When I begin thy praise,
Where will the growing numbers end,
   The numbers of thy grace?

2 I trust in thy eternal word;
   Thy goodness I adore:
Send down thy grace, O blessed Lord,
   That I may love thee more.

3 My feet shall travel all the length
   Of the celestial road;
And march, with courage in thy strength,
   To see the Lord my God.

4 Awake! awake! my tuneful powers,
   With this delightful song;
And entertain the darkest hours,
   Nor think the season long.
                        ISAAC WATTS, M.F

Doxology.

To Father, Son, and Holy Ghost,
   The God whom we adore,
Be glory, as it was, is now,
   And shall be evermore!
                        TATE AND BRADY.

HOLY CROSS.　　C. M.　　　　　　　　　　UNKNOWN.

FIRST PART.

700 *The sweetest name.*

1 JESUS, the very thought of thee
　With sweetness fills the breast;
But sweeter far thy face to see,
　And in thy presence rest.

2 No voice can sing, no heart can frame,
　Nor can the memory find
A sweeter sound than Jesus' name,
　The Saviour of mankind.

3 O Hope of every contrite heart,
　O Joy of all the meek,
To those who ask, how kind thou art!
　How good to those who seek!

4 But what to those who find? Ah, this
　Nor tongue nor pen can show:
The love of Jesus, what it is,
　None but his loved ones know.

5 Jesus, our only joy be thou,
　As thou our prize wilt be;
In thee be all our glory now,
　And through eternity.
　　BERNARD OF CLAIRVAUX.　TR. BY E. CASWALL.

SECOND PART.

701 *The conqueror renowned.*

1 O JESUS, King most wonderful,
　Thou Conqueror renowned,
Thou sweetness most ineffable,
　In whom all joys are found!

2 When once thou visitest the heart,
　Then truth begins to shine,
Then earthly vanities depart,
　Then kindles love divine.

3 O Jesus, Light of all below,
　Thou Fount of living fire,
Surpassing all the joys we know,
　And all we can desire!

4 Jesus, may all confess thy name,
　Thy wondrous love adore,
And, seeking thee, themselves inflame
　To seek thee more and more.

5 Thee, Jesus, may our voices bless;
　Thee may we love alone;
And ever in our lives express
　The image of thine own.
　　BERNARD OF CLAIRVAUX.　TR. BY E. CASWALL.

THIRD PART.

702 *The King in his beauty.*

1 O JESUS, thou the beauty art
　Of angel-worlds above;
Thy name is music to the heart,
　Inflaming it with love.

2 O Jesus, Saviour, hear the sighs
　Which unto thee we send;
To thee our inmost spirit cries,
　To thee our prayers ascend.

3 Abide with us, and let thy light
　Shine, Lord, on every heart;
Dispel the darkness of our night,
　And joy to all impart.

4 Jesus, our love and joy! to thee,
　The Virgin's holy Son,
All might, and praise, and glory be,
　While endless ages run!
　　BERNARD OF CLAIRVAUX.　TR. BY E. CASWALL.

ROSCOE.   C. M.

EDWARD L. WHITE.

703   *The rapture of love.*

1 O 'TIS delight without alloy,
  Jesus, to hear thy name:
My spirit leaps with inward joy;
  I feel the sacred flame.

2 My passions hold a pleasing reign,
  When love inspires my breast,—
Love, the divinest of the train,
  The sovereign of the rest.

3 This is the grace must live and sing,
  When faith and hope shall cease,
And sound from every joyful string
  Through all the realms of bliss.

4 Swift I ascend the heavenly place,
  And hasten to my home;
I leap to meet thy kind embrace;
  I come, O Lord, I come.

5 Sink down, ye separating hills!
  Let sin and death remove;
'Tis love that drives my chariot wheels,
  And death must yield to love.
                                ISAAC WATTS.

704   *Triumphant joy.*

1 MY God, the spring of all my joys,
  The life of my delights,
The glory of my brightest days,
  And comfort of my nights!

2 In darkest shades, if thou appear,
  My dawning is begun;
Thou art my soul's bright morning star,
  And thou my rising sun.

3 The opening heavens around me shine
  With beams of sacred bliss,
If Jesus shows his mercy mine,
  And whispers I am his.

4 My soul would leave this heavy clay
  At that transporting word,
Run up with joy the shining way,
  To see and praise my Lord.

5 Fearless of hell and ghastly death,
  I'd break through every foe;
The wings of love and arms of faith
  Would bear me conqueror through.
                                ISAAC WATTS.

705   *Perpetual praise.*

1 YES, I will bless thee, O my God,
  Through all my fleeting days;
And to eternity prolong
  Thy vast, thy boundless praise.

2 Nor shall my tongue alone proclaim
  The honors of my God;
My life, with all its active powers,
  Shall spread thy praise abroad.

3 Nor will I cease thy praise to sing
  When death shall close mine eyes;
My thoughts shall then to nobler heights
  And sweeter raptures rise.

4 Then shall my lips, in endless praise,
  Their grateful tribute pay;
The theme demands an angel's tongue,
  And an eternal day.
                        OTTIWELL HEGINBOTHAM.

SALOME.   C. M.   LUDWIG VON BEETHOVEN.

706 *Prayer.*

1 PRAYER is the breath of God in man,
  Returning whence it came;
Love is the sacred fire within,
  And prayer the rising flame.

2 It gives the burdened spirit ease,
  And soothes the troubled breast;
Yields comfort to the mourners here,
  And to the weary rest.

3 When God inclines the heart to pray,
  He hath an ear to hear;
To him there's music in a groan,
  And beauty in a tear.

4 The humble suppliant cannot fail
  To have his wants supplied,
Since He for sinners intercedes,
  Who once for sinners died.
                              BENJAMIN BEDDOME.

707 *Prayer moves Omnipotence.*

1 THERE is an eye that never sleeps
  Beneath the wing of night;
There is an ear that never shuts,
  When sink the beams of light.

2 There is an arm that never tires,
  When human strength gives way;
There is a love that never fails,
  When earthly loves decay.

3 That eye is fixed on seraph throngs;
  That arm upholds the sky;
That ear is filled with angel songs;
  That love is throned on high.

4 But there's a power which man can wield,
  When mortal aid is vain,

That eye, that arm, that love to reach,
  That listening ear to gain.

5 That power is prayer, which soars on high,
  Through Jesus, to the throne,
And moves the hand which moves the world,
  To bring salvation down.
                              JOHN A. WALLACE.

708 *The two worlds.*

1 UNVEIL, O Lord, and on us shine
  In glory and in grace;
The gaudy world grows pale before
  The beauty of thy face.

2 Till thou art seen, it seems to be
  A sort of fairy ground,
Where suns unsetting light the sky,
  And flowers and fruits abound.

3 But when thy keener, purer beam
  Is poured upon our sight,
It loses all its power to charm,
  And what was day is night.

4 Its noblest toils are then the scourge
  Which made thy blood to flow;
Its joys are but the treacherous thorns
  Which circled round thy brow.

5 And thus, when we renounce for thee
  Its restless aims and fears,
The tender memories of the past,
  The hopes of coming years,—

6 Poor is our sacrifice, whose eyes
  Are lighted from above;
We offer what we cannot keep,
  What we have ceased to love.
                              JOHN H. NEWMAN.

WOODSTOCK.   C. M.   DEODATUS DUTTON, JR.

709   *Evening—solitude.*

1 I LOVE to steal awhile away
  From every cumbering care,
And spend the hours of setting day
  In humble, grateful prayer.

2 I love in solitude to shed
  The penitential tear,
And all his promises to plead
  Where none but God can hear.

3 I love to think on mercies past,
  And future good implore,
And all my cares and sorrows cast
  On him whom I adore.

4 I love by faith to take a view
  Of brighter scenes in heaven;
The prospect doth my strength renew,
  While here by tempests driven.

5 Thus, when life's toilsome day is o'er,
  May its departing ray
Be calm as this impressive hour,
  And lead to endless day.
          MRS. PHŒBE H. BROWN.

710   *What is prayer?*

1 PRAYER is the soul's sincere desire,
  Uttered or unexpressed;
The motion of a hidden fire
  That trembles in the breast.

2 Prayer is the burden of a sigh,
  The falling of a tear,
The upward glancing of an eye,
  When none but God is near.

3 Prayer is the simplest form of speech
  That infant lips can try;

Prayer the sublimest strains that reach
  The Majesty on high.

4 Prayer is the contrite sinner's voice,
  Returning from his ways;
While angels in their songs rejoice
  And cry, "Behold, he prays!"

5 Prayer is the Christian's vital breath,
  The Christian's native air,
His watchword at the gates of death;
  He enters heaven with prayer.

6 O Thou, by whom we come to God,
  The Life, the Truth, the Way;
The path of prayer thyself hast trod:
  Lord, teach us how to pray!
          JAMES MONTGOMERY.

711   *Communion with God.*

1 SWEET is the prayer whose holy stream
  In earnest pleading flows;
Devotion dwells upon the theme,
  And warm and warmer glows.

2 Faith grasps the blessing she desires;
  Hope points the upward gaze;
And Love, celestial Love, inspires
  The eloquence of praise.

3 But sweeter far the still small voice,
  Unheard by human ear,
When God has made the heart rejoice,
  And dried the bitter tear.

4 No accents flow, no words ascend;
  All utterance faileth there;
But God himself doth comprehend
  And answer silent prayer.
          UNKNOWN.

262

712 *Talking with God.*

1 TALK with us, Lord, thyself reveal,
  While here o'er earth we rove;
Speak to our hearts, and let us feel
  The kindling of thy love.

2 With thee conversing, we forget
  All time, and toil, and care;
Labor is rest, and pain is sweet,
  If thou, my God, art here.

3 Here, then, my God, vouchsafe to stay,
  And bid my heart rejoice;
My bounding heart shall own thy sway,
  And echo to thy voice.

4 Thou callest me to seek thy face,—
  'Tis all I wish to seek;
To attend the whispers of thy grace,
  And hear thee inly speak.

5 Let this my every hour employ,
  Till I thy glory see;
Enter into my Master's joy,
  And find my heaven in thee.
                        CHARLES WESLEY.

713 *Retirement and meditation.*

1 FAR from the world, O Lord, I flee,
  From strife and tumult far;
From scenes where Satan wages still
  His most successful war.

2 The calm retreat, the silent shade,
  With prayer and praise agree,
And seem by thy sweet bounty made
  For those who follow thee.

3 There, if thy Spirit touch the soul,
  And grace her mean abode,
O with what peace, and joy, and love,
  Does she commune with God!

4 Author and Guardian of my life,
  Sweet Source of light divine,
And all harmonious names in one,
  My Saviour! thou art mine!

5 The thanks I owe thee, and the love,
  A boundless, endless store,
Shall echo through the realms above
  When time shall be no more.
                        WILLIAM COWPER.

714 *Whom having not seen, ye love.*
  1 Pet. 1: 8.

1 JESUS, these eyes have never seen
  That radiant form of thine;
The veil of sense hangs dark between
  Thy blessed face and mine.

2 I see thee not, I hear thee not,
  Yet art thou oft with me;

And earth hath ne'er so dear a spot
  As where I meet with thee.

3 Like some bright dream that comes unsought
  When slumbers o'er me roll,
Thine image ever fills my thought,
  And charms my ravished soul.

4 Yet though I have not seen, and still
  Must rest in faith alone,
I love thee, dearest Lord, and will,
  Unseen, but not unknown.

5 When death these mortal eyes shall seal,
  And still this throbbing heart,
The rending veil shall thee reveal,
  All-glorious as thou art.
                        RAY PALMER.

715 *Pray without ceasing.*

1 SHEPHERD Divine, our wants relieve
  In this our evil day;
To all thy tempted followers give
  The power to watch and pray.

2 Long as our fiery trials last,
  Long as the cross we bear,
O let our souls on thee be cast
  In never-ceasing prayer.

3 Till thou thy perfect love impart,
  Till thou thyself bestow,
Be this the cry of every heart,
  "I will not let thee go;

4 "I will not let thee go, unless
  Thou tell thy name to me,
With all thy great salvation bless,
  And make me all like thee.

5 "Then let me on the mountain-top
  Behold thy open face,
Where faith in sight is swallowed up,
  And prayer in endless praise."
                        CHARLES WESLEY.

716 *The Lord's Prayer.*

1 OUR Father, God, who art in heaven,
  All hallowed be thy name;
Thy kingdom come; thy will be done
  In heaven and earth the same.

2 Give us this day our daily bread;
  And as we those forgive
Who sin against us, so may we
  Forgiving grace receive.

3 Into temptation lead us not;
  From evil set us free;
And thine the kingdom, thine the power
  And glory, ever be.
                        ADONIRAM JUDSON.

HENDON. 7.

FROM REV. HENRI ABRAHAM CÆSAR MALAN.

717 *God every-where.*

1 THEY who seek the throne of grace,
Find that throne in every place;
If we live a life of prayer,
God is present every-where.

2 In our sickness or our health,
In our want or in our wealth,
If we look to God in prayer,
God is present every-where.

3 When our earthly comforts fail,
When the foes of life prevail,
'Tis the time for earnest prayer;
God is present every-where.

4 Then, my soul, in every strait
To thy Father come and wait;
He will answer every prayer;
God is present every-where.

OLIVER HOLDEN, ALT

718 *Encouragements to pray.*

1 COME, my soul, thy suit prepare,
Jesus loves to answer prayer;
He himself invites thee near,
Bids thee ask him, waits to hear.

2 Lord, I come to thee for rest;
Take possession of my breast;
There thy blood-bought right maintain,
And without a rival reign.

3 While I am a pilgrim here,
Let thy love my spirit cheer;
As my guide, my guard, my friend,
Lead me to my journey's end.

4 Show me what I have to do;
Every hour my strength renew;
Let me live a life of faith,
Let me die thy people's death.

JOHN NEWTON.

SEYMOUR. 7.

FROM CARL MARIA VON WEBER.

719 *Partnership of the saints in light.*

1 JESUS is our common Lord,
He our loving Saviour is;
By his death to life restored,
Misery we exchange for bliss;

2 Bliss to carnal minds unknown,
O 'tis more than tongue can tell!
Only to believers shown,
Glorious and unspeakable.

3 Christ, our Brother and our Friend
Shows us his eternal love:
Never shall our triumphs end,
Till we take our seats above.

4 Let us walk with him in white,
For our bridal day prepare,
For our partnership in light,
For our glorious meeting there

CHARLES WESLEY.

VIENNA. 7.

ARR. FROM REV. WILLIAM HENRY HAVERGAL.

720 *The pilgrims' song.*

1 CHILDREN of the heavenly King,
As we journey let us sing;
Sing our Saviour's worthy praise,
Glorious in his works and ways.

2 We are traveling home to God,
In the way our fathers trod;
They are happy now, and we
Soon their happiness shall see.

3 O ye banished seed, be glad;
Christ our Advocate is made:
Us to save our flesh assumes,
Brother to our souls becomes.

4 Lift your eyes, ye sons of light;
Zion's city is in sight;
There our endless home shall be,
There our Lord we soon shall see.

5 Fear not, brethren, joyful stand
On the borders of our land;
Jesus Christ, our Father's Son,
Bids us undismayed go on.

6 Lord, obediently we'll go,
Gladly leaving all below:
Only thou our Leader be,
And we still will follow thee.

JOHN CENNICK.

721 *Christ, the source of every blessing.*

1 CHRIST, of all my hopes the ground,
Christ, the spring of all my joy,
Still in thee may I be found,
Still for thee my powers employ.

2 Fountain of o'erflowing grace,
Freely from thy fullness give;
Till I close my earthly race,
May I prove it "Christ to live!"

3 Firmly trusting in thy blood,
Nothing shall my heart confound;
Safely I shall pass the flood,
Safely reach Immanuel's ground.

4 When I touch the blessed shore,
Back the closing waves shall roll,
Death's dark stream shall nevermore
Part from thee my ravished soul.

5 Thus, O thus an entrance give
To the land of cloudless sky;
Having known it "Christ to live,"
Let me know it "Gain to die."

RALPH WARDLAW.

722 *For humility and protection.*

1 GOD of love, who hearest prayer,
Kindly for thy people care,
Who on thee alone depend:
Love us, save us to the end.

2 Save us, in the prosperous hour,
From the flattering tempter's power,
From his unsuspected wiles,
From the world's pernicious smiles.

3 Save us from the great and wise,
Till they sink in their own eyes,
Tamely to thy yoke submit,
Lay their honor at thy feet.

4 Never let the world break in;
Fix a mighty gulf between;
Keep us little and unknown,
Prized and loved by God alone.

5 Let us still to thee look up,
Thee, thy Israel's strength and hope;
Nothing know, or seek, beside
Jesus, and him crucified.

CHARLES WESLEY.

SPANISH HYMN. 7. D.   SPANISH MELODY.

723   *The Litany.*

1 SAVIOUR, when, in dust, to thee
Low we bend the adoring knee;
When, repentant, to the skies
Scarce we lift our weeping eyes;
O by all the pains and woe
Suffered once for man below,
Bending from thy throne on high,
Hear our solemn litany!

2 By thy helpless infant years;
By thy life of want and tears;
By thy days of sore distress,
In the savage wilderness;
By the dread mysterious hour
Of the insulting tempter's power;
Turn, O turn a favoring eye,
Hear our solemn litany!

3 By the sacred griefs that wept
O'er the grave where Lazarus slept;
By the boding tears that flowed
Over Salem's loved abode;
By the anguished sigh that told
Treachery lurked within thy fold;
From thy seat above the sky,
Hear our solemn litany!

4 By thine hour of dire despair;
By thine agony of prayer;
By the cross, the nail, the thorn,
Piercing spear, and torturing scorn;
By the gloom that veiled the skies
O'er the dreadful sacrifice;
Listen to our humble cry,
Hear our solemn litany!

5 By thy deep, expiring groan;
By the sad sepulchral stone;
By the vault whose dark abode
Held in vain the rising God;
O from earth to heaven restored,
Mighty, re-ascended Lord,
Listen, listen to the cry
Of our solemn litany!

SIR ROBERT GRANT.

BLUMENTHAL. 7. D.   JACOB BLUMENTHAL.

BETHANY. 6, 4, 6. LOWELL MASON.

724 *Nearer, my God, to thee.*

1 NEARER, my God, to thee!
  Nearer to thee,
E'en though it be a cross
  That raiseth me;
Still all my song shall be,
Nearer, my God, to thee,
  Nearer to thee!

2 Though like the wanderer,
  The sun gone down,
Darkness be over me,
  My rest a stone,
Yet in my dreams I'd be
Nearer, my God, to thee,
  Nearer to thee!

3 There let the way appear,
  Steps unto heaven;
All that thou sendest me,
  In mercy given;
Angels to beckon me
Nearer, my God, to thee,
  Nearer to thee!

4 Then, with my waking thoughts
  Bright with thy praise,
Out of my stony griefs
  Bethel I'll raise;
So by my woes to be
Nearer, my God, to thee,
  Nearer to thee!

5 Or if, on joyful wing
  Cleaving the sky,
Sun, moon, and stars forgot,
  Upward I fly,
Still all my song shall be,
Nearer, my God, to thee,
  Nearer to thee!

MRS. SARAH F. ADAMS.

MORE LOVE TO THEE. 6, 4, 6. WILLIAM HOWARD DOANE.

725 *More love to thee.*

1 MORE love to thee, O Christ,
  More love to thee!
Hear thou the prayer I make,
  On bended knee;
This is my earnest plea,
More love, O Christ, to thee,
  More love to thee!

2 Once earthly joy I craved,
  Sought peace and rest;

Now thee alone I seek,
  Give what is best;
This all my prayer shall be,
More love, O Christ, to thee,
  More love to thee!

3 Then shall my latest breath
  Whisper thy praise;
This be the parting cry
  My heart shall raise,
This still its prayer shall be,
More love, O Christ, to thee,
  More 'ove to thee!

MRS. ELIZABETH P. PRENTISS.

NETTLETON.   8, 7. D.   UNKNOWN.

726 *Hitherto hath the Lord helped us.*
1 Sam. 7 : 12.

1 COME, thou Fount of every blessing,
　Tune my heart to sing thy grace;
Streams of mercy, never ceasing,
　Call for songs of loudest praise.
Teach me some melodious sonnet,
　Sung by flaming tongues above;
Praise the mount—I'm fixed upon it—
　Mount of thy redeeming love!

2 Here I'll raise mine Ebenezer;
　Hither by thy help I'm come;
And I hope, by thy good pleasure,
　Safely to arrive at home.
Jesus sought me when a stranger,
　Wandering from the fold of God;
He, to rescue me from danger,
　Interposed his precious blood.

3 O to grace how great a debtor
　Daily I'm constrained to be!
Let thy goodness, like a fetter,
　Bind my wandering heart to thee:
Prone to wander, Lord, I feel it,
　Prone to leave the God I love;
Here's my heart, O take and seal it;
　Seal it for thy courts above.

ROBERT ROBINSON.

727   *The harmonious chorus.*

1 HERE on earth, where foes surround us,
　While our trembling souls within
Feel the fetters which have bound us,
　Feel the burden of our sin;
Lord, on thee alone relying,
　Strength we crave to burst our chain,
Ever pleading, ever crying,
　"Lord, for us the Lamb was slain."

2 In those high and holy regions
　Where the blest thy praise prolong,
Cherubs and seraphic legions
　Know no theme of nobler song;
White-robed saints, who there adore thee
　Throned above the glassy main,
Sing, and cast their crowns before thee,
　"Lord, for us the Lamb was slain."

3 Thus thy Church, whate'er her dwelling,
　Heaven above or earth below,
One harmonious chorus swelling,
　Loves her Saviour's praise to show:
Here in trial, there in glory,
　Changeless rings the immortal strain,
Changeless sounds the wondrous story,
　"Lord, for us the Lamb was slain."

UNKNOWN.

WHAT A FRIEND WE HAVE IN JESUS. 8, 7. D.   C. C. CONVERSE.

728 *What a Friend we have in Jesus.*

1 WHAT a Friend we have in Jesus,
  All our sins and griefs to bear!
What a privilege to carry
  Every thing to God in prayer!
O what peace we often forfeit,
  O what needless pain we bear,
All because we do not carry
  Every thing to God in prayer!

2 Have we trials and temptations?
  Is there trouble anywhere?
We should never be discouraged,
  Take it to the Lord in prayer.
Can we find a friend so faithful
  Who will all our sorrows share?
Jesus knows our every weakness,
  Take it to the Lord in prayer.

3 Are we weak and heavy laden,
  Cumbered with a load of care?—
Precious Saviour, still our refuge,—
  Take it to the Lord in prayer.
Do thy friends despise, forsake thee?
  Take it to the Lord in prayer;
In his arms he'll take and shield thee,
  Thou wilt find a solace there.
                    HORATIUS BONAR.

729   *Praise to the Deity.*

1 O MY God, how thy salvation
  Fills my soul with peace and joy,
Patience gives, and consolation
  Which the world cannot destroy!
Praise to God, the glorious giver,
  Christ, the Saviour of the lost,
And the Comforter forever,
  Father, Son, and Holy Ghost!

2 For that love whose tender mercies
  Purest joys do daily bring,
I will in my life confess thee,
  With my mouth thy praises sing:
Praise to God, the glorious giver,
  Christ, the Saviour of the lost,
And the Comforter forever,
  Father, Son, and Holy Ghost!
                    JOHN S. B. MONSELL.

Doxology.

PRAISE the God of our salvation;
  Praise the Father's boundless love;
Praise the Lamb, our expiation;
  Praise the Spirit from above,
Author of the new creation,
  Him by whom our spirits live;
Undivided adoration
  To the one Jehovah give!
                    JOSIAH CONDER, ALT.

THE CHRISTIAN—PRAYER AND PRAISE.

DULCETTA. 8, 7.

FROM LUDWIG VON BEETHOVEN.

730 *Before His cross.*

1 SWEET the moments, rich in blessing,
  Which before the cross I spend;
Life, and health, and peace possessing,
  From the sinner's dying Friend.

2 Truly blessed is this station,
  Low before his cross to lie,
While I see divine compassion
  Beaming in his gracious eye.

3 Here it is I find my heaven
  While upon the cross I gaze;
Love I much? I've much forgiven;
  I'm a miracle of grace.

4 Love and grief my heart dividing,
  With my tears his feet I'll bathe;
Constant still, in faith abiding,
  Life deriving from his death.

5 Here in tender, grateful sorrow
  With my Saviour will I stay;
Here new hope and strength will borrow;
  Here will love my fears away.
    JAMES ALLEN, ALT. BY WALTER SHIRLEY.

731 *Lo, I am with you alway.*

1 ALWAYS with us, always with us;—
  Words of cheer and words of love;
Thus the risen Saviour whispers,
  From his dwelling-place above.
With us when we toil in sadness,
  Sowing much, and reaping none;
Telling us that in the future
  Golden harvests shall be won.

2 With us when the storm is sweeping
  O'er our pathway dark and drear;

Waking hope within our bosoms,
  Stilling every anxious fear.
With us in the lonely valley,
  When we cross the chilling stream;
Lighting up the steps to glory
  With salvation's radiant beam.
    EDWIN H. NEVIN.

732 *Life of life.*

1 LABORING and heavy laden,
  Wanting help in time of need,
Fainting by the way from hunger,
  "Bread of life!" on thee we feed.

2 Thirsting for the springs of waters
  That, by love's eternal law,
From the stricken Rock are flowing,
  "Well of life!" from thee we draw.

3 In the land of cloud and shadow,
  Where no human eye can see,
Light to those who sit in darkness,
  "Light of life!" we walk in thee.

4 Thou the grace of life supplying,
  Thou the crown of life wilt give;
Dead to sin, and daily dying,
  "Life of life!" in thee we live.
    JOHN S. B. MONSELL.

Doxology.

PRAISE the God of our salvation;
  Praise the Father's boundless love.
Praise the Lamb, our expiation;
  Praise the Spirit from above.
Author of the new creation,
  Him by whom our spirits live;
Undivided adoration
  To the one Jehovah give.
    JOSIAH CONDER, ALT.

REGENT SQUARE. 8, 7, 4, or 8, 7. D. HENRY SMART.

733 *Hallelujah.*

1 O THOU God of my salvation,
My Redeemer from all sin;
Moved by thy divine compassion,
Who hast died my heart to win,
I will praise thee;
Where shall I thy praise begin?

2 Though unseen, I love the Saviour;
He hath brought salvation near;
Manifests his pardoning favor;
And when Jesus doth appear,
Soul and body
Shall his glorious image bear.

3 While the angel choirs are crying,
"Glory to the great I AM,"
I with them will still be vying—
Glory! glory to the Lamb!
O how precious
Is the sound of Jesus' name!

4 Angels now are hovering round us,
Unperceived amid the throng;
Wondering at the love that crowned us,
Glad to join the holy song:
Hallelujah,
Love and praise to Christ belong.
THOMAS OLIVERS.

734 *King of heaven, God of grace.*

1 PRAISE, my soul, the King of heaven;
To his feet thy tribute bring;
Ransomed, healed, restored, forgiven,
Evermore his praises sing:
Hallelujah! Hallelujah!
Praise the everlasting King.

2 Praise him for his grace and favor
To our fathers in distress;
Praise him, still the same as ever,
Slow to chide, and swift to bless:
Hallelujah! Hallelujah!
Glorious in his faithfulness.

3 Father-like, he tends and spares us,
Well our feeble frame he knows;
In his hands he gently bears us,
Rescues us from all our foes:
Hallelujah! Hallelujah!
Praise with us the God of grace.
HENRY F. LYTE AND SIR HENRY W. BAKER.

Doxology.

GREAT Jehovah! we adore thee,
God the Father, God the Son,
God the Spirit, joined in glory
On the same eternal throne:
Endless praises
To Jehovah, Three in One.
WILLIAM GOODE.

ST. CATHERINE. L. M. 6l. ADAPTED BY J. G. WALTON.

735 *The power of prayer.*

1 O WONDROUS power of faithful prayer!
  What tongue can tell the almighty grace?
God's hands or bound or open are,
  As Moses or Elijah prays:
Let Moses in the Spirit groan,
And God cries out, "Let me alone!

2 "Let me alone, that all my wrath
  May rise the wicked to consume;
While justice hears thy praying faith,
  It cannot seal the sinner's doom:
My Son is in my servant's prayer,
And Jesus forces me to spare."

Father, we ask in Jesus' name,
  In Jesus' power and spirit pray;
Divert thy vengeful thunder's aim,
  O turn thy threatening wrath away!
Our guilt and punishment remove,
And magnify thy pardoning love.

4 Father, regard thy pleading Son!
  Accept his all-availing prayer,
And send a peaceful answer down,
  In honor of our Spokesman there,
Whose blood proclaims our sins forgiven,
And speaks thy rebels up to heaven.
CHARLES WESLEY.

736 *Jesus all, and in all.*

1 THOU hidden Source of calm repose,
  Thou all-sufficient Love divine,
My help and refuge from my foes,
  Secure I am while thou art mine:
And lo! from sin, and grief, and shame,
I hide me, Jesus, in thy name.

2 Thy mighty name salvation is,
  And keeps my happy soul above:
Comfort it brings, and power, and peace,
  And joy, and everlasting love:
To me, with thy great name, are given
Pardon, and holiness, and heaven.

3 Jesus, my all in all thou art;
  My rest in toil, my ease in pain;
The medicine of my broken heart;
  In war, my peace; in loss, my gain;
My smile beneath the tyrant's frown;
In shame, my glory and my crown:

4 In want, my plentiful supply;
  In weakness, my almighty power;
In bonds, my perfect liberty;
  My light, in Satan's darkest hour;
In grief, my joy unspeakable;
My life in death, my all in all.
CHARLES WESLEY.

FIRST PART.

737 *Wrestling Jacob—the struggle.*

1 COME, O thou Traveler unknown,
  Whom still I hold but cannot see;
My company before is gone,
  And I am left alone with thee:
With thee all night I mean to stay,
And wrestle till the break of day.

2 I need not tell thee who I am,
  My sin and misery declare;
Thyself hast called me by my name,
  Look on thy hands, and read it there:
But who, I ask thee, who art thou?
Tell me thy name, and tell me now.

3 In vain thou strugglest to get free,
  I never will unloose my hold:
Art thou the Man that died for me?
  The secret of thy love unfold:
Wrestling, I will not let thee go,
Till I thy name, thy nature know.

4 Wilt thou not yet to me reveal
  Thy new, unutterable name?
Tell me, I still beseech thee, tell;
  To know it now resolved I am:
Wrestling, I will not let thee go,
Till I thy name, thy nature know.

5 What though my shrinking flesh complain,
  And murmur to contend so long?
I rise superior to my pain;
  When I am weak, then I am strong:
And when my all of strength shall fail,
I shall with the God-man prevail.
CHARLES WESLEY.

SECOND PART.

738 *The name revealed.*

1 YIELD to me now, for I am weak,
  But confident in self-despair;
Speak to my heart, in blessing speak,
  Be conquered by my instant prayer:
Speak, or thou never hence shalt move,
And tell me if thy name be Love.

2 'Tis Love! 'tis Love! thou diedst for me!
  I hear thy whisper in my heart;
The morning breaks, the shadows flee;
  Pure, universal love thou art:
To me to all, thy bowels move;
Thy nature and thy name is Love.

3 My prayer hath power with God; the grace
  Unspeakable I now receive;
Through faith I see thee face to face,
  I see thee face to face, and live!
In vain I have not wept and strove;
Thy nature and thy name is Love.

4 I know thee, Saviour, who thou art,
  Jesus, the feeble sinner's Friend;
Nor wilt thou with the night depart,
  But stay and love me to the end:
Thy mercies never shall remove;
Thy nature and thy name is Love.
CHARLES WESLEY.

THIRD PART.

739 *Victorious rapture.*

1 THE Sun of righteousness on me
  Hath risen with healing in his wings:
Withered my nature's strength, from thee
  My soul its life and succor brings:
My help is all laid up above;
Thy nature and thy name is Love.

2 Contented now, upon my thigh
  I halt, till life's short journey end;
All helplessness, all weakness, I
  On thee alone for strength depend,
Nor have I power from thee to move:
Thy nature and thy name is Love.

3 Lame as I am, I take the prey;
  Hell, earth, and sin, with ease o'ercome;
I leap for joy, pursue my way,
  And as a bounding hart fly home,
Through all eternity to prove
Thy nature and thy name is Love.
CHARLES WESLEY.

[L. P. M. Tune, Nashville. Page 178.]

740 *Everlasting praises.*

1 I'LL praise my Maker while I've breath,
  And when my voice is lost in death,
  Praise shall employ my nobler powers:
My days of praise shall ne'er be past,
While life, and thought, and being last,
  Or immortality endures.

2 Happy the man whose hopes rely
  On Israel's God; he made the sky,
  And earth, and seas, with all their train;
His truth forever stands secure;
He saves the oppressed, he feeds the poor
  And none shall find his promise vain.

3 The Lord pours eye-sight on the blind;
  The Lord supports the fainting mind;
  He sends the laboring conscience peace;
He helps the stranger in distress,
The widow and the fatherless,
  And grants the prisoner sweet release.

4 I'll praise him while he lends me breath,
  And when my voice is lost in death,
  Praise shall employ my nobler powers;
My days of praise shall ne'er be past,
While life, and thought, and being last,
  Or immortality endures.
ISAAC WATTS.

FADE, FADE, EACH EARTHLY JOY. 6, 4, 6.

THEODORE E. PERKINS.

741 *Jesus is mine.*

1 FADE, fade, each earthly joy;
    Jesus is mine.
Break every tender tie;
    Jesus is mine.
Dark is the wilderness,
Earth has no resting-place,
Jesus alone can bless;
    Jesus is mine.

2 Tempt not my soul away;
    Jesus is mine.
Here would I ever stay;
    Jesus is mine.
Perishing things of clay,
Born but for one brief day,
Pass from my heart away;
    Jesus is mine.

3 Farewell, ye dreams of night;
    Jesus is mine.
Lost in this dawning bright,
    Jesus is mine.
All that my soul has tried
Left but a dismal void;
Jesus has satisfied;
    Jesus is mine.

4 Farewell, mortality;
    Jesus is mine.
Welcome, eternity;
    Jesus is mine.
Welcome, O loved and blest,
Welcome, sweet scenes of rest,
Welcome, my Saviour's breast;
    Jesus is mine.

MRS. HORATIUS BONAR.

742 *I give myself to Thee.*

1 SAVIOUR, who died for me.
I give myself to thee;
Thy love, so full, so free.
    Claims all my powers.
Be this my purpose high,
To serve thee till I die,
Whether my path shall lie
    'Mid thorns or flowers.

2 But, Lord, the flesh is weak;
Thy gracious aid I seek,
For thou the word must speak,
    That makes me strong.
Then let me hear thy voice,
Thou art my only choice;
O bid my heart rejoice,
    Be thou my song.

3 May it be joy to me
To follow only thee;
Thy faithful servant be,
    Thine to the end.
For thee, I'll do and dare,
For thee, the cross I'll bear,
To thee direct my prayer,
    On thee depend.

4 Saviour, with me abide;
Be ever near my side;
Support, defend, and guide;
    I look to thee.
I lay my hand in thine,
And fleeting joys resign,
If I may call thee mine
    Eternally.

MISS MARY J. MASON.

ARIEL. C. P. M. ARR. BY LOWELL MASON.

743 *Make His praise glorious.*

1 O COULD I speak the matchless worth,
O could I sound the glories forth,
  Which in my Saviour shine,
I'd soar and touch the heavenly strings,
And vie with Gabriel while he sings
  In notes almost divine.

2 I'd sing the precious blood he spilt,
My ransom from the dreadful guilt
  Of sin, and wrath divine;
I'd sing his glorious righteousness,
In which all-perfect, heavenly dress
  My soul shall ever shine.

3 I'd sing the characters he bears,
And all the forms of love he wears,
  Exalted on his throne;
In loftiest songs of sweetest praise
  would to everlasting days
Make all his glories known.

4 Well, the delightful day will come
When my dear Lord will bring me home,
  And I shall see his face;
Then with my Saviour, Brother, Friend,
A blest eternity I'll spend,
  Triumphant in his grace.

SAMUEL MEDLEY.

744 *Always rejoicing.*

1 How happy, gracious Lord, are we,
Divinely drawn to follow thee!
  Whose hours divided are
Betwixt the mount and multitude;
Our day is spent in doing good,
  Our night in praise and prayer.

2 With us no melancholy void,
No moment lingers unemployed,
  Or unimproved, below:
Our weariness of life is gone,
Who live to serve our God alone,
  And only thee to know.

3 The winter's night, the summer's day,
Glide imperceptibly away,
  Too short to sing thy praise:
Too few we find the happy hours,
And haste to join those heavenly powers
  In everlasting lays.

4 With all who chant thy name on high,
And, "Holy, holy, holy," cry,—
  A bright, harmonious throng!
We long thy praises to repeat,
And ceaseless sing around thy seat
  The new, eternal song.

CHARLES WESLEY.

BROMLEY.　7, 6, 7.　　　　　　　　　　　　LONDON TUNE BOOK.

FIRST PART.

745 *My help cometh from the Lord.*
Ps. 121 : 2.

1 To the hills I lift mine eyes,
　The everlasting hills;
Streaming thence in fresh supplies,
　My soul the Spirit feels:
Will he not his help afford?
　Help, while yet I ask, is given:
God comes down; the God and Lord
　Who made both earth and heaven.

2 Faithful soul, pray always; pray,
　And still in God confide;
He thy feeble steps shall stay,
　Nor suffer thee to slide;
Lean on thy Redeemer's breast;
　He thy quiet spirit keeps;
Rest in him, securely rest;
　Thy Watchman never sleeps.

3 Neither sin, nor earth, nor hell,
　Thy Keeper can surprise;
Careless slumbers cannot steal
　On his all-seeing eyes;
He is Israel's sure defense;
　Israel all his care shall prove;
Kept by watchful providence,
　And ever-waking love.
　　　　　　　　　CHARLES WESLEY.

SECOND PART.

746 *The Lord is thy Keeper.*—Ps. 121 : 5.

1 SEE the Lord, thy Keeper, stand
　Omnipotently near:
Lo! he holds thee by thy hand,
　And banishes thy fear:
Shadows with his wings thy head;
　Guards from all impending harms;
Round thee and beneath are spread
　The everlasting arms.

2 Christ shall bless thy going out,
　Shall bless thy coming in;
Kindly compass thee about,
　Till thou art saved from sin;
Like thy spotless Master, thou,
　Filled with wisdom, love, and power
Holy, pure, and perfect now,
　Henceforth, and evermore.
　　　　　　　　　CHARLES WESLEY.

Doxology.　　　　7, 6, 8.

FATHER, Son, and Holy Ghost,
　Thy Godhead we adore,
Join we with the heavenly host,
　To praise thee evermore!
Live, by earth and heaven adored,
　The Three in One, the One in Three;
Holy, holy, holy Lord,
　All glory be to thee!
　　　　　　　　　CHARLES WESLEY.

CONTRAST. 8.

Lewis Edson.

747 *Preciousness of Jesus.*

1 How tedious and tasteless the hours
  When Jesus no longer I see!
Sweet prospects, sweet birds, and sweet
    flowers,
  Have all lost their sweetness to me;
The midsummer sun shines but dim,
  The fields strive in vain to look gay;
But when I am happy in him,
  December's as pleasant as May.

2 His name yields the richest perfume,
  And sweeter than music his voice;
His presence disperses my gloom,
  And makes all within me rejoice;
I should, were he always thus nigh,
  Have nothing to wish or to fear;
No mortal so happy as I,
  My summer would last all the year.

3 Content with beholding his face,
  My all to his pleasure resigned,
No changes of season or place
  Would make any change in my mind:
While blest with a sense of his love,
  A palace a toy would appear;
And prisons would palaces prove,
  If Jesus would dwell with me there.

4 My Lord, if indeed I am thine,
  If thou art my sun and my song,
Say, why do I languish and pine?
  And why are my winters so long?
O drive these dark clouds from my sky,
  Thy soul-cheering presence restore;
Or take me to thee up on high,
  Where winter and clouds are no more.
          JOHN NEWTON.

748 *Longing for closer communion.*

1 THOU Shepherd of Israel, and mine,
  The joy and desire of my heart,
For closer communion I pine,
  I long to reside where thou art:
The pasture I languish to find,
  Where all, who their Shepherd obey,
Are fed, on thy bosom reclined,
  And screened from the heat of the day.

2 'Tis there, with the lambs of thy flock,
  There only, I covet to rest;
To lie at the foot of the rock,
  Or rise to be hid in thy breast:
'Tis there I would always abide,
  And never a moment depart,
Concealed in the cleft of thy side,
  Eternally held in thy heart.
          CHARLES WESLEY

WHITEFIELD. S. M.   EDWARD MILLER

749 *The tender mercy of the Lord.*

1 O BLESS the Lord, my soul!
    His grace to thee proclaim;
And all that is within me, join
    To bless his holy name.

2 The Lord forgives thy sins,
    Prolongs thy feeble breath;
He healeth thine infirmities,
    And ransoms thee from death.

3 He clothes thee with his love,
    Upholds thee with his truth;
And like the eagle he renews
    The vigor of thy youth.

4 Then bless his holy name
    Whose grace hath made thee whole;
Whose loving-kindness crowns thy days:
    O bless the Lord, my soul!
                                ISAAC WATTS, ALT.

750 *Pray evermore.*

1 COME at the morning hour,
    Come, let us kneel and pray;
Prayer is the Christian pilgrim's staff
    To walk with God all day.

2 At noon, beneath the Rock
    Of ages, rest and pray;
Sweet is that shelter from the sun
    In weary heat of day.

3 At evening, in thy home,
    Around its altar, pray;
And finding there the house of God,
    With heaven then close the day.

4 When midnight veils our eyes,
    O it is sweet to say,
"I sleep, but my heart waketh, Lord,
    With thee to watch and pray."
                                JAMES MONTGOMERY.

751 *Heaven upon earth.*

1 MY God, my Life, my Love,
    To thee, to thee I call;
I cannot live if thou remove,
    For thou art all in all.

2 Thy shining grace can cheer
    This dungeon where I dwell;
'Tis paradise when thou art here;
    If thou depart, 'tis hell.

3 The smilings of thy face,
    How amiable they are!
'Tis heaven to rest in thine embrace,
    And nowhere else but there.

4 Not all the harps above
    Can make a heavenly place,
If God his residence remove,
    Or but conceal his face.

5 Thou art the sea of love,
    Where all my pleasures roll:
The circle where my passions move,
    And center of my soul.
                                ISAAC WATTS.

Doxology.

To God, the Father, Son,
    And Spirit, One in Three,
Be glory, as it was, is now,
    And shall forever be.
                                JOHN WESLEY.

THE HOUR OF PRAYER. 8, 8, 8, 4. Rev. John Bacchus Dykes.

752 *The hour of prayer.*

1 MY God, is any hour so sweet,
   From blush of morn to evening star,
As that which calls me to thy feet,
      The hour of prayer?

2 Blest is that tranquil hour of morn,
   And blest that solemn hour of eve,
When, on the wings of prayer upborne,
      The world I leave.

3 Then is my strength by thee renewed;
   Then are my sins by thee forgiven;
Then dost thou cheer my solitude
      With hopes of heaven.

4 No words can tell what sweet relief
   Here for my every want I find;
What strength for warfare, balm for grief,
      What peace of mind.

5 Hushed is each doubt, gone every fear;
   My spirit seems in heaven to stay;
And e'en the penitential tear
      Is wiped away.

6 Lord, till I reach that blissful shore,
   No privilege so dear shall be,
As thus my inmost soul to pour
      In prayer to thee.

CHARLOTTE ELLIOTT.

SUPPLICATION. S. M. JOSEPH BARNBY.

753 *The spirit of prayer.*

1 THE praying spirit breathe,
   The watching power impart,
From all entanglements beneath
   Call off my peaceful heart;
My feeble mind sustain,
   By worldly thoughts oppressed;
Appear, and bid me turn again
   To my eternal rest.

2 Swift to my rescue come,
   Thine own this moment seize;
Gather my wandering spirit home,
   And keep in perfect peace:
Suffered no more to rove
   O'er all the earth abroad,
Arrest the prisoner of thy love,
   And shut me up in God.

CHARLES WESLEY.

ST. HILDA. 7, 6. Rev. H. Husband.

4 I long to be like Jesus,
  Meek, loving, lowly, mild;
I long to be like Jesus,
  The Father's holy child:
I long to be with Jesus
  Amid the heavenly throng,
To sing with saints his praises,
  And learn the angels' song.
                    HORATIUS BONAR.

754 *I lay my sins on Jesus.*

1 I LAY my sins on Jesus,
   The spotless Lamb of God;
He bears them all, and frees us
   From the accursèd load:
I bring my guilt to Jesus,
   To wash my crimson stains
White in his blood most precious,
   Till not a stain remains.

2 I lay my wants on Jesus;
   All fullness dwells in him;
He healeth my diseases,
   He doth my soul redeem:
I lay my griefs on Jesus,
   My burdens and my cares;
He from them all releases,
   He all my sorrows shares.

3 I rest my soul on Jesus,
   This weary soul of mine;
His right hand me embraces,
   I on his breast recline:
I love the name of Jesus,
   Immanuel, Christ, the Lord;
Like fragrance on the breezes,
   His name abroad is poured.

755 *Never separated from Christ.*

1 I KNOW no life divided,
   O Lord of life, from thee;
In thee is life provided
   For all mankind and me:
I know no death, O Jesus,
   Because I live in thee;
Thy death it is which frees us
   From death eternally.

2 I fear no tribulation,
   Since, whatsoe'er it be,
It makes no separation
   Between my Lord and me.
If thou, my God and Teacher,
   Vouchsafe to be my own,
Though poor, I shall be richer
   Than monarch on his throne.

3 If, while on earth I wander,
   My heart is light and blest,
Ah, what shall I be yonder,
   In perfect peace and rest?
O blessed thought! in dying
   We go to meet the Lord,
Where there shall be no sighing,
   A kingdom our reward.
          CARL J. P. SPITTA. TR. BY R. MASSIE.

I LOVE TO TELL THE STORY. 7, 6.

William G. Fischer.

CHORUS.

756 *I love to tell the story.*

1 I LOVE to tell the story,
  Of unseen things above,
Of Jesus and his glory,
  Of Jesus and his love.
I love to tell the story,
  Because I know 'tis true;
It satisfies my longings,
  As nothing else can do.
    I love to tell the story,
      'Twill be my theme in glory,
    To tell the old, old story
      Of Jesus and his love.

2 I love to tell the story;
  More wonderful it seems
Than all the golden fancies
  Of all our golden dreams.
I love to tell the story,
  It did so much for me;

And that is just the reason
  I tell it now to thee.

3 I love to tell the story;
  'Tis pleasant to repeat
What seems, each time I tell it,
  More wonderfully sweet.
I love to tell the story;
  For some have never heard
The message of salvation
  From God's own holy word.

4 I love to tell the story;
  For those who know it best
Seem hungering and thirsting
  To hear it like the rest.
And when, in scenes of glory,
  I sing the new, new song,
'Twill be the old, old story
  That I have loved so long.
      CATHARINE HANKEY.

KELBROOK.   11, 12.   J. RILEY.

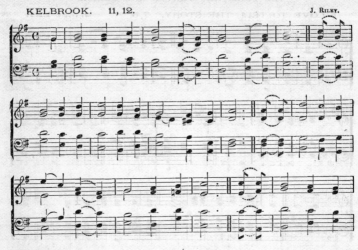

757   *The foretaste of endless bliss.*

1 MY God, I am thine; what a comfort divine,
What a blessing to know that my Jesus is mine!
In the heavenly Lamb thrice happy I am,
And my heart doth rejoice at the sound of his name.

2 True pleasures abound in the rapturous sound,
And whoever hath found it, hath paradise found:
My Redeemer to know, to feel his blood flow,
This is life everlasting—'tis heaven below.

Yet onward I haste to the heavenly feast:
That indeed is the fullness, but this is the taste;
And this I shall prove, till with joy I remove
To the heaven of heavens in Jesus's love.
CHARLES WESLEY.

[10, 11. Tune, Lyons. Page 168.]

758   *Worldly vanity renounced.*

1 O TELL me no more of this world's vain store,
The time for such trifles with me now is o'er;

A country I've found where true joys abound,
To dwell I'm determined on that happy ground.

2 The souls that believe in paradise live,
And me in that number will Jesus receive:
My soul, don't delay; he calls thee away;
Rise, follow thy Saviour, and bless the glad day.

3 No mortal doth know what he can bestow,
What light, strength, and comfort—go after him, go;
Lo, onward I move to a city above,
None guesses how wondrous my journey will prove.

4 Great spoils I shall win from death, hell, and sin,
'Midst outward afflictions shall feel Christ within:
And when I'm to die, "Receive me," I'll cry,
For Jesus hath loved me, I cannot tell why:

5 But this I do find, we two are so joined,
He'll not live in glory and leave me behind:
So this is the race I'm running through grace,
Henceforth, till admitted to see my Lord's face.

6 And now I'm in care my neighbors may share
These blessings: to seek them will none of you dare?
In bondage, O why, and death will you lie,
When one here assures you free grace is so nigh?
JOHN GAMBOLD.

MEDITATION. 11, 8. FREEMAN LEWIS, ARR. BY HUBERT P. MAIN.

759 *My Beloved.*

1 O THOU, in whose presence my soul takes delight,
    On whom in affliction I call,
My comfort by day, and my song in the night,
    My hope, my salvation, my all!

2 Where dost thou, dear Shepherd, resort with thy sheep,
    To feed them in pastures of love?
Say, why in the valley of death should I weep,
    Or alone in this wilderness rove?

3 O why should I wander an alien from thee,
    Or cry in the desert for bread?
Thy foes will rejoice when my sorrows they see,
    And smile at the tears I have shed.

4 Ye daughters of Zion, declare, have you seen
    The star that on Israel shone?
Say, if in your tents my Beloved has been,
    And where with his flocks he is gone.

5 He looks! and ten thousands of angels rejoice,
    And myriads wait for his word;
He speaks! and eternity, filled with his voice,
    Re-echoes the praise of the Lord.

6 Dear Shepherd, I hear, and will follow thy call;
    I know the sweet sound of thy voice;
Restore and defend me, for thou art my all,
    And in thee I will ever rejoice.
                                    JOSEPH SWAIN.

I NEED THEE EVERY HOUR. 6, 4, 7. REV. ROBERT LOWRY.

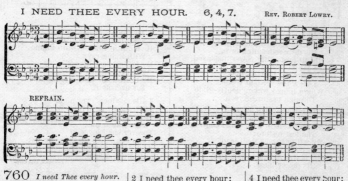

REFRAIN.

760 *I need Thee every hour.*

1 I NEED thee every hour,
    Most gracious Lord;
No tender voice like thine
    Can peace afford.
    I need thee, O I need thee;
    Every hour I need thee;
    O bless me now, my Saviour,
    I come to thee!

2 I need thee every hour;
    Stay thou near by;
Temptations lose their power
    When thou art nigh.

3 I need thee every hour,
    In joy or pain;
Come quickly and abide,
    Or life is vain.

4 I need thee every hour;
    Teach me thy will;
And thy rich promises
    In me fulfill.

5 I need thee every hour,
    Most Holy One;
O make me thine indeed,
    Thou blessed Son!
              MRS. ANNIE S. HAWKS.

THE CHRISTIAN---PRAYER AND PRAISE.

BROWNE. 6, 8, 4.   * MISS BROWNE.

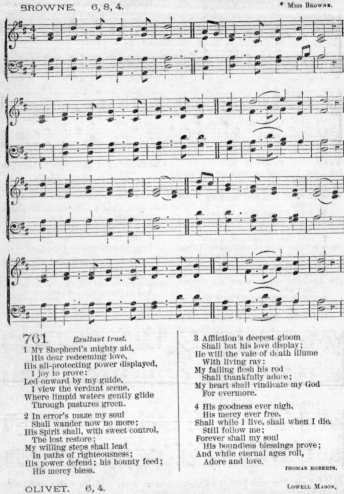

761   *Exultant trust.*

1 My Shepherd's mighty aid,
　His dear redeeming love,
His all-protecting power displayed,
　I joy to prove:
Led onward by my guide,
　I view the verdant scene,
Where limpid waters gently glide
　Through pastures green.

2 In error's maze my soul
　Shall wander now no more;
His Spirit shall, with sweet control,
　The lost restore:
My willing steps shall lead
　In paths of righteousness;
His power defend; his bounty feed;
　His mercy bless.

3 Affliction's deepest gloom
　Shall but his love display;
He will the vale of death illume
　With living ray:
My failing flesh his rod
　Shall thankfully adore;
My heart shall vindicate my God
　For evermore.

4 His goodness ever nigh,
　His mercy ever free,
Shall while I live, shall when I die,
　Still follow me;
Forever shall my soul
　His boundless blessings prove;
And while eternal ages roll,
　Adore and love.
                              THOMAS ROBERTS.

OLIVET. 6, 4.   LOWELL MASON.

284

OLIVET. 6, 4.—*Continued.*

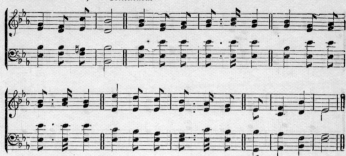

762 *Before the cross.*

1 My faith looks up to thee,
Thou Lamb of Calvary,
　Saviour divine:
Now hear me while I pray,
Take all my guilt away,
O let me from this day
　Be wholly thine.

2 May thy rich grace impart
Strength to my fainting heart,
　My zeal inspire;
As thou hast died for me,
O may my love to thee
Pure, warm, and changeless be,—
　A living fire.

3 While life's dark maze I tread,
And griefs around me spread,
　Be thou my guide;
Bid darkness turn to day,
Wipe sorrow's tears away,
Nor let me ever stray
　From thee aside.

4 When ends life's transient dream,
When death's cold, sullen stream
　Shall o'er me roll;
Blest Saviour, then, in love,
Fear and distrust remove:
O bear me safe above,—
　A ransomed soul.

RAY PALMER.

NEW HAVEN. 6, 4.　　　　　THOMAS HASTINGS.

ST. ANN S.   C. M.   William Croft.

763 *The Church immovable.*

1 O where are kings and empires now,
    Of old that went and came?
But, Lord, thy Church is praying yet,
    A thousand years the same.

2 We mark her goodly battlements,
    And her foundations strong;
We hear within the solemn voice
    Of her unending song.

3 For not like kingdoms of the world
    Thy holy Church, O God!
Though earthquake shocks are threaten-
        ing her,
    And tempests are abroad;

4 Unshaken as eternal hills,
    Immovable she stands,
A mountain that shall fill the earth,
    A house not made by hands.
                        A. CLEVELAND COXE.

764 *Founded on a Rock.*

1 With stately towers and bulwarks strong,
    Unrivaled and alone,
    ved theme of many a sacred song,
God's holy city shone.

    Thus fair was Zion's chosen seat,
        The glory of all lands;
Yet fairer, and in strength complete,
    The Christian temple stands.

3 The faithful of each clime and age
    This glorious Church compose;
Built on a Rock, with idle rage
    The threatening tempest blows.

4 Fear not; though hostile bands alarm,
    Thy God is thy defense;
And weak and powerless every arm
    Against Omnipotence.   HARRIET AUBER.

765 *The kingdoms one.*

1 Happy the souls to Jesus join d-
    And saved by grace alone;
Walking in all his ways, they find
    Their heaven on earth begun.

2 The Church triumphant in thy l ve,
    Their mighty joys we know:
They sing the Lamb in hymns above,
    And we in hymns below.

3 Thee in thy glorious realm they praise,
    And bow before thy throne;
We in the kingdom of thy grace:
    The kingdoms are but one.

4 The holy to the holiest leads,
    And thence our spirits rise;
For he that in thy statutes treads
    Shall meet thee in the skies.
                        CHARLES WESLEY.

766 *The sure Foundation.*

1 Behold the sure Foundation-stone
    Which God in Zion lays,
To build our heavenly hopes upon,
    And his eternal praise.

2 Chosen of God, to sinners dear,
    We now adore thy name;
We trust our whole salvation here,
    Nor can we suffer shame.

3 The foolish builders, scribe and priest,
    Reject it with disdain;
Yet on this Rock the Church shall rest,
    And envy rage in vain.

4 What though the gates of hell withstood,
    Yet must this building rise;
'Tis thine own work, Almighty God,
    And wondrous in our eyes.   ISAAC WATTS

ZION. 8, 7, 4. THOMAS HASTINGS.

767 *Good news for Zion.*

1 ON the mountain's top appearing,
Lo! the sacred herald stands,
Welcome news to Zion bearing,
Zion, long in hostile lands:
Mourning captive!
God himself shall loose thy bands.

2 Has thy night been long and mournful?
Have thy friends unfaithful proved?
Have thy foes been proud and scornful,
By thy sighs and tears unmoved?
Cease thy mourning;
Zion still is well beloved.

3 God, thy God, will now restore thee;
He himself appears thy Friend;
All thy foes shall flee before thee;
Here their boasts and triumphs end:
Great deliverance
Zion's King will surely send.

4 Peace and joy shall now attend thee;
All thy warfare now is past;
God thy Saviour will defend thee;
Victory is thine at last:
All thy conflicts
End in everlasting rest.

THOMAS KELLY.

768 *Jehovah, the defense of Zion.*

1 ZION stands with hills surrounded,
Zion, kept by power divine:
All her foes shall be confounded,
Though the world in arms combine:
Happy Zion,
What a favored lot is thine!

2 Every human tie may perish;
Friend to friend unfaithful prove;

Mothers cease their own to cherish;
Heaven and earth at last remove;
But no changes
Can attend Jehovah's love.

3 In the furnace God may prove thee,
Thence to bring thee forth more bright,
But can never cease to love thee:
Thou art precious in his sight:
God is with thee,
God, thine everlasting light.

THOMAS KELLY.

[C. M. Tune, St. Ann's. Page 286.]

769 *The truly blest.*

1 How lovely are thy dwellings, Lord,
From noise and trouble free!
How beautiful the sweet accord
Of souls that pray to thee!

2 Lord God of hosts that reign'st on high,
They are the truly blest
Who only will on thee rely,
In thee alone will rest.

3 They pass refreshed the thirsty vale,
The dry and barren ground,
As through a fruitful, watery dale,
Where springs and showers abound.

4 They journey on from strength to
strength,
With joy and gladsome cheer,
Till all before our God at length
In Zion's courts appear.

JOHN MILTON.

Doxology.

GREAT Jehovah! we adore thee,
God the Father, God the Son,
God the Spirit, joined in glory
On the same eternal throne:
Endless praises
To Jehovah, Three in One!

WILLIAM GOODE.

AMANTUS. S. M. REV. WILLIAM AUGUSTUS MUHLENBERG, D.D.

770 *Love for Zion.*

1 I LOVE thy kingdom, Lord,
    The house of thine abode,
The Church our blest Redeemer saved
    With his own precious blood.

2 I love thy Church, O God!
    Her walls before thee stand,
Dear as the apple of thine eye,
    And graven on thy hand.

3 For her my tears shall fall,
    For her my prayers ascend;
To her my cares and toils be given,
    Till toils and cares shall end.

4 Beyond my highest joy
    I prize her heavenly ways,
Her sweet communion, solemn vows,
    Her hymns of love and praise.

5 Sure as thy truth shall last,
    To Zion shall be given
The brightest glories earth can yield,
    And brighter bliss of heaven.
                    TIMOTHY DWIGHT.

771 *For a revival.*

1 O LORD, thy work revive,
    In Zion's gloomy hour,
And let our dying graces live
    By thy restoring power.

2 O let thy chosen few
    Awake to earnest prayer;
Their covenant again renew,
    And walk in filial fear.

3 Thy Spirit then will speak
    Through lips of humble clay,
Till hearts of adamant shall break,
    Till rebels shall obey.

4 Now lend thy gracious ear;
    Now listen to our cry:
O come, and bring salvation near;
    Our souls on thee rely.
                    PHŒBE H. BROWN.

772 *The Church's confidence and security.*

1 WHO in the Lord confide,
    And feel his sprinkled blood,
In storms and hurricanes abide
    Firm as the mount of God:
Steadfast, and fixed, and sure,
    His Zion cannot move;
His faithful people stand secure
    In Jesus' guardian love.

2 As round Jerusalem
    The hilly bulwarks rise,
So God protects and covers them
    From all their enemies.
On every side he stands,
    And for his Israel cares;
And safe in his almighty hands
    Their souls forever bears.
                    CHARLES WESLEY.

Doxology.

To God, the Father, Son,
    And Spirit, One in Three,
Be glory, as it was, is now,
    And shall forever be.
                    JOHN WESLEY.

APPLETON.   L. M.

WILLIAM BOYCE.

773   *The forty-sixth Psalm.*

1 GOD is the refuge of his saints,
   When storms of sharp distress invade;
Ere we can offer our complaints,
   Behold him present with his aid.

2 Let mountains from their seats be hurled
   Down to the deep, and buried there,
Convulsions shake the solid world,—
   Our faith shall never yield to fear.

3 Loud may the troubled ocean roar,
   In sacred peace our souls abide;
While every nation, every shore,
   Trembles, and dreads the swelling tide.

4 There is a stream whose gentle flow
   Supplies the city of our God,
Life, love, and joy, still gliding through,
   And watering our divine abode.

5 That sacred stream, thine holy word,
   Our grief allays, our fear controls;
Sweet peace thy promises afford,
   And give new strength to fainting souls.

   Zion enjoys her Monarch's love,
   Secure against a threatening hour;
Nor can her firm foundation move,
   Built on his truth, and armed with power.
                                    ISAAC WATTS.

774   *The river of life.*

1 GREAT Source of being and of love!
Thou waterest all the worlds above;
And all the joys which mortals know,
From thine exhaustless fountain flow.

2 A sacred spring, at thy command,
From Zion's mount, in Canaan's land,
Beside thy temple cleaves the ground,
And pours its limpid stream around.

3 Close by its banks, in order fair,
The blooming trees of life appear;
Their blossoms fragrant odors give,
And on their fruit the nations live.

4 Flow, wondrous stream, with glory
     crowned,
Flow on to earth's remotest bound;
And bear us, on thy gentle wave,
To him who all thy virtues gave.
                              PHILIP DODDRIDGE.

775   *Awake, Jerusalem, awake!*

1 AWAKE, Jerusalem, awake!
   No longer in thy sins lie down:
The garment of salvation take;
   Thy beauty and thy strength put on.

2 Shake off the dust that blinds thy sight,
   And hides the promise from thine eyes;
Arise, and struggle into light;
   The great Deliverer calls, "Arise!"

3 Shake off the bands of sad despair;
   Zion, assert thy liberty;
Look up, thy broken heart prepare,
   And God shall set the captive free.

4 Vessels of mercy, sons of grace,
   Be purged from every sinful stain;
Be like your Lord, his word embrace,
   Nor bear his hallowed name in vain.
                              CHARLES WESLEY.

AUSTRIA. 8, 7. D.   FRANCIS JOSEPH HAYDN.

776 *God in the midst of her.*

1 GLORIOUS things of thee are spoken,
    Zion, city of our God;
He, whose word cannot be broken,
    Formed thee for his own abode;
On the Rock of ages founded,
    What can shake thy sure repose?
With salvation's walls surrounded,
    Thou mayst smile at all thy foes.

2 See, the streams of living waters,
    Springing from eternal love,
Still supply thy sons and daughters,
    And all fear of want remove:
Who can faint while such a river
    Ever flows our thirst to assuage?
Grace, which, like the Lord, the giver,
    Never fails from age to age.

3 Round each habitation hovering,
    See the cloud and fire appear,
For a glory and a covering,
    Showing that the Lord is near!
He who gives us daily manna,
    He who listens when we cry,
Let him hear the loud hosanna
    Rising to his throne on high.
                                        JOHN NEWTON.

777 *God her everlasting light.*

1 HEAR what God the Lord hath spoken:
    O my people, faint and few,
Comfortless, afflicted, broken,
    Fair abodes I build for you.
Scenes of heartfelt tribulation
    Shall no more perplex your ways;
You shall name your walls "Salvation,"
    And your gates shall all be "Praise."

2 There, like streams that feed the garden,
    Pleasures without end shall flow,
For the Lord, your faith rewarding
    All his bounty shall bestow.
Still in undisturbed possession,
    Peace and righteousness shall reign;
Never shall you feel oppression,
    Hear the voice of war again.

3 Ye, no more your suns descending,
    Waning moons no more shall see;
But, your griefs forever ending,
    Find eternal noon in me:
God shall rise, and, shining o'er you,
    Change to day the gloom of night;
He, the Lord, shall be your glory,
    God your everlasting light.
                                        WILLIAM COWPER.

HANOVER. 11.   JOHANN C. W. A. MOZART.

HANOVER. 11.—*Continued.*

778   *Daughter of Zion.*

1 DAUGHTER of Zion, awake from thy sadness;
  Awake, for thy foes shall oppress thee no more;
Bright o'er thy hills dawns the day-star of gladness;
  Arise, for the night of thy sorrow is o'er.

2 Strong were thy foes; but the arm that subdued them,
  And scattered their legions, was mightier far;
They fled like the chaff from the scourge that pursued them;
  Vain were their steeds and their chariots of war.

3 Daughter of Zion, the power that hath saved thee
  Extolled with the harp and the timbrel should be;
Shout, for the foe is destroyed that enslaved thee;
  The oppressor is vanquished, and Zion is free!

UNKNOWN.

ROSEFIELD.   7, 61.

REV. CÆSAR HENRI ABRAHAM MALAN.

779   *For the extension of the Church.*

1 ON thy Church, O Power divine,
Cause thy glorious face to shine,
Till the nations, from afar,
Hail her as their guiding star;
Till her sons from zone to zone,
Make thy great salvation known.

2 Then shall God, with lavish hand,
Scatter blessings o'er the land;
Earth shall yield her rich increase,
Every breeze shall whisper peace,
And the world's remotest bound
With the voice of praise resound.

HARRIET AUBER.

THE CHURCH—FELLOWSHIP AND UNITY.

HERMON. C. M. LOWELL MASON.

780 *The golden chain.*

1 How sweet, how heavenly is the sight,
　When those who love the Lord
In one another's peace delight,
　And so fulfill his word!

2 When each can feel his brother's sigh,
　And with him bear a part!
When sorrow flows from eye to eye,
　And joy from heart to heart!

3 When, free from envy, scorn, and pride,
　Our wishes all above,
Each can his brother's failings hide,
　And show a brother's love!

4 Let love, in one delightful stream,
　Through every bosom flow,
And union sweet, and dear esteem,
　In every action glow.

5 Love is the golden chain that binds
　The happy souls above;
And he's an heir of heaven who finds
　His bosom glow with love.
JOSEPH SWAIN.

781 *Come with us.*

C Come in, thou blessed of the Lord,
　Stranger nor foe art thou:
We welcome thee with warm accord,
　Our friend, our brother, now.

2 The hand of fellowship, the heart
　Of love, we offer thee:
Leaving the world, thou dost but part
　From lies and vanity.

3 Come with us; we will do thee good,
　As God to us hath done;

Stand but in him as those have stood
　Whose faith the victory won.

4 And when, by turns, we pass away,
　As star by star grows dim,
May each, translated into day,
　Be lost and found in him.
JAMES MONTGOMERY.

782 *United—though separate.*

1 Blest be the dear uniting love,
　That will not let us part;
Our bodies may far off remove,
　We still are one in heart.

2 Joined in one spirit to our Head,
　Where he appoints we go;
And still in Jesus' footsteps tread,
　And show his praise below.

3 O may we ever walk in him,
　And nothing know beside;
Nothing desire, nothing esteem,
　But Jesus crucified.

4 Closer and closer let us cleave
　To his beloved embrace;
Expect his fullness to receive,
　And grace to answer grace.

5 Partakers of the Saviour's grace,
　The same in mind and heart,
Nor joy, nor grief, nor time, nor place,
　Nor life, nor death can part.

6 Then let us hasten to the day
　Which shall our flesh restore;
When death shall all be done away,
　And bodies part no more.
CHARLES WESLEY.

CORNELL.   C. M.   JOHN HENRY CORNELL.

783 *Love, the test of discipleship.*

1 OUR God is love; and all his saints
    His image bear below:
The heart with love to God inspired,
    With love to man will glow.

2 Teach us to love each other, Lord,
    As we are loved by thee;
None who are truly born of God
    Can live in enmity.

3 Heirs of the same immortal bliss,
    Our hopes and fears the same,
With bonds of love our hearts unite,
    With mutual love inflame.

4 So may the unbelieving world
    See how true Christians love;
And glorify our Saviour's grace,
    And seek that grace to prove.
                    THOMAS COTTERILL.

784   *The law of Christ.*

1 TRY us, O God, and search the ground
    Of every sinful heart;
Whate'er of sin in us is found,
    O bid it all depart.

2 If to the right or left we stray,
    Leave us not comfortless;
But guide our feet into the way
    Of everlasting peace.

3 Help us to help each other, Lord,
    Each other's cross to bear;
Let each his friendly aid afford,
    And feel his brother's care.

4 Help us to build each other up,
    Our little stock improve;

Increase our faith, confirm our hope,
    And perfect us in love.

5 Up into thee, our living Head,
    Let us in all things grow,
Till thou hast made us free indeed,
    And spotless here below.

6 Then, when the mighty work is wrought,
    Receive thy ready bride:
Give us in heaven a happy lot
    With all the sanctified.
                    CHARLES WESLEY.

785   *The loadstone of His love.*

1 JESUS, united by thy grace,
    And each to each endeared,
With confidence we seek thy face,
    And know our prayer is heard.

2 Still let us own our common Lord,
    And bear thine easy yoke;
A band of love, a threefold cord,
    Which never can be broke.

3 Make us into one spirit drink;
    Baptize into thy name;
And let us alway kindly think,
    And sweetly speak, the same.

4 Touched by the loadstone of thy love,
    Let all our hearts agree,
And ever toward each other move,
    And ever move toward thee.
                    CHARLES WESLEY.

Doxology.

To Father, Son, and Holy Ghost,
    The God whom we adore,
Be glory, as it was, is now,
    And shall be evermore!
                    TATE AND BRADY.

THE CHURCH—FELLOWSHIP AND UNITY.

HUMMEL.   C. M.   HEINRICH CHRISTOPHER ZEUNER.

786   *Rejoicing in hope.*

1 LIFT up your hearts to things above,
   Ye followers of the Lamb,
And join with us to praise his love,
   And glorify his name.

2 To Jesus' name give thanks and sing,
   Whose mercies never end:
Rejoice! rejoice! the Lord is King;
   The King is now our friend!

3 We for his sake count all things loss;
   On earthly good look down;
And joyfully sustain the cross,
   Till we receive the crown.

4 O let us stir each other up,
   Our faith by works to approve,
By holy, purifying hope,
   And the sweet task of love.

5 Let all who for the promise wait,
   The Holy Ghost receive;
And, raised to our unsinning state,
   With God in Eden live:—

6 Live, till the Lord in glory come,
   And wait his heaven to share:
He now is fitting up your home;
   Go on, we'll meet you there.
                        CHARLES WESLEY.

787   *Ye are come unto Mount Sion.*
           Heb. 12 : 22.

1 NOT to the terrors of the Lord,
   The tempest, fire, and smoke;
Not to the thunder of that word
   Which God on Sinai spoke:—

2 But we are come to Zion's hill,
   The city of our God;
Where milder words declare his will,
   And speak his love abroad.

3 Behold the innumerable host
   Of angels clothed in light!
Behold the spirits of the just,
   Whose faith is turned to sight!

4 Behold the blest assembly there,
   Whose names are writ in heaven,
And God, the Judge of all, declare
   Their vilest sins forgiven!

5 The saints on earth and all the dead
   But one communion make;
All join in Christ, their living Head
   And of his grace partake.

6 In such society as this
   My weary soul would rest:
The man that dwells where Jesus is,
   Must be forever blest.
                        ISAAC WATTS.

788   *The bond of love.*

1 THE glorious universe around,
   The heavens with all their train,
Sun, moon, and stars, are firmly bound
   In one mysterious chain.

2 In one fraternal bond of love,
   One fellowship of mind,
The saints below and saints above
   Their bliss and glory find.

3 Here, in their house of pilgrimage,
   Thy statutes are their song;
There, through one bright, eternal age.
   Thy praises thee prolong.

4 Lord, may our union form a part
   Of that thrice happy whole;
Derive its pulse from thee, the heart,
   Its life from thee, the soul.
                        JAMES MONTGOMERY.

ARMENIA.   C. M.   SYLVANUS BILLINGS POND.

789   *Harmony and joy unspeakable.*

1 ALL praise to our redeeming Lord,
  Who joins us by his grace,
And bids us, each to each restored,
  Together seek his face.

2 He bids us build each other up;
  And, gathered into one,
To our high calling's glorious hope,
  We hand in hand go on.

3 The gift which he on one bestows,
  We all delight to prove;
The grace through every vessel flows,
  In purest streams of love.

4 E'en now we think and speak the same,
  And cordially agree,
United all, through Jesus' name,
  In perfect harmony.

5 We all partake the joy of one;
  The common peace we feel;
A peace to sensual minds unknown,
  A joy unspeakable.

6 And if our fellowship below
  In Jesus be so sweet,
What height of rapture shall we know
  When round his throne we meet!

CHARLES WESLEY.

ELIZABETHTOWN.   C. M.   GEORGE KINGSLEY.

790   *Safety in union.*

1 JESUS, great Shepherd of the sheep,
  To thee for help we fly;
Thy little flock in safety keep,
  For O, the wolf is nigh!

2 He comes, of hellish malice full,
  To scatter, tear, and slay;
He seizes every straggling soul
  As his own lawful prey.

3 Us into thy protection take,
  And gather with thine arm;
Unless the fold we first forsake,
  The wolf can never harm.

4 We laugh to scorn his cruel power
  While by our Shepherd's side;
The sheep he never can devour,
  Unless he first divide.

5 O do not suffer him to part
  The souls that here agree;
But make us of one mind and heart,
  And keep us one in thee.

6 Together let us sweetly live,
  Together let us die;
And each a starry crown receive,
  And reign above the sky.

CHARLES WESLEY.

TICHORAH. L. M.  LOWELL MASON.

791 *Welcome to Church fellowship.*

1 BRETHREN in Christ, and well beloved,
 To Jesus and his servants dear,
Enter, and show yourselves approved;
 Enter, and find that God is here.

2 Welcome from earth: lo, the right hand
 Of fellowship to you we give!
With open hearts and hands we stand,
 And you in Jesus' name receive.

3 Jesus, attend; thyself reveal;
 Are we not met in thy great name?
Thee in the midst we wait to feel;
 We wait to catch the spreading flame.

4 Truly our fellowship below
 With thee and with the Father is:
In thee eternal life we know,
 And heaven's unutterable bliss.

5 Though but in part we know thee here,
 We wait thy coming from above;
And we shall then behold thee near,
 And be forever lost in love.
CHARLES WESLEY.

FIRST PART.

792 *Striving together for the faith
 of the gospel.*

1 UNCHANGEABLE, almighty Lord,
 Our souls upon thy truth we stay;
Accomplish now thy faithful word,
 And give, O give us all one way.

2 O let us all join hand in hand,
 Who seek redemption in thy blood;
Fast in one mind and spirit stand,
 And build the temple of our God.

3 Thou only canst our wills control,
 Our wild, unruly passions bind,
Tame the old Adam in our soul,
 And make us of one heart and mind.

4 Speak but the reconciling word,—
 The winds shall cease, the waves sub-
 side;
We all shall praise our common Lord,
 Our Jesus, and him crucified.
CHARLES WESLEY.

SECOND PART.

793 *One fold and one Shepherd.*

1 GIVER of peace and unity,
 Send down thy mild, pacific Dove;
We all shall then in one agree,
 And breathe the spirit of thy love.

2 We all shall think and speak the same
 Delightful lesson of thy grace;
One undivided Christ proclaim,
 And jointly glory in thy praise.

3 O let us take a softer mold,
 Blended and gathered into thee;
Under one Shepherd make one fold,
 Where all is love and harmony.

4 Regard thine own eternal prayer,
 And send a peaceful answer down;
To us thy Father's name declare;
 Unite and perfect us in one.

5 So shall the world believe and know,
 That God hath sent thee from above,
When thou art seen in us below,
 And every soul displays thy love.
CHARLES WESLEY.

LINWOOD. L. M.   GIOACCHINO ROSSINI.

794 *The heavenly Guest invited.*

1 SAVIOUR of all, to thee we bow,
  And own thee faithful to thy word;
We hear thy voice, and open now
  Our hearts to entertain our Lord.

2 Come in, come in, thou heavenly Guest;
  Delight in what thyself hast given;
On thy own gifts and graces feast,
  And make the contrite heart thy heaven.

3 Smell the sweet odor of our prayers;
  Our sacrifice of praise approve;
And treasure up our gracious tears,
  Who rest in thy redeeming love.

4 Beneath thy shadow let us sit;
  Call us thy friends, and love, and bride,
And bid us freely drink and eat
  Thy dainties, and be satisfied.
                              CHARLES WESLEY.

795 *Glorious and spotless.*

1 JESUS, from whom all blessings flow,
Great Builder of thy Church below,
If now thy Spirit move my breast,
Hear, and fulfill thine own request.

2 The few that truly call thee Lord,
And wait thy sanctifying word,
And thee their utmost Saviour own,—
Unite and perfect them in one.

3 O let them all thy mind express,
Stand forth thy chosen witnesses,
Thy power unto salvation show,
And perfect holiness below.

4 In them let all mankind behold
How Christians lived in days of old;
Mighty their envious foes to move,
A proverb of reproach—and love.
                              CHARLES WESLEY.

796 *One now, one forever.*

1 STILL one in life and one in death,
  One in our hope of rest above,
One in our joy, our trust, our faith,
  One in each other's faithful love;

2 Yet must we part, and parting weep;
  What else has earth for us in store?
Our farewell pangs, how sharp and deep!
  Our farewell words, how sad and sore!

3 Yet shall we meet again in peace,
  To sing the song of festal joy,
Where none shall bid our gladness cease,
  And none our fellowship destroy:

4 Where none shall beckon us away,
  Nor bid our festival be done;
Our meeting-time the eternal day,
  Our meeting-place the eternal throne.

5 There, hand in hand, firm-linked at last,
  And heart to heart enfolded all,
We'll smile upon the troubled past,
  And wonder why we wept at all.
                              HORATIUS BONAR.

Doxology.

PRAISE God, from whom all blessings flow,
Praise him, all creatures here below;
Praise him above, ye heavenly host;
Praise Father, Son, and Holy Ghost!
                              THOMAS KEN.

THE CHURCH—FELLOWSHIP AND UNITY.

DENNIS.   S. M.   HANS GEORGE NAEGELI.

797   *Sympathy and mutual love.*

1 BLEST be the tie that binds
   Our hearts in Christian love;
The fellowship of kindred minds
   Is like to that above.

2 Before our Father's throne,
   We pour our ardent prayers;
Our fears, our hopes, our aims are one,
   Our comforts and our cares.

3 We share our mutual woes,
   Our mutual burdens bear;
And often for each other flows
   The sympathizing tear.

4 When we asunder part,
   It gives us inward pain;
But we shall still be joined in heart,
   And hope to meet again.

5 This glorious hope revives
   Our courage by the way;
While each in expectation lives,
   And longs to see the day.

6 From sorrow, toil, and pain,
   And sin we shall be free;
And perfect love and friendship reign
   Through all eternity.
                                        JOHN FAWCETT.

798   *Meeting, after absence.*

1 AND are we yet alive,
   And see each other's face?
Glory and praise to Jesus give,
   For his redeeming grace.

Preserved by power divine
   To full salvation here,
Again in Jesus' praise we join,
   And in his sight appear.

2 What troubles have we seen,
   What conflicts have we passed,
Fightings without, and fears within,
   Since we assembled last!
But out of all the Lord
   Hath brought us by his love;
And still he doth his help afford,
   And hides our life above.

3 Then let us make our boast
   Of his redeeming power,
Which saves us to the uttermost,
   Till we can sin no more:
Let us take up the cross,
   Till we the crown obtain;
And gladly reckon all things loss,
   So we may Jesus gain.
                                        CHARLES WESLEY.

799   *Blest communion.*

1 BLEST are the sons of peace,
   Whose hearts and hopes are one;
Whose kind designs to serve and please
   Through all their actions run.

2 Blest is the pious house
   Where zeal and friendship meet;
Their songs of praise, their mingled vows,
   Make their communion sweet.

3 Thus on the heavenly hills
   The saints are blest above,
Where joy like morning dew distills,
   And all the air is love.
                                        ISAAC WATTS.

ST. EBBE. H. M.   RICHARD REDHEAD.

One Lord, one faith, one baptism.
Eph. 4 : 5.

1 ONE sole baptismal sign,
  One Lord below, above,
One faith, one hope divine,
  One only watchword, love:
From different temples though it rise,
One song ascendeth to the skies.

2 Our Sacrifice is one;
  One Priest before the throne,
The slain, the risen Son,
  Redeemer, Lord alone:
Thou who didst raise him from the dead,
Unite thy people in their Head.

3 O may that holy prayer,
  His tenderest and his last,
His constant, latest care
  Ere to his throne he passed,
No longer unfulfilled remain,
The world's offense, his people's stain!

4 Head of thy Church beneath,
  The catholic, the true,
On all her members breathe,
  Her broken frame renew:
Then shall thy perfect will be done,
When Christians love and live as one.
                GEORGE ROBINSON.

801 *Bear ye one another's burdens.*

1 THOU God of truth and love,
  We seek thy perfect way,
Ready thy choice to approve,
  Thy providence to obey;

Enter into thy wise design,
And sweetly lose our will in thine.

2 Why hast thou cast our lot
  In the same age and place?
And why together brought
  To see each other's face;
To join with softest sympathy,
And mix our friendly souls in thee?

3 Didst thou not make us one,
  That we might one remain;
Together travel on,
  And bear each other's pain;
Till all thy utmost goodness prove,
And rise renewed in perfect love?

4 Surely thou didst unite
  Our kindred spirits here,
That all hereafter might
  Before thy throne appear;
Meet at the marriage of the Lamb,
And all thy gracious love proclaim.

5 Then let us ever bear
  The blessed end in view,
And join, with mutual care,
  To fight our passage through;
And kindly help each other on,
Till all receive the starry crown.

6 O may thy Spirit seal
  Our souls unto that day,
With all thy fullness fill,
  And then transport away,—
Away to our eternal rest,
Away to our Redeemer's breast!
                CHARLES WESLEY.

NUREMBERG. 7.

JOHANN RUDOLF AHLE.

802 *Sweet counsel.*

1 GLORY be to God above,
  God, from whom all blessings flow;
Make we mention of his love,
  Publish we his praise below:

2 Called together by his grace,
  We are met in Jesus' name;
See with joy each other's face,
  Followers of the bleeding Lamb.

3 Build we each the other up;
  Pray we for our faith's increase;
Solid comfort, settled hope,
  Constant joy, and lasting peace.

4 More and more let love abound;
  Let us never, never rest,
Till we are in Jesus found,
  Of our paradise possessed.
                          CHARLES WESLEY.

803 *Love, the bond of union.*

1 WHILE we walk with God in light,
God our hearts doth still unite;
Dearest fellowship we prove,
Fellowship in Jesus' love:
Sweetly each, with each combined,
In the bonds of duty joined,
Feels the cleansing blood applied,
Daily feels that Christ hath died.

2 Still, O Lord, our faith increase,
Cleanse from all unrighteousness;
Thee the unholy cannot see,
Make, O make us meet for thee;
Every vile affection kill,
Root out every seed of ill,
Utterly abolish sin,
Write thy law of love within.

3 Hence may all our actions flow,
Love the proof that Christ we know;
Mutual love the token be,
Lord, that we belong to thee:
Love, thine image, love impart;
Stamp it now on every heart:
Only love to us be given;
Lord, we ask no other heaven.
                          CHARLES WESLEY.

804 *Of one heart and mind.*

1 JESUS, Lord, we look to thee;
Let us in thy name agree;
Show thyself the Prince of peace;
Bid our jars forever cease.

2 By thy reconciling love,
Every stumbling-block remove;
Each to each unite, endear,
Come, and spread thy banner here.

3 Make us of one heart and mind,
Courteous, pitiful, and kind,
Lowly, meek, in thought and word,
Altogether like our Lord.

4 Let us for each other care,
Each the other's burden bear;
To thy Church the pattern give,
Show how true believers live.

5 Free from anger and from pride,
Let us thus in God abide;
All the depths of love express,
All the heights of holiness.

6 Let us then with joy remove
To the family above;
On the wings of angels fly;
Show how true believers die.
                          CHARLES WESLEY.

THE CHURCH—FELLOWSHIP AND UNITY.

ONIDO.   7. D.

IGNACE PLEYEL.

805 *Witnesses for Jesus.*

1 COME, and let us sweetly join,
Christ to praise in hymns divine;
Give we all, with one accord,
Glory to our common Lord;
Hands, and hearts, and voices raise;
Sing as in the ancient days;
Anticipate the joys above,
Celebrate the feast of love.

2 Strive we, in affection strive;
Let the purer flame revive,
Such as in the martyrs glowed,
Dying champions for their God:
We like them may live and love;
Called we are their joys to prove,
Saved with them from future wrath,
Partners of like precious faith.

3 Sing we, then, in Jesus' name,
Now as yesterday the same;
One in every time and place,
Full for all of truth and grace:
We for Christ, our Master, stand,
Lights in a benighted land:
We our dying Lord confess;
We are Jesus' witnesses.

CHARLES WESLEY.

806   *Many, but one.*

1 CHRIST, from whom all blessings flow,
Perfecting the saints below,
Hear us, who thy nature share,
Who thy mystic body are.
Join us, in one spirit join,
Let us still receive of thine;
Still for more on thee we call,
Thou who fillest all in all.

2 Move, and actuate, and guide,
Divers gifts to each divide;
Placed according to thy will,
Let us all our work fulfill;
Never from our office move;
Needful to each other prove;
Let us daily growth receive,
More and more in Jesus live.

3 Sweetly may we all agree,
Touched with softest sympathy;
Kindly for each other care;
Every member feel its share.
Many are we now and one,
We who Jesus have put on;
Names, and sects, and parties fall:
Thou, O Christ, art all in all.

CHARLES WESLEY.

UNITY. 6, 5. LOWELL MASON.

807 *When shall we meet again?*

1 WHEN shall we meet again,
    Meet ne'er to sever?
When will peace wreathe her chain
    Round us forever?
Our hearts will ne'er repose,
Safe from each blast that blows,
In this dark vale of woes,
    Never—no, never!

2 When shall love freely flow
    Pure as life's river?
When shall sweet friendship glow
    Changeless forever?
Where joys celestial thrill,
Where bliss each heart shall fill,
And fears of parting chill
    Never—no, never!

3 Up to that world of light
    Take us, dear Saviour;
May we all there unite,
    Happy forever;
Where kindred spirits dwell,
There may our music swell,
And time our joys dispel
    Never—no, never!

4 Soon shall we meet again,
    Meet ne'er to sever;
Soon shall peace wreathe her chain
    Round us forever:
Our hearts will then repose
Secure from worldly woes;
Our songs of praise shall close
    Never—no, never!

ALARIC A. WATTS.

302

CLARE. 7, 6.   HUBERT P. MAIN.

808 *Ministers' prayer.*

1 LORD of the living harvest
    That whitens o'er the plain,
Where angels soon shall gather
    Their sheaves of golden grain;
Accept these hands to labor,
    These hearts to trust and love,
And deign with them to hasten
    Thy kingdom from above.

2 As laborers in thy vineyard,
    Send us, O Christ, to be
Content to bear the burden
    Of weary days for thee;
We ask no other wages,
    When thou shalt call us home,
But to have shared the travail
    Which makes thy kingdom come.

3 Come down, thou Holy Spirit!
    And fill our souls with light,
Clothe us in spotless raiment.
    In linen clean and white;
Beside thy sacred altar
    Be with us, where we stand,
To sanctify thy people
    Through all this happy land.

JOHN S. B. MONSELL.

[C. P. M. Tune, Meribah. Page 358.]

809 *Entire dependence on Christ.*

1 EXCEPT the Lord conduct the plan,
The best concerted schemes are vain,
    And never can succeed;
We spend our wretched strength for naught
But if our works in thee be wrought,
    They shall be blest indeed.

2 Lord, if thou didst thyself inspire
Our souls with this intense desire
    Thy goodness to proclaim;
Thy glory if we now intend,
O let our deeds begin and end
    Complete in Jesus' name.

3 Now, Jesus, now thy love impart,
To govern each devoted heart,
    And fit us for thy will;
Deep founded in the truth of grace,
Build up thy rising Church, and place
    The city on the hill.

4 O let our love and faith abound;
O let our lives, to all around,
    With purest luster shine;
That all around our works may see,
And give the glory, Lord, to thee,
    The heavenly light divine.

CHARLES WESLEY.

MIGDOL. L. M. LOWELL MASON.

810 *Heralds of the cross.*

1 Go forth, ye heralds, in My name,
  Sweetly the gospel trumpet sound;
The glorious jubilee proclaim,
  Where'er the human race is found.

2 The joyful news to all impart,
  And teach them where salvation lies;
With care bind up the broken heart,
  And wipe the tears from weeping eyes.

3 Be wise as serpents, where you go,
  But harmless as the peaceful dove;
And let your heaven-taught conduct show
  Ye are commissioned from above.

4 Freely from me ye have received,
  Freely, in love, to others give;
Thus shall your doctrines be believed,
  And, by your labors, sinners live.
                              JOHN LOGAN.

811 *He giveth the increase.*

1 HIGH on his everlasting throne,
  The King of saints his work surveys;
Marks the dear souls he calls his own,
  And smiles on the peculiar race.

2 He rests well pleased their toils to see;
  Beneath his easy yoke they move;
With all their heart and strength agree
  In the sweet labor of his love.

3 See where the servants of the Lord,
  A busy multitude, appear;
For Jesus day and night employed,
  His heritage they toil to clear.

4 The love of Christ their hearts constrains,
  And strengthens their unwearied hands;
They spend their sweat, and blood, and pains,
  To cultivate Immanuel's lands.

5 Jesus their toil delighted sees,
  Their industry vouchsafes to crown;
He kindly gives the wished increase,
  And sends the promised blessing down.
        AUGUSTUS G. SPANGENBERG. TR. BY J. WESLEY.

812 *The ministry instituted.*

1 THE Saviour, when to heaven he rose,
In splendid triumph o'er his foes,
Scattered his gifts on men below,
And still his royal bounties flow.

2 Hence sprang the apostles' honored name,
Sacred beyond heroic fame:
In humbler forms, before our eyes,
Pastors and teachers hence arise.

3 From Christ they all their gifts derive,
And, fed by Christ, their graces live;
While, guarded by his mighty hand,
'Midst all the rage of hell they stand.

4 So shall the bright succession run
Through all the courses of the sun;
While unborn churches, by their care,
Shall rise and flourish large and fair.

5 Jesus, now teach our hearts to know
The spring whence all these blessings flow;
Pastors and people shout thy praise,
Through the long round of endless days.
                              PHILIP DODDRIDGE.

BARTHOLDY.   L. M.   FELIX MENDELSSOHN-BARTHOLDY.

FIRST PART.

813   *Boldness in the gospel.*

1 SHALL I, for fear of feeble man,
The Spirit's course in me restrain?
Or, undismayed in deed and word,
Be a true witness of my Lord?

2 Awed by a mortal's frown, shall I
Conceal the word of God most high?
How then before thee shall I dare
To stand, or how thine anger bear?

3 Shall I, to soothe the unholy throng,
Soften thy truth, or smooth my tongue,
To gain earth's gilded toys, or flee
The cross endured, my Lord, by thee?

4 What, then, is he whose scorn I dread,
Whose wrath or hate makes me afraid?
A man! an heir of death! a slave
To sin! a bubble on the wave!

5 Yea, let men rage; since thou wilt spread
Thy shadowing wings around my head;
Since in all pain thy tender love
Will still my sure refreshment prove.
          JOHANN J. WINKLER.   TR. BY J. WESLEY.

SECOND PART.

814   *Christ's constraining love.*

1 SAVIOUR of men, thy searching eye
Doth all mine inmost thoughts descry;
Doth aught on earth my wishes raise,
Or the world's pleasures, or its praise?

2 The love of Christ doth me constrain
To seek the wandering souls of men;
With cries, entreaties, tears, to save,—
To snatch them from the gaping grave.

3 For this let men revile my name;
No cross I shun, I fear no shame:
All hail, reproach; and welcome, pain;
Only thy terrors, Lord, restrain.

4 My life, my blood, I here present,
If for thy truth they may be spent;
Fulfill thy sovereign counsel, Lord;
Thy will be done, thy name adored.

5 Give me thy strength, O God of power.
Then let winds blow, or thunders roar,
Thy faithful witness will I be:
'Tis fixed; I can do all through thee.
          JOHANN J. WINKLER.   TR. BY J. WESLEY.

815   *The angels of the Churches.*

1 DRAW near, O Son of God, draw near,
Us with thy flaming eye behold;
Still in thy Church do thou appear,
And let our candlestick be gold.

2 Still hold the stars in thy right hand,
And let them in thy luster glow,
The lights of a benighted land,
The angels of thy Church below.

3 Make good their apostolic boast;
Their high commission let them prove;
Be temples of the Holy Ghost,
And filled with faith, and hope, and
love.

4 Give them an ear to hear thy word;
Thou speakest to the churches now:
And let all tongues confess their Lord;
Let every knee to Jesus bow.
                    CHARLES WESLEY.

OLMUTZ.   S. M.   GREGORIAN CHANT, ARR. BY LOWELL MASON.

816 *Laborers in the vineyard.*

1 AND let our bodies part,
  To different climes repair;
Inseparably joined in heart
  The friends of Jesus are.

2 O let us still proceed
  In Jesus' work below;
And, following our triumphant Head,
  To further conquests go.

3 The vineyard of the Lord
  Before his laborers lies;
And lo! we see the vast reward
  Which waits us in the skies.

4 O that our heart and mind
  May evermore ascend,
That haven of repose to find,
  Where all our labors end;

5 Where all our toils are o'er,
  Our suffering and our pain!
Who meet on that eternal shore
  Shall never part again.

6 O happy, happy place,
  Where saints and angels meet!
There we shall see each other's face,
  And all our brethren greet:

7 The Church of the first-born,
  We shall with them be blest,
And, crowned with endless joy, return
  To our eternal rest.
                        CHARLES WESLEY.

817 *Success certain.*

1 LORD, if at thy command
  The word of life we sow,
Watered by thy almighty hand,
  The seed shall surely grow:

The virtue of thy grace
  A large increase shall give,
And multiply the faithful race
  Who to thy glory live.

2 Now, then, the ceaseless shower
  Of gospel blessings send,
And let the soul-converting power
  Thy ministers attend.
On multitudes confer
  The heart-renewing love,
And by the joy of grace prepare
  For fuller joys above.
                        CHARLES WESLEY.

818 *The laborers are few.*

1 LORD of the harvest, hear
  Thy needy servants' cry;
Answer our faith's effectual prayer,
  And all our wants supply.

2 On thee we humbly wait;
  Our wants are in thy view;
The harvest, truly, Lord, is great,
  The laborers are few.

3 Convert and send forth more
  Into thy Church abroad,
And let them speak thy word of power
  As workers with their God.

4 O let them spread thy name,
  Their mission fully prove;
Thy universal grace proclaim,
  Thine all-redeeming love.
                        CHARLES WESLEY.

Doxology.

To God, the Father, Son,
  And Spirit, One in Three,
Be glory, as it was, is now,
  And shall forever be.
                        JOHN WESLEY.

GRISWOLD.　　L. M.　　　　　　　　　　　　　　　　UNKNOWN.

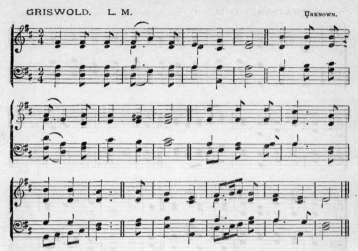

819 *For the success of ministers.*

1 FATHER of mercies, bow thine ear,
 Attentive to our earnest prayer:
We plead for those who plead for thee;
 Successful pleaders may they be.

2 O clothe their words with power divine,
 And let those words be ever thine;
To them thy sacred truth reveal;
 Suppress their fear, inflame their zeal.

3 Teach them to sow the precious seed;
 Teach them thy chosen flock to feed;
Teach them immortal souls to gain,
 Nor let them labor, Lord, in vain.

4 Let thronging multitudes around
 Hear from their lips the joyful sound,
In humble strains thy grace implore,
 And feel thy Spirit's living power.
　　　　　　　　　　　　BENJAMIN BEDDOME.

[L. M. Missionary Chant. Page 220.]

820　　　*The commission.*

1 "GO, preach my gospel," saith the Lord,
 "Bid the whole world my grace receive;
He shall be saved who trusts my word;
 He shall be damned who won't believe.

2 "I'll make your great commission known;
 And ye shall prove my gospel true,
By all the works that I have done,
 By all the wonders ye shall do.

3 "Teach all the nations my commands,
 I'm with you till the world shall end;
All power is trusted in my hands,
 I can destroy, and I defend."
　　　　　　　　　　　　ISAAC WATTS.

[S. M. Tune, Olmutz. Page 306.]

821　　　*The joyful sound.*

1 How beauteous are their feet
 Who stand on Zion's hill,
Who bring salvation on their tongues,
 And words of peace reveal!

2 How charming is their voice,
 How sweet the tidings are!
"Zion, behold thy Saviour King;
 He reigns and triumphs here."

3 How happy are our ears,
 That hear the joyful sound,
Which kings and prophets waited for,
 And sought, but never found!

4 How blessed are our eyes,
 That see this heavenly light!
Prophets and kings desired it long,
 But died without the sight.

5 The watchmen join their voice,
 And tuneful notes employ;
Jerusalem breaks forth in songs,
 And deserts learn the joy.

6 The Lord makes bare his arm
 Through all the earth abroad;
Let every nation now behold
 Their Saviour and their God.
　　　　　　　　　　　　ISAAC WATTS.

Doxology.

PRAISE God, from whom all blessings flow
Praise him, all creatures here below;
Praise him above, ye heavenly host;
Praise Father, Son, and Holy Ghost.
　　　　　　　　　　　　THOMAS KEN.

CORONATION. C. M.   OLIVER HOLDEN.

822 *The minister's only business.*

1 JESUS! the name high over all,
  In hell, or earth, or sky;
Angels and men before it fall,
  And devils fear and fly.

2 Jesus! the name to sinners dear,
  The name to sinners given;
It scatters all their guilty fear;
  It turns their hell to heaven.

3 Jesus the prisoner's fetters breaks,
  And bruises Satan's head;
Power into strengthless souls he speaks,
  And life into the dead.

4 O that the world might taste and see
  The riches of his grace!
The arms of love that compass me
  Would all mankind embrace.

5 His only righteousness I show,
  His saving truth proclaim:
'Tis all my business here below,
  To cry, "Behold the Lamb!"

6 Happy, if with my latest breath
  I may but gasp his name;
Preach him to all, and cry in death,
  "Behold, behold the Lamb!"
                                CHARLES WESLEY.

823 *The pastoral office.*

1 LET Zion's watchmen all awake,
  And take the alarm they give;
Now let them from the mouth of God
  Their solemn charge receive.

2 'Tis not a cause of small import
  The pastor's care demands;
But what might fill an angel's heart,
  And filled a Saviour's hands.

3 They watch for souls for which the Lord
  Did heavenly bliss forego;
For souls which must forever live
  In raptures or in woe.

4 May they that Jesus, whom they preach,
  Their own Redeemer see;
And watch thou daily o'er their souls,
  That they may watch for thee.
                                PHILIP DODDRIDGE.

824 *Clothed with salvation.*

1 JESUS, the word of mercy give,
  And let it swiftly run;
And let the priests themselves believe,
  And put salvation on.

2 Jesus, let all thy servants shine
  Illustrious as the sun;
And, bright with borrowed rays divine,
  Their glorious circuit run.

3 As giants may they run their race,
  Exulting in their might;
As burning luminaries, chase
  The gloom of hellish night.

4 As the bright Sun of righteousness
  Their healing wings display;
And let their luster still increase
  Unto the perfect day.
                                CHARLES WESLEY.

VALETE. L. M. 6l.

Sir Arthur Seymour Sullivan.

825 *Training the soldiers of Christ.*

1 CAPTAIN of our salvation, take
    The souls we here present to thee,
And fit for thy great service make
    These heirs of immortality;
And let them in thine image rise,
And then transplant to paradise.

2 Unspotted from the world, and pure,
    Preserve them for thy glorious cause,
Accustomed daily to endure
    The welcome burden of thy cross;
Inured to toil and patient pain,
Till all thy perfect mind they gain.

3 Train up thy hardy soldiers, Lord,
    In all their Captain's steps to tread;
Or send them to proclaim the word,
    Thy gospel through the world to spread;
Freely as they receive to give,
And preach the death by which we live.

CHARLES WESLEY.

826 *Baptismal hymn.*

1 I AM baptized into thy name,
    O Father, Son, and Holy Ghost!
Among thy seed a place I claim,
    Among thy consecrated host;
Buried with Christ and dead to sin,
Thy Spirit now shall live within.

2 My loving Father, here dost thou
    Proclaim me as thy child and heir;
Thou, faithful Saviour, bidd'st me now
    The fruit of all thy sorrows share;
Thou, Holy Ghost, wilt comfort me
When darkest clouds around I see.

3 Hence, Prince of darkness! hence, my
        foe!
    Another Lord hath purchased me;
My conscience tells of sin, yet know,
    Baptized in Christ, I fear not thee:
Away, vain world! sin, leave me now!
I turn from you; God hears my vow.

4 And never let me waver more,
    O Father, Son, and Holy Ghost;
Till at thy will this life is o'er,
    Still keep me in thy faithful host,
So unto thee I live and die,
And praise thee evermore on high.

J. J. RAMBACH. TR. BY MISS C. WINKWORTH

Doxology.

IMMORTAL honor, endless fame,
Attend the almighty Father's name:
The Saviour Son be glorified,
Who for lost man's redemption died;
And equal adoration be,
Eternal Comforter, to thee!

JOHN DRYDEN.

SERENITY.   C. M.   WILLIAM VINCENT WALLACE.

827 *Suffer the little ones to come unto Me.*

1 SEE, Israel's gentle Shepherd stands
    With all-engaging charms;
Hark, how he calls the tender lambs,
    And folds them in his arms!

2 "Permit them to approach," he cries,
    "Nor scorn their humble name;
For 'twas to bless such souls as these
    The Lord of angels came."

3 We bring them, Lord, in thankful hands,
    And yield them up to thee;
Joyful that we ourselves are thine,
    Thine let our offspring be.
                        PHILIP DODDRIDGE.

828 *Children in the arms of Jesus.*

1 BEHOLD what condescending love
    Jesus on earth displays!
To little children he extends
    The riches of his grace.

2 He still the ancient promise keeps,
    To our forefathers given;
Our infants in his arms he takes,
    And calls them heirs of heaven.

3 Forbid them not, whom Jesus calls,
    Nor dare the claim resist,
Since his own lips to us declare
    Of such will heaven consist.

4 With flowing tears, and thankful hearts,
    We give them up to thee;
Receive them, Lord, into thine arms;
    Thine may they ever be.
        JOHN PEACOCK, AUGUSTUS M. TOPLADY.

829 *Significance of baptism.*

1 O LORD, while we confess the worth
    Of this the outward seal,

Do thou the truths herein set forth
    To every heart reveal.

2 Death to the world we here avow,
    Death to each fleshly lust;
Newness of life our calling now,
    A risen Lord our trust.

3 And we, O Lord, who now partake
    Of resurrection life,
With every sin, for thy dear sake,
    Would be at constant strife.

4 Baptized into the Father's name,
    We'd walk as sons of God;
Baptized in thine, we own thy claim
    As ransomed by thy blood.

5 Baptized into the Holy Ghost,
    We'd keep his temple pure,
And make thy grace our only boast,
    And by thy strength endure.
                        MARY P. BOWLY.

[S. M.   Tune, Dennis.   Page 298.

830   *Rites inefficacious.*

1 RITES cannot change the heart,
    Undo the evil done,
Or with the uttered name impart
    The nature of thy Son.

2 To meet our desperate want,
    There gushed a crimson flood:
O from his heart's o'erflowing font
    Baptize this soul with blood!

3 Be grace from Christ our Lord,
    And love from God supreme,
By the communing Spirit poured
    In a perpetual stream!
                    WILLIAM M. BUNTING.

WARD. L. M.   SCOTCH TUNE, ARR. BY LOWELL MASON.

831 *The sacramental seal.*

1 COME, Father, Son, and Holy Ghost,
  Honor the means ordained by thee;
Make good our apostolic boast,
  And own thy glorious ministry.

2 We now thy promised blessing claim;
  Sent to disciple all mankind,
Sent to baptize into thy name,
  We now thy promised presence find.

3 Father, in these reveal thy Son;
  In these, for whom we seek thy face,
The hidden mystery make known,
  The inward, pure, baptizing grace.

4 Jesus, with us thou always art;
  Effectual make the sacred sign;
The gift unspeakable impart,
  And bless the ordinance divine.

5 Eternal Spirit, from on high,
  Baptizer of our spirits thou,
The sacramental seal apply,
  And witness with the water now.
                              CHARLES WESLEY.

832 *At a child's baptism.*

1 THIS child we dedicate to thee,
O God of grace and purity!
Shield it from sin and threatening wrong,
And let thy love its life prolong.

2 O may thy Spirit gently draw
Its willing soul to keep thy law;
May virtue, piety, and truth,
Dawn even with its dawning youth.

3 We, too, before thy gracious sight,
once shared the blest baptismal rite,

And would renew its solemn vow
With love, and thanks, and praises, now.

4 Grant that, with true and faithful heart,
We still may act the Christian's part.
Cheered by each promise thou hast given,
And laboring for the prize in heaven.
                              TR. BY S. GILMAN.

[L. M. 61. Tune, Selena. Page 82.]

833 *The Lord's Supper instituted.*

1 IN that sad, memorable night,
  When Jesus was for us betrayed,
He left his death-recording rite:
  He took, and blest, and brake the bread:
And gave his own their last bequest,
And thus his love's intent expressed:

2 "Take, eat, this is my body, given
  To purchase life and peace for you,
Pardon, and holiness, and heaven:
  Do this, my dying love to show:
Accept your precious legacy,
And thus, my friends, remember me."

3 He took into his hands the cup,
  To crown the sacramental feast,
And, full of kind concern, looked up,
  And gave to them what he had blest;
And, "Drink ye all of this," he said,
"In solemn memory of the dead."

4 "This is my blood, which seals the new
  Eternal covenant of my grace;
My blood, so freely shed for you,
  For you and all the sinful race;
My blood, that speaks your sins forgiven,
And justifies your claim to heaven."
                              CHARLES WESLEY.

DUNDEE.   C. M.

GUILLAUME FRANC.

834   *The invitation.*

1 THE King of heaven his table spreads,
 And blessings crown the board;
Not paradise, with all its joys, .
 Could such delight afford.

2 Pardon and peace to dying men,
 And endless life are given,
Through the rich blood that Jesus shed
 To raise our souls to heaven.

3 Millions of souls, in glory now,
 Were fed and feasted here;
And millions more, still on the way,
 Around the board appear.

4 All things are ready, come away,
 Nor weak excuses frame;
Crowd to your places at the feast,
 And bless the Founder's name.
 PHILIP DODDRIDGE.

835   *Approaching the table.*

1 JESUS, at whose supreme command,
 We now approach to God,
Before us in thy vesture stand,
 Thy vesture dipped in blood.

2 The tokens of thy dying love
 O let us all receive,
And feel the quickening Spirit move,
 And sensibly believe.

3 The cup of blessing, blest by thee,
 Let it thy blood impart;
The bread thy mystic body be,
 To cheer each languid heart.

4 The living bread sent down from heaven,
 In us vouchsafe to be:
Thy flesh for all the world is given,
 And all may live by thee.
 CHARLES WESLEY.

836   *Grateful remembrance.*

1 ACCORDING to thy gracious word.
 In meek humility,
This will I do, my dying Lord,
 I will remember thee!

2 Thy body, broken for my sake,
 My bread from heaven shall be;
Thy testamental cup I take,
 And thus remember thee!

3 Gethsemane can I forget?
 Or there thy conflict see,
Thine agony and bloody sweat,
 And not remember thee?

4 When to the cross I turn mine eyes,
 And rest on Calvary,
O Lamb of God, my Sacrifice,
 I must remember thee!

5 Remember thee, and all thy pains,
 And all thy love to me;
Yea, while a breath, a pulse remains,
 Will I remember thee!

6 And when these failing lips grow dumb,
 And mind and memory flee,
When thou shalt in thy kingdom come,
 Jesus, remember me!
 JAMES MONTGOMERY.

SIMPSON.   C. M.

FROM LOUIS SPOHR.

837 *Rich gifts of gospel grace.*

1 O LOVE divine! O matchless grace!
  Which in this sacred rite
Shines forth so full, so free, in rays
  Of purest living light.

2 O wondrous death! O precious blood!
  For us so freely spilt,
To cleanse our sin-polluted souls
  From every stain of guilt.

3 O covenant of life and peace,
  By blood and suffering sealed!
All the rich gifts of gospel grace
  Are here to faith revealed.

4 Jesus, we bow our souls to thee,
  Our life, our hope, our all,
While we, with thankful, contrite hearts,
  Thy dying love recall.

5 O may thy pure and perfect love
  Be written on our minds;
Nor earth, nor self, nor sin obscure
  The ever-radiant lines.

EDWARD TURNEY.

838 *The sacred feast.*

1 In memory of the Saviour's love,
  We keep the sacred feast,
Where every humble, contrite heart
  Is made a welcome guest.

2 By faith we take the bread of life,
  With which our souls are fed;
The cup, in token of his blood,
  That was for sinners shed.

3 Under his banner thus we sing
  The wonders of his love,
And thus anticipate by faith
  The heavenly feast above.

UNKNOWN.

839 *Gratitude and love.*

1 If human kindness meets return,
  And owns the grateful tie;
If tender thoughts within us burn
  To feel a friend is nigh;

2 O shall not warmer accents tell
  The gratitude we owe
To Him who died our fears to quell,
  And save from endless woe?

3 While yet in anguish he surveyed
  Those pangs he would not flee,
What love his latest words displayed!
  "Meet, and remember me."

4 Remember thee! thy death, thy shame,
  The griefs which thou didst bear!
O memory, leave no other name
  So deeply graven there.

GERARD T. NOEL.

840 *He died for me.*

1 THAT doleful night before his death,
  The Lamb, for sinners slain,
Did, almost with his dying breath,
  This solemn feast ordain.

2 To keep the feast, Lord, we have met,
  And to remember thee:
Help each poor trembler to repeat,
  "For me he died, for me!"

3 Thy sufferings, Lord, each sacred sign
  To our remembrance brings;
We eat the bread, and drink the wine,
  But think on nobler things.

4 O tune our tongues, and set in frame
  Each heart that pants for thee,
To sing, "Hosanna to the Lamb,
  The Lamb that died for me!"

JOSEPH HART.

PRAYER. S. M.   LEONARD MARSHALL.

841   *Universal gladness.*

1 GLORY to God on high,
  Our peace is made with Heaven;
The Son of God came down to die,
  That we might be forgiven.

2 His precious blood was shed,
  His body bruised, for sin:
Remember this in eating bread,
  And this in drinking wine.

3 Approach his royal board,
  In his rich garments clad;
Join every tongue to praise the Lord,
  And every heart be glad.

4 The Father gives the Son;
  The Son, his flesh and blood;
The Spirit seals; and faith puts on
  The righteousness of God.
                  JOSEPH HART.

842   *A foretaste of glory.*

1 O WHAT delight is this,
  Which now in Christ we know,
An earnest of our glorious bliss,
  Our heaven begun below!

2 When he the table spreads,
  How royal is the cheer!
With rapture we lift up our heads,
  And own that God is here.

3 The Lamb for sinners slain,
  Who died to die no more,
Let all the ransomed sons of men,
  With all his hosts, adore.

4 Let earth and heaven be joined,
  His glories to display,
And hymn the Saviour of mankind
  In one eternal day.
                  CHARLES WESLEY.

843   *His the pain—ours the joy.*

1 No gospel like this feast
  Spread for Thy Church by thee;
Nor prophet nor evangelist
  Preach the glad news so free.

2 All our redemption cost,
  All our redemption won;
All it has won for us, the lost;
  All it cost thee, the Son.

3 Thine was the bitter price,
  Ours is the free gift, given;
Thine was the blood of sacrifice,
  Ours is the wine of heaven.

4 Here we would rest midway,
  As on a sacred height,
That darkest and that brightest day
  Meeting before our sight.

5 From that dark depth of woes
  Thy love for us has trod,
Up to the heights of blest repose
  Thy love prepares with God;

6 Till from self's chains released,
  One sight alone we see,
Still at the cross, as at the feast,
  Behold thee, only thee.
                  J. C. RYLE.

NASSAU.   7, 6l.   JOHANN ROSENMÜLLER.

Let the little while between
In their golden light be seen;
Let us think how heaven and home
Lie beyond that—"Till he come."

2 When the weary ones we love
Enter on their rest above,
Seems the earth so poor and vast,
All our life-joy overcast;
Hush, be every murmur dumb;
It is only—"Till he come."

3 See, the feast of love is spread,
Drink the wine, and break the bread:
Sweet memorials,—till the Lord
Call us round his heavenly board;
Some from earth, from glory some,
Severed only—"Till he come."
EDWARD H. BICKERSTETH.

844   *The memorial feast maintained.*

1 MANY centuries have fled
Since our Saviour broke the bread,
And this sacred feast ordained,
Ever by his Church retained:
Those his body who discern,
Thus shall meet till his return.

2 Through the Church's long eclipse,
When, from priest or pastor's lips,
Truth divine was never heard,—
'Mid the famine of the word,
Still these symbols witness gave
To his love who died to save.

3 All who bear the Saviour's name,
Here their common faith proclaim;
Though diverse in tongue or rite,
Here, one body, we unite;
Breaking thus one mystic bread,
Members of one common Head.

4 Come, the blessed emblems share,
Which the Saviour's death declare;
Come, on truth immortal feed;
For his flesh is meat indeed;
Saviour, witness with the sign,
That our ransomed souls are thine.
JOSIAH CONDER.

845   *Till He come.*

1 "TILL He come:" O let the words
Linger on the trembling chords:

[S. M. Tune, Prayer. Page 314.]

846   *Our Paschal Lamb.*

1 LET all who truly bear
The bleeding Saviour's name,
Their faithful hearts with us prepare,
And eat the Paschal Lamb.

2 This eucharistic feast
Our every want supplies,
And still we by his death are blest,
And share his sacrifice.

3 Who thus our faith employ,
His sufferings to record,
E'en now we mournfully enjoy
Communion with our Lord.

4 We too with him are dead,
And shall with him arise;
The cross on which he bows his head
Shall lift us to the skies.
CHARLES WESLEY.

INNOCENTS. 7.   ANON., ARR. BY WILLIAM HENRY MONK.

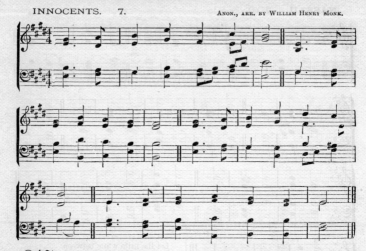

847 *Praise to our victorious King.*

1 AT the Lamb's high feast we sing
Praise to our victorious King,
Who hath washed us in the tide
Flowing from his piercéd side;

2 Praise we him, whose love divine
Gives his sacred blood for wine,
Gives his body for the feast,
Christ the Victim, Christ the Priest.

3 Where the paschal blood is poured,
Death's dark angel sheathes his sword;
Israel's hosts triumphant go
Through the wave that drowns the foe.

4 Praise we Christ, whose blood was shed,
Paschal Victim, paschal Bread;
With sincerity and love
Eat we manna from above.

5 Mighty Victim from the sky!
Hell's fierce powers beneath thee lie;
Thou hast conquered in the fight,
Thou hast brought us life and light:

6 Now no more can death appall,
Now no more the grave enthrall,
Thou hast opened paradise,
And in thee thy saints shall rise.
                ROMAN BREVIARY. TR. BY R. CAMPBELL.

848 *Discerning the Lord's body.*

1 JESUS, all-redeeming Lord,
Magnify thy dying word;
In thine ordinance appear;
Come, and meet thy followers here.

2 In the rite thou hast enjoined,
Let us now our Saviour find;
Drink thy blood for sinners shed,
Taste thee in the broken bread.

3 Thou our faithful hearts prepare;
Thou thy pardoning grace declare;
Thou that hast for sinners died,
Show thyself the Crucified!

4 All the power of sin remove;
Fill us with thy perfect love;
Stamp us with the stamp divine;
Seal our souls forever thine.
                                        CHARLES WESLEY.

[7, 6. Tune, St. Hilda. Page 280.]

849   *Angels' food.*

1 O BREAD to pilgrims given,
    O Food that angels eat,
O Manna sent from heaven,
    For heaven-born natures meet;
Give us, for thee long pining,
    To eat till richly filled;
Till, earth's delights resigning,
    Our every wish is stilled.

2 O Water, life bestowing,
    From out the Saviour's heart,
A fountain purely flowing,
    A fount of love thou art:
O let us, freely tasting,
    Our burning thirst assuage;
Thy sweetness, never wasting,
    Avails from age to age.

3 Jesus, this feast receiving,
    We thee unseen adore;
Thy faithful word believing,
    We take, and doubt no more:
Give us, thou true and loving,
    On earth to live in thee;
Then, death the veil removing,
    Thy glorious face to see.
                        FROM THE LATIN. TR. BY R. PALMER.

NAUFORD. 8, 8, 8, 4. Sir Arthur Seymour Sullivan.

850 *Until He come.*

1 By Christ redeemed, in Christ restored,
We keep the memory adored,
And show the death of our dear Lord,
    Until he come.

2 His body broken in our stead
Is here, in this memorial bread;
And so our feeble love is fed,
    Until he come.

3 His fearful drops of agony,
His life-blood shed for us we see:
The wine shall tell the mystery,
    Until he come.

4 And thus that dark betrayal night,
With the last advent we unite—
The shame, the glory, by this rite,
    Until he come.

5 Until the trump of God be heard,
Until the ancient graves be stirred,
And with the great commanding word,
    The Lord shall come.

6 O blessed hope! with this elate
Let not our hearts be desolate,
But strong in faith, in patience wait,
    Until he come!

GEORGE RAWSON.

ST. ALBAN. L. M. St. Alban's Tune Book.

851 *Figure and means of saving grace.*

1 AUTHOR of our salvation, thee,
With lowly, thankful hearts, we praise;
Author of this great mystery,
    Figure and means of saving grace.

2 The sacred, true, effectual sign,
Thy body and thy blood it shows;
The glorious instrument divine,
    Thy mercy and thy strength bestows.

3 We see the blood that seals our peace;
Thy pardoning mercy we receive;
The bread doth visibly express
    The strength through which our spirits
      live.

4 Our spirits drink a fresh supply,
    And eat the bread so freely given,
Till, borne on eagle wings, we fly,
    And banquet with our Lord in heaven.

CHARLES WESLEY.

852 *Rejoicing at the table.*

1 To Jesus, our exalted Lord,
The name by heaven and earth adored,
Fain would our hearts and voices raise
A cheerful song of sacred praise.

2 But all the notes which mortals know
Are weak, and languishing, and low;
Far, far above our humble songs,
The theme demands immortal tongues.

3 Yet while around his board we meet,
And humbly worship at his feet,
O let our warm affections move,
In glad returns of grateful love.

4 Let humble, penitential woe,
In tears of godly sorrow flow;
And thy forgiving smiles impart
Life, hope, and joy to every heart.

ANNE STEELE.

AUTUMN. 8, 7. D.

SPANISH MELODY. FROM MARECHIO.

853 *The heavenly banquet.*

1 JESUS spreads his banner o'er us,
  Cheers our famished souls with food;
He the banquet spreads before us,
  Of his mystic flesh and blood.
Precious banquet; bread of heaven;
  Wine of gladness, flowing free;
May we taste it, kindly given,
  In remembrance, Lord, of thee.

2 In thy holy incarnation,
  When the angels sang thy birth;
In thy fasting and temptation;
  In thy labors on the earth;
In thy trial and rejection;
  In thy sufferings on the tree;
In thy glorious resurrection;
  May we, Lord, remember thee.

ROSWELL PARK.

854 *The Spirit's quickening influences.*

1 COME, thou everlasting Spirit,
  Bring to every thankful mind
All the Saviour's dying merit,
  All his sufferings for mankind:
True Recorder of his passion,
  Now the living faith impart;

Now reveal his great salvation
  Unto every faithful heart.

2 Come, thou Witness of his dying;
  Come, Remembrancer divine;
Let us feel thy power applying
  Christ to every soul, and mine:
Let us groan thy inward groaning;
  Look on him we pierced, and grieve,
All partake the grace atoning,
  All the sprinkled blood receive.

CHARLES WESLEY.

[8, 7, 4. Tune, Regent Square. Page 319.]

855 *Bless us in parting.*

1 NOW in parting, Father, bless us;
  Saviour, still thy peace bestow;
Gracious Comforter, be with us,
  As we from thy table go.
    Bless us, bless us,
  Father, Son, and Spirit, now.

2 Bless us here, while still as strangers
  Onward to our home we move;
Bless us with eternal blessings,
  In our Father's house above,
    Ever, ever
  Dwelling in the light of love.

HORATIUS BONAR.

REGENT SQUARE.   8, 7. 61.   HENRY SMART.

856   *Christ the Head and Corner Stone.*

1 CHRIST is made the sure Foundation,
  Christ the Head and Corner Stone,
Chosen of the Lord, and precious,
  Binding all the Church in one,
Holy Zion's help forever,
  And her confidence alone.

2 To this temple, where we call thee,
  Come, O Lord of hosts, to-day:
With thy wonted loving-kindness,
  Hear thy servants as they pray;
And thy fullest benediction
  Shed within its walls alway.

3 Here vouchsafe to all thy servants
  What they ask of thee to gain,
What they gain from thee forever
  With the blessed to retain,
And hereafter in thy glory
  Evermore with thee to reign.
        FROM THE LATIN. TR. BY J. M. NEALE.

[7. Tune, Hall. Page 202.]

857   *Christ, the Corner-stone.*

1 ON this stone, now laid with prayer,
Let thy church rise, strong and fair;
Ever, Lord, thy name be known,
Where we lay this corner-stone.

2 Let thy holy Child, who came
Man from error to reclaim,
And for sinners to atone,
Bless, with thee, this corner-stone.

3 May thy Spirit here give rest
To the heart by sin oppressed,
And the seeds of truth be sown,
Where we lay this corner-stone.

4 Open wide, O God, thy door,
For the outcast and the poor,
Who can call no house their own,
Where we lay this corner-stone.

5 By wise master-builders squared,
Here be living stones prepared
For the temple near thy throne,—
Jesus Christ its Corner-stone.
        JOHN PIERPONT.

[7. Tune, Nuremberg   Page 300.]

858   *Prayer and praise.*

1 LORD of hosts! to thee we raise
Here a house of prayer and praise:
Thou thy people's hearts prepare
Here to meet for praise and prayer.

2 Let the living here be fed
With thy word, the heavenly bread:
Here, in hope of glory blest,
May the dead be laid to rest.

3 Here to thee a temple stand,
While the sea shall gird the land:
Here reveal thy mercy sure,
While the sun and moon endure.

4 Hallelujah! earth and sky
To the joyful sound reply:
Hallelujah! hence ascend
Prayer and praise till time shall end.
        JAMES MONTGOMERY.

319

DUKE STREET. L. M. JOHN HATTON.

859 *Laying the foundation.*

1 O LORD of hosts, whose glory fills
The bounds of the eternal hills,
And yet vouchsafes, in Christian lands,
To dwell in temples made with hands;

2 Grant that all we who here to-day
Rejoicing this foundation lay,
May be in very deed thine own,
Built on the precious Corner-stone.

3 Endue the creatures with thy grace
That shall adorn thy dwelling-place;
The beauty of the oak and pine,
The gold and silver, make them thine.

4 To thee they all pertain; to thee
The treasures of the earth and sea;
And when we bring them to thy throne
We but present thee with thine own.

5 The heads that guide endue with skill;
The hands that work preserve from ill;
That we, who these foundations lay,
May raise the topstone in its day.
J. MASON NEALE.

860 *Jehovah's presence.*

1 NOT heaven's wide range of hallowed
space
Jehovah's presence can confine;
Nor angels' claims restrain his grace,
Whose glories through creation shine.

2 It beamed on Eden's guilty days,
And traced redemption's wondrous plan;
From Calvary, in brightest rays,
It glowed to guide benighted man.

3 Its sacred shrine it fixes there,
Where two or three are met to raise

Their holy hands in humble prayer,
Or tune their hearts to grateful praise.

4 Be this, O Lord, that honored place,
The house of God, the gate of heaven;
And may the fullness of thy grace
To all who here shall meet be given.

5 And hence, in spirit, may we soar
To those bright courts where seraphs
bend;
With awe like theirs, on earth adore,
Till with their anthems ours shall blend.
UNKNOWN.

861 *God's guardian presence.*

1 THIS stone to thee in faith we lay;
To thee this temple, Lord, we build;
Thy power and goodness here display,
And be it with thy presence filled.

2 Here, when thy people seek thy face,
And dying sinners pray to live,
Hear thou in heaven, thy dwelling-place,
And when thou hearest, Lord, forgive!

3 Here, when thy messengers proclaim
The blessed gospel of thy Son,
Still, by the power of his great name,
Be mighty signs and wonders done.

4 But will indeed Jehovah deign
Here to abide, no transient guest?
Here will the world's Redeemer reign?
And here the Holy Spirit rest?

5 Thy glory never hence depart;
Yet choose not, Lord, this house alone;
Thy kingdom come to every heart,
In every bosom fix thy throne.
JAMES MONT.

HURSLEY. L. M.

PETER RITTER, ARR. BY WILLIAM HENRY MONK.

862 *The earthly and the heavenly temple.*

1 ENTER thy temple, glorious King!
And write thy name upon its shrine,
Thy peace to shed, thy joy to bring,
And seal its courts forever thine.

2 Abide with us, O Lord, we pray,
Our strength, our comfort, and our light;
Sun of our joy's unclouded day!
Star of our sorrow's troubled night!

3 If from thy paths our souls should stray,
Yet turn to seek thy pardoning grace,
Cast not our contrite prayer away,
But hear from heaven, thy dwelling-place.

4 Grant us to walk in peace and love,
And find, at last, some humble place
In that great temple built above,
Where dwell thy saints before thy face.
MRS. EMILY H. MILLER.

863 *A humble offering to Jehovah.*

1 THE perfect world, by Adam trod,
Was the first temple, built by God;
His fiat laid the corner-stone,
And heaved its pillars one by one.

2 He hung its starry roof on high,
The broad expanse of azure sky;
He spread its pavement, green and bright,
And curtained it with morning light.

3 The mountains in their places stood,
The sea, the sky; and all was good;
And when its first pure praises rang,
"The morning stars together sang."

4 Lord, 'tis not ours to make the sea,
And earth, and sky, a house for thee:
But in thy sight our offering stands,
A humbler temple, "made with hands."
NATHANIEL P. WILLIS.

ST. FAITH. L. M.

BAMBERG HYMN BOOK.

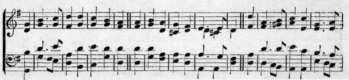

864 *Seeking a tabernacle.*

1 WHEN to the exiled seer were given
Those rapturous views of highest heaven,
All glorious though the visions were,
Yet he beheld no temple there.

2 The new Jerusalem on high
Hath one pervading sanctity;
No sin to mourn, no grief to mar,
God and the Lamb its temple are.

3 But we, frail sojourners below,
The pilgrim heirs of guilt and woe,
Must seek a tabernacle where
Our scattered souls may blend in prayer.

4 O Thou, who o'er the cherubim
Didst shine in glories veiled and dim,
With purer light our temple cheer,
And dwell in unveiled glory here.
GEORGE ROBINSON.

MURRAY. H. M. GERMAN.

And grateful praise ascend,
Like incense, to the skies:
Here may thy word melodious sound,
And spread celestial joys around.

865 *Invoking God's presence.*

1 GREAT King of glory, come,
And with thy favor crown
This temple as thy home,
This people as thine own:
Beneath this roof, O deign to show
How God can dwell with men below.

2 Here may thine ears attend
Our interceding cries,

3 Here may our unborn sons
And daughters sound thy praise,
And shine, like polished stones,
Through long-succeeding days:
Here, Lord, display thy saving power,
While temples stand and men adore.

4 Here may the listening throng
Receive thy truth in love;
Here Christians join the song
Of seraphim above;
Till all, who humbly seek thy face,
Rejoice in thy abounding grace.
BENJAMIN FRANCIS.

MENDON. L. M. GERMAN.

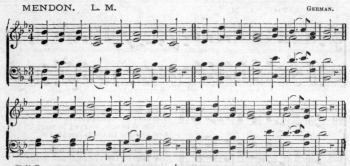

866 *Dedication of a hall of science.*

1 THE Lord our God alone is strong;
His hands build not for one brief day;
His wondrous works, through ages long,
His wisdom and his power display.

2 His mountains lift their solemn forms,
To watch in silence o'er the land;

The rolling ocean, rocked with storms,
Sleeps in the hollow of his hand.

3 Beyond the heavens he sits alone,
The universe obeys his nod;
The lightning-rifts disclose his throne,
And thunders voice the name of God.

4 Thou sovereign God, receive this gift
  Thy willing servants offer thee;
Accept the prayers that thousands lift,
  And let these halls thy temple be.

5 And let those learn, who here shall meet,
  True wisdom is with reverence crowned,
And Science walks with humble feet
  To seek the God that Faith hath found.
                        CALEB T. WINCHESTER.

867   *The tokens of His grace.*

1 AND will the great eternal God
  On earth establish his abode?

And will he, from his radiant throne
  Accept our temples for his own?

2 These walls we to thy honor raise;
  Long may they echo with thy praise:
And thou, descending, fill the place
  With choicest tokens of thy grace.

3 Here let the great Redeemer·reign,
  With all the graces of his train;
While power divine his word attends,
  To conquer foes, and cheer his friends.

4 And in the great decisive day,
  When God the nations shall survey,
May it before the world appear
  That crowds were born to glory here.
                        PHILIP DODDRIDGE.

PORTUGUESE HYMN.   11.   UNKNOWN.

868   *Where is the house that ye build unto Me?*—Isa. 66: 1.

1 WE rear not a temple, like Judah's of old,
Whose portals were marble, whose vault-
    ings were gold;
No incense is lighted, no victims are slain,
No monarch kneels praying to hallow the
    fane.

2 More simple and lowly the walls that we
    raise,
And humbler the pomp of procession and
    praise,
Where the heart is the altar whence in-
    cense shall roll,
And Messiah the King who shall pray for
    the soul.

3 O Father, come in! but not in the cloud
Which filled the bright courts where thy
    chosen ones bowed;

But come in that Spirit of glory and grace,
Which beams on the soul and illumines the
    race.

4 O come in the power of thy life-giving
    word,
And reveal to each heart its Redeemer and
    Lord;
Till faith bring the peace to the penitent
    given,
And love fill the air with the fragrance o
    heaven.

5 The pomp of Moriah has long passed
    away,
And soon shall our frailer erection decay;
But the souls that are builded in worship
    and love
Shall be temples to God, everlasting above.
                        HENRY WARE, JR.

DUNDEE. C. M.

GUILLAUME FRANC.

869 *Dedication hymn.*

1 O THOU, whose own vast temple stands,
    Built over earth and sea,
Accept the walls that human hands
    Have raised to worship thee!

2 Lord, from thine inmost glory send,
    Within these courts to bide,
The peace that dwelleth without end,
    Serenely by thy side!

3 May erring minds that worship here
    Be taught the better way;
And they who mourn, and they who fear,
    Be strengthened as they pray.

4 May faith grow firm, and love grow warm,
    And pure devotion rise,
While round these hallowed walls the storm,
    Of earthborn passion dies.

WILLIAM C. BRYANT.

870 *Blessings entreated.*

1 O GOD, though countless worlds of light
    Thy power and glory show,
Though round thy throne, above all height,
    Immortal seraphs glow,—

Yet, Lord, where'er thy saints apart
    Are met for praise and prayer,
Wherever sighs a contrite heart,
    Thou, gracious God, art there.

3 With grateful joy, thy children rear
    This temple, Lord, to thee;
Long may they sing thy praises here,
    And here thy beauty see.

4 Here, Saviour, deign thy saints to meet;
    With peace their hearts to fill;

And here, like Sharon's odors sweet,
    May grace divine distill.

5 Here may thy truth fresh triumphs win,
    Eternal Spirit, here,
In many a heart now dead in sin,
    A living temple rear.

J. D. KNOWLES.

[S. M. Tune, St. Thomas. Page 186.]

871 *The honor and safety of a nation.*

1 GREAT is the Lord our God,
    And let his praise be great;
He makes his churches his abode,
    His most delightful seat.

2 These temples of his grace,
    How beautiful they stand!
The honors of our native place,
    And bulwarks of our land.

3 In Zion God is known,
    A refuge in distress;
How bright has his salvation shone
    Through all her palaces!

4 In every new distress
    We'll to his house repair;
We'll think upon his wondrous grace
    And seek deliverance there.

ISAAC WATTS.

Doxology.

To Father, Son, and Holy Ghost,
    The God whom we adore,
Be glory, as it was, is now,
    And shall be evermore.

TATE AND BRADY.

SAVIOUR, LIKE A SHEPHERD. 8, 7, 4.

WILLIAM B. BRADBURY.

872 *For the Shepherd's care.*

1 SAVIOUR, like a shepherd lead us,
Much we need thy tenderest care;
In thy pleasant pastures feed us,
For our use thy folds prepare:
Blessed Jesus,
Thou hast bought us, thine we are.

2 We are thine, do thou befr'end us,
Be the guardian of our way;
Keep thy flock, from sin defend us,
Seek us when we go astray:
Blessed Jesus,
Hear, O hear us, when we pray.

3 Thou hast promised to receive us,
Poor and sinful though we be;
Thou hast mercy to relieve us,
Grace to cleanse, and power to free:
Blessed Jesus,
We will early turn to thee.

4 Early let us seek thy favor,
Early let us do thy will;
Blessed Lord and only Saviour,
With thy love our bosoms fill:
Blessed Jesus,
Thou hast loved us, love us still
DOROTHY A. THRUPP.

873 *For early piety.*

1 GOD has said, "Forever blessed
Those who seek me in their youth;
They shall find the path of wisdom,
And the narrow way of truth:"
Guide us, Saviour,
In the narrow way of truth.

2 Be our strength, for we are weakness;
Be our wisdom and our guide;
May we walk in love and meekness,
Nearer to our Saviour's side:
Naught can harm us,
While we thus in thee abide.

3 Thus, when evening shades shall gather,
We may turn our tearless eye
To the dwelling of our Father,
To our home beyond the sky;
Gently passing
To the happy land on high.
UNKNOWN.

874 *Children's hymn.*

1 CHILDREN, loud hosannas singing,
Hymned Thy praise in olden time,
Judah's ancient temple filling
With the melody sublime;
Infant voices
Joined to swell the holy chime.

2 Though no more the incarnate Saviour
We behold in latter days;
Though a temple far less glorious
Echoes now the songs we raise;
Still in glory
Thou wilt hear our notes of praise.

3 Loud we'll swell the pealing anthem,
All thy wondrous acts proclaim,
Till all heaven and earth resounding,
Echo with thy glorious name;
Hallelujah,
Hallelujah to the Lamb!
MRS. H. B. STEELE.

SILOAM. C. M.

Isaac Baker Woodbury.

875 *The Christian child.*

1 By cool Siloam's shady rill
  How sweet the lily grows!
How sweet the breath, beneath the hill,
  Of Sharon's dewy rose!

2 Lo! such the child whose early feet
  The paths of peace have trod;
Whose secret heart, with influence sweet,
  Is upward drawn to God.

3 By cool Siloam's shady rill
  The lily must decay;
The rose that blooms beneath the hill
  Must shortly fade away.

4 And soon, too soon, the wintry hour
  Of man's maturer age
Will shake the soul with sorrow's power,
  And stormy passion's rage.

5 O Thou, whose infant feet were found
  Within thy Father's shrine,
Whose years, with changeless virtue
    crowned,
  Were all alike divine;

6 Dependent on thy bounteous breath,
  We seek thy grace alone,
In childhood, manhood, age, and death,
  To keep us still thine own.
                    REGINALD HEBER.

876 *Children praising Christ.*

1 Come, Christian children, come, and raise
  Your voice with one accord;
Come, sing in joyful songs of praise
  The glories of your Lord.

2 Sing of the wonders of his love,
  And loudest praises give
To him who left his throne above,
  And died that you might live.

3 Sing of the wonders of his truth,
  And read in every page
The promise made to earliest youth
  Fulfilled to latest age.

4 Sing of the wonders of his power,
  Who with his own right arm
Upholds and keeps you hour by hour,
  And shields from every harm.
                    UNKNOWN.

877 *Blessedness of instructing the young.*

1 Delightful work! young souls to win
  And turn the rising race
From the deceitful paths of sin,
  To seek redeeming grace.

2 Children our kind protection claim;
  And God will well approve
When infants learn to lisp his name,
  And their Redeemer love.

3 Be ours the bliss, in wisdom's way
  To guide untutored youth,
And show the mind which went astray
  The Way, the Life, the Truth.

4 Almighty God, thine influence shed,
  To aid this blest design;
The honors of thy name be spread,
  And all the glory thine.
                    JOSEPH STRAPHAN.

NEW BRUNSWICK. 7, 5, or 7, D.

Rev. John Black.

878 *Sunday-school anniversary.*

1 WILT thou hear the voice of praise
Which the little children raise,
Thou who art, from endless days,
    Glorious God of all?
While the circling year has sped,
Thou hast heavenly blessings shed,
Like the dew, upon each head;
    Still on thee we call.

2 Still thy constant care bestow;
Let us each in wisdom grow,
And in favor while below,
    With the God above.
In our hearts the Spirit mild,
Which adorned the Saviour-child,
Gently soothe each impulse wild
    To the sway of love.

3 Thine example, kept in view,
Jesus, help us to pursue;
Lead us all our journey through
    By thy guiding hand;
And when life on earth is o'er,
Where the blest dwell evermore,
May we praise thee and adore,
    An unbroken band.

MRS. CAROLINE L. RICE.

879 *Little travelers Zionward.*

1 LITTLE travelers Zionward,
    Each one entering into rest,
In the kingdom of your Lord,
    In the mansions of the blest;
There, to welcome, Jesus waits,
    Gives the crowns his followers win
Lift your heads, ye golden gates!
    Let the little travelers in!

2 Who are they whose little feet,
    Pacing life's dark journey through,
Now have reached that heavenly seat
    They had ever kept in view?
"I, from Greenland's frozen land;"
    "I, from India's sultry plain;"
"I, from Afric's barren sand;"
    "I, from islands of the main."

3 "All our earthly journey past,
    Every tear and pain gone by,
Here together met at last,
    At the portal of the sky!"
Each the welcome "Come" awaits
    Conquerors over death and sin!
Lift your heads, ye golden gates!
    Let the little travelers in!

JAMES EDMESTON.

SWEET STORY.   11, 8, 12, 9.   ENGLISH.

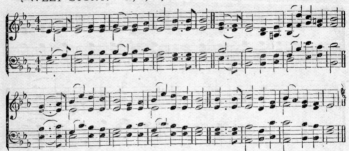

880   *That sweet story of old.*

1 I THINK, when I read that sweet story
    of old,
When Jesus was here among men,
How he called little children as lambs to
    his fold,
I should like to have been with him then.

2 I wish that his hands had been placed on
    my head,
That his arms had been thrown around
    me,
That I might have seen his kind look when
    he said,
"Let the little ones come unto me."

3 Yet still to his footstool in prayer I may
    go,
And ask for a share in his love;
And if I thus earnestly seek him below,
I shall see him and hear him above:

4 In that beautiful place he has gone to
    prepare,
For all who are washed, and forgiven;
And many dear children are gath ring there,
"For of such is the kingdom of heaven."
                                    MRS. JEMIMA LUKE.

[7. Tune, Hendon.   Page 264.]

881   *A blessing for teachers.*

1 MIGHTY One, before whose face
    Wisdom had her glorious seat,
When the orbs that people space
    Sprang to birth beneath thy feet!

2 Source of truth, whose beams alone
    Light the mighty world of mind;
God of love, who from thy throne
    Kindly watchest all mankind!

3 Shed on those who in thy name
    Teach the way of truth and right,
Shed that love's undying flame,
    Shed that wisdom's guiding light.
                              WILLIAM C. BRYANT.

COLMAN.   C. M.   GEORGE KINGSLEY.

882   *The children's jubilee.*

1 HOSANNA! be the children's song,
    To Christ, the children's King;
His praise, to whom our souls belong,
    Let all the children sing.

2 Hosanna! sound from hill to hill,
    And spread from plain to plain,
While louder, sweeter, clearer still,
    Woods echo to the strain.

3 Hosanna! on the wings of light,
    O'er earth and ocean fly,
Till morn to eve, and noon to night,
    And heaven to earth, reply.

4 Hosanna! then, our song shall be;
    Hosanna to our King!
This is the children's jubilee;
    Let all the children sing.
                              JAMES MONTGOMERY.

328

MIRIAM. 7, 6.

JOSEPH P. HOLBROOK.

883 *The Lord's love to children.*

1 WHEN, his salvation bringing,
   To Zion Jesus came,
The children all stood singing
   Hosanna to his name;
Nor did their zeal offend him,
   But as he rode along,
He let them still attend him,
   And smiled to hear their song.

2 And since the Lord retaineth
   His love to children still,
Though now as King he reigneth
   On Zion's heavenly hill,
We'll flock around his banner,
   We'll bow before his throne,
And cry aloud, "Hosanna
   To David's royal Son."

3 For should we fail proclaiming
   Our great Redeemer's praise,
The stones, our silence shaming,
   Would their hosannas raise.
But shall we only render
   The tribute of our words?
No; while our hearts are tender,
   They too shall be the Lord's.

JOHN KING.

884 *Grateful praise.*

1 WE bring no glittering treasures,
   No gems from earth's deep mine;
We come, with simple measures,
   To chant Thy love divine.
Children, thy favors sharing,
   Their voice of thanks would raise,
Father, accept our offering,
   Our song of grateful praise.

2 The dearest gift of Heaven,
   Love's written word of truth,
To us is early given,
   To guide our steps in youth;
We hear the wondrous story,
   The tale of Calvary;
We read of homes in glory,
   From sin and sorrow free.

3 Redeemer, grant thy blessing!
   O teach us how to pray,
That each, thy fear possessing,
   May tread life's onward way;
Then, where the pure are dwelling
   We hope to meet again,
And, sweeter numbers swelling,
   Forever praise thy name.

HARRIET PHILLIPS.

TIVOLI. 6, 4.

EDWARD JOHN HOPKINS.

5 So now, and till we die,
Sound we thy praises high,
And joyful sing:
Infants, and the glad throng
Who to thy Church belong,
Unite to swell the song
To Christ our King.

CLEMENT OF ALEXANDRIA, (220.)
TR. BY H. M. DEXTER.

885 *Shepherd of tender youth.*

1 SHEPHERD of tender youth,
Guiding in love and truth
Through devious ways;
Christ our triumphant King,
We come thy name to sing,
Hither our children bring
To shout thy praise.

2 Thou art our holy Lord,
The all-subduing Word,
Healer of strife:
Thou dost thyself abase,
That from sin's deep disgrace
Thou mightest save our race,
And give us life.

3 Thou art the great High Priest;
Thou hast prepared the feast
Of heavenly love;
While in our mortal pain
None calls on thee in vain;
Help thou dost not disdain,
Help from above.

4 Ever be thou our guide,
Our shepherd and our pride,
Our staff and song:
Jesus, thou Christ of God,
By thy perennial word
Lead us where thou hast trod,
Make our faith strong.

[7, 6. Tune, Miriam. Page 329.

886 *Early piety.*

1 I LOVE to hear the story
Which angel voices tell,
How once the King of glory
Came down on earth to dwell.
I am both weak and sinful,
But this I surely know,
The Lord came down to save me,
Because he loved me so.

2 I'm glad my blessed Saviour
Was once a child like me,
To show how pure and holy
His little ones may be;
And if I try to follow
His footsteps here below,
He never will forget me,
Because he loves me so.

3 To sing his love and mercy
My sweetest songs I'll raise;
And though I cannot see him
I know he hears my praise;
For he has kindly promised
That even I may go
To sing among his angels,
Because he loves me so.

MRS. EMILY M. MILLER.

GAYLORD.   8, 7. D.

ARR. BY JOSEPH P. HOLBROOK.

887   *For a blessing on children.*

1 HOLY Father, send thy blessing
    On thy children gathered here;
Let them all, thy name confessing,
    Be to thee forever dear.
Holy Saviour, who in meekness
    Didst vouchsafe a child to be;
Guide their steps and help their weakness,
    Bless, and make them like to thee.

2 Bear the lambs, when they are weary,
    In thine arms and at thy breast;
Through life's desert dark and dreary
    Bring them to thy heavenly rest.
Spread thy wings of blessing o'er them,
    Holy Spirit, from above;
Guide, and lead, and go before them,
    Give them peace, and joy, and love.
                                    UNKNOWN.

888   *The lambs enfolded.*

1 SAVIOUR, who thy flock art feeding
    With the shepherd's kindest care,
All the feeble gently leading,
    While the lambs thy bosom share;
Now, these little ones receiving,
    Fold them in thy gracious arm;
There, we know, thy word believing,
    Only there, secure from harm.

2 Never, from thy pasture roving,
    Let them be the lion's prey;
Let thy tenderness, so loving,
    Keep them all life's dangerous way:
Then, within thy fold eternal,
    Let them find a resting-place,
Feed in pastures ever vernal,
    Drink the rivers of thy grace.
                        WILLIAM A. MUHLENBERG

889   *He shall gather the lambs with his arm.*—Isa. 40: 11.

1 GRACIOUS Saviour, gentle Shepherd,
    Little ones are dear to thee;
Gathered with thine arms, and carried
    In thy bosom may we be;
Sweetly, fondly, safely tended,
    From all want and danger free.

2 Tender Shepherd, never leave us
    From thy fold to go astray;
By thy look of love directed
    May we walk the narrow way;
Thus direct us, and protect us,
    Lest we fall an easy prey.

3 Taught to lisp the holy praises
    Which on earth thy children sing,
Both with lips and hearts unfeigned
    May we our thank-offerings bring;
Then with all thy saints in glory
    Join to praise our Lord and King.
            JANE E. LEESON AND J. WHITTEMORE

BOYLSTON. S. M. LOWELL MASON.

890 *The evils of intemperance.*

1 MOURN for the thousands slain,
  The youthful and the strong;
Mourn for the wine-cup's fearful reign,
  And the deluded throng.

2 Mourn for the tarnished gem—
  For reason's light divine,
Quenched from the soul's bright diadem,
  Where God had bid it shine.

3 Mourn for the ruined soul—
  Eternal life and light
Lost by the fiery, maddening bowl,
  And turned to hopeless night.

4 Mourn for the lost,—but call,
  Call to the strong, the free;
Rouse them to shun that dreadful fall,
  And to the refuge flee.

5 Mourn for the lost,—but pray,
  Pray to our God above,
To break the fell destroyer's sway,
  And show his saving love.
                                  UNKNOWN.

891 *Christian sympathy.*

1 O PRAISE our God to-day,
  His constant mercy bless,
Whose love hath helped us on our way,
  And granted us success.

2 His arm the strength imparts
  Our daily toil to bear;
His grace alone inspires our hearts,
  Each other's load to share.

3 O happiest work below,
  Earnest of joy above,
To sweeten many a cup of woe,
  By deeds of holy love!

4 Lord, may it be our choice
  This blessed rule to keep,
"Rejoice with them that do rejoice,
  And weep with them that weep."

5 God of the widow, hear,
  Our work of mercy bless;
God of the fatherless, be near,
  And grant us good success.
                         SIR HENRY W. BAKER.

892 *Ye have done it unto Me.*

1 WE give thee but thine own,
  Whate'er the gift may be:
All that we have is thine alone,
  A trust, O Lord, from thee.

2 May we thy bounties thus
  As stewards true receive,
And gladly, as thou blessest us,
  To thee our first-fruits give.

3 O, hearts are bruised and dead,
  And homes are bare and cold,
And lambs for whom the Shepherd bled,
  Are straying from the fold!

4 To comfort and to bless,
  To find a balm for woe,
To tend the lone and fatherless,
  Is angels' work below.

5 The captive to release,
  To God the lost to bring,
To teach the way of life and peace,—
  It is a Christ-like thing.

6 And we believe thy word,
  Though dim our faith may be;
Whate'er for thine we do, O Lord,
  We do it unto thee.
                          WILLIAM W. HOW.

INVITATION. C. M.

THOMAS HASTINGS.

893 *Acts of charity.*

1 JESUS, my Lord, how rich thy grace,
  Thy bounties how complete!
How shall I count the matchless sum?
  How pay the mighty debt?

2 High on a throne of radiant light
  Dost thou exalted shine;
What can my poverty bestow,
  When all the worlds are thine?

3 But thou hast brethren here below,
  The partners of thy grace,
And wilt confess their humble names
  Before thy Father's face.

4 In them thou mayst be clothed and fed,
  And visited and cheered;
And in their accents of distress
  My Saviour's voice is heard.

5 Thy face with reverence and with love,
  I in thy poor would see;
Orather let me beg my bread,
  Than hold it back from thee.

PHILIP DODDRIDGE

894 *Sympathy with the afflicted.*

1 FATHER of mercies, send thy grace,
  All-powerful, from above,
To form in our obedient souls
  The image of thy love.

2 O may our sympathizing breasts
  That generous pleasure know,
Kindly to share in others' joy,
  And weep for others' woe.

3 When poor and helpless sons of grief
  In deep distress are laid,

Soft be our hearts their pains to feel
  And swift our hands to aid.

4 So Jesus looked on dying man,
  When, throned above the skies,
And in the Father's bosom blest,
  He felt compassion rise.

5 On wings of love the Saviour flew,
  To bless a ruined race;
We would, O Lord, thy steps pursue,
  Thy bright example trace.

PHILIP DODDRIDGE.

895 *Prayer for the intemperate.*

1 'TIS thine alone, almighty Name,
  To raise the dead to life,
The lost inebriate to reclaim
  From passion's fearful strife.

2 What ruin hath intemperance wrought!
  How widely roll its waves!
How many myriads hath it brought
  To fill dishonored graves!

3 And see, O Lord, what numbers still
  Are maddened by the bowl,
Led captive at the tyrant's will
  In bondage, heart and soul.

4 Stretch forth thy hand, O God, our King
  And break the galling chain;
Deliverance to the captive bring,
  And end the usurper's reign.

5 The cause of temperance is thine own
  Our plans and efforts bless;
We trust, O Lord, in thee alone
  To crown them with success.

EDWIN F. HATFIELD.

RETURN.   C. M.

THEODORE FREELINGHUYSEN SEWARD.

896   *The box of spikenard.*

1 SHE loved her Saviour, and to him
  Her costliest present brought;
To crown his head, or grace his name,
  No gift too rare she thought.

2 So let the Saviour be adored,
  And not the poor despised;
Give to the hungry from your hoard,
  But all, give all to Christ.

3 Go, clothe the naked, lead the blind,
  Give to the weary rest;
For sorrow's children comfort find,
  And help for all distressed;

4 But give to Christ alone thy heart,
  Thy faith, thy love supreme;
Then for his sake thine alms impart,
  And so give all to him.
                        WILLIAM CUTTER.

897   *Ye have the poor always with you.*
          Matt. 26 : 11.

1 LORD, lead the way the Saviour went,
  By lane and cell obscure,
And let love's treasures still be spent,
  Like his, upon the poor.

2 Like him, through scenes of deep distress,
  Who bore the world's sad weight,
We, in their crowded loneliness,
  Would seek the desolate.

3 For thou hast placed us side by side
  In this wide world of ill;
And that thy followers may be tried,
  The poor are with us still.

4 Mean are all offerings we can make;
  Yet thou hast taught us, Lord,
If given for the Saviour's sake,
  They lose not their reward.
                        WILLIAM CROSWELL.

898   *Thy neighbor.*

1 WHO is thy neighbor ? He whom thou
  Hast power to aid or bless;
Whose aching heart or burning brow
  Thy soothing hand may press.

2 Thy neighbor? 'Tis the fainting poor,
  Whose eye with want is dim;
O enter thou his humble door,
  With aid and peace for him.

3 Thy neighbor? He who drinks the cup
  When sorrow drowns the brim;
With words of high, sustaining hope,
  Go thou and comfort him.

4 Thy neighbor? Pass no mourner by;
  Perhaps thou canst redeem
A breaking heart from misery;
  Go, share thy lot with him.
                        WILLIAM B. O. PEABODY.

899   *For the inebriate.*

1 LIFE from the dead, Almighty God,
  'Tis thine alone to give;
To lift the poor inebriate up,
  And bid the helpless live.

2 Life from the dead! For those we plead
  Fast bound in passion's chain,
That, from their iron fetters freed,
  They wake to life again.

3 Life from the dead! Quickened by thee
  Be all their powers inclined
To temperance, truth, and piety,
  And pleasures pure, refined.

4 And may they by thy help abide,
  The tempter's power withstand:
By grace restored and purified,
  In Christ accepted stand.
                        UNKNOWN.

HEBRON. L. M.

.LOWELL MASON.

900 *For mercy on the drunkard.*

1 WHEN, doomed to death, the apostle lay
  At night in Herod's dungeon cell,
A light shone round him like the day,
  And from his limbs the fetters fell.

2 A messenger from God was there,
  To break his chain and bid him rise;
And lo! the saint, as free as air,
  Walked forth beneath the open skies.

3 Chains yet more strong and cruel bind
  The victims of that deadly thirst
Which drowns the soul, and from the mind
  Blots the bright image stamped at first.

4 O God of love and mercy, deign
  To look on those with pitying eye
Who struggle with that fatal chain,
  And send them succor from on high!

5 Send down, in its resistless might,
  Thy gracious Spirit, we implore,
And lead the captive forth to light,
  A rescued soul, a slave no more!
                              WILLIAM C. BRYANT.

901 *Temperance hymn.*

1 BONDAGE and death the cup contains;
2 Dash to the earth the poisoned bowl!
ofter than silk are iron chains,
  Compared with those that chafe the soul.

  Hosannas, Lord, to thee we sing,
  Whose power the giant fiend obeys;
What countless thousands tribute bring,
  For happier homes and brighter days!

3 Thou wilt not break the bruised reed,
  Nor leave the broken heart unbound;
The wife regains a husband freed!
  The orphan clasps a father found!

4 Spare, Lord, the thoughtless, guide the
    blind,
  Till man no more shall deem it just

To live by forging chains to bind
  His weaker brother in the dust.
                              LUCIUS M. SARGENT.

[C. M. . Tune, Return. Page 334.]

902 *Deeds of love rewarded.*

1 How blest the children of the Lord,
  Who, walking in his sight,
Make all the precepts of his word
  Their study and delight!

2 That precious wealth shall be their dower,
  Which cannot know decay;
Which moth or rust shall ne'er devour,
  Or spoiler take away.

3 For them that heavenly light shall spread
  Whose cheering rays illume
The darkest hours of life, and shed
  A halo round the tomb.

4 Their works of piety and love,
  Performed through Christ, their Lord,
Forever registered above,
  Shall meet a sure reward.
                              HARRIET AUBER.

[C. M. Tune, Return. Page 334.]

903 *Treasures in heaven.*

1 RICH are the joys which cannot die,
  With God laid up in store;
Treasures beyond the changing sky,
  Brighter than golden ore.

2 The seeds which piety and love
  Have scattered here below,
In the fair fertile fields above
  To ample harvests grow.

3 All that my willing hands can give
  At Jesus' feet I lay;
Grace shall the humble gift receive,
  Abounding grace repay.
                              PHILIP DODDRIDGE.

ERNAN. L. M.

LOWELL MASON.

904 *More blessed to give than to receive.*
Acts 20 : 35.

1 HELP us, O Lord, thy yoke to wear,
　Delighting in thy perfect will;
Each other's burdens learn to bear,
　And thus thy law of love fulfill.

2 He that hath pity on the poor
　Lendeth his substance to the Lord;
And, lo! his recompense is sure,
　For more than all shall be restored.

3 Teach us, with glad, ungrudging heart,
　As thou hast blest our various store,
From our abundance to impart
　A liberal portion to the poor.

4 To thee our all devoted be,
　In whom we breathe, and move, and live;
Freely we have received from thee;
　Freely may we rejoice to give.
THOMAS COTTERILL.

905 *For a charitable occasion.*

1 DEAR ties of mutual succor bind
　The children of our feeble race,
And if our brethren were not kind,
　This earth were but a weary place.

2 We lean on others as we walk
　Life's twilight path, with pitfalls strewn;
And 'twere an idle boast to talk
　Of treading that dim path alone.

3 Amid the snares misfortune lays
　Unseen, beneath the steps of all,
Blest is the love that seeks to raise,
　And stay, and strengthen those who fall;

4 Till, taught by Him who for our sake
　Bore every form of life's distress,
With every passing year we make
　The sum of human sorrow less.
WILLIAM C. BRYANT.

[7. Tune, Pleyel's Hymn. Page 141.]
906 *The wanderer exhorted.*

1 BROTHER, hast thou wandered far
　From thy Father's happy home,
With thyself and God at war?
　Turn thee, brother; homeward come.

2 Hast thou wasted all the powers
　God for noble uses gave?
Squandered life's most golden hours?
　Turn thee, brother; God can save!

3 Is a mighty famine now
　In thy heart and in thy soul?
Discontent upon thy brow?
　Turn thee; God will make thee whole.

4 He can heal thy bitterest wound,
　He thy gentlest prayer can hear;
Seek him, for he may be found;
　Call upon him; he is near.
JAMES F. CLARKE.

[C. M. Tune, Return. Page 334.]
907 *The guiding star.*

1 As shadows, cast by cloud and sun,
　Flit o'er the summer grass,
So, in thy sight, Almighty One,
　Earth's generations pass.

2 And as the years, an endless host,
　Come swiftly pressing on,
The brightest names that earth can boast
　Just glisten and are gone.

3 Yet doth the star of Bethlehem shed
　A luster pure and sweet;
And still it leads, as once it led,
　To the Messiah's feet.

4 O Father, may that holy star
　Grow every year more bright,
And send its glorious beams afar
　To fill the world with light.
WILLIAM C. BRYANT.

HUMMEL. C. M. HEINRICH CHRISTOPHER ZEUNER.

908 *Christ, the Conqueror.*

1 JESUS, immortal King, arise;
Assert thy rightful sway,
Till earth, subdued, its tribute brings,
And distant lands obey.

2 Ride forth, victorious Conqueror, ride,
Till all thy foes submit,
And all the powers of hell resign
Their trophies at thy feet.

3 Send forth thy word, and let it fly
The spacious earth around,
Till every soul beneath the sun
Shall hear the joyful sound.

4 O may the great Redeemer's name
Through every clime be known,
And heathen gods, forsaken, fall,
And Jesus reign alone.

5 From sea to sea, from shore to shore,
Be thou, O Christ, adored,
And earth, with all her millions, shout
Hosannas to the Lord.
A. C. HOBART SEYMOUR.

909 *Returning to Zion with hymns of joy.*

1 DAUGHTER of Zion, from the dust
Exalt thy fallen head;
Again in thy Redeemer trust;
He calls thee from the dead.

2 Awake, awake, put on thy strength,
Thy beautiful array;
The day of freedom dawns at length,
The Lord's appointed day.

3 Rebuild thy walls, thy bounds enlarge,
And send thy heralds forth;
Say to the South, "Give up thy charge!"
And, "Keep not back, O North!"

4 They come, they come; thine exiled bands,
Where'er they rest or roam,
Have heard thy voice in distant lands,
And hasten to their home.

5 Thus, though the universe shall burn,
And God his works destroy,
With songs thy ransomed shall return,
And everlasting joy.
JAMES MONTGOMERY.

910 *The gospel for all nations.*

1 GREAT God, the nations of the earth
Are by creation thine;
And in thy works, by all beheld,
Thy radiant glories shine.

2 But, Lord, thy greater love has sent
Thy gospel to mankind,
Unveiling what rich stores of grace
Are treasured in thy mind.

3 Lord, when shall these glad tidings spread
The spacious earth around,
Till every tribe and every soul
Shall hear the joyful sound?

4 Smile, Lord, on each divine attempt
To spread the gospel's rays,
And build on sin's demolished throne
The temples of thy praise.
THOMAS GIBBONS.

IBSTONE.   6.   MARIA TIDDEMAN.

911   *The seed of the Church.*

1 FLUNG to the heedless winds,
    Or on the waters cast,
The martyrs' ashes, watched,
    Shall gathered be at last;
And from that scattered dust,
    Around us and abroad,
Shall spring a plenteous seed
    Of witnesses for God.

2 The Father hath received
    Their latest living breath;
And vain is Satan's boast
    Of victory in their death:
Still, still, though dead, they speak,
    And, trumpet-tongued, proclaim,
To many a wakening land,
    The one availing name.

MARTIN LUTHER. TR. BY W. J. FOX.

[11, 10. Tune, Hanover. Page 69.]

912   *Zion's glad morning.*

1 HAIL to the brightness of Zion's glad
    morning!
Joy to the lands that in darkness have lain!
Hushed be the accents of sorrow and
    mourning;
Zion in triumph begins her mild reign.

2 Hail to the brightness of Zion's glad
    morning,
    Long by the prophets of Israel foretold;
Hail to the millions from bondage return-
    ing;
Gentiles and Jews the blest vision behold.

3 Lo, in the desert rich flowers are spring-
    ing;
Streams ever copious are gliding along;
Loud from the mountain-tops echoes are
    ringing;
Wastes rise in verdure, and mingle in
    song.

4 See, from all lands, from the isles of
    the ocean,
    Praise to Jehovah ascending on high;
Fallen are the engines of war and com-
    motion;
Shouts of salvation are rending the sky.

THOMAS HASTINGS.

[6, 4. Tune, Dort. Page 87.]

913   *Let there be light.*

1 THOU, whose almighty word
Chaos and darkness heard,
    And took their flight;
Hear us, we humbly pray,
And where the gospel day
Sheds not its glorious ray,
    "Let there be light."

2 Thou, who didst come to bring
On thy redeeming wing,
    Healing and sight,
Health to the sick in mind,
Sight to the inly blind;
O now, to all mankind,
    "Let there be light."

3 Spirit of truth and love,
Life-giving, holy Dove,
    Speed forth thy flight;
Move o'er the waters' face
By thine almighty grace;
And in earth's darkest place,
    "Let there be light."

4 Blessed and holy Three,
Glorious Trinity,
    Wisdom, Love, Might;
Boundless as ocean's tide
Rolling in fullest pride,
O'er the world far and wide,
    "Let there be light."

JOHN MARRIOTT.

NEWBOLD. C. M. GEORGE KINGSLEY.

914 *The Morning Star.*

1 LIGHT of the lonely pilgrim's heart,
　Star of the coming day,
Arise, and with thy morning beams
　Chase all our griefs away!

2 Come, blessed Lord, let every shore
　And answering island sing
The praises of thy royal name,
　And own thee as their King.

3 Bid the whole earth, responsive now
　To the bright world above,
Break forth in sweetest strains of joy,
　In memory of thy love.

4 Jesus, thy fair creation groans,
　The air, the earth, the sea,
In unison with all our hearts,
　And calls aloud for thee.

5 Thine was the cross, with all its fruits
　Of grace and peace divine:
Be thine the crown of glory now,
　The palm of victory thine!
　　　　　　　　SIR EDWARD DENNY.

915 *Reign of Christ foretold.*

1 THE Lord will come, and not be slow;
　His footsteps cannot err;
Before him Righteousness shall go,
　His royal harbinger.

2 Mercy and Truth, that long were missed,
　Now joyfully are met;
Sweet Peace and Righteousness have kissed,
　And hand in hand are set.

5 The nations all whom thou hast made
　Shall come, and all shall frame

To bow them low before thee, Lord!
　And glorify thy name.

4 Truth from the earth, like to a flower,
　Shall bud and blossom then,
And Justice, from her heavenly bower,
　Look down on mortal men.

5 Thee will I praise, O Lord, my God!
　Thee honor and adore
With my whole heart; and blaze abroad
　Thy name for evermore!
　　　　　　　　JOHN MILTON.

916 *The earth renewed in righteousness.*

1 ALMIGHTY Spirit, now behold
　A world by sin destroyed:
Creating Spirit, as of old,
　Move on the formless void.

2 Give thou the word; that healing sound
　Shall quell the deadly strife;
And earth again, like Eden crowned,
　Bring forth the tree of life.

3 If sang the morning stars for joy,
　When nature rose to view,
What strains will angel-harps employ,
　When thou shalt all renew!

4 And if the sons of God rejoice
　To hear a Saviour's name,
How will the ransomed raise their voice
　To whom that Saviour came!

5 Lo, every kindred, every tribe,
　Assembling round the throne,
The new creation shall ascribe,
　To sovereign love alone!
　　　　　　　　JAMES MONTGOMERY.

MIGDOL.　L. M.　　　　　　　　　　　　　　LOWELL MASON.

917　*That glorious anthem.*

1 SOON may the last glad song arise,
Through all the millions of the skies;
That song of triumph which records
That all the earth is now the Lord's.

2 Let thrones, and powers, and king-
doms be
Obedient, mighty God, to thee;
And over land, and stream, and main,
Now wave the scepter of thy reign.

3 O let that glorious anthem swell;
Let host to host the triumph tell,
Till not one rebel heart remains,
But over all the Saviour reigns.
　　　　　　　　　　　　　MRS. VOKE.

918　*The time to favor Zion.*

1 SOVEREIGN of worlds! display thy power;
Be this thy Zion's favored hour;
O bid the morning star arise,
O point the heathen to the skies.

2 Set up thy throne where Satan reigns,
In western wilds and eastern plains;
Far let the gospel's sound be known;
Make thou the universe thine own.

3 Speak, and the world shall hear thy voice;
Speak, and the desert shall rejoice;
Dispel the gloom of heathen night;
Bid every nation hail the light.
　　　　　　　　　　　　　MRS. VOKE.

919　*Christ's all-embracing empire.*

1 JESUS shall reign where'er the sun
Does his successive journeys run;

His kingdom spread from shore to shore,
Till moons shall wax and wane no more.

2 From north to south the princes meet,
To pay their homage at his feet;
While western empires own their Lord,
And savage tribes attend his word.

3 To him shall endless prayer be made,
And endless praises crown his head;
His name like sweet perfume shall rise
With every morning sacrifice.

4 People and realms of every tongue
Dwell on his love with sweetest song,
And infant voices shall proclaim
Their early blessings on his name.
　　　　　　　　　　　　　ISAAC WATTS.

920　*Triumphs of mercy.*

1 ARM of the Lord, awake, awake!
Put on thy strength, the nations shake,
And let the world, adoring, see
Triumphs of mercy wrought by thee.

2 Say to the heathen, from thy throne,
"I am Jehovah, God alone:"
Thy voice their idols shall confound,
And cast their idols to the ground.

3 No more let creature blood be spilt,
Vain sacrifice for human guilt!
But to each conscience be applied
The blood that flowed from Jesus' side.

4 Almighty God, thy grace proclaim,
In every land, of every name;
Till adverse powers before thee fall,
And crown the Saviour, Lord of all.
　　　　　　　　　　　WILLIAM SHRUBSOLE, JR.

ARNHEIM.   L. M.   SAMUEL HOLYOKE.

921 *The triumph near.*

1 ETERNAL Father, thou hast said,
That Christ all glory shall obtain;
That he who once a sufferer bled
Shall o'er the world a conqueror reign.

2 We wait thy triumph, Saviour King;
Long ages have prepared thy way;
Now all abroad thy banner fling,
Set time's great battle in array.

3 Thy hosts are mustered to the field;
"The Cross! the Cross!" the battle-call;
The old grim towers of darkness yield,
And soon shall totter to their fall.

4 On mountain tops the watch-fires glow,
Where scattered wide the watchmen
      stand;
Voice echoes voice, and onward flow
The joyous shouts from land to land.

5 O fill thy Church with faith and power,
Bid her long night of weeping cease;
To groaning nations haste the hour
Of life and freedom, light and peace.

6 Come, Spirit, make thy wonders known,
Fulfill the Father's high decree;
Then earth, the might of hell o'erthrown,
Shall keep her last great jubilee.
                                    RAY PALMER.

922 *Missionary meeting.*

1 ASSEMBLED at thy great command,
Before thy face, dread King, we stand;
The voice that marshaled every star
Has called thy people from afar.

2 We meet through distant lands to spread
The truth for which the martyrs bled;
Along the line, to either pole,
The anthem of thy praise to roll.

3 Our prayers assist; accept our praise,
Our hopes revive; our courage raise;
Our counsels aid; to each impart
The single eye, the faithful heart.

4 Forth with thy chosen heralds come;
Recall the wandering spirits home;
From Zion's mount send forth the sound,
To spread the spacious earth around.
                           WILLIAM B. COLLYER.

923 *The latter-day glory.*

1 BEHOLD, the heathen waits to know
The joy the gospel will bestow;
The exiled captive, to receive
The freedom Jesus has to give.

2 Come, let us, with a grateful heart,
In this blest labor share a part;
Our prayers and offerings gladly bring
To aid the triumphs of our King.

3 Our hearts exult in songs of praise
That we have seen these latter days,
When our Redeemer shall be known
Where Satan long hath held his throne.

4 Where'er his hand hath spread the skies
Sweet incense to his name shall rise;
And slave and freeman, Greek and Jew,
By sovereign grace be formed anew.
                                    MRS. VOKE.

THE CHURCH—CHURCH WORK: MISSIONS.

PROMISE. L. M.

FRANÇOIS HIPPOLYTE BARTHELEMON.

924 *For Jews and Gentiles.*

1 HEAD of the Church, whose Spirit fills
  And flows through every faithful soul,
Unites in mystic love, and seals
  Them one, and sanctifies the whole;

2 "Come, Lord," thy glorious Spirit cries,
  And souls beneath the altar groan;
"Come, Lord," the bride on earth replies,
  "And perfect all our souls in one."

3 Pour out the promised gift on all;
  Answer the universal "Come!"
The fullness of the Gentiles call,
  And take thine ancient people home.

4 To thee let all the nations flow;
  Let all obey the gospel word;
Let all their bleeding Saviour know,
  Filled with the glory of the Lord.

5 O for thy truth and mercy's sake
  The purchase of thy passion claim;
Thine heritage, the Gentiles, take,
  And cause the world to know thy name.
                          CHARLES WESLEY.

925 *Light for those who sit in darkness.*

1 THOUGH now the nations sit beneath
  The darkness of o'erspreading death,
God will arise with light divine,
  On Zion's holy towers to shine.

2 That light shall shine on distant lands,
  And wandering tribes, in joyful bands,
Shall come, thy glory, Lord, to see,
  And in thy courts to worship thee.

3 O light of Zion, now arise!
  Let the glad morning bless our eyes;
Ye nations, catch the kindling ray,
  And hail the splendors of the day.
                          LEONARD BACON.

926 *Prepare ye the way of the Lord.*
     Matt. 3: 3.

1 COMFORT, ye ministers of grace,
  Comfort the people of your Lord;
O lift ye up the fallen race,
  And cheer them by the gospel word.

2 Go into every nation, go;
  Speak to their trembling hearts, and cry,—
Glad tidings unto all we show:
  Jerusalem, thy God is nigh.

3 Hark! in the wilderness a cry,
  A voice that loudly calls,—Prepare!
Prepare your hearts, for God is nigh,
  And waits to make his entrance there.

4 The Lord your God shall quickly come;
  Sinners, repent, the call obey:
Open your hearts to make him room;
  Ye desert souls, prepare the way.

5 The Lord shall clear his way through all
  Whate'er obstructs, obstructs in vain;
The vale shall rise, the mountain fall,
  Crooked be straight, and rugged plain.

6 The glory of the Lord displayed
  Shall all mankind together view;
And what his mouth in truth hath said
  His own almighty hand shall do.
                          CHARLES WESLEY.

APPLETON. L. M. WILLIAM BOYCE.

927 *Souls perishing for lack of knowledge.*

1 SHEPHERD of souls, with pitying eye
  The thousands of our Israel see;
To thee in their behalf we cry,
  Ourselves but newly found in thee.

2 See where o'er desert wastes they err,
  And neither food nor feeder have,
Nor fold, nor place of refuge near,
  For no man cares their souls to save.

3 Thy people, Lord, are sold for naught,
  Nor know they their Redeemer nigh;
They perish, whom thyself hast bought;
  Their souls for lack of knowledge die.

4 The pit its mouth hath opened wide,
  To swallow up its careless prey:
Why should they die, when thou hast died,
  Hast died to bear their sins away?

5 Why should the foe thy purchase seize?
  Remember, Lord, thy dying groans:
The meed of all thy sufferings these;
  O claim them for thy ransomed ones!
                              CHARLES WESLEY.

928 *The Saviour's coming awaited.*

1 JESUS, thy Church, with longing eyes,
  For thine expected coming waits:
When will the promised light arise,
  And glory beam on Zion's gates?

2 E'en now, when tempests round us fall,
  And wintry clouds o'ercast the sky,
Thy words with pleasure we recall,
  And deem that our redemption's nigh.

3 O come, and reign o'er every land;
  Let Satan from his throne be hurled,
All nations bow to thy command,
  And grace revive a dying world.

4 Teach us, in watchfulness and prayer,
  To wait for thine appointed hour;
And fit us, by thy grace, to share
  The triumphs of thy conquering power.
                          WILLIAM H. BATHURST.

929 *For home missions.*

1 LOOK from thy sphere of endless day,
  O God of mercy and of might!
In pity look on those who stray,
  Benighted, in this land of light.

2 In peopled vale, in lonely glen,
  In crowded mart, by stream or sea,
How many of the sons of men
  Hear not the message sent from thee!

3 Send forth thy heralds, Lord, to call
  The thoughtless young, the hardened old,
A scattered, homeless flock, till all
  Be gathered to thy peaceful fold.

4 Send them thy mighty word to speak,
  Till faith shall dawn, and doubt depart
To awe the bold, to stay the weak,
  And bind and heal the broken heart.

5 Then all these wastes, a dreary scene,
  That make us sadden as we gaze,
Shall grow with living waters green,
  And lift to heaven the voice of praise.
                          WILLIAM C. BRYANT.

MISSIONARY HYMN. 7, 6.   LOWELL MASON.

930 *Missionary hymn.*

1 FROM Greenland's icy mountains,
    From India's coral strand;
Where Afric's sunny fountains
    Roll down their golden sand;
From many an ancient river,
    From many a palmy plain,
They call us to deliver
    Their land from error's chain.

2 What though the spicy breezes
    Blow soft o'er Ceylon's isle;
Though every prospect pleases,
    And only man is vile?
In vain with lavish kindness
    The gifts of God are strown;
The heathen in his blindness
    Bows down to wood and stone.

3 Shall we, whose souls are lighted
    With wisdom from on high,
Shall we to men benighted
    The lamp of life deny?
Salvation! O salvation!
    The joyful sound proclaim,
Till earth's remotest nation
    Has learned Messiah's name.

4 Waft, waft, ye winds, his story,
    And you, ye waters, roll,
Till, like a sea of glory,
    It spreads from pole to pole:
Till o'er our ransomed nature
    The Lamb for sinners slain,
Redeemer, King, Creator,
    In bliss returns to reign.
                        REGINALD HEBER.

931 *Departing missionaries.*

1 ROLL on, thou mighty ocean!
    And, as thy billows flow,
Bear messengers of mercy
    To every land below.
Arise, ye gales, and waft them
    Safe to the destined shore;
That man may sit in darkness,
    And death's black shade, no more.

2 O thou eternal Ruler,
    Who holdest in thine arm
The tempests of the ocean,
    Protect them from all harm!
Thy presence, Lord, be with them,
    Wherever they may be;
Though far from us who love them,
    Still let them be with thee.
                        JAMES EDMESTON.

WEBB. 7, 6.

GEORGE JAMES WEBB

932 *The morning light is breaking.*

1 THE morning light is breaking;
  The darkness disappears;
The sons of earth are waking
  To penitential tears;
Each breeze that sweeps the ocean
  Brings tidings from afar,
Of nations in commotion,
  Prepared for Zion's war.

2 See heathen nations bending
  Before the God we love,
And thousand hearts ascending
  In gratitude above;
While sinners, now confessing,
  The gospel call obey,
And seek the Saviour's blessing,
  A nation in a day.

3 Blest river of salvation,
  Pursue thine onward way;
Flow thou to every nation,
  Nor in thy richness stay:
Stay not till all the lowly
  Triumphant reach their home;
Stay not till all the holy
  Proclaim, "The Lord is come!"

SAMUEL F. SMITH.

933 *Domestic missions.*

1 OUR country's voice is pleading,
  Ye men of God, arise!
His providence is leading,
  The land before you lies;
Day-gleams are o'er it brightening,
  And promise clothes the soil;
Wide fields, for harvest whitening,
  Invite the reaper's toil.

2 Go where the waves are breaking
  On California's shore,
Christ's precious gospel taking,
  More rich than golden ore;
On Alleghany's mountains,
  Through all the western vale,
Beside Missouri's fountains,
  Rehearse the wondrous tale.

3 The love of Christ unfolding,
  Speed on from east to west,
Till all, his cross beholding,
  In him are fully blest.
Great Author of salvation,
  Haste, haste the glorious day,
When we, a ransomed nation,
  Thy scepter shall obey!

MRS. MARIA F. ANDERSON

934 *The universal anthem.*

1 WHEN shall the voice of singing
  Flow joyfully along,
When hill and valley, ringing
  With one triumphant song,
Proclaim the contest ended,
  And Him who once was slain,
Again to earth descended,
  In righteousness to reign?

2 Then from the craggy mountains
  The sacred shout shall fly;
And shady vales and fountains
  Shall echo the reply.
High tower and lowly dwelling
  Shall send the chorus round,
All hallelujahs swelling
  In one eternal sound!

JAMES EDMESTON. ALT

WATCHMAN. 7. D.   LOWELL MASON.

935 *The watchman's report.*

1 WATCHMAN, tell us of the night,
  What its signs of promise are.
Traveler, o'er yon mountain's height
  See that glory-beaming star!
Watchman, does its beauteous ray
  Aught of hope or joy foretell?
Traveler, yes; it brings the day,
  Promised day of Israel.

2 Watchman, tell us of the night;
  Higher yet that star ascends.
Traveler, blessedness and light,
  Peace and truth, its course portends!
Watchman, will its beams alone
  Gild the spot that gave them birth?
Traveler, ages are its own,
  See, it bursts o'er all the earth!

3 Watchman, tell us of the night,
  For the morning seems to dawn.
Traveler, darkness takes its flight,
  Doubt and terror are withdrawn.
Watchman, let thy wandering cease;
  Hie thee to thy quiet home!
Traveler, lo! the Prince of peace,
  Lo! the Son of God is come!
                    SIR JOHN BOWRING.

936 *The word glorified.*

1 SEE how great a flame aspires,
  Kindled by a spark of grace!
Jesus' love the nations fires,
  Sets the kingdoms on a blaze.
To bring fire on earth he came;
  Kindled in some hearts it is:
O that all might catch the flame,
  All partake the glorious bliss!

2 When he first the work begun,
  Small and feeble was his day:
Now the word doth swiftly run;
  Now it wins its widening way:
More and more it spreads and grows,
  Ever mighty to prevail;
Sin's strongholds it now o'erthrows.
  Shakes the trembling gates of hell.

3 Sons of God, your Saviour praise!
  He the door hath opened wide;
He hath given the word of grace;
  Jesus' word is glorified.
Jesus, mighty to redeem,
  He alone the work hath wrought;
Worthy is the work of him,
  Him who spake a world from naught.

4 Saw ye not the cloud arise,
  Little as a human hand?
Now it spreads along the skies,
  Hangs o'er all the thirsty land ·
Lo! the promise of a shower
  Drops already from above;
But the Lord will shortly pour
  All the Spirit of his love.
                    CHARLES WESLEY.

ELTHAM. 7, 6l.

LOWELL MASON.

937 *Christ's universal reign.*

HASTEN, Lord, the glorious time,
  When, beneath Messiah's sway,
Every nation, every clime,
  Shall the gospel call obey.

2 Mightiest kings his power shall own;
  Heathen tribes his name adore;
Satan and his host, o'erthrown,
  Bound in chains, shall hurt no more.

3 Then shall wars and tumults cease;
  Then be banished grief and pain;
Righteousness, and joy, and peace,
  Undisturbed, shall ever reign.

4 Bless we, then, our gracious Lord;
  Ever praise his glorious name;
All his mighty acts record,
  All his wondrous love proclaim.
                    HARRIET AUBER.

938 *The song of jubilee.*

1 HARK! the song of jubilee;
  Loud as mighty thunders roar,
Or the fullness of the sea,
  When it breaks upon the shore:
Hallelujah! for the Lord
  God omnipotent shall reign;
Hallelujah! let the word
  Echo round the earth and main.

2 Hallelujah!—hark! the sound,
  From the center to the skies,
Wakes above, beneath, around,
  All creation's harmonies:
See Jehovah's banner furled,
  Sheathed his sword: he speaks—'tis done,
And the kingdoms of this world
  Are the kingdoms of his Son.

3 He shall reign from pole to pole
  With illimitable sway;
He shall reign, when, like a scroll,
  Yonder heavens have passed away:
Then the end;—beneath his rod,
  Man's last enemy shall fall;
Hallelujah! Christ in God,
  God in Christ, is all in all.
                    JAMES MONTGOMERY.

939 *The banner of the cross.*

1 Go, ye messengers of God;
  Like the beams of morning, fly;
Take the wonder-working rod;
  Wave the banner-cross on high.

2 Where the lofty minaret
  Gleams along the morning skies,
Wave it till the crescent set,
  And the "Star of Jacob" rise.

3 Go to many a tropic isle
  In the bosom of the deep,
Where the skies forever smile,
  And the oppressed forever weep.

4 O'er the pagan's night of care
  Pour the living light of heaven;
Chase away his dark despair,
  Bid him hope to be forgiven.

5 Where the golden gates of day
  Open on the palmy East,
High the bleeding cross display;
  Spread the gospel's richest feast.

6 Bear the tidings round the ball,
  Visit every soil and sea;
Preach the cross of Christ to all,
  Christ, whose love is full and free.
                    JOSHUA MARSDEN.

HAMDEN. 8, 7, 4.   LOWELL MASON.

940 *The conquest of the gospel.*

1 O'ER the gloomy hills of darkness,
  Cheered by no celestial ray,
Sun of righteousness, arising,
  Bring the bright, the glorious day!
    Send the gospel
  To the earth's remotest bound.

2 Kingdoms wide that sit in darkness,—
  Grant them, Lord, the glorious light:
And, from eastern coast to western,
  May the morning chase the night;
    And redemption,
  Freely purchased, win the day.

3 Fly abroad, thou mighty Gospel!
  Win and conquer, never cease;
May thy lasting, wide dominion
  Multiply and still increase;
    Sway thy scepter,
  Saviour, all the world around!
                            WILLIAM WILLIAMS.

941 *The Macedonian cry.*

1 SOULS in heathen darkness lying,
  Where no light has broken through,
Souls that Jesus bought by dying,
  Whom his soul in travail knew,—
    Thousand voices
  Call us, o'er the waters blue.

2 Christians, hearken: none has taught them
    Of his love so deep and dear;
Of the precious price that bought them;
  Of the nail, the thorn, the spear;
    Ye who know him,
  Guide them from their darkness drear.

3 Haste, O haste, and spread the tidings
  Wide to earth's remotest strand;
Let no brother's bitter chidings
  Rise against us when we stand
    In the judgment,
  From some far, forgotten land.

4 Lo! the hills for harvest whiten,
  All along each distant shore;
Seaward far the islands brighten;
  Light of nations, lead us o'er!
    When we seek them,
  Let thy Spirit go before.
                    MRS. CECIL F. ALEXANDER.

942 *Fields white to the harvest.*

1 WHO but thou, almighty Spirit,
  Can the heathen world reclaim?
Men may preach, but till thou favor,
  Heathens will be still the same:
    Mighty Spirit!
  Witness to the Saviour's name.

2 Thou hast promised by thy prophets
  Glorious light in latter days:
Come, and bless bewildered nations,
  Change our prayers and tears to praise
    Promised Spirit!
  Round the world diffuse thy rays.

3 All our hopes, and prayers, and labors
  Must be vain without thine aid:
But thou wilt not disappoint us,
  All is true that thou hast said:
    Faithful Spirit!
  O'er the world thine influence shed.
                            UNKNOWN.

FABEN. 8, 7. D.   JOHN HENRY WILCOX.

943 *The Light of the world.*

1 LIGHT of those whose dreary dwelling
    Borders on the shades of death,
Come, and, by thyself revealing,
    Dissipate the clouds beneath.
Thou, new heaven and earth's Creator,
    In our deepest darkness rise;
Scattering all the night of nature,
    Pouring day upon our eyes.

2 Still we wait for thine appearing;
    Life and joy thy beams impart,
Chasing all our fears, and cheering
    Every poor, benighted heart.
Come, and manifest thy favor
    To our ruined, guilty race;
Come, thou universal Saviour;
    Come, and bring the gospel grace.

3 Save us in thy great compassion,
    O thou mild, pacific Prince;
Give the knowledge of salvation,
    Give the pardon of our sins:
By thine all-atoning merit,
    Every burdened soul release;
Every weary, wandering spirit,
    Guide into thy perfect peace.
                                CHARLES WESLEY.

944 *So shall He sprinkle many nations.*
Isa. 52: 15.

1 SAVIOUR, sprinkle many nations,
    Fruitful let thy sorrows be;
By thy pains and consolations,
    Draw the Gentiles unto thee:
Of thy cross the wondrous story,
    Be it to the nations told;
Let them see thee in thy glory,
    And thy mercy manifold.

2 Far and wide, though all unknowing,
    Pants for thee each mortal breast;
Human tears for thee are flowing,
    Human hearts in thee would rest;
Thirsting, as for dews of even,
    As the new-mown grass for rain,
Thee they seek, as God of heaven,
    Thee, as Man for sinners slain.

3 Saviour, lo! the isles are waiting,
    Stretched the hand, and strained the
        sight,
For thy Spirit, new creating
    Love's pure flame and wisdom's light;
Give the word, and of the preacher
    Speed the foot, and touch the tongue,
Till on earth by every creature
    Glory to the Lamb be sung.
                            A. CLEVELAND COXE.

ST. MARTIN'S.   C. M.   WILLIAM TANSUR.

945   *Renewing the covenant.*

1 COME, let us use the grace divine,
  And all, with one accord,
In a perpetual covenant join
  Ourselves to Christ the Lord;

2 Give up ourselves, through Jesus' power,
  His name to glorify;
And promise, in this sacred hour,
  For God to live and die.

3 The covenant we this moment make
  Be ever kept in mind;
We will no more our God forsake,
  Or cast his words behind.

4 We never will throw off his fear
  Who hears our solemn vow;
And if thou art well pleased to hear,
  Come down, and meet us now.

5 Thee, Father, Son, and Holy Ghost,
  Let all our hearts receive;
Present with the celestial host,
  The peaceful answer give.

6 To each the covenant blood apply,
  Which takes our sins away;
And register our names on high,
  And keep us to that day.
                              CHARLES WESLEY.

946   *Praise and thanksgiving.*

1 SING to the great Jehovah's praise;
  All praise to him belongs;
Who kindly lengthens out our days,
  Demands our choicest songs:

2 His providence hath brought us through
  Another various year;

We all, with vows and anthems new,
  Before our God appear.

3 Father, thy mercies past we own,
  Thy still continued care;
To thee presenting, through thy Son,
  Whate'er we have or are.

4 Our lips and lives shall gladly show
  The wonders of thy love,
While on in Jesus' steps we go
  To seek thy face above.

5 Our residue of days or hours
  Thine, wholly thine, shall be;
And all our consecrated powers
  A sacrifice to thee:

6 Till Jesus in the clouds appear
  To saints on earth forgiven,
And bring the grand Sabbatic year,
  The jubilee of heaven.
                              CHARLES WESLEY.

947   *A midnight song.*

1 JOIN, all ye ransomed sons of grace,
  The holy joy prolong,
And shout to the Redeemer's praise
  A solemn midnight song.

2 Blessing, and thanks, and love, and
      might,
  Be to our Jesus given,
Who turns our darkness into light,
  Who turns our hell to heaven.

3 Thither our faithful souls he leads;
  Thither he bids us rise,
With crowns of joy upon our heads,
  To meet him in the skies.
                              CHARLES WESLEY.

FROME.   C. M.   Hugh Bond.

948   *Close of the year.*

1 Awake, ye saints, and raise your eyes,
   And raise your voices high:
Awake, and praise that sovereign love,
   That shows salvation nigh.

2 On all the wings of time it flies,
   Each moment brings it near;
Then welcome each declining day,
   Welcome each closing year.

3 Not many years their rounds shall run,
   Nor many mornings rise,
Ere all its glories stand revealed
   To our admiring eyes.

4 Ye wheels of nature, speed your course!
   Ye mortal powers, decay!
Fast as ye bring the night of death,
   Ye bring eternal day.

                        PHILIP DODDRIDGE.

949   *The opening year.*

1 The year is gone, beyond recall,
   With all its hopes and fears,
With all its bright and gladdening smiles,
   With all its mourners' tears;

2 Thy thankful people praise thee, Lord,
   For countless gifts received;
And pray for grace to keep the faith
   Which saints of old believed.

3 To thee we come, O gracious Lord,
   The newborn year to bless;
Defend our land from pestilence;
   Give peace and plenteousness;

4 Forgive this nation's many sins;
   The growth of vice restrain;
And help us all with sin to strive,
   And crowns of life to gain.

5 From evil deeds that stain the past
   We now desire to flee;
And pray that future years may all
   Be spent, good Lord, for thee.

6 O Father, let thy watchful eye
   Still look on us in love,
That we may praise thee, year by year,
   With angel-hosts above.

                  FROM THE LATIN. TR. BY F. POTT.

[S. M. Tune, State Street. Page 115.]

950   *Beginning a new year.*

1 Our few revolving years,
   How swift they glide away!
How short the term of life appears
   When past—but as a day!—

2 A dark and cloudy day,
   Clouded by grief and sin;
A host of enemies without,
   Distressing fears within.

3 Lord, through another year
   If thou permit our stay,
With diligence may we pursue
   The true and living way.

                        BENJAMIN BEDDOME.

Doxology.

To Father, Son, and Holy Ghost,
   The God whom we adore,
Be glory, as it was, is now,
   And shall be evermore!

                        TATE AND BRADY.

351

STELLA. L. M. 6l.

FROM CROWN OF JESUS.

951 *A living sacrifice.*

1 WISDOM ascribe, and might, and praise,
To God, who lengthens out our days;
Who spares us yet another year,
And makes us see his goodness here:
O may we all the time redeem,
And henceforth live and die to him!

2 How often, when his arm was bared,
Hath he our sinful Israel spared!
"Let me alone!" his mercy cried,
And turned the vengeful bolt aside;
Indulged another kind reprieve,
And strangely suffered us to live.

3 Merciful God, how shall we raise
Our hearts to pay thee all thy praise?
Our hearts shall beat for thee alone;
Our lives shall make thy goodness known;
Our souls and bodies shall be thine,
A living sacrifice divine.

CHARLES WESLEY.

952 *A solemn vigil.*

1 How many pass the guilty night
In reveling and frantic mirth!
The creature is their sole delight,
Their happiness the things of earth:
For us suffice the season past;
We choose the better part at last.

2 We will not close our wakeful eyes,
We will not let our eyelids sleep,

But humbly lift them to the skies,
And all a solemn vigil keep;
So many years on sin bestowed,
Can we not watch one night for God?

3 We can, O Jesus, for thy sake,
Devote our every hour to thee;
Speak but the word, our souls shall wake,
And sing with cheerful melody:
Thy praise shall our glad tongues employ,
And every heart shall dance for joy.

4 Blest object of our faith and love,
We listen for thy welcome voice;
Our persons and our works approve,
And bid us in thy strength rejoice;
Now let us hear the mighty cry,
And shout to find the Bridegroom nigh.

5 Shout in the midst of us, O King
Of saints, and let our joys abound;
Let us rejoice, give thanks, and sing,
And triumph in redemption found:
We ask in faith for every soul;
O let our glorious joy be full!

6 O may we all triumphant rise;
With joy upon our heads return;
And, far above these nether skies,
By thee on eagle wings upborne,
Through all yon radiant circles move,
And gain the highest heaven of love!

CHARLES WESLEY.

ZEBULON.   H. M.   LOWELL MASON.

953   *The barren fig-tree.*

1 THE Lord of earth and sky,
   The God of ages, praise,
Who reigns enthroned on high,
   Ancient of endless days;
Who lengthens out our trials here,
And spares us yet another year.

2 Barren and withered trees,
   We cumbered long the ground;
No fruit of holiness
   On our dead souls was found;
Yet doth he us in mercy spare,
Another and another year.

3 When justice bared the sword
   To cut the fig-tree down,
The pity of the Lord
   Cried, "Let it still alone:"
The Father mild inclines his ear,
And spares us yet another year.

4 Jesus, thy speaking blood
   From God obtained the grace,
Who therefore hath bestowed
   On us a longer space;
Thou didst in our behalf appear,
And, lo, we see another year!

5 Then dig about the root,
   Break up our fallow ground,
And let our gracious fruit
   To thy great praise abound;
O let us all thy praise declare,
And fruit unto perfection bear.
                           CHARLES WESLEY.

954   *The Bridegroom cometh.*

1 YE virgin souls, arise,
   With all the dead, awake!
Unto salvation wise,
   Oil in your vessels take;
Upstarting at the midnight cry,
"Behold the heavenly Bridegroom nigh!"

2 He comes, he comes to call
   The nations to his bar,
And take to glory all
   Who meet for glory are;
Made ready for your full reward,
Go forth with joy to meet your Lord.

3 Go, meet him in the sky,
   Your everlasting Friend;
Your Head to glorify,
   With all his saints ascend:
Ye pure in heart, obtain the grace
To see, without a veil, his face.

4 The everlasting doors
   Shall soon the saints receive,
With seraphs, thrones, and powers,
   In glorious joy to live;
Far from a world of grief and sin,
With God eternally shut in.

5 Then let us wait to hear
   The trumpet's welcome sound;
To see our Lord appear,
   May we be watching found;
And when thou dost the heavens bow,
Be found—as, Lord, thou find'st us now
                           CHARLES WESLEY.

LUCAS. 10, 5, 11. JAMES LUCAS.

955 *Renewed devotedness.*

1 COME, let us anew our journey pursue,
    Roll round with the year,
And never stand still till the Master appear.
His adorable will let us gladly fulfill,
    And our talents improve,
By the patience of hope, and the labor of love.

2 Our life is a dream; our time, as a stream,
    Glides swiftly away,
And the fugitive moment refuses to stay.

The arrow is flown,—the moment is gone;
    The millennial year
Rushes on to our view, and eternity's here

3 O that each in the day of his coming may say,
    "I have fought my way through;
I have finished the work thou didst give me to do!"
O that each from his Lord may receive the glad word,
    "Well and faithfully done!
Enter into my joy, and sit down on m throne!"

CHARLES WESLEY.

BENEVENTO. 7. D. SAMUEL WEBBE.

BENEVENTO.—*Continued.*

956 *Retrospect of the year.*

1 WHILE, with ceaseless course, the sun
Hasted through the former year,
Many souls their race have run,
Never more to meet us here:
Fixed in an eternal state,
They have done with all below;
We a little longer wait,
But how little—none can know.

2 As the winged arrow flies
Speedily the mark to find;
As the lightning from the skies
Darts, and leaves no trace behind

Swiftly thus our fleeting days
Bear us down life's rapid stream;
Upward, Lord, our spirits raise;
All below is but a dream.

3 Thanks for mercies past receive;
Pardon of our sins renew;
Teach us henceforth how to live
With eternity in view:
Bless thy word to young and old;
Fill us with a Saviour's love;
And when life's short tale is told,
May we dwell with him above.

JOHN NEWTON.

SHAWMUT. S. M.   ARR. BY LOWELL MASON.

957 *Nearing the end.*

1 A FEW more years shall roll,
A few more seasons come;
And we shall be with those that rest,
Asleep within the tomb.

2 A few more storms shall beat
On this wild rocky shore;
And we shall be where tempests cease,
And surges swell no more.

3 A few more struggles here,
A few more partings o'er,
A few more toils, a few more tears,
And we shall weep no more.

4 Then, O my Lord, prepare
My soul for that blest day;
O wash me in thy precious blood,
And take my sins away!

HORATIUS BONAR.

958 *Our fathers; where are they?*

1 How swift the torrent rolls
That bears us to the sea,
The tide that hurries thoughtless souls
To vast eternity!

2 Our fathers, where are they,
With all they called their own?
Their joys and griefs, and hopes and cares,
And wealth and honor gone.

3 God of our fathers, hear,
Thou everlasting Friend!

While we, as on life's utmost verge,
Our souls to thee commend.

4 Of all the pious dead
May we the footsteps trace,
Till with them, in the land of light,
We dwell before thy face.

PHILIP DODDRIDGE.

959 *Plea for sparing mercy.*

1 LORD, let me know mine end,
My days, how brief their date;
That I may timely comprehend
How frail my best estate.

2 My life is but a span;
Mine age is naught with thee;
And, in his highest honor, man
Is dust and vanity.

3 At thy rebuke the bloom
Of earthly beauty flies;
And grief shall like a moth consume
All that delights our eyes.

4 Have pity on my fears;
Hearken to my request;
Turn not in silence from my tears,
But give the mourner rest.

5 O spare me yet, I pray;
Awhile my strength restore,
Ere I am summoned hence away,
And seen on earth no more.

JAMES MONTGOMERY.

SEASONS. L. M.

IGNACE PLEYEL.

960 *Earthly things vain and transitory.*

1 How vain is all beneath the skies!
  How transient every earthly bliss!
How slender all the fondest ties
  That bind us to a world like this!

2 The evening cloud, the morning dew,
  The withering grass, the fading flower,
Of earthly hopes are emblems true,
  The glory of a passing hour.

3 But though earth's fairest blossoms die,
  And all beneath the skies is vain,
There is a brighter world on high,
  Beyond the reach of care and pain.

4 Then let the hope of joys to come
  Dispel our cares, and chase our fears:
If God be ours, we're traveling home,
  Though passing through a vale of tears.
                                    DAVID E. FORD.

961 *A peaceful death besought.*

1 SHRINKING from the cold hand of death,
  I soon shall gather up my feet;
Shall soon resign this fleeting breath,
  And die, my fathers' God to meet.

2 Numbered among thy people, I
  Expect with joy thy face to see:
Because thou didst for sinners die,
  Jesus, in death remember me!

3 O that without a lingering groan
  I may the welcome word receive;
My body with my charge lay down,
  And cease at once to work and live!

4 Walk with me through the dreadful
      shade,
  And, certified that thou art mine,

My spirit, calm and undismayed,
  I shall into thy hands resign.

5 No anxious doubt, no guilty gloom,
  Shall damp whom Jesus' presence cheers
My Light, my Life, my God is come,
  And glory in his face appears.
                                    CHARLES WESLEY.

962 *The soul's best portion.*

1 ALMIGHTY Maker of my frame,
  Teach me the measure of my days;
Teach me to know how frail I am,
  And spend the remnant to thy praise.

2 My days are shorter than a span;
  A little point my life appears;
How frail, at best, is dying man!
  How vain are all his hopes and fears!

3 Vain his ambition, noise, and show;
  Vain are the cares which rack his mind:
He heaps up treasures mixed with woe,
  And dies, and leaves them all behind.

4 O be a nobler portion mine!
  My God, I bow before thy throne;
Earth's fleeting treasures I resign,
  And fix my hope on thee alone.
                                    ANNE STEELE.

963 *The way of all the earth.*

1 PASS a few swiftly fleeting years,
  And all that now in bodies live
Shall quit, like me, the vale of tears,
  Their righteous sentence to receive.

2 But all, before they hence remove,
  May mansions for themselves prepare
In that eternal house above;
  And, O my God, shall I be there?
                                    CHARLES WESLEY.

MEAR. C. M.

WELSH AIR. AARON WILLIAMS.

964 *Man frail—God eternal.*

1 O GOD, our help in ages past,
Our hope for years to come,
Our shelter from the stormy blast,
And our eternal home!

2 Under the shadow of thy throne
Still may we dwell secure;
Sufficient is thine arm alone,
And our defense is sure.

3 Before the hills in order stood,
Or earth received her frame,
From everlasting thou art God,
To endless years the same.

4 A thousand ages, in thy sight,
Are like an evening gone;
Short as the watch that ends the night,
Before the rising sun.

5 The busy tribes of flesh and blood,
With all their cares and fears,
Are carried downward by the flood,
And lost in following years.

6 Time, like an ever-rolling stream,
Bears all its sons away;
They fly, forgotten, as a dream
Dies at the opening day.

7 O God, our help in ages past,
Our hope for years to come;
Be thou our guide while life shall last,
And our perpetual home!

ISAAC WATTS.

965 *Frailty of life.*

1 THEE we adore, eternal Name,
And humbly own to thee
How feeble is our mortal frame,
What dying worms are we.

2 Our wasting lives grow shorter still,
As days and months increase;
And every beating pulse we tell
Leaves but the number less.

3 The year rolls round, and steals away
The breath that first it gave:
Whate'er we do, where'er we be,
We're traveling to the grave.

4 Dangers stand thick through all the
ground
To push us to the tomb;
And fierce diseases wait around,
To hurry mortals home.

5 Infinite joy, or endless woe,
Attends on every breath;
And yet how unconcerned we go,
Upon the brink of death!

6 Waken, O Lord, our drowsy sense
To walk this dangerous road;
And if our souls are hurried hence,
May they be found with God!

ISAAC WATTS.

Doxology.

To Father, Son, and Holy Ghost,
The God whom we adore,
Be glory, as it was, is now,
And shall be evermore.

TATE AND BRADY.

MERIBAH. C. P. M

Lowell Mason.

966 *The brink of fate.*

1 THOU God of glorious majesty,
To thee, against myself, to thee,
  A worm of earth, I cry;
A half-awakened child of man,
An heir of endless bliss or pain,
  A sinner born to die.

2 Lo! on a narrow neck of land,
'Twixt two unbounded seas, I stand,
  Secure, insensible:
A point of time, a moment's space,
Removes me to that heavenly place,
  Or shuts me up in hell.

3 O God, mine inmost soul convert,
And deeply on my thoughtful heart
  Eternal things impress:
Give me to feel their solemn weight,
And tremble on the brink of fate,
  And wake to righteousness.

4 Before me place in dread array,
The pomp of that tremendous day,
  When thou with clouds shalt come
To judge the nations at thy bar;
And tell me, Lord, shall I be there
  To meet a joyful doom?

5 Be this my one great business here,
With serious industry and fear
  Eternal bliss to insure;
Thine utmost council to fulfill,
And suffer all thy righteous will,
  And to the end endure

6 Then, Saviour, then my soul receive,
Transported from this vale, to live
  And reign with thee above,
Where faith is sweetly lost in sight,
And hope in full, supreme delight,
  And everlasting love.

CHARLES WESLEY.

VENETIA. C. P. M.

LONDON TUNE BOOK.

VENETIA.—*Continued.*

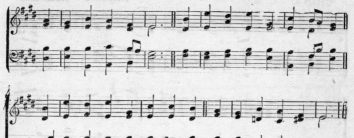

967 *Death of a friend.*

1 IF death my friend and me divide,
Thou dost not, Lord, my sorrow chide,
    Or frown my tears to see;
Restrained from passionate excess,
Thou bidd'st me mourn in calm distress
    For them that rest in thee.

2 I feel a strong immortal hope,
Which bears my mournful spirit up,
    Beneath its mountain load;
Redeemed from death, and grief and pain,
I soon shall find my friend again
    Within the arms of God.

3 Pass a few fleeting moments more,
And death the blessing shall restore
    Which death has snatched away;
For me thou wilt the summons send,
And give me back my parted friend,
    In that eternal day.
                              CHARLES WESLEY.

968 *The momentous question.*

1 AND am I only born to die?
And must I suddenly comply
    With nature's stern decree?
What after death for me remains?
Celestial joys, or hellish pains,
    To all eternity!

2 How then ought I on earth to live,
While God prolongs the kind reprieve,
    And props the house of clay?
My sole concern, my single care,
To watch, and tremble, and prepare
    Against that fatal day.

3 No room for mirth or trifling here,
For worldly hope, or worldly fear,
    If life so soon is gone;
If now the Judge is at the door,
And all mankind must stand before
    The inexorable throne!

4 No matter which my thoughts employ,
A moment's misery or joy;
    But O! when both shall end,

Where shall I find my destined place?
Shall I my everlasting days
    With fiends, or angels spend?

5 Nothing is worth a thought beneath,
But how I may escape the death
    That never, never dies;
How make mine own election sure;
And, when I fail on earth, secure
    A mansion in the skies.

6 Jesus, vouchsafe a pitying ray;
Be thou my guide, be thou my way
    To glorious happiness.
Ah! write the pardon on my heart,
And whensoe'er I hence depart,
    Let me depart in peace.
                              CHARLES WESLEY.

969 *The dying Christian to his soul.*

1 VITAL spark of heavenly flame,
Quit, O quit this mortal frame;
Trembling, hoping, lingering, flying,
O the pain, the bliss of dying!
Cease, fond nature, cease thy strife,
And let me languish into life.

2 Hark! they whisper: angels say,
"Sister spirit, come away!"
What is this absorbs me quite—
Steals my senses, shuts my sight,
Drowns my spirit, draws my breath?—
Tell me, my soul, can this be death?

3 The world recedes—it disappears;
Heaven opens on my eyes; my ears
    With sounds seraphic ring!
Lend, lend your wings! I mount! I fly!
"O Grave, where is thy victory?
    O Death, where is thy sting?"
                              ALEXANDER POPE.

Doxology.

To Father, Son, and Holy Ghost,
The God whom heaven's triumphant host
    And saints on earth adore;
Be glory as in ages past,
And now it is, and so shall last,
    When time shall be no more!
                              TATE AND BRADY.

CHINA. C. M. TIMOTHY SWAN.

970 *We mourn not as those without hope.*

1 WHY do we mourn for dying friends,
　Or shake at death's alarms?
'Tis but the voice that Jesus sends,
　To call them to his arms.

2 Are we not tending upward too,
　As fast as time can move?
Nor should we wish the hours more slow,
　To keep us from our love.

3 Why should we tremble to convey
　Their bodies to the tomb?
There once the flesh of Jesus lay,
　And left a long perfume.

4 The graves of all his saints he blest,
　And softened every bed:
Where should the dying members rest,
　But with their dying Head?

5 Thence he arose, ascending high,
　And showed our feet the way:
Up to the Lord our flesh shall fly,
　At the great rising-day.

6 Then let the last loud trumpet sound,
　And bid our kindred rise:
Awake, ye nations under ground;
　Ye saints, ascend the skies!
　　　　　　　　　ISAAC WATTS.

971　*To die is gain.*

1 WHY should our tears in sorrow flow
　When God recalls his own,
And bids them leave a world of woe,
　For an immortal crown?

2 Is not e'en death a gain to those
　Whose life to God was given?
Gladly to earth their eyes they close,
　To open them in heaven.

3 Their toils are past, their work is done,
　And they are fully blest;
They fought the fight, the victory won,
　And entered into rest.

4 Then let our sorrows cease to flow:
　God has recalled his own;
But let our hearts, in every woe,
　Still say, "Thy will be done."
　　　　　　　　WILLIAM H. BATHURST.

972　*A voice from the tombs.*

1 HARK! from the tombs a doleful sound
　My ears, attend the cry:
"Ye living men, come view the ground
　Where you must shortly lie.

2 "Princes, this clay must be your bed,
　In spite of all your towers;
The tall, the wise, the reverend head,
　Must lie as low as ours."

3 Great God! is this our certain doom?
　And are we still secure?
Still walking downward to the tomb,
　And yet prepared no more?

4 Grant us the power of quickening grace
　To fit our souls to fly;
Then, when we drop this dying flesh,
　We'll rise above the sky.
　　　　　　　　ISAAC WATTS.

DITSON.   C. M.   UNKNOWN.

973   *Through death to life.*

1 THROUGH sorrow's night, and danger's
            path,
    Amid the deepening gloom,
We, followers of our suffering Lord,
    Are marching to the tomb.

2 There, when the turmoil is no more,
    And all our powers decay,
Our cold remains in solitude
    Shall sleep the years away.

3 Our labors done, securely laid
    In this our last retreat,
Unheeded, o'er our silent dust,
    The storms of earth shall beat.

4 Yet not thus buried, or extinct,
    The vital spark shall lie;
For o'er life's wreck that spark shall rise
    To seek its kindred sky.

5 These ashes, too, this little dust,
    Our Father's care shall keep,
Till the last angel rise and break
    The long and dreary sleep.
                              H. KIRKE WHITE.

974   *Peaceful departure.*

1 BEHOLD the western evening light!
    It melts in deepening gloom;
So calmly Christians sink away,
    Descending to the tomb.

2 The winds breathe low, the withering leaf
    Scarce whispers from the tree :
So gently flows the parting breath,
    When good men cease to be.

3 How beautiful on all the hills
    The crimson light is shed!
'Tis like the peace the Christian gives
    To mourners round his bed.

4 How mildly on the wandering cloud
    The sunset beam is cast !
'Tis like the memory left behind
    When loved ones breathe their last.

5 And now above the dews of night
    The rising star appears :
So faith springs in the heart of those
    Whose eyes are bathed in tears.

6 But soon the morning's happier light
    Its glory shall restore;
And eyelids that are sealed in death
    Shall wake to close no more.
                      WILLIAM B. O. PEABODY.

975   *Thou art with me.*—Ps. 23 : 4.

1 THAT solemn hour will come for me,
    When, though their charms I own,
All human ties resigned must be ;
    For I must die alone.

2 All earthly pleasures will be o'er,
    All earthly labors done,
And I shall tread the eternal shore,
    And I must die alone.

3 But O, I will not view with dread
    That shadowy vale unknown :
I see a light within it shed ;
    I shall not die alone!

4 One will be with me there, whose voice
    I long have loved and known ;
To die is now my wish, my choice :
    I shall not die alone!
                              UNKNOWN

TIME AND ETERNITY—DEATH AND RESURRECTION.

BRISTOL. L. M.   EDWARD L. WHITE.

976 *Christ's presence makes dying easy.*

1 WHY should we start, and fear to die?
    What timorous worms we mortals are!
Death is the gate to endless joy,
    And yet we dread to enter there.

2 The pains, the groans, the dying strife,
    Fright our approaching souls away;
And we shrink back again to life,
    Fond of our prison and our clay.

3 O would my Lord his servant meet,
    My soul would stretch her wings in haste,
Fly fearless through death's iron gate,
    Nor feel the terrors as she passed.

4 Jesus can make a dying bed
    Feel soft as downy pillows are,
While on his breast I lean my head,
    And breathe my life out sweetly there.
                                    ISAAC WATTS.

977 *Sown in dishonor—raised in glory.*

1 THE morning flowers display their sweets,
    And gay their silken leaves unfold,
As careless of the noontide heats,
    As fearless of the evening cold.

2 Nipped by the wind's unkindly blast,
    Parched by the sun's directer ray,
The momentary glories waste,
    The short-lived beauties die away.

3 So blooms the human face divine,
    When youth its pride of beauty shows:
Fairer than spring the colors shine,
    And sweeter than the virgin rose.

4 Or worn by slowly rolling years,
    Or broke by sickness in a day,
The fading glory disappears,
    The short-lived beauties die away.

5 Yet these, new rising from the tomb,
    With luster brighter far shall shine,
Revive with ever-during bloom,
    Safe from diseases and decline.

6 Let sickness blast, let death devour,
    If heaven must recompense our pains;
Perish the grass, and fade the flower,
    If firm the word of God remains.
                                    SAMUEL WESLEY, JR.

978 *The memory of the just is blessed*
         Prov. 10: 7.

1 EARTH'S transitory things decay;
    Its pomps, its pleasures, pass away;
But the sweet memory of the good
Survives in the vicissitude.

2 As, 'mid the ever-rolling sea,
    The eternal isles established be,
'Gainst which the surges of the main
Fret, dash, and break themselves in vain

3 As, in the heavens, the urns divine
    Of golden light forever shine;
Though clouds may darken, storms may
        rage,
They still shine on from age to age;

4 So, through the ocean-tide of years,
    The memory of the just appears;
So, through the tempest and the gloom,
The good man's virtues light the tomb.
                                    SIR JOHN BOWRING.

TIME AND ETERNITY—DEATH AND RESURRECTION.

REST. L. M.

WILLIAM BATCHELDER BRADBURY.

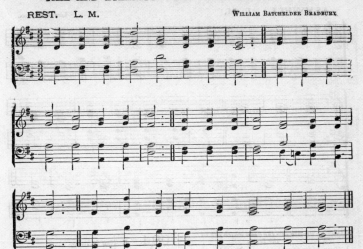

979 *Asleep in Jesus.*

1 ASLEEP in Jesus! blessed sleep,
From which none ever wakes to weep!
A calm and undisturbed repose,
Unbroken by the last of foes.

2 Asleep in Jesus! O how sweet
To be for such a slumber meet!
With holy confidence to sing,
That Death hath lost his venomed sting.

3 Asleep in Jesus! peaceful rest,
Whose waking is supremely blest!
No fear, no woe, shall dim that hour
That manifests the Saviour's power.

4 Asleep in Jesus! O for me
May such a blissful refuge be!
Securely shall my ashes lie,
Waiting the summons from on high.

5 Asleep in Jesus! far from thee
Thy kindred and their graves may be;
But thine is still a blessed sleep,
From which none ever wakes to weep.
MRS. MARGARET MACKAY.

980 *The Christian's parting hour.*

1 How sweet the hour of closing day,
When all is peaceful and serene,
And when the sun, with cloudless ray,
Sheds mellow luster o'er the scene!

2 Such is the Christian's parting hour;
So peacefully he sinks to rest,
When faith, endued from heaven with
power,
Sustains and cheers his languid breast.

3 Mark but that radiance of his eye,
That smile upon his wasted cheek,
They tell us of his glory nigh,
In language that no tongue can speak

4 A beam from heaven is sent to cheer
The pilgrim on his gloomy road;
And angels are attending near,
To bear him to their bright abode.

5 Who would not wish to die like those
Whom God's own Spirit deigns to bless?
To sink into that soft repose,
Then wake to perfect happiness?
WILLIAM H. BATHURST.

981 *The vision of faith.*

1 SHALL man, O God of light and life,
Forever molder in the grave?
Canst thou forget thy glorious work,
Thy promise, and thy power to save?

2 In those dark, silent realms of night,
Shall peace and hope no more arise?
No future morning light the tomb,
Nor day-star gild the darksome skies?

3 Cease, cease, ye vain, desponding fears:
When Christ, our Lord, from darkness
sprang,
Death, the last foe, was captive led,
And heaven with praise and wonder rang

4 Faith sees the bright, eternal doors
Unfold, to make his children way;
They shall be clothed with endless life,
And shine in everlasting day.
TIMOTHY DWIGHT

TIME AND ETERNITY—DEATH AND RESURRECTION.

ASHWELL.   L. M.

LOWELL MASON.

982   *Blessed are the dead which die in the Lord.*

1 How blest the righteous when he dies!
  When sinks a weary soul to rest,
How mildly beam the closing eyes,
  How gently heaves the expiring breast!

2 So fades a summer cloud away;
  So sinks the gale when storms are o'er;
So gently shuts the eye of day;
  So dies a wave along the shore.

3 A holy quiet reigns around,
  A calm which life nor death destroys;
And naught disturbs that peace profound
  Which his unfettered soul enjoys.

4 Farewell, conflicting hopes and fears,
  Where lights and shades alternate dwell;
How bright the unchanging morn appears!
  Farewell, inconstant world, farewell!

5 Life's labor done, as sinks the clay,
  Light from its load the spirit flies,
While heaven and earth combine to say,
  "How blest the righteous when he dies!"
                    MRS. ANNA L. BARBAULD, ALT.

983   *Disembodied saints.*

1 THE saints who die of Christ possessed,
  Enter into immediate rest;
For them no further test remains,
  Of purging fires and torturing pains.

2 Who trusting in their Lord depart,
  Cleansed from all sin, and pure in heart,
The bliss unmixed, the glorious prize,
  They find with Christ in paradise.

3 Yet, glorified by grace alone,
  They cast their crowns before the throne,
And fill the echoing courts above
  With praises of redeeming love.
                          CHARLES WESLEY.

984   *Resting in peace.*

1 UNVEIL thy bosom, faithful tomb;
  Take this new treasure to thy trust,
And give these sacred relics room
  To slumber in the silent dust.

2 Nor pain, nor grief, nor anxious fear
  Invade thy bounds; no mortal woes
Can reach the peaceful sleeper here,
  While angels watch the soft repose.

3 So Jesus slept; God's dying Son
  Passed through the grave, and blest the
      bed;
Rest here, blest saint, till from his throne
  The morning break, and pierce the shade.

4 Break from his throne, illustrious morn!
  Attend, O earth, his sovereign word!
Restore thy trust; a glorious form
  Shall then ascend to meet the Lord.
                            ISAAC WATTS.

[C. M. Tune, Mount Auburn. Page 365.]

985   *Victory over death.*

1 O FOR an overcoming faith,
  To cheer my dying hours,
To triumph o'er approaching Death,
  And all his frightful powers!

2 Joyful, with all the strength I have,
  My quivering lips should sing,
"Where is thy boasted victory, Grave?
  And where, O Death, thy sting?"

3 If sin be pardoned, I'm secure;
  Death has no sting beside:
The law gives sin its damning power,
  But Christ, my ransom, died.

4 Now to the God of victory
  Immortal thanks be paid,
Who makes us conquerors, while we die,
  Through Christ, our living Head.
                            ISAAC WATTS.

MOUNT AUBURN.   C. M.   GEORGE KINGSLEY.

986   *Planted to bloom in paradise.*

1 WHO shall forbid our chastened woe,
    Our tears of love to start?
There's balm in their assuaging flow,
    To heal the wounded heart!

2 This lovely child, thus early torn
    From our fond breasts away,
With silent grief is gently borne
    To its lone bed of clay.

3 Here sleep thou, till our longer race
    And heavier toils shall close;
Then shall we seek thy resting-place,
    And share thy long repose.

4 We plant thee here, with tears bedewed,
    Bright flower of heavenly dye;
And often shall our griefs renewed,
    These flowing founts supply.

5 But thou shalt yet in beauty bloom,
    A plant of paradise;
And gladden with thy sweet perfume
    Our mansion in the skies.
                        WILLIAM HUNTER.

987   *Death of children.*

1 THY life I read, my gracious Lord,
    With transport all divine;
Thine image trace in every word,
    Thy love in every line.

2 Methinks I see a thousand charms
    Spread o'er thy lovely face,
While infants in thy tender arms
    Receive the smiling grace.

3 "I take these little lambs," said he,
    "And lay them in my breast;
Protection they shall find in me,
    In me be ever blest.

4 "Death may the bands of life unloose,
    But can't dissolve my love;
Millions of infant souls compose
    The family above."
                        SAMUEL STENNETT.

988   *The sharpness of death overcome.*

1 CALM on the bosom of thy God,
    Fair spirit, rest thee now!
E'en while with us thy footsteps trod,
    His seal was on thy brow.

2 Dust, to its narrow house beneath!
    Soul, to its place on high!
They that have seen thy look in death,
    No more may fear to die.

3 Lone are the paths, and sad the bowers,
    Whence thy meek smile is gone;
But O, a brighter home than ours,
    In heaven is now thine own.
                        MRS. FELICIA D. HEMANS.

989   *Death vanquished.*

1 WHEN the last trumpet's awful voice
    This rending earth shall shake;
When opening graves shall yield their charge
    And dust to life awake;

2 Those bodies that corrupted fell
    Shall incorrupt arise,
And mortal forms shall spring to life
    Immortal in the skies.

3 Behold, what heavenly prophets sung
    Is now at last fulfilled;
And Death yields up his ancient reign,
    And, vanquished, quits the field.

4 Let Faith exalt her joyful voice,
    And now in triumph sing:
"O Grave, where is thy victory?
    And where, O Death, thy sting?"
                        WILLIAM CAMERON.

OWEN. S. M.

Joseph E. Sweetser.

990 *Let me die the death of the righteous.*

1 O FOR the death of those
Who slumber in the Lord!
O be like theirs my last repose,
Like theirs my last reward!

2 Their bodies in the ground,
In silent hope may lie,
Till the last trumpet's joyful sound
Shall call them to the sky.

3 Their ransomed spirits soar,
On wings of faith and love,
To meet the Saviour they adore,
And reign with him above.

4 O for the death of those
Who slumber in the Lord!
O be like theirs my last repose,
Like theirs my last reward!
JAMES MONTGOMERY.

991 *The conqueror crowned.*

1 SERVANT of God, well done!
Thy glorious warfare 's past;
The battle 's fought, the race is won,
And thou art crowned at last;

2 Of all thy heart's desire
Triumphantly possessed;
Lodged by the ministerial choir
In thy Redeemer's breast.

3 In condescending love,
Thy ceaseless prayer he heard;
And bade thee suddenly remove
To thy complete reward.

4 With saints enthroned on high,
Thou dost thy Lord proclaim,
And still to God salvation cry,
Salvation to the Lamb!

5 O happy, happy soul!
In ecstasies of praise,
Long as eternal ages roll,
Thou seest thy Saviour's face.

6 Redeemed from earth and pain,
Ah! when shall we ascend,
And all in Jesus' presence reign
With our translated friend?
CHARLES WESLEY.

992 *Death of a pastor.*

1 REST from thy labor, rest,
Soul of the just, set free!
Blest be thy memory, and blest
Thy bright example be!

2 Now, toil and conflict o'er,
Go, take with saints thy place;
But go, as each has gone before,
A sinner saved by grace.

3 Saviour, into thy hands
Our pastor we resign,
And now we wait thine own commands.
We were not his but thine.

4 Thou art thy Church's Head;
And when the members die,
Thou raisest others in their stead;
To thee we lift our eye.

5 On thee our hopes depend,
We gather round our Rock;
Send whom thou wilt, but condescend
Thyself to feed the flock.
JAMES MONTGOMERY.

TIME AND ETERNITY—DEATH AND RESURRECTION.

CAPELLO.   S. M.

LOWELL MASON.

993   *It is not death to die.*

1 It is not death to die,—
   To leave this weary road,
And, 'mid the brotherhood on high,
   To be at home with God.

2 It is not death to close
   The eye long dimmed by tears,
And wake, in glorious repose
   To spend eternal years.

3 It is not death to bear
   The wrench that sets us free
From dungeon chain, to breathe the air
   Of boundless liberty.

4 It is not death to fling
   Aside this sinful dust,
And rise, on strong exulting wing,
   To live among the just.

5 Jesus, thou Prince of life,
   Thy chosen cannot die!
Like thee, they conquer in the strife,
   To reign with thee on high.
           ABRAHAM H. C. MALAN. TR. BY G. W. BETHUNE.

994   *Resting in hope.*

1 Rest for the toiling hand,
   Rest for the anxious brow,
Rest for the weary, way-sore feet,
   Rest from all labor now.

2 Rest for the fevered brain,
   Rest for the throbbing eye;
Through these parched lips of thine no
      more
   Shall pass the moan or sigh.

3 Soon shall the trump of God
   Give out the welcome sound,

That shakes thy silent chamber-walls,
   And breaks the turf-sealed ground.

4 Ye dwellers in the dust,
   Awake, come forth and sing!
Sharp has your frost of winter been,
   But bright shall be your spring.

5 'Twas sown in weakness here,
   'Twill then be raised in power:
That which was sown an earthly seed,
   Shall rise a heavenly flower.
                    HORATIUS BONAR.

995   *Because I live, ye shall live also.*

1 And must this body die,
   This well-wrought frame decay?
And must these active limbs of mine
   Lie moldering in the clay?

2 God, my Redeemer, lives,
   And ever from the skies
Looks down, and watches all my dust,
   Till he shall bid it rise.

3 Arrayed in glorious grace
   Shall these vile bodies shine,
And every shape, and every face,
   Be heavenly and divine.

4 These lively hopes we owe,
   Lord, to thy dying love:
O may we bless thy grace below,
   And sing thy grace above!

5 Saviour, accept the praise
   Of these our humble songs,
Till tunes of nobler sound we raise
   With our immortal tongues.
                    ISAAC WATTS.

TIOGA. S. M.

THOMAS HASTINGS.

FINE.

D.S.

996 *Solemn thoughts of the future.*

1 AND am I born to die?
  To lay this body down?
And must my trembling spirit fly
  Into a world unknown,—
A land of deepest shade,
  Unpierced by human thought,
The dreary regions of the dead,
  Where all things are forgot?

2 Soon as from earth I go,
  What will become of me?
Eternal happiness or woe
  Must then my portion be:
Waked by the trumpet's sound,
  I from my grave shall rise,
And see the Judge, with glory crowned,
  And see the flaming skies!

3 Who can resolve the doubt
  That tears my anxious breast?
Shall I be with the damned cast out,
  Or numbered with the blest?
I must from God be driven,
  Or with my Saviour dwell,
Must come at his command to heaven,
  Or else—depart to hell!

4 O thou who wouldst not have
  One wretched sinner die;
Who diedst thyself my soul to save
  From endless misery;

Show me the way to shun
  Thy dreadful wrath severe,
That when thou comest on thy throne
  I may with joy appear.
                        CHARLES WESLEY.

997 *For victory in death.*

1 WHEN on the brink of death
  My trembling soul shall stand,
Waiting to pass that awful flood,
  Great God, at thy command,—

2 When every scene of life
  Stands ready to depart,
And the last sigh that shakes the frame
  Shall rend this bursting heart,—

3 Thou Source of joy supreme,
  Whose arm alone can save,
Dispel the darkness that surrounds
  The entrance to the grave.

4 Lay thy supporting hand
  Beneath my sinking head;
And with a ray of love divine
  Illume my dying bed.

5 Leaning on Jesus' breast,
  May I resign my breath;
And in his kind embraces lose
  The bitterness of death.
                        WILLIAM B. COLLYER, ALT.

FREDERICK. 11, or 13, 11, 12.   GEORGE KINGSLEY

998   *I would not live alway.*

1 I WOULD not live alway; I ask not to stay
Where storm after storm rises dark o'er the way:
The few lurid mornings that dawn on us here
Are enough for life's woes, full enough for its cheer.

2 I would not live alway; no, welcome the tomb!
Since Jesus hath lain there, I dread not its gloom;
There sweet be my rest till he bid me arise,
To hail him in triumph descending the skies.

3 Who, who would live alway, away from his God;
Away from yon heaven, that blissful abode,
Where the rivers of pleasure flow o'er the bright plains,
And the noontide of glory eternally reigns?

4 Where the saints of all ages in harmony meet,
Their Saviour and brethren transported to greet;
While the anthems of rapture unceasingly roll,
And the smile of the Lord is the feast of the soul.

WILLIAM A. MUHLENBERG.

999   *Thou art gone to the grave.*

1 THOU art gone to the grave; but we will not deplore thee,
Though sorrows and darkness encompass the tomb;
Thy Saviour has passed through its portal before thee,
And the lamp of his love is thy guide through the gloom.

2 Thou art gone to the grave; we no longer behold thee,
Nor tread the rough path of the world by thy side:
But the wide arms of mercy are spread to enfold thee,
And sinners may die, for the Sinless hath died.

3 Thou art gone to the grave; and, its mansion forsaking,
Perchance thy weak spirit in fear lingered long;
But the mild rays of paradise beamed on thy waking,
And the sound which thou heardst was the seraphim's song.

4 Thou art gone to the grave; but we will not deplore thee,
Whose God was thy ransom, thy guardian, and guide;
He gave thee, he took thee, and he will restore thee;
And death has no sting, for the Saviour has died.

REGINALD HEBER.

TIME AND ETERNITY—DEATH AND RESURRECTION.

LEAVITT. 7. D.

JOSEPH P. HOLBROOK.

1000 *Clothed with immortality.*

1 "SPIRIT, leave thy house of clay;
  Lingering dust, resign thy breath!
Spirit, cast thy chains away;
  Dust, be thou dissolved in death!"
Thus the mighty Saviour speaks,
  While the faithful Christian dies;
Thus the bonds of life he breaks,
  And the ransomed captive flies.

2 "Prisoner, long detained below,
  Prisoner, now with freedom blest,
Welcome from a world of woe;
  Welcome to a land of rest!"
Thus the choir of angels sing,
  As they bear the soul on high,
While with hallelujahs ring
  All the regions of the sky.

3 Grave, the guardian of our dust,
  Grave, the treasury of the skies,
Every atom of thy trust
  Rests in hope again to rise:
Hark! the judgment-trumpet calls,
  "Soul, rebuild thy house of clay;
Immortality thy walls,
  And eternity thy day!"

JAMES MONTGOMERY, ALT.

1001 *Dying in the Lord.*

1 HARK! a voice divides the sky,—
  Happy are the faithful dead!
In the Lord who sweetly die,
  They from all their toils are freed:
Them the Spirit hath declared
  Blest, unutterably blest;
Jesus is their great reward,
  Jesus is their endless rest.

2 Followed by their works they go,
  Where their Head is gone before:
Reconciled by grace below,
  Grace hath opened mercy's door;
Justified through faith alone,
  Here they knew their sins forgiven,
Here they laid their burden down,
  Hallowed and made meet for heaven

3 Who can now lament the lot
  Of a saint in Christ deceased?
Let the world, who know us not,
  Call us hopeless and unblest:
When from flesh the spirit freed
  Hastens homeward to return,
Mortals cry, "A man is dead!"
  Angels sing, "A child is born!"

4 Born into the world above,
  They our happy brother greet;
Bear him to the throne of love,
  Place him at the Saviour's feet:
Jesus smiles, and says, "Well done!
  Good and faithful servant thou!
Enter, and receive thy crown,
  Reign with me triumphant now."

CHARLES WESLEY.

TALMAR. 8, 7.   ISAAC BAKER WOODBURY.

1002 *Bereavement and resignation.*

1 JESUS, while our hearts are bleeding
   O'er the spoils that death has won,
We would, at this solemn meeting,
   Calmly say, "Thy will be done."

2 Though cast down, we're not forsaken;
   Though afflicted, not alone:
Thou didst give, and thou hast taken;
   Blessed Lord, "Thy will be done."

3 Though to-day we're filled with mourning,
   Mercy still is on the throne;
With thy smiles of love returning,
   We can sing, "Thy will be done."

4 By thy hands the boon was given;
   Thou hast taken but thine own:
Lord of earth, and God of heaven,
   Evermore, "Thy will be done."
                              THOMAS HASTINGS.

1003 *Conflict ended—crown waiting.*

1 HAPPY soul, thy days are ended,
   All thy mourning days below;
Go, by angel guards attended,
   To the sight of Jesus go!
Waiting to receive thy spirit,
   Lo! the Saviour stands above;
Shows the purchase of his merit,
   Reaches out the crown of love.

2 Struggle through thy latest passion,
   To thy great Redeemer's breast,
To his uttermost salvation,
   To his everlasting rest.
For the joy he sets before thee,
   Bear a momentary pain;
Die, to live a life of glory;
   Suffer, with thy Lord to reign.
                              CHARLES WESLEY.

[7. D. Tune, Leavitt. Page 370.]

1004 *The dying believer.*

1 DEATHLESS spirit, now arise;
Soar, thou native of the skies!
Pearl of price by Jesus bought,
To his glorious likeness wrought,—

2 Go, to shine before the throne;
Deck the Mediator's crown;
Go, his triumphs to adorn;
Made for God, to God return.

3 Lo! he beckons from on high;
Fearless to his presence fly;
Thine the merit of his blood,
Thine the righteousness of God.

4 Angels, joyful to attend,
Hovering round thy pillow, bend;
Wait to catch the signal given,
And convey thee quick to heaven.

5 Shudder not to pass the stream;
Venture all thy care on him,—
Him, whose dying love and power
Stilled its tossings, hushed its roar.

6 Safe is the expanded wave,
Gentle as a summer's eve;
Not one object of his care
Ever suffered shipwreck there.

7 See the haven full in view;
Love divine shall bear thee through
Trust to that propitious gale;
Weigh thine anchor, spread thy sail.

8 Saints in glory, perfect made,
Wait thy passage through the shade,
Ardent for thy coming o'er,
See, they throng the blissful shore.
                       AUGUSTUS M. TOPLADY.

OUR FATHER. 6, 4.

EDWARD L. WHITE.

1005 *Our stay in death.*

1 LOWLY and solemn be
Thy children's cry to thee,
 Father divine!
A hymn of suppliant breath,
Owning that life and death
 Alike are thine.

2 O Father, in that hour,
When earth all helping power
 Shall disavow;
When spear, and shield, and crown,
In faintness are cast down;
 Sustain us, thou!

3 By Him who bowed to take
The death-cup for our sake,
 The thorn, the rod;
From whom the last dismay
Was not to pass away;
 Aid us, O God!

4 Tremblers beside the grave,
We call on thee to save,
 Father divine!

Hear, hear our suppliant breath,
Keep us in life and death,
 Thine, only thine.

MRS. FELICIA D. HEMANS.

[7, 6 l. Tune, Gethsemane. Page 407.]

1006 *Death of a child.*

1 WHEREFORE should I make my moan
 Now the darling child is dead?
He to early rest is gone,
 He to paradise is fled;
I shall go to him, but he
Never shall return to me.

2 God forbids his longer stay;
 God recalls the precious loan;
God hath taken him away,
 From my bosom to his own:
Surely what he wills is best;
Happy in his will I rest.

3 Faith cries out, "It is the Lord,
 Let him do as seems him good!"
Be thy holy name adored;
 Take the gift awhile bestowed:
Take the child no longer mine;
Thine he is, forever thine.

CHARLES WESLEY.

THE LONG HOME. 7, 8, 7. Sir Arthur Seymour Sullivan.

1007 *On the death of a little child.*

1 TENDER Shepherd, thou hast stilled
  Now thy little lamb's brief weeping:
Ah, how peaceful, pale, and mild
  In its narrow bed 'tis sleeping!
And no sigh of anguish sore
Heaves that little bosom more.

2 In this world of care and pain,
  Lord, thou wouldst no longer leave it;
To the sunny heavenly plain
  Thou dost now with joy receive it;
Clothed in robes of spotless white,
Now it dwells with thee in light.

3 Ah, Lord Jesus, grant that we
  Where it lives may soon be living,
And the lovely pastures see
  That its heavenly food are giving;
Then the gain of death we prove,
Though thou take what most we love.
FROM THE GERMAN. TR. BY MISS C. WINKWORTH.

[6. Tune, Jewett. Page 241.]

1008 *For a child's funeral.*

1 Go to thy rest, fair child!
  Go to thy dreamless bed,

Gentle, and meek, and mild,
  With blessings on thy head.
Fresh roses in thy hand,
  Buds on thy pillow laid,
Haste from this blighting land,
  Where flowers so quickly fade.

2 Before thy heart could learn
  In waywardness to stray;
Before thy feet could turn
  The dark and downward way:
Ere sin could wound thy breast,
  Or sorrow wake the tear;
Rise to thy home of rest,
  In yon celestial sphere!

3 Because thy smile was fair,
  Thy lip and eye so bright,
Because thy cradle-care
  Was such a fond delight;
Shall love, with weak embrace
  Thy heavenward flight detain?
No, angel! seek thy place
  Amid yon cherub train.
MRS. LYDIA H. SIGOURNEY.

REQUIEM. 6, 8, 8. THOMAS HASTINGS.

1009 *Friends separated.*

1 FRIEND after friend departs:
  Who hath not lost a friend?
There is no union here of hearts
  That finds not here an end:
Were this frail world our only rest,
Living or dying, none were blest.

2 Beyond the flight of time,
  Beyond this vale of death,
There surely is some blessed clime
  Where life is not a breath,
Nor life's affection transient fire,
Whose sparks fly upward to expire.

3 There is a world above,
  Where parting is unknown;
A whole eternity of love,
  Formed for the good alone:
And faith beholds the dying here
Translated to that happier sphere.

4 Thus star by star declines,
  Till all are passed away,
As morning high and higher shines,
  To pure and perfect day;
Nor sink those stars in empty night;
They hide themselves in heaven's own
  light.

JAMES MONTGOMERY.

[7, 6. Tune, Munich. Page 83.]

1010 *Present with the Lord.*

1 THE precious seed of weeping
  To-day we sow once more,
The form of one now sleeping,
  Whose pilgrimage is o'er.
Ah! death but safely lands him
  Where we too would attain:
Our Father's voice demands him,
  And death to him is gain.

2 He has what we are wanting,
  He sees what we believe;
The sins on earth so haunting
  Have there no power to grieve;
Safe in his Saviour's keeping,
  Who sent him calm release,—
'Tis only we are weeping,—
  He dwells in perfect peace.

3 The crown of life he weareth,
  He bears the shining palm,
The "Holy, holy," shareth,
  And joins the angels' psalm;
But we, poor pilgrims, wander
  Still through this land of woe
Till we shall meet him yonder,
  And all his joy shall know.

CARL J. F. SPITTA. TR. BY MISS C. WINKWORTH.

VERNON.　8.　　　　　　　　　　　　　　GERMAN.

1011 *Safe in the harbor.*

1 WEEP not for a brother deceased,
　Our loss is his infinite gain;
A soul out of prison released,
　And freed from its bodily chain;
With songs let us follow his flight,
　And mount with his spirit above,
Escaped to the mansions of light,
　And lodged in the Eden of love.

2 Our brother the haven hath gained,
　Outflying the tempest and wind;
His rest he hath sooner obtained,
　And left his companions behind,
Still tossed on a sea of distress,
　Hard toiling to make the blest shore,
Where all is assurance and peace,
　And sorrow and sin are no more.

3 There all the ship's company meet,
　Who sailed with the Saviour beneath;
With shouting each other they greet,
　And triumph o'er sorrow and death:
The voyage of life's at an end;
　The mortal affliction is past;
The age that in heaven they spend,
　Forever and ever shall last.

CHARLES WESLEY.

1012 *The grave disarmed.*

1 MAN dieth and wasteth away,
　And where is he?—Hark! from the skies,
I hear a voice answer and say,
　"The spirit of man never dies!
His body, which came from the earth,
　Must mingle again with the sod;
His soul, which in heaven had birth,
　Returns to the bosom of God."

2 No terror has death, or the grave,
　To those who believe in the Lord,
Who know the Redeemer can save,
　And lean on the faith of his word:
While ashes to ashes, and dust
　We give unto dust, in our gloom,
The light of salvation we trust,
　Which hangs like a lamp in the tomb.

3 O Lord God Almighty! to thee
　We turn, as our solace above;
The waters may fail from the sea,
　But never thy fountains of love:
O teach us thy will to obey,
　And sing with one heart and accord,
"He gave, and he taketh away,
　And praised be the name of the Lord."

GEORGE P. MORRIS.

NOVELLO.　8, 7, 4.

VINCENT NOVELLO.

1013　*The second advent.*

1 Lo! He comes, with clouds descending,
　Once for favored sinners slain;
Thousand thousand saints attending,
　Swell the triumph of his train:
　　Hallelujah!
　God appears on earth to reign.

2 Every eye shall now behold him
　Robed in dreadful majesty;
Those who set at naught and sold him,
　Pierced and nailed him to the tree,
　　Deeply wailing,
　Shall the true Messiah see.

3 All the tokens of his passion
　Still his dazzling body bears,
Cause of endless exultation
　To his ransomed worshipers;
　　With what rapture
　Gaze we on those glorious scars!

4 Yea, Amen! let all adore thee,
　High on thy eternal throne;
Saviour, take the power and glory,
　Claim the kingdom for thine own:
　　Jah! Jehovah!
　Everlasting God, come down!

CHARLES WESLEY.

1014　*Judgment terrors—judgment raptures.*

1 Lift your heads, ye friends of Jesus,
　Partners in his patience here.
Christ, to all believers precious,
　Lord of lords, shall soon appear:
　　Mark the tokens
　Of his heavenly kingdom near.

2 Sun and moon are both confounded,
　Darkened into endless night,
When, with angel-hosts surrounded,
　In his Father's glory bright,
　　Beams the Saviour,
　Shines the everlasting light.

3 See the stars from heaven falling;
　Hark, on earth the doleful cry,
Men on rocks and mountains calling,
　While the frowning Judge draws nigh
　　"Hide us, hide us,
　Rocks and mountains, from his eye!"

4 With what different exclamation
　Shall the saints his banner see!
By the tokens of his passion,
　By the marks received for me,
　　All discern him;
　All with shouts cry out, "'Tis he!"

5 Lo! 'tis he! our hearts' desire,
　Come for his espoused below;
Come to join us with his choir,
　Come to make our joys o'erflow;
　　Palms of victory,
　Crowns of glory, to bestow.

CHARLES WESLEY.

PILGRIMAGE. 8, 7, 4. ANCIENT MELODY.

5 With my lamp well trimmed and
burning,
Swift to hear, and slow to roam,
Watching for thy glad returning
To restore me to my home;
Come, my Saviour,
O my Saviour, quickly come!
JOHN S. B. MONSELL.

1015 *O'er the distant mountains
breaking.*

1 O'ER the distant mountains breaking,
Comes the reddening dawn of day;
Rise, my soul, from sleep awaking,
Rise, and sing, and watch, and pray:
'Tis thy Saviour,
On his bright returning way.

2 O thou long-expected, weary
Waits my anxious soul for thee;
Life is dark, and earth is dreary
Where thy light I do not see:
O my Saviour,
When wilt thou return to me?

3 Long, too long, in sin and sadness,
Far away from thee I pine;
When, O when, shall I the gladness
Of thy Spirit feel in mine?
O my Saviour,
When shall I be wholly thine?

4 Nearer is my soul's salvation,
Spent the night, the day at hand;
Keep me in my lowly station,
Watching for thee, till I stand,
O my Saviour,
In thy bright and promised land.

1016 *Christ is coming.*

1 CHRIST is coming! let creation
Bid her groans and travail cease;
Let the glorious proclamation
Hope restore, and faith increase;
Christ is coming!
Come, thou blessed Prince of peace!

2 Earth can now but tell the story
Of thy bitter cross and pain;
She shall yet behold thy glory
When thou comest back to reign;
Christ is coming!
Let each heart repeat the strain.

3 Long thy exiles have been pining,
Far from rest, and home, and thee;
But, in heavenly vesture shining,
Soon they shall thy glory see;
Christ is coming!
Haste the joyous jubilee.

4 With that "blessed hope" before us,
Let no harp remain unstrung;
Let the mighty advent chorus
Onward roll from tongue to tongue;
Christ is coming!
Come, Lord Jesus, quickly come!
JOHN R. MACDUFF.

GRACE CHURCH. L. M.

IGNACE PLEYEL.

1017 *The dreadful day.*

1 THE day of wrath, that dreadful day,
When heaven and earth shall pass away!
What power shall be the sinner's stay?
How shall he meet that dreadful day?

2 When, shriveling like a parchéd scroll,
The flaming heavens together roll;
And louder yet, and yet more dread,
Swells the high trump that wakes the dead!

3 O, on that day, that wrathful day,
When man to judgment wakes from clay,
Be thou, O Christ, the sinner's stay,
Though heaven and earth shall pass away!
SIR WALTER SCOTT.

1018 *The Judge severe.*

1 HE comes! He comes! the Judge severe!
The seventh trumpet speaks him near;
His lightnings flash, his thunders roll;
How welcome to the faithful soul!

2 From heaven angelic voices sound;
See the almighty Jesus crowned,
Girt with omnipotence and grace!
And glory decks the Saviour's face.

3 Descending on his great white throne,
He claims the kingdoms for his own;
The kingdoms all obey his word,
And hail him their triumphant Lord.

4 Shout, all the people of the sky,
And all the saints of the Most High;
Our Lord, who now his right obtains,
Forever and forever reigns.
CHARLES WESLEY.

1019 *Safety amid general dissolution.*

1 THE great archangel's trump shall sound,
While twice ten thousand thunders roar,
Tear up the graves, and cleave the ground,
And make the greedy sea restore.

2 The greedy sea shall yield her dead;
The earth no more her slain conceal;
Sinners shall lift their guilty head,
And shrink to see a yawning hell.

3 But we, who now our Lord confess,
And faithful to the end endure,
Shall stand in Jesus' righteousness;
Stand, as the Rock of ages, sure.

4 We, while the stars from heaven shall fall,
And mountains are on mountains huried,
Shall stand unmoved amidst them all,
And smile to see a burning world.

5 The earth and all the works therein
Dissolve, by raging flames destroyed,
While we survey the awful scene,
And mount above the fiery void.

6 By faith we now transcend the skies,
And on that ruined world look down:
By love above all height we rise,
And share the everlasting throne.
CHARLES WESLEY.

Doxology.

PRAISE God, from whom all blessings flow;
Praise him, all creatures here below;
Praise him above, ye heavenly host;
Praise Father, Son, and Holy Ghost!
THOMAS KEN.

WINDSOR. C. M.

GEORGE KIRBYE.

1020 *The awful sentence.*

1 THAT awful day will surely come,
  The appointed hour makes haste,
When I must stand before my Judge,
  And pass the solemn test.

2 Jesus, thou Source of all my joys,
  Thou Ruler of my heart,
How could I bear to hear thy voice
  Pronounce the word, "Depart!"

3 The thunder of that awful word
  Would so torment my ear,
'Twould tear my soul asunder, Lord,
  With most tormenting fear.

4 What! to be banished from my Lord,
  And yet forbid to die!
To linger in eternal pain,
  And death forever fly!

5 O wretched state of deep despair,
  To see my God remove,
And fix my doleful station where
  I must not taste his love!

ISAAC WATTS.

1021 *The final account.*

1 AND must I be to judgment brought,
  And answer in that day
For every vain and idle thought,
  And every word I say?

2 Yes, every secret of my heart
  Shall shortly be made known,
And I receive my just desert
  For all that I have done.

3 How careful, then, ought I to live,
  With what religious fear!

Who such a strict account must give
  For my behavior here.

4 Thou awful Judge of quick and dead,
  The watchful power bestow;
So shall I to my ways take heed,—
  To all I speak or do.

5 If now thou standest at the door,
  O let me feel thee near;
And make my peace with God, before
  I at thy bar appear.

CHARLES WESLEY.

[L. M. Tune, Grace Church. Page 378.]

1022 *Be pitiful, O God.*

1 O SON of God, in glory crowned,
  The Judge ordained of quick and dead)
O Son of man, so pitying found
  For all the tears thy people shed!

2 Be with us in this darkened place,—
  This weary, restless, dangerous night;
And teach, O teach us, by thy grace,
  To struggle onward into light!

3 And since, in God's recording book,
  Our sins are written, every one,—
The crime, the wrath, the wandering look,
  The good we knew, and left undone;

4 Lord, ere the last dread trump be heard,
  And ere before thy face we stand,
Look thou on each accusing word,
  And blot it with thy bleeding hand.

5 And by the love that brought thee here,
  And by the cross, and by the grave,
Give perfect love for conscious fear,
  And in the day of judgment save.

MRS. CECIL F. ALEXANDER.

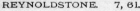

REYNOLDSTONE.   7, 61.   Rev. T. R. Matthews.

FROM MENDELSSOHN.

5 Thou, who bad'st the sinner cease
From her tears and go in peace,—
Thou, who to the dying thief
Spakest pardon and relief,—
Thou, O Lord, to me hast given,
E'en to me, the hope of heaven.
THOMAS OF CELANO. TR. BY A. R. STANLEY.

[S. M. Tune, Tioga. Page 863.]

1023   Day of wrath.

1 DAY of wrath, O dreadful day!
When this world shall pass away
And the heavens together roll,
Shriveling like a parchéd scroll,
Long foretold by saint and sage,
David's harp, and sibyl's page.

2 Day of terror, day of doom,
When the Judge at last shall come!
Through the deep and silent gloom,
Shrouding every human tomb,
Shall the archangel's trumpet tone
Summon all before the throne.

3 Then the writing shall be read,
Which shall judge the quick and dead;
Then the Lord of all our race
Shall appoint to each his place;
Every wrong shall be set right,
Every secret brought to light.

4 O just Judge, to whom belongs
Vengeance for all earthly wrongs,
Grant forgiveness, Lord, at last,
Ere the dread account be past.
Lo, my sighs, my guilt, my shame!
Spare me for thine own great name.

1024   The inexorable Judge.

1 THOU Judge of quick and dead,
Before whose bar severe,
With holy joy or guilty dread,
We all shall soon appear;
Our cautioned souls prepare
For that tremendous day,
And fill us now with watchful care,
And stir us up to pray:

2 To pray, and wait the hour,
That awful hour unknown,
When, robed in majesty and power,
Thou shalt from heaven come down,
The immortal Son of man,
To judge the human race,
With all thy Father's dazzling train,
With all thy glorious grace.

3 O may we all be found
Obedient to thy word,
Attentive to the trumpet's sound,
And looking for our Lord.
O may we thus insure
A lot among the blest;
And watch a moment to secure
An everlasting rest.
CHARLES WESLEY.

FALKIRK. 7, 6, 8.

FROM THOMAS AUGUSTINE ARNE.

1025 *The omnipotent decree.*

1 STAND the omnipotent decree!
  Jehovah's will be done!
Nature's end we wait to see,
  And hear her final groan.
Let this earth dissolve, and blend
  In death the wicked and the just;
Let those ponderous orbs descend,
  And grind us into dust :—

2 Rests secure the righteous man,
  At his Redeemer's beck,
Sure to emerge and rise again,
  And mount above the wreck:

Lo! the heavenly spirit towers,
  Like flames o'er nature's funeral pyre,
Triumphs in immortal powers,
  And claps his wings of fire!

3 Nothing hath the just to lose,
  By worlds on worlds destroyed:
Far beneath his feet he views,
  With smiles, the flaming void;
Sees this universe renewed,
  The grand millennial reign begun;
Shouts, with all the sons of God,
  Around the eternal throne.

CHARLES WESLEY

25

CHARLES. 8, 7. J. PARKER.

1026 *Day of life.*

1 Lo, the day, the day of life!
Day of unimagined light,
Day when death itself shall die,
And there shall be no more night!

2 See the King desired for ages,
By the just expected long,
Long implored, at length he hasteth,
Cometh with salvation strong.

3 O how past all utterance happy,
Sweet and joyful it will be
When they who, unseen, have loved him,
Jesus face to face shall see!

4 Blessed then, earth's patient mourners,
Who for Christ have toiled and died,
Driven by the world's rough pressure
In those mansions to abide!

5 What will be the bliss and rapture
None can dream and none can tell,
There to reign among the angels,
In that heavenly home to dwell.
FROM THE LATIN. TR. BY MRS. E. CHARLES.

[C. P. M. Tune, Meribah. Page 358.]

1027 *Supplication.*

1 WHEN thou, my righteous Judge,
shalt come
To take thy ransomed people home,
Shall I among them stand?
Shall such a worthless worm as I,
Who sometimes am afraid to die,
Be found at thy right hand?

2 I love to meet thy people now,
Before thy feet with them to bow,
Though vilest of them all;
But, can I bear the piercing thought,
What if my name should be left out,
When thou for them shalt call?

3 O Lord, prevent it by thy grace;
Be thou my only hiding-place,
In this the accepted day;
Thy pardoning voice O let me hear,
To still my unbelieving fear,
Nor let me fall, I pray.

4 Among thy saints let me be found,
Whene'er the archangel's trump shall
sound,
To see thy smiling face;
Then loudest of the throng I'll sing,
While heaven's resounding mansions
ring
With shouts of sovereign grace.
SELINA, COUNTESS OF HUNTINGDON.

JUDGMENT HYMN. 8, 7. (Peculiar.) JOSEPH KLUG'S GESANGBUCH.

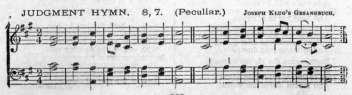

JUDGMENT HYMN.—*Continued.*

1028 *The end of things created.*

1 GREAT God! what do i see and hear!
The end of things created!
The Judge of man I see appear,
On clouds of glory seated:
The trumpet sounds; the graves restore
The dead which they contained before;
Prepare, my soul, to meet him!

2 The dead in Christ shall first arise,
At the last trumpet's sounding,

Caught up to meet him in the skies,
With joy their Lord surrounding:
No gloomy fears their souls dismay;
His presence sheds eternal day
On those prepared to meet him.

3 But sinners, filled with guilty fears,
Behold his wrath prevailing;
For they shall rise and find their tears
And sighs are unavailing:
The day of grace is past and gone,
Trembling they stand before the throne,
All unprepared to meet him.

4 Great God! what do I see and hear!
The end of things created!
The Judge of man I see appear,
On clouds of glory seated:
Beneath his cross I view the day
When heaven and earth shall pass away,
And thus prepare to meet him.

BARTHOLOMÄUS RINGWALDT, ALT.
TR. BY W. B. COLLYER.

BREST.   8, 7, 4.

LOWELL MASON.

1029 *The judgment-day.*

1 DAY of judgment, day of wonders!
Hark! the trumpet's awful sound,
Louder than a thousand thunders,
Shakes the vast creation round:
How the summons
Will the sinner's heart confound!

2 See the Judge, our nature wearing,
Clothed in majesty divine!
You who long for his appearing,
Then shall say, "This God is mine:"
Glorious Saviour,
Own me in that day for thine!

3 At his call the dead awaken,
Rise to life from earth and sea;
All the powers of nature, shaken
By his voice, prepare to flee:
Careless sinner,
What will then become of thee?

4 But to those who have confessed,
Loved and served the Lord below,
He will say, "Come near, ye blessed:
See the kingdom I bestow;
You forever
Shall my love and glory know."

JOHN NEWTON.

DEVIZES.   C. M.   ISAAC TUCKER

FIRST PART.

1030 *The full assurance of hope.*

1 How happy every child of grace,
  Who knows his sins forgiven!
"This earth," he cries, "is not my place,
  I seek my place in heaven,—
A country far from mortal sight;
  Yet O, by faith I see
The land of rest, the saints' delight,
  The heaven prepared for me."

2 O what a blessed hope is ours!
  While here on earth we stay,
We more than taste the heavenly powers,
  And antedate that day:
We feel the resurrection near,
  Our life in Christ concealed,
And with his glorious presence here
  Our earthen vessels filled.

3 O would he more of heaven bestow.
  And let the vessels break,
And let our ransomed spirits go
  To grasp the God we seek;
In rapturous awe on him to gaze,
  Who bought the sight for me;
And shout and wonder at his grace
  Through all eternity!
                        CHARLES WESLEY.

SECOND PART.

1031 *Endless bliss in prospect.*

1 A STRANGER in the world below
  I calmly sojourn here;
Nor can its happiness or woe
  Provoke my hope or fear:

Its evils in a moment end,
  Its joys as soon are past;
But O, the bliss to which I tend
  Eternally shall last!

2 To that Jerusalem above,
  With singing I repair;
While in the flesh, my hope and love,
  My heart and soul, are there.
There my exalted Saviour stands,
  My merciful High Priest;
And still extends his wounded hands,
  To take me to his breast.
                        CHARLES WESLEY.

THIRD PART.

1032 *The prospect joyous.*

1 AND let this feeble body fail,
  And let it faint or die;
My soul shall quit the mournful vale,
  And soar to worlds on high;
Shall join the disembodied saints,
  And find its long-sought rest,
That only bliss for which it pants,
  In the Redeemer's breast.

2 In hope of that immortal crown
  I now the cross sustain,
And gladly wander up and down,
  And smile at toil and pain:
I suffer on my threescore years,
  Till my Deliverer come,
And wipe away his servant's tears,
  And take his exile home.

3 O what hath Jesus bought for me!
  Before my ravished eyes

Rivers of life divine I see,
  And trees of paradise:
I see a world of spirits bright,
  Who taste the pleasures there;
They all are robed in spotless white,
  And conquering palms they bear.

4 O what are all my sufferings here,
  If, Lord, thou count me meet
With that enraptured host to appear,
  And worship at thy feet!
Give joy or grief, give ease or pain,
  Take life or friends away,
But let me find them all again
  In that eternal day.

CHARLES WESLEY.

FOURTH PART.

1033 *Communion with saints in heaven.*

1 COME, let us join our friends above
  That have obtained the prize,
And on the eagle wings of love
  To joys celestial rise.
Let all the saints terrestrial sing,
  With those to glory gone;
For all the servants of our King,
  In earth and heaven, are one.

2 One family we dwell in him,
  One church above, beneath,
Though now divided by the stream,
  The narrow stream, of death.
One army of the living God,
  To his command we bow;
Part of his host have crossed the flood,
  And part are crossing now.

3 Ten thousand to their endless home
  This solemn moment fly;
And we are to the margin come,
  And we expect to die.
His militant embodied host,
  With wishful looks we stand,
And long to see that happy coast,
  And reach the heavenly land.

4 Our old companions in distress
  We haste again to see,
And eager long for our release,
  And full felicity.
E'en now by faith we join our hands
  With those that went before;
And greet the blood-besprinkled bands
  On the eternal shore.

5 Our spirits, too, shall quickly join,
  Like theirs with glory crowned,
And shout to see our Captain's sign,
  To hear his trumpet sound.
O that we now might grasp our Guide!
  O that the word were given!
Come, Lord of hosts, the waves divide,
  And land us all in heaven!

CHARLES WESLEY.

Doxology.

THE God of mercy be adored,
  Who calls our souls from death,
Who saves by his redeeming word,
  And new-creating breath;
To praise the Father, and the Son,
  And Spirit all-divine,—
The One in Three, and Three in One,—
  Let saints and angels join.

ISAAC WATTS.

BURLINGTON.   C. M.   JOHN FRECKLETON BURROWES.

TIME AND ETERNITY—HEAVEN.

HARRIS.   C. M.   ARR. FROM DEVEREUX.

1034   *Farewell to earth—heaven welcomed.*

1 YE golden lamps of heaven, farewell,
  With all your feeble light;
Farewell, thou ever-changing moon,
  Pale empress of the night.

2 And thou, refulgent orb of day,
  In brighter flames arrayed,
My soul, that springs beyond thy sphere,
  No more demands thine aid.

3 Ye stars are but the shining dust,
  Of my divine abode,
The pavement of those heavenly courts
  Where I shall reign with God.

4 The Father of eternal light
  Shall there his beams display,
Nor shall one moment's darkness mix
  With that unvaried day.

5 No more the drops of piercing grief
  Shall swell into mine eyes,
Nor the meridian sun decline
  Amid those brighter skies.

6 There all the millions of his saints
  Shall in one song unite,
And each the bliss of all shall view
  With infinite delight.

PHILIP DODDRIDGE.

1035   *The New Jerusalem.*

1 Lo, what a glorious sight appears
  To our believing eyes!
The earth and seas are passed away,
  And the old rolling skies.

2 From the third heaven, where God re-
    sides,
  That holy, happy place,
The New Jerusalem comes down,
  Adorned with shining grace.

3 Attending angels shout for joy,
  And the bright armies sing,
"Mortals, behold the sacred seat
  Of your descending King!

4 "The God of glory down to men
  Removes his blest abode;
Men, the dear objects of his grace,
  And he the loving God.

5 "His own soft hand shall wipe the tears
  From every weeping eye;
And pains, and groans, and griefs, and
    fears,
  And death itself, shall die."

6 How long, dear Saviour, O how long
  Shall this bright hour delay?
Fly swifter round, ye wheels of time,
  And bring the welcome day!

ISAAC WATTS.

1036   *In the desert—heaven before us.*

1 FORTH to the land of promise bound,
  Our desert path we tread;
God's fiery pillar for our guide,
  His Captain at our head.

2 E'en now we faintly trace the hills,
  And catch their distant blue;
And the bright city's gleaming spires
  Rise dimly on our view.

3 Soon, when the desert shall be crossed,
  The flood of death passed o'er,
Our pilgrim hosts shall safely land
  On Canaan's peaceful shore.

4 There love shall have its perfect **work**,
  And prayer be lost in praise;
And all the servants of our God
  Their endless anthems raise.

HENRY ALFORD.

VARINA.   C. M.   JOHANN CHRISTIAN HEINRICH RINK.

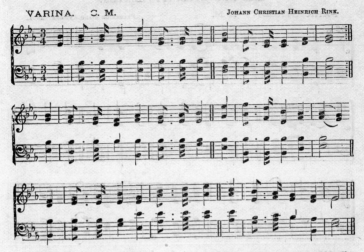

1037 *The heavenly Canaan.*

1 THERE is a land of pure delight,
   Where saints immortal reign;
Infinite day excludes the night,
   And pleasures banish pain.

2 There everlasting spring abides,
   And never-withering flowers:
Death, like a narrow sea, divides
   This heavenly land from ours.

3 Sweet fields beyond the swelling flood
   Stand dressed in living green;
So to the Jews old Canaan stood,
   While Jordan rolled between.

4 Could we but climb where Moses
      stood,
   And view the landscape o'er,
Not Jordan's stream, nor death's cold
      flood,
   Should fright us from the shore.
                           ISAAC WATTS.

1038 *The promised land.*

1 ON Jordan's stormy banks I stand,
   And cast a wishful eye
To Canaan's fair and happy land,
   Where my possessions lie.

2 O the transporting, rapturous scene,
   That rises to my sight!
Sweet fields arrayed in living green,
   And rivers of delight.

3 O'er all those wide-extended plains
   Shines one eternal day;
There God the Son forever reigns,
   And scatters night away.

4 No chilling winds, or poisonous breath,
   Can reach that healthful shore;
Sickness and sorrow, pain and death,
   Are felt and feared no more.

5 When shall I reach that happy place,
   And be forever blest?
When shall I see my Father's face,
   And in his bosom rest?

6 Filled with delight, my raptured soul
   Would here no longer stay:
Though Jordan's waves around me roll,
   Fearless I'd launch away.
                        SAMUEL STENNETT.

[8, 6. Tune, Tappan. Page 56.]

1039 *The land of rest.*

1 THERE is an hour of peaceful rest,
   To mourning wanderers given;
There is a joy for souls distressed,
   'Tis found above, in heaven.

2 There is a home for weary souls
   By sin and sorrow driven,
When tossed on life's tempestuous shoals,
   Where storms arise and ocean rolls,
   And all is drear; 'tis heaven.

3 There faith lifts up the tearless eye.
   To brighter prospects given;
And views the tempest passing by,
The evening shadows quickly fly,
   And all serene in heaven.

4 There fragrant flowers immortal bloom,
   And joys supreme are given;
There rays divine disperse the gloom
Beyond the confines of the tomb
   Appears the dawn of heaven.
                     WILLIAM B. TAPPAN.

PARK STREET. L. M.

FREDERICK MARC ANTOINE VENUA.

1040 *The redeemed in heaven.*

1 Lo! round the throne, à glorious band,
The saints in countless myriads stand;
Of every tongue redeemed to God,
Arrayed in garments washed in blood.

2 Through tribulation great they came;
They bore the cross, despised the shame;
But now from all their labors rest,
In God's eternal glory blest.

3 They see the Saviour face to face;
They sing the triumph of his grace;
And day and night, with ceaseless praise,
To him their loud hosannas raise.

4 O may we tread the sacred road
That holy saints and martyrs trod,
Wage to the end the glorious strife,
And win, like them, a crown of life!

MARY L. DUNCAN.

1041 *They shall behold the land that is very far off.*—Isa. 33 : 17.

1 THERE is a land mine eye hath seen
In visions of enraptured thought,
So bright, that all which spreads between
Is with its radiant glories fraught.

A land upon whose blissful shore
There rests no shadow, falls no stain;
There those who meet shall part no more,
And those long parted meet again.

2 Its skies are not like earthly skies,
With varying hues of shade and light;
It hath no need of suns to rise
To dissipate the gloom of night.

4 There sweeps no desolating wind
Across that calm, serene abode;
The wanderer there a home may find
Within the paradise of God.

GURDON ROBINE.

1042 *Perfection in heaven.*

1 WHAT sinners value I resign;
Lord, 'tis enough that thou art mine;
I shall behold thy blissful face,
And stand complete in righteousness.

2 This life 's a dream, an empty show;
But the bright world to which I go
Hath joys substantial and sincere;
When shall I wake, and find me there?

3 O glorious hour! O blest abode!
I shall be near, and like my God;
And flesh and sin no more control
The sacred pleasures of the soul.

4 My flesh shall slumber in the ground,
Till the last trumpet's joyful sound;
Then burst the chains, with sweet surprise,
And in my Saviour's image rise.

ISAAC WATTS.

1043 *The heavenly Zion.*

1 ARM of the Lord, awake, awake!
Thine own immortal strength put on!
With terror clothed, hell's kingdom shake,
And cast thy foes with fury down.

2 By death and hell pursued in vain,
To thee the ransomed seed shall come;
Shouting, their heavenly Zion gain,
And pass through death triumphant home.

3 The pain of life shall then be o'er,
The anguish and distracting care;
There sighing grief shall weep no more,
And sin shall never enter there.

4 Where pure, essential joy is found,
The Lord's redeemed their heads shall raise,
With everlasting gladness crowned,
And filled with love, and lost in praise.

CHARLES WESLEY.

NEWBOLD.   C. M.   GEORGE KINGSLEY

1044   *The heavenly city.*

1 JERUSALEM, my happy home!
  Name ever dear to me!
When shall my labors have an end,
  In joy and peace in thee?

2 When shall these eyes thy heaven-built walls
  And pearly gates behold?
Thy bulwarks with salvation strong,
  And streets of shining gold?

3 O when, thou city of my God,
  Shall I thy courts ascend,
Where congregations ne'er break up,
  And Sabbath has no end?

4 There happier bowers than Eden's bloom,
  Nor sin nor sorrow know:
Blest seats! through rude and stormy scenes
  I onward press to you.

5 Apostles, martyrs, prophets, there
  Around my Saviour stand;
And soon my friends in Christ below
  Will join the glorious band.

6 Jerusalem, my happy home!
  My soul still pants for thee;
Then shall my labors have an end,
  When I thy joys shall see.

    UNKNOWN.

1045   *The saints in glory.*

1 GIVE me the wings of faith, to rise
  Within the veil, and see
The saints above, how great their joys,
  How bright their glories be.

2 Once they were mourners here below,
  And poured out cries and tears;
They wrestled hard, as we do now,
  With sins, and doubts, and fears.

3 I ask them whence their victory came:
  They, with united breath,
Ascribe their conquest to the Lamb,
  Their triumph to his death.

4 They marked the footsteps that he trod;
  His zeal inspired their breast;
And, following their incarnate God,
  Possess the promised rest.

5 Our glorious Leader claims our praise
  For his own pattern given;
While the long cloud of witnesses
  Show the same path to heaven.
    ISAAC WATTS.

1046   *We shall see Him as he is.*

1 THE heavenly treasure now we have
  In a vile house of clay;
But Christ will to the utmost save,
  And keep us to that day.

2 Our souls are in his mighty hand,
  And he shall keep them still;
And you and I shall surely stand
  With him on Zion's hill.

3 Him eye to eye we there shall see,
  Our face like his shall shine;
O what a glorious company,
  When saints and angels join!

4 O what a joyful meeting there!
  In robes of white arrayed,
Palms in our hands we all shall bear,
  And crowns upon our head.

5 Then let us lawfully contend,
  And fight our passage through;
Bear in our faithful minds the end,
  And keep the prize in view.
    CHARLES WESLEY.

GREEK HYMN. 6, 5.

1047 *In the conflict.*

1 CHRISTIAN, dost thou see them,
   On the holy ground,
How the powers of darkness
   Rage thy steps around?
Christian, up and smite them,
   Counting gain but loss;
In the strength that cometh
   By the holy cross!

2 Christian, dost thou feel them,
   How they work within,
Striving, tempting, luring,
   Goading into sin?
Christian, never tremble;
   Never be downcast;
Gird thee for the battle,
   Watch, and pray, and fast!

3 Christian, dost thou hear them,
   How they speak thee fair?
"Always fast and vigil?
   Always watch and prayer?"
Christian, answer boldly:
   "While I breathe I pray!"
Peace shall follow battle,
   Night shall end in day.

4 "Well I know thy trouble,
   O my servant true;
Thou art very weary,
   I was weary too;
But that toil shall make thee
   Some day all mine own,
And the end of sorrow
   Shall be near my throne."

ANDREW OF CRETE. TR. BY J. M. NEALE.

[S. M. Tune, Vigil. Page 391.]

1048 *The pilgrim's home.*

1 WHILE through this world we roam,
   From infancy to age,
Heaven is the Christian pilgrim's home
   His rest at every stage.

2 Thither his soul ascends,
   Eternal joys to share;
There his adoring spirit bends
   While here he kneels in prayer.

3 His freed affections rise,
   To fix on things above,
Where all his hope of glory lies,
   Where all is perfect love.

4 There we our treasure place;
   There let our hearts be found;
That still, where sin abounded, grace
   May more and more abound.

5 Henceforth our converse be
   With Christ before the throne;
Ere long we eye to eye shall see,
   And know as we are known.

JAMES MONTGOMERY.

[S. M. Tune, Vigil. Page 391.]

1049 *No night in heaven.*

1 THERE is no night in heaven;
   In that blest world above
Work never can bring weariness,
   For work itself is love.

2 There is no grief in heaven;
   For life is one glad day,
And tears are of those former things
   Which all have passed away.

3 There is no sin in heaven;
   Behold that blessed throng,
All holy in their spotless robes,
   All holy in their song.

4 There is no death in heaven;
   For they who gain that shore
Have won their immortality,
   And they can die no more.

FREDERICK D. HUNTINGTON.

VIGIL. S. M.

St. Alban's Tune Book.

1050 *At home in heaven.*

1 "FOREVER with the Lord!"
 Amen, so let it be!
Life from the dead is in that word,
 'Tis immortality.

2 Here in the body pent,
 Absent from him I roam,
Yet nightly pitch my moving tent
 A day's march nearer home.

3 "Forever with the Lord!"
 Father, if 'tis thy will,
The promise of that faithful word,
 E'en here to me fulfill.

4 So when my latest breath
 Shall rend the veil in twain,
By death I shall escape from death,
 And life eternal gain.

5 Knowing as I am known,
 How shall I love that word,
And oft repeat before the throne,
 "Forever with the Lord!"

JAMES MONTGOMERY.

1051 *The goodly land.*

1 FAR from these scenes of night,
 Unbounded glories rise,
And realms of joy and pure delight,
 Unknown to mortal eyes.

2 Fair land! could mortal eyes
 But half its charms explore,
How would our spirits long to rise,
 And dwell on earth no more!

3 No cloud those regions know,
 Realms ever bright and fair;

For sin, the source of mortal woe,
 Can never enter there.

4 O may the prospect fire
 Our hearts with ardent love,
Till wings of faith, and strong desire,
 Bear every thought above.

5 Prepared, by grace divine,
 For thy bright courts on high,
Lord, bid our spirits rise and join
 The chorus of the sky.

ANNE STEELE.

1052 *The land of peace.*

1 COME to the land of peace;
 From shadows come away;
Where all the sounds of weeping cease,
 And storms no more have sway.

2 Fear hath no dwelling here;
 But pure repose and love
Breathe through the bright, celestial air
 The spirit of the dove.

3 Come to the bright and blest,
 Gathered from every land;
For here thy soul shall find its rest
 Amid the shining band.

4 In this divine abode
 Change leaves no saddening trace;
Come, trusting spirit, to thy God,
 Thy holy resting-place.

5 "Come to our peaceful home,"
 The saints and angels say,
"Forsake the world, no longer roam;
 O wanderer come away!"

UNKNOWN.

CAR. 6. (Irregular.)   EBEN TOURJÉE. AD. BY L. FRANKLIN SNOW.

1053 *Nearer home.*

1 ONE sweetly solemn thought
Comes to me o'er and o'er,—
I am nearer home to-day
Than I ever have been before.

2 Nearer my Father's house,
Where the many mansions be;
Nearer the great white throne;
Nearer the crystal sea.

3 Nearer the bound of life,
Where we lay our burdens down;
Nearer leaving the cross;
Nearer gaining the crown.

4 But lying darkly between,
Winding down through the night,
Is the deep and unknown stream,
That leads at last to the light.

5 Father, perfect my trust!
Strengthen the might of my faith;
Let me feel as I would when I stand
On the rock of the shore of death:

6 Feel as I would when my feet
Are slipping over the brink;
For it may be, I'm nearer home—
Nearer now than I think!

PHŒBE CARY.

THE SAINT'S HOME.   11.   SIR HENRY ROWLEY BISHOP.

1054 *Home! home! sweet, sweet home.*

1 'MID scenes of confusion and creature complaints,
How sweet to the soul is communion
with saints!
To find at the banquet of mercy there's
room,
And feel in the presence of Jesus at
home.
Home! home! sweet, sweet home!
Prepare me, dear Saviour, for glory,
my home.

2 Sweet bonds that unite all the children of peace!
And, thrice precious Jesus, whose love cannot
cease,
Though oft from thy presence in sadness I roam,
I long to behold thee in glory, at home.

3 I sigh from this body of sin to be free,
Which hinders my joy and communion with
thee;
Though now my temptation like billows may
foam,
All, all will be peace, when I'm with thee at
home.

4 While here in the valley of conflict I stay,
O give me submission, and strength as my day;
In all my afflictions to thee would I come,
Rejoicing in hope of my glorious home.

5 Whate'er thou deniest, O give me thy grace,
The Spirit's sure witness, and smiles of thy face;

Endue me with patience to wait at thy throne,
And find, even now, a sweet foretaste of home.

6 I long, dearest Lord, in thy beauties to shine;
No more as an exile in sorrow to pine;
And in thy dear image arise from the tomb,
With glorified millions to praise thee at home.

DAVID DENHAM.

HAVERHILL. S. M.

LOWELL MASON.

1055 *Repose in heaven.*

1 AND is there, Lord, a rest,
  For weary souls designed,
Where not a care shall stir the breast,
  Or sorrow entrance find?

2 Is there a blissful home,
  Where kindred minds shall meet,
And live and love, nor ever roam
  From that serene retreat?

3 Are there bright, happy fields,
  Where naught that blooms shall die;
Where each new scene fresh pleasure yields,
  And healthful breezes sigh?

4 Are there celestial streams,
  Where living waters glide,
With murmurs sweet as angel-dreams,
  And flowery banks beside?

5 Forever blessed they,
  Whose joyful feet shall stand,
While endless ages waste away,
  Amid that glorious land!

6 My soul would thither tend,
  While toilsome years are given;
Then let me, gracious God, ascend
  To sweet repose in heaven.

RAY PALMER.

1056 *The house not made with hands.*

1 WE know, by faith we know,
  If this vile house of clay,
This tabernacle, sink below,
  In ruinous decay,—

2 We have a house above,
  Not made with mortal hands;

And firm as our Redeemer's love
  That heavenly fabric stands.

3 It stands securely high,
  Indissolubly sure:
Our glorious mansion in the sky
  Shall evermore endure.

4 Full of immortal hope,
  We urge the restless strife,
And hasten to be swallowed up
  Of everlasting life.

5 Lord, let us put on thee
  In perfect holiness,
And rise prepared thy face to see,
  Thy bright, unclouded face.

6 Thy grace with glory crown,
  Who hast the earnest given,
And then triumphantly come down,
  And take our souls to heaven!

CHARLES WESLEY.

1057 *The mighty change.*

1 O WHAT a mighty change
  Shall Jesus' sufferers know,
While o'er the happy plains they range
  Incapable of woe!
No ill-requited love
  Shall there our spirits wound:
No base ingratitude above,
  No sin in heaven is found.

2 No slightest touch of pain,
  Nor sorrow's least alloy,
Can violate our rest, or stain
  Our purity of joy:
In that eternal day
  No clouds or tempests rise;
There gushing tears are wiped away
  Forever from our eyes.

CHARLES WESLEY.

RIMBAULT. 7, 6. CHAS. D'URHAN, ARR. BY EDWARD FRANCIS RIMBAULT.

1058 *O sweet and blessed country.*

1 THE world is very evil,
  The times are waxing late:
Be sober and keep vigil,
  The Judge is at the gate;
The Judge that comes in mercy,
  The Judge that comes with might,
To terminate the evil,
  To diadem the right.

2 Arise, arise, good Christian,
  Let right to wrong succeed;
Let penitential sorrow
  To heavenly gladness lead,
To light that hath no evening,
  That knows no moon nor sun,
The light so new and golden,
  The light that is but one.

3 O home of fadeless splendor,
  Of flowers that fear no thorn,
Where they shall dwell as children
  Who here as exiles mourn!
'Midst power that knows no limit,
  Where wisdom has no bound,
The beatific vision
  Shall glad the saints around.

4 O happy, holy portion,
  Refection for the blest,
True vision of true beauty,
  Sweet cure of all distressed!
Strive, man, to win that glory;
  Toil, man, to gain that light;
Send hope before to grasp it,
  Till hope be lost in sight.

5 O sweet and blessed country,
  The home of God's elect!
O sweet and blessed country
  That eager hearts expect!
Jesus, in mercy bring us
  To that dear land of rest;
Who art, with God the Father,
  And Spirit, ever blest.
    BERNARD OF CLUNY. TR. BY J. M. NEALE.

Doxology.

To thee be praise forever,
  Thou glorious King of kings!
Thy wondrous love and favor
  Each ransomed spirit sings;
We'll celebrate thy glory,
  With all thy saints above,
And shout the joyful story
  Of thy redeeming love.
    UNKNOWN.

394

TIME AND ETERNITY—HEAVEN.

GAUNTLETT. 7, 6.

HENRY JOHN GAUNTLETT.

1059 *Brief sorrow—eternal rest.*

1 BRIEF life is here our portion;
  Brief sorrow, short-lived care;
The life that knows no ending,
  The tearless life, is there.
O happy retribution!
  Short toil, eternal rest;
For mortals and for sinners
  A mansion with the blest!

2 And now we fight the battle,
  But then shall wear the crown
Of full and everlasting
  And passionless renown:
But He whom now we trust in
  Shall then be seen and known;
And they that know and see him
  Shall have him for their own.

3 The morning shall awaken,
  The shadows shall decay,
And each true-hearted servant
  Shall shine as doth the day.
There God, our King and Portion,
  In fullness of his grace,
Shall we behold forever,
  And worship face to face.

4 O sweet and blessed country,
  The home of God's elect!
O sweet and blessed country
  That eager hearts expect!
Jesus, in mercy bring us
  To that dear land of rest;
Who art, with God the Father,
  And Spirit, ever blest.

BERNARD OF CLUNY. TR. BY J. M. NEALE.

WEBB. 7, 6.

GEORGE JAMES WEBB.

FINE.

D. S.

BERNARD. 7, 6.

JOSEPH P. HOLBROOK.

1060 *Paradise of joy.*

1 For thee, O dear, dear country,
  Mine eyes their vigils keep;
For very love, beholding
  Thy happy name, they weep.
The mention of thy glory
  Is unction to the breast,
And medicine in sickness,
  And love, and life, and rest.

2 O one, O only mansion,
  O paradise of joy!
Where tears are ever banished,
  And smiles have no alloy;
The Lamb is all thy splendor,
  The Crucified thy praise;
His laud and benediction
  Thy ransomed people raise.

3 With jasper glow thy bulwarks,
  Thy streets with emerald blaze;
The sardius and the topaz
  Unite in thee their rays;
Thine ageless walls are bonded
  With amethyst unpriced;
Thy saints build up its fabric,
  And the corner-stone is Christ.

4 Thou hast no shore, fair ocean;
  Thou hast no time, bright day:
Dear fountain of refreshment
  To pilgrims far away:
Upon the Rock of ages
  They raise thy holy tower;
Thine is the victor's laurel,
  And thine the golden dower.

5 O sweet and blessed country,
  The home of God's elect!
O sweet and blessed country
  That eager hearts expect!
Jesus, in mercy bring us
  To that dear land of rest;
Who art, with God the Father,
  And Spirit, ever blest.

BERNARD OF CLUNY. TR. BY J. M. NEALE.

Doxology.

To thee be praise forever,
  Thou glorious King of kings!
Thy wondrous love and favor
  Each ransomed spirit sings:
We'll celebrate thy glory,
  With all thy saints above,
And shout the joyful story
  Of thy redeeming love.

UNKNOWN.

EWING. 7, 6.

ALEXANDER EWING.

1061 *The home of God's elect.*

1 JERUSALEM the golden,
  With milk and honey blest,
Beneath thy contemplation
  Sink heart and voice oppressed:
I know not, O I know not
  What social joys are there;
What radiancy of glory,
  What light beyond compare.

2 They stand, those halls of Zion,
  All jubilant with song,
And bright with many an angel,
  And all the martyr throng:
The Prince is ever in them,
  The daylight is serene;
The pastures of the blessed
  Are decked in glorious sheen.

3 There is the throne of David;
  And there, from care released,
The song of them that triumph,
  The shout of them that feast;
And they who, with their Leader,
  Have conquered in the fight,
Forever and forever
  Are clad in robes of white.

4 O sweet and blessed country,
  The home of God's elect!
O sweet and blessed country
  That eager hearts expect!
Jesus, in mercy bring us
  To that dear land of rest;
Who art, with God the Father,
  And Spirit, ever blest.

BERNARD OF CLUNY. TR. BY J. M. NEALE.

26

ALFORD. 7, 6, 8, 6.　　　　　　　　REV. JOHN BACCHUS DYKES.

1062 *The armies of the living God.*

1 TEN thousand times ten thousand,
　In sparkling raiment bright,
The armies of the ransomed saints
　Throng up the steeps of light:
'Tis finished, all is finished,
　Their fight with death and sin:
Fling open wide the golden gates,
　And let the victors in.

2 What rush of hallelujahs
　Fills all the earth and sky!
What ringing of a thousand harps
　Bespeaks the triumph nigh!
O day, for which creation
　And all its tribes were made!
O joy, for all its former woes
　A thousand fold repaid!

3 O then what raptured greetings
　On Canaan's happy shore,
What knitting severed friendships up,
　Where partings are no more!
Then eyes with joy shall sparkle,
　That brimmed with tears of late,
Orphans no longer fatherless,
　Nor widows desolate.

　　　　　　　　　　　HENRY ALFORD.

[8. Tune, Desire. Page 399.]

1063 *The heavenly Jerusalem.*

1 AWAY with our sorrow and fear,
　We soon shall recover our home;
The city of saints shall appear,
　The day of eternity come.
From earth we shall quickly remove,
　And mount to our native abode,
The house of our Father above,
　The palace of angels and God.

2 By faith we already behold
　That lovely Jerusalem here:
Her walls are of jasper and gold,
　As crystal her buildings are clear;
Immovably founded in grace,
　She stands as she ever hath stood,
And brightly her Builder displays,
　And flames with the glory of God.

3 No need of the sun in that day
　Which never is followed by night,
Where Jesus's beauties display
　A pure and a permanent light·
The Lamb is their light and their sun,
　And lo! by reflection they shine;
With Jesus ineffably one,
　And bright in effulgence divine.

　　　　　　　　　　　CHARLES WESLEY.

398

DESIRE. 8. J. B.

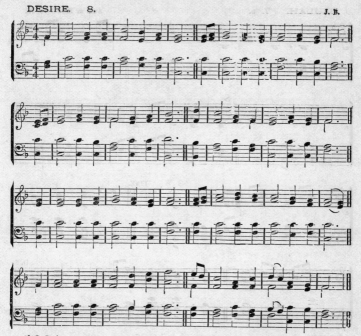

1064 *Desiring to depart.*

1 I LONG to behold Him arrayed
    With glory and light from above;
The King in his beauty displayed,
    His beauty of holiest love:
I languish and sigh to be there,
    Where Jesus hath fixed his abode;
O when shall we meet in the air,
    And fly to the mountain of God!

2 With him I on Zion shall stand,
    For Jesus hath spoken the word;
The breadth of Immanuel's land
    Survey by the light of my Lord:
But when, on thy bosom reclined,
    Thy face I am strengthened to see,
My fullness of rapture I find,
    My heaven of heavens in thee.

3 How happy the people that dwell
    Secure in the city above!
No pain the inhabitants feel,
    No sickness or sorrow shall prove.
Physician of souls, unto me
    Forgiveness and holiness give;
And then from the body set free,
    And then to the city receive.

CHARLES WESLEY.

1065 *To be with Christ is far better.*

1 O WHEN shall we sweetly remove,
    O when shall we enter our rest,
Return to the Zion above,
    The mother of spirits distressed!
That city of God the great King,
    Where sorrow and death are no more,
But saints our Immanuel sing,
    And cherub and seraph adore.

2 Not all the archangels can tell
    The joys of that holiest place,
Where Jesus is pleased to reveal
    The light of his heavenly face:
When, caught in the rapturous flame,
    The sight beatific they prove,
And walk in the light of the Lamb,
    Enjoying the beams of his love.

3 Thou know'st in the spirit of prayer
    We long thy appearing to see,
Resigned to the burden we bear,
    But longing to triumph with thee:
'Tis good at thy word to be here;
    'Tis better in thee to be gone,
And see thee in glory appear,
    And rise to a share in thy throne.

CHARLES WESLEY.

BEULAH. 7. D.

ARR. BY ELAM IVES, JR.

1066 *In white array.*

1 WHO are these arrayed in white,
  Brighter than the noonday sun,
Foremost of the sons of light,
  Nearest the eternal throne?
These are they that bore the cross,
  Nobly for their Master stood;
Sufferers in his righteous cause,
  Followers of the dying God.

2 Out of great distress they came,
  Washed their robes by faith below,
In the blood of yonder Lamb,
  Blood that washes white as snow;
Therefore are they next the throne,
  Serve their Maker day and night;
God resides among his own,
  God doth in his saints delight.

3 More than conquerors at last,
  Here they find their trials o'er;
They have all their sufferings passed,
  Hunger now and thirst no more.
He that on the throne doth reign,
  Them the Lamb shall always feed,
With the tree of life sustain,
  To the living fountains lead.

CHARLES WESLEY

1067 *Night lost in day.*

1 HIGH in yonder realms of light,
  Dwell the raptured saints above;
Far beyond our feeble sight,
  Happy in Immanuel's love:
Pilgrims in this vale of tears,
  Once they knew, like us below,
Gloomy doubts, distressing fears,
  Torturing pain, and heavy woe.

2 But these days of weeping o'er,
  Passed this scene of toil and pain,
They shall feel distress no more,
  Never, never weep again:
'Mid the chorus of the skies,
  'Mid the angelic lyres above,
Hark, their songs melodious rise,
  Songs of praise to Jesus' love!

3 All is tranquil and serene,
  Calm and undisturbed repose.
There no cloud can intervene,
  There no angry tempest blows:
Every tear is wiped away,
  Sighs no more shall heave the breast,
Night is lost in endless day,
  Sorrow, in eternal rest.

THOMAS RAFFLES.

AMSTERDAM. 7, 6, 7. JAMES NARES.

1068 *The better portion.*

1 RISE, my soul, and stretch thy wings,
  Thy better portion trace;
Rise from transitory things
  Toward heaven, thy native place:
Sun, and moon, and stars decay;
  Time shall soon this earth remove;
Rise, my soul, and haste away
  To seats prepared above.

2 Rivers to the ocean run,
  Nor stay in all their course;
Fire ascending seeks the sun;
  Both speed them to their source:
So a soul that 's born of God,
  Pants to view his glorious face;
Upward tends to his abode,
  To rest in his embrace.

3 Cease, ye pilgrims, cease to mourn,
  Press onward to the prize;
Soon our Saviour will return.
  Triumphant in the skies:
There we 'll join the heavenly train,
  Welcomed to partake the bliss;
Fly from sorrow, care, and pain,
  To realms of endless peace.

ROBERT SEAGRAVE.

[7. D. Tune, Beulah. Page 400.]

1069 *Saints and angels round the throne*

1 LIFT your eyes of faith, and see
  Saints and angels joined in one:
What a countless company
  Stand before yon dazzling throne!
Each before his Saviour stands,
  All in whitest robes arrayed;
Palms they carry in their hands,
  Crowns of glory on their head.

2 Saints begin the endless song,
  Cry aloud in heavenly lays,
Glory doth to God belong,
  God, the glorious Saviour, praise:
All salvation from him came,
  Him, who reigns enthroned on high
Glory to the bleeding Lamb,
  Let the morning stars reply.

3 Angel powers the throne surround,
  Next the saints in glory they;
Lulled with the transporting sound,
  They their silent homage pay:
Prostrate on their face, before
  God and his Messiah fall;
Then in hymns of praise adore,
  Shout the Lamb that died for all.

CHARLES WESLEY.

ANGELS' SONG. 11, 10.

REV. JOHN BACCHUS DYKES.

CHORUS.

1070 *The night is far spent, the day is at hand.*—ROM. 13 : 12.

1 HARK, hark, my soul! angelic songs are swelling
O'er earth's green fields and ocean's wave-beat shore:
How sweet the truth those blessed strains are telling
Of that new life when sin shall be no more!
Angels of Jesus, angels of light,
Singing to welcome the pilgrims of the night!

2 Onward we go, for still we hear them singing,
"Come, weary souls, for Jesus bids you come;"
And through the dark, its echoes sweetly ringing,
The music of the gospel leads us home.

3 Far, far away, like bells at evening pealing,
The voice of Jesus sounds o'er land and sea,
And laden souls by thousands, meekly stealing,
Kind Shepherd, turn their weary steps to thee.

4 Rest comes at length, though life be long and dreary;
The day must dawn, and darksome night be past;
All journeys end in welcome to the weary,
And heaven, the heart's true home, will come at last.

5 Angels, sing on! your faithful watches keeping,
Sing us sweet fragments of the songs above;
Till morning's joy shall end the night of weeping,
And life's long shadows break in cloudless love.

FREDERICK W. FABER.

PARADISE. 8, 6, 6.   JOSEPH BARNBY.

1071   *Paradise.*

1 O PARADISE! O paradise!
  Who doth not crave for rest?
Who would not seek the happy land
  Where they that loved are blest;
    Where loyal hearts and true
    Stand ever in the light,
  All rapture through and through,
    In God's most holy sight?

2 O paradise! O paradise!
  The world is growing old;
Who would not be at rest and free
  Where love is never cold;
    Where loyal hearts and true, etc.

3 O paradise! O paradise!
  'Tis weary waiting here;
I long to be where Jesus is,
  To feel, to see him near;
    Where loyal hearts and true, etc.

4 O paradise! O paradise!
  I want to sin no more,
I want to be as pure on earth
  As on thy spotless shore;
    Where loyal hearts and true, etc.

5 O paradise! O paradise!
  I greatly long to see
The special place my dearest Lord
  In love prepares for me;
    Where loyal hearts and true, etc.
    FREDERICK W. FABER.

GOING HOME. L. M.

ARR. REV. WILLIAM McDONALD.

1072 *The heavenly home.*

1 My heavenly home is bright and fair:
Nor pain nor death can enter there;
Its glittering towers the sun outshine;
That heavenly mansion shall be mine.
　I'm going home, I'm going home,
　I'm going home to die no more;
　To die no more, to die no more,
　I'm going home to die no more.

2 My Father's house is built on high,
Far, far above the starry sky.
When from this earthly prison free,
That heavenly mansion mine shall be.

3 While here, a stranger far from home,
Affliction's waves may round me foam;
Although, like Lazarus, sick and poor,
My heavenly mansion is secure.

4 Let others seek a home below,
Which flames devour, or waves o'erflow,
Be mine the happier lot to own
A heavenly mansion near the throne.

5 Then fail the earth, let stars decline,
And sun and moon refuse to shine,
All nature sink and cease to be,
That heavenly mansion stands for me.
　　　　　　　WILLIAM HUNTER.

[12, 9. Tune, Rapture. Page 164.]

1073 *Rapturous anticipation.*

1 Come, let us ascend,
My companion and friend,
To a taste of the banquet above:
　If thy heart be as mine,
　If for Jesus it pine,
Come up into the chariot of love.

2 Who in Jesus confide,
　We are bold to outride
The storms of affliction beneath;
　With the prophet we soar
　To the heavenly shore,
And outfly all the arrows of death.

3 By faith we are come
　To our permanent home;
By hope we the rapture improve:
　By love we still rise,
　And look down on the skies,
For the heaven of heavens is love.

4 Who on earth can conceive
　How happy we live,
In the palace of God the great King?
　What a concert of praise,
　When our Jesus's grace
The whole heavenly company sing!

5 What a rapturous song,
　When the glorified throng
In the spirit of harmony join;
　Join all the glad choirs,
　Hearts, voices, and lyres,
And the burden is, "Mercy divine!"

6 "Hallelujah," they cry,
　To the King of the sky,
To the great everlasting I AM;
　To the Lamb that was slain,
　And that liveth again,
"Hallelujah to God and the Lamb!"
　　　　　　　CHARLES WESLEY.

Doxology.

Praise God, from whom all blessings flow
Praise him, all creatures here below;
Praise him above, ye heavenly host;
Praise Father, Son, and Holy Ghost!
　　　　　　　THOMAS KEN

TIME AND ETERNITY—HEAVEN.

NEW YEAR'S HYMN. 10, 5, 11.

SAMUEL WEBBE.

1074 *Eternity near.*

1 COME, let us anew our journey pursue,
  With vigor arise,
And press to our permanent place in the
  skies.
Of heavenly birth, though wandering on
  earth,
  This is not our place,
But strangers and pilgrims ourselves we
  confess.

2 At Jesus's call, we gave up our all;
  And still we forego,
For Jesus's sake, our enjoyments below.
No longing we find for the country behind;
  But onward we move,
And still we are seeking a country above:

3 A country of joy without any alloy;
  We thither repair;
Our hearts and our treasure already are
  there.
We march hand in hand to Immanuel's
  land;
  No matter what cheer
We meet with on earth, for eternity's near.

4 The rougher our way, the shorter our
  stay;
  The tempests that rise
Shall gloriously hurry our souls to the skies:
The fiercer the blast, the sooner 'tis past;
  The troubles that come
Shall come to our rescue, and hasten us
  home.

CHARLES WESLEY.

LEONI. 6, 8, 4.

AD. BY RABBI LEONI.

FIRST PART.

1075 *The God of Abraham.*

1 THE God of Abrah'm praise,
  Who reigns enthroned above,
Ancient of everlasting days,
  And God of love:
Jehovah, great I AM,
  By earth and heaven confessed;
I bow and bless the sacred name,
  Forever blest.

2 The God of Abrah'm praise,
  At whose supreme command
From earth I rise, and seek the joys
  At his right hand:
I all on earth forsake,
  Its wisdom, fame, and power;
And him my only portion make,
  My shield and tower.

3 The God of Abrah'm praise,
  Whose all-sufficient grace
Shall guide me all my happy days
  In all his ways;
He calls a worm his friend,
  He calls himself my God!
And he shall save me to the end,
  Through Jesus' blood.

4 He by himself hath sworn,
  I on his oath depend;
I shall, on eagle wings upborne,
  To heaven ascend;
I shall behold his face,
  I shall his power adore,
And sing the wonders of his grace
  For evermore.   THOMAS OLIVERS.

SECOND PART.

1076 *Pressing toward the mark.*

1 THOUGH nature's strength decay,
  And earth and hell withstand,

To Canaan's bounds I urge my way,
  At his command;
The watery deep I pass,
  With Jesus in my view;
And through the howling wilderness
  My way pursue.

2 The goodly land I see,
  With peace and plenty blest;
A land of sacred liberty,
  And endless rest.
There milk and honey flow,
  And oil and wine abound,
And trees of life forever grow,
  With mercy crowned.

3 There dwells the Lord our King,
  The Lord our Righteousness,
Triumphant o'er the world and sin,
  The Prince of peace;
On Zion's sacred height,
  His kingdom still maintains;
And, glorious, with his saints in light
  Forever reigns.

4 He keeps his own secure;
  He guards them by his side;
Arrays in garments white and pure
  His spotless bride;
With streams of sacred bliss,
  With groves of living joys,
With all the fruits of paradise,
  He still supplies.

5 Before the great Three One
  They all exulting stand,
And tell the wonders he hath done
  Through all their land:
The listening spheres attend,
  And swell the growing fame;
And sing, in songs which never end,
  The wondrous name.
                    THOMAS OLIVERS

TIME AND ETERNITY—HEAVEN.

[6, 8, 4. Tune, Leoni. Page 406.]

THIRD PART.

1077 *Joining the heavenly choir*

1 THE God who reigns on high
  The great archangels sing,
And, "Holy, holy, holy," cry,
  "Almighty King!"
Who was and is the same,
  And evermore shall be;
Jehovah, Father, great I AM,
  We worship thee."

2 Before the Saviour's face
  The ransomed nations bow;
O'erwhelmed at his almighty grace,
  Forever new;
He shows his prints of love,—
  They kindle to a flame,
And sound through all the worlds above,
  The slaughtered Lamb!

3 The whole triumphant host
  Give thanks to God on high;
"Hail, Father, Son, and Holy Ghost,"
  They ever cry:
Hail, Abrah'm's God, and mine!—
  I join the heavenly lays,—
All might and majesty are thine,
  And endless praise.

THOMAS OLIVERS.

[C. P. M. Tune, Ganges. Page 433.]

1078 *The pilgrim's lot.*

1 How happy is the pilgrim's lot,
How free from every anxious thought,
  From worldly hope and fear!
Confined to neither court nor cell,
His soul disdains on earth to dwell,
  He only sojourns here.

2 This happiness in part is mine,
Already saved from low design,
  From every creature-love;
Blest with the scorn of finite good,
My soul is lightened of its load,
  And seeks the things above.

3 There is my house and portion fair;
My treasure and my heart are there,
  And my abiding home;
For me my elder brethren stay,
And angels beckon me away,
  And Jesus bids me come.

4 "I come," thy servant, Lord, replies,
"I come to meet thee in the skies,
  And claim my heavenly rest!
Now let the pilgrim's journey end;
Now, O my Saviour, Brother, Friend,
  Receive me to thy breast!"

JOHN WESLEY.

GETHSEMANE.   7, 6l.

RICHARD REDHEAD.

1079 *The debt unknown.*

1 WHEN this passing world is done,
When has sunk yon glaring sun,
When we stand with Christ in glory,
Looking o'er life's finished story;
Then, Lord, shall I fully know,
Not till then, how much I owe.

2 When I stand before the throne,
Dressed in beauty not my own;

When I see thee as thou art,
Love thee with unsinning heart;
Then, Lord, shall I fully know,
Not till then, how much I owe.

3 When the praise of heaven I hear,
Loud as thunders to the ear,
Loud as many waters' noise,
Sweet as harp's melodious voice;
Then, Lord, shall I fully know,
Not till then, how much I owe.

ROBERT M. M'CHEYNE.

SOUTHWELL. C. M. HERBERT S. IRONS.

1080 *The fruit of the seasons.*

1 LORD, in thy name thy servants plead,
And thou hast sworn to hear;
Thine is the harvest, thine the seed,
The fresh and fading year.

2 Our hope, when autumn winds blew wild,
We trusted, Lord, with thee;
And still, now spring has on us smiled,
We wait on thy decree.

3 The former and the latter rain,
The summer sun and air,
The green ear, and the golden grain,
All thine, are ours by prayer.

4 Thine, too, by right, and ours by grace,
The wondrous growth unseen,
The hopes that soothe, the fears that brace,
The love that shines serene.
JOHN KEBLE.

1081 *Bountiful goodness.*

1 FOUNTAIN of mercy, God of love,
How rich thy bounties are!
The rolling seasons, as they move,
Proclaim thy constant care.

2 When in the bosom of the earth
The sower hid the grain,
Thy goodness marked its secret birth,
And sent the early rain.

3 The spring's sweet influence, Lord, was thine;
The plants in beauty grew;
Thou gav'st refulgent suns to shine,
And the refreshing dew.

4 These various mercies from above
Matured the swelling grain;
A kindly harvest crowns thy love,
And plenty fills the plain.

5 We own and bless thy gracious sway;
Thy hand all nature hails:
Seed-time nor harvest, night nor day,
Summer nor winter, fails.
MRS. ALICE FLOWERDEW.

[L. M. Tune, Duke Street. Page 320.]

1082 *Eternal Source of every joy.*

1 ETERNAL Source of every joy,
Well may thy praise our lips employ,
While in thy temple we appear,
Whose goodness crowns the circling year.

2 The flowery spring, at thy command,
Embalms the air and paints the land;
The summer rays with vigor shine,
To raise the corn and cheer the vine.

3 Thy hand in autumn richly pours
Through all our coasts redundant stores;
And winters, softened by thy care,
No more a face of horror wear.

4 Seasons, and months, and weeks, and days,
Demand successive songs of praise;
Still be the cheerful homage paid,
With opening light and evening shade.

5 Here in thy house shall incense rise,
And circling Sabbaths bless our eyes,
Till to those lofty heights we soar,
Where days and years revolve no more.
PHILIP DODDRIDGE.

ST. GEORGE. 7. D. Sir George J. Elvey.

1083 *Harvest-home.*

1 COME, ye thankful people, come,
Raise the song of harvest-home:
All is safely gathered in,
Ere the winter storms begin;
God, our Maker, doth provide
For our wants to be supplied:
Come to God's own temple, come,
Raise the song of harvest-home.

2 All the world is God's own field,
Fruit unto his praise to yield;
Wheat and tares together sown,
Unto joy or sorrow grown;
First the blade, and then the ear,
Then the full corn shall appear:
Lord of harvest, grant that we
Wholesome grain and pure may be.

3 For the Lord our God shall come,
And shall take his harvest home;
From his field shall in that day
All offenses purge away;
Give his angels charge at last
In the fire the tares to cast;
But the fruitful ears to store
In his garner evermore.

4 Even so, Lord, quickly come
To thy final harvest-home;
Gather thou thy people in,
Free from sorrow, free from sin;
There, forever purified,
In thy presence to abide:
Come, with all thine angels, come,
Raise the glorious harvest-home.
HENRY ALFORD.

1084 *Thanksgiving hymn.*

1 PRAISE to God, immortal praise,
For the love that crowns our days!
Bounteous Source of every joy,
Let thy praise our tongues employ.

2 For the blessings of the field,
For the stores the gardens yield;
For the fruits in full supply,
Ripened 'neath the summer sky;

3 All that spring with bounteous hand
Scatters o'er the smiling land;
All that liberal autumn pours
From her rich, o'erflowing stores;

4 These to thee, my God, we owe,
Source whence all our blessings flow;
And for these my soul shall raise
Grateful vows and solemn praise.

5 Should thine altered hand restrain
The early and the latter rain;
Blast each opening bud of joy,
And the rising year destroy;

6 Yet to thee my soul should raise
Grateful vows and solemn praise;
And, when every blessing 's flown,
Love thee for thyself alone.
MRS. ANNA L. BARBAULD, ALT.

Doxology.

SING we to our God above,
Praise eternal as his love;
Praise him, all ye heavenly host,
Father, Son, and Holy Ghost!
CHARLES WESLEY.

ST. JAMES.   7, 6.   From Lindeman's Koral Bog.

1085 *Praise to the Lord of harvest.*

1 SING to the Lord of harvest!
   Sing songs of love and praise!
With joyful hearts and voices
   Your hallelujahs raise:
By him the rolling seasons
   In fruitful order move;
Sing to the Lord of harvest
   A song of happy love.

2 By him the clouds drop fatness,
   The deserts bloom and spring,
The hills leap up in gladness,
   The valleys laugh and sing:
He filleth with his fullness
   All things with large increase,
He crowns the year with goodness,
   With plenty, and with peace.

3 Heap on his sacred altar
   The gifts his goodness gave,
The golden sheaves of harvest,
   The souls he died to save:
Your hearts lay down before him
   When at his feet ye fall,
And with your lives adore him
   Who gave his life for all.

4 To God, the gracious Father,
   Who made us "very good,"
To Christ, who, when we wandered
   Restored us with his blood,

And to the Holy Spirit,
   Who doth upon us pour
His blessed dews and sunshine,
   Be praise for evermore!
                    JOHN S. B. MONSELL.

1086 *God's gifts in nature.*

1 WE plow the fields and scatter
   The good seed on the land,
But it is fed and watered
   By God's almighty hand;
He sends the snow in winter,
   The warmth to swell the grain,
The breezes and the sunshine,
   And soft refreshing rain.

2 He only is the Maker
   Of all things near and far;
He paints the wayside flower,
   He lights the evening star;
The winds and waves obey him,
   By him the birds are fed;
Much more to us, his children,
   He gives our daily bread.

3 We thank thee, then, O Father,
   For all things bright and good,
The seed-time and the harvest,
   Our life, our health, our food:
Accept the gifts we offer
   For all thy love imparts,
And, what thou most desirest,
   Our humble, thankful hearts.
       FROM THE GERMAN OF MATTHIAS CLAUDIUS.

RIGHINI. 6, 4.

VINCENZO RIGHINI.

1087 *Praise to the God of harvest.*

1 THE God of harvest praise;
In loud thanksgiving raise
  Hand, heart, and voice;
The valleys laugh and sing,
Forests and mountains ring,
The plains their tribute bring,
  The streams rejoice.

2 Yea, bless his holy name,
And joyful thanks proclaim
  Through all the earth;
To glory in your lot
Is comely,—but be not
God's benefits forgot,
  Amid your mirth.

3 The God of harvest praise;
Hands, hearts, and voices raise
  With one accord;
From field to garner throng,
Bearing your sheaves along,
And in your harvest song
  Bless ye the Lord.

JAMES MONTGOMERY.

[7, 6. Tune, St. James. Page 410.]

1088 *The preaching leaves.*

1 THE leaves, around me falling,
Are preaching of decay,
The hollow winds are calling,
  "Come, pilgrim, come away!"

The day, in night declining,
  Says I must, too, decline;
The year, its life resigning,—
  Its lot foreshadows mine.

2 The light my path surrounding,
  The loves, to which I cling,
The hopes within me bounding,
  The joys that round me wing,—
All melt, like stars of even,
  Before the morning's ray,
Pass upward unto heaven,
  And chide at my delay.

3 The friends, gone there before me,
  Are calling from on high;
And joyous angels o'er me
  Tempt sweetly to the sky:
"Why wait," they say, "and wither
  'Mid scenes of death and sin?
O rise to glory, hither,
  And find true life begin."

4 I hear the invitation,
  And fain would rise and come,—
A sinner, to salvation;
  An exile, to his home:
But, while I here must linger,
  Thus, thus let all I see
Point on, with faithful finger,
  To heaven, O Lord, and thee.

HENRY F. LYTE.

411

AMERICA. 6, 4. HENRY CAREY.

1089 *National hymn.*

1 My country! 'tis of thee,
Sweet land of liberty,
  Of thee I sing:
Land where my fathers died!
Land of the pilgrims' pride!
From every mountain side
  Let freedom ring!

2 My native country, thee,
Land of the noble, free,
  Thy name I love;
I love thy rocks and rills,
Thy woods and templed hills;
My heart with rapture thrills
  Like that above.

3 Let music swell the breeze,
And ring from all the trees
  Sweet freedom's song:
Let mortal tongues awake;
Let all that breathe partake;
Let rocks their silence break,
  The sound prolong.

4 Our fathers' God! to thee,
Author of liberty,
  To thee we sing:
Long may our land be bright
With freedom's holy light;
Protect us by thy might,
  Great God, our King!
SAMUEL F. SMITH.

1090 *Our native land.*

1 God bless our native land!
Firm may she ever stand,
  Through storm and night:

When the wild tempests rave,
Ruler of wind and wave,
  Do thou our country save
    By thy great might!

* 2 For her our prayer shall rise
To God, above the skies;
  On him we wait:
Thou who art ever nigh,
Guarding with watchful eye,
To thee aloud we cry,
  God save the State!
JOHN S. DWIGHT.

[8, 7. Tune, Wilmot. Page 70.]

1091 *Pardon for national sins.*

1 Dread Jehovah! God of nations!
  From thy temple in the skies,
Hear thy people's supplications;
  Now for their deliverance rise.

2 Lo! with deep contrition turning,
  In thy holy place we bend;
Hear us, fasting, praying, mourning;
  Hear us, spare us, and defend.

3 Though our sins, our hearts confound
    ing,
  Long and loud for vengeance call,
Thou hast mercy more abounding;
  Jesus' blood can cleanse them all.

4 Let that mercy veil transgression;
  Let that blood our guilt efface:
Save thy people from oppression;
  Save from spoil thy holy place.
UNKNOWN.

RUSSIAN HYMN. 11, 10, 9. ALEXIS THEODORE LWOFF.

1092 *Prayer for peace.*

1 GOD, the All-Terrible! thou who ordainest
Thunder thy clarion, and lightning thy
sword;
Show forth thy pity on high where thou
reignest;
Give to us peace in our time, O Lord.

2 God, the Omnipotent! mighty Avenger,
Watching invisible, judging unheard;
Save us in mercy, O save us from danger;
Give to us peace in our time, O Lord.

3 God, the All-Merciful! earth hath for-
saken
Thy ways all holy, and slighted thy word;
Let not thy wrath in its terror awaken;
Give to us pardon and peace, O Lord.

4 So will thy people, with thankful devo-
tion,
Praise him who saved them from peril
and sword,
Shouting in chorus, from ocean to ocean,
Peace to the nations, and praise to the
Lord.

HENRY F. CHORLEY.

JEFFERSON. 7. HANS GEORGE NAEGELI, ARR. BY JOSEPH P. HOLBROOK.

1093 *Thanksgiving choral.*

1 SWELL the anthem, raise the song;
Praises to our God belong;
Saints and angels join to sing
Praises to the heavenly King.

2 Blessings from his liberal hand
Flow around this happy land:
Kept by him, no foes annoy;
Peace and freedom we enjoy.

3 Here, beneath a virtuous sway
May we cheerfully obey;
Never feel oppression's rod,
Ever own and worship God.

4 Hark! the voice of nature sings
Praises to the King of kings;
Let us join the choral song,
And the grateful notes prolong.

NATHAN STRONG.

ZELZAH.   C. M.   GERMAN MELODY.

1094   *Mercy implored.*

1 GREAT King of nations, hear our prayer,
  While at thy feet we fall,
And humbly, with united cry,
  To thee for mercy call.

2 The guilt is ours, but grace is thine,
  O turn us not away;
But hear us from thy lofty throne,
  And help us when we pray.

3 Our fathers' sins were manifold,
  And ours no less we own,
Yet wondrously from age to age
  Thy goodness hath been shown.

4 When dangers, like a stormy sea,
  Beset our country round,
To thee we looked, to thee we cried,
  And help in thee was found.

5 With one consent we meekly bow
  Beneath thy chastening hand,
And, pouring forth confession meet,
  Mourn with our mourning land.

6 With pitying eye behold our need,
  As thus we lift our prayer;
Correct us with thy judgments, Lord,
  Then let thy mercy spare.
                    JOHN H. GURNEY.

1095   *For protection in pestilence.*

1 IN grief and fear to thee, O Lord,
  We now for succor fly;
Thine awful judgments are abroad,
  O shield us, lest we die.

2 The fell disease on every side
  Walks forth with tainted breath;

And pestilence, with rapid stride,
  Bestrews the land with death.

3 O look with pity on the scene
  Of sadness and of dread;
And let thine angel stand between
  The living and the dead.

4 With contrite hearts, to thee, our King,
  We turn who oft have strayed;
Accept the sacrifice we bring,
  And let the plague be stayed.
                    WILLIAM BULLOCK.

1096   *Impending judgments.*

1 COME, let our souls adore the Lord,
  Whose judgments yet delay;
Who yet suspends the lifted sword,
  And gives us time to pray.

2 Great is our guilt, our fears are great,
  But let us not despair;
Still open is the mercy-seat
  To penitence and prayer.

3 Kind Intercessor, to thy love
  This blessed hope we owe:
O let thy merits plead above,
  While we implore below.

4 Though justice near thy awful throne
  Attends thy dread command,
Lord, hear thy servants, hear thy Son,
  And save a guilty land.
                    ANNE STEELE.

Doxology.

To Father, Son, and Holy Ghost,
  The God whom we adore,
Be glory, as it was, is now,
  And shall be evermore!
                    TATE AND BRADY.

PALESTRINA.　　C. M.　　　　　　GIOVANNI PETRI ALOYSIUS PALESTRINA.

1097 *National deliverance ascribed to God.*

1 O LORD, our fathers oft have told,
　In our attentive ears,
Thy wonders in their days performed,
　And in more ancient years.

2 'Twas not their courage, nor their sword,
　To them salvation gave;
'Twas not their number, nor their strength,
　That did their country save;

3 But thy right hand, thy powerful arm,
　Whose succor they implored;
Thy providence protected them,
　Who thy great name adored.

4 As thee their God our fathers owned,
　So thou art still our King;
O, therefore, as thou didst to them,
　To us deliverance bring.

5 To thee the glory we ascribe,
　From whom salvation came;
In God, our shield, we will rejoice,
　And ever bless thy name.
　　　　　　　　TATE AND BRADY.

1098 *Prayer for our native land.*

1 LORD, while for all mankind we pray,
　Of every clime and coast,
O hear us for our native land,—
　The land we love the most.

2 O guard our shores from every foe;
　With peace our borders bless,
Our cities with prosperity,
　Our fields with plenteousness.

3 Unite us in the sacred love
　Of knowledge, truth, and thee;
And let our hills and valleys shout
　The songs of liberty.

4 Lord of the nations, thus to thee
　Our country we commend;
Be thou her refuge and her trust,
　Her everlasting friend.
　　　　　　　　JOHN R. WREFORD.

1099 *Strong to heal and save.*

1 THINE arm, O Lord, in days of old
　Was strong to heal and save;
It triumphed o'er disease and death,
　O'er darkness and the grave:
To thee they went, the blind, the dumb,
　The palsied and the lame,
The leper with his tainted life,
　The sick with fevered frame.

2 And lo, thy touch brought life and health,
　Gave speech, and strength, and sight,
And youth renewed and frenzy calmed
　Owned thee, the Lord of light:
And now, O Lord, be near to bless,
　Almighty as of yore,
In crowded street, by restless couch,
　As by Gennesareth's shore.

3 Be thou our great Deliverer still,
　Thou Lord of life and death;
Restore and quicken, soothe and bless
　With thine almighty breath.
To hands that work, and eyes that see,
　Give wisdom's heavenly lore,
That whole and sick, and weak and strong,
　May praise thee evermore.
　　　　　　　　EDWARD H. PLUMPTRE.

MENDON. L. M.

GERMAN MELODY.

1100 *National blessings.*

1 GREAT God of nations, now to thee
  Our hymn of gratitude we raise;
With humble heart, and bending knee,
  We offer thee our song of praise.

2 Thy name we bless, Almighty God,
  For all the kindness thou hast shown
To this fair land the pilgrims trod,—
  This land we fondly call our own.

3 Here freedom spreads her banner wide,
  And casts her soft and hallowed ray;
Here thou our fathers' steps didst guide
  In safety through their dangerous way.

4 We praise thee that the gospel's light
  Through all our land its radiance sheds;
Dispels the shades of error's night,
  And heavenly blessings round us spreads.

5 Great God, preserve us in thy fear;
  In danger still our guardian be;
O spread thy truth's bright precepts here;
  Let all the people worship thee.

UNKNOWN.

1101 *Thanksgiving for national peace.*

1 GREAT Ruler of the earth and skies,
  A word of thine almighty breath
Can sink the world, or bid it rise:
  Thy smile is life, thy frown is death.

2 When angry nations rush to arms,
  And rage, and noise, and tumult reign,
And war resounds its dire alarms,
  And slaughter dyes the hostile plain,—

3 Thy sovereign eye looks calmly down,
  And marks their course, and bounds their
    power;
Thy law the angry nations own,
  And noise and war are heard no more.

4 Then peace returns with balmy wing;
  Sweet peace, with her what blessings fled!
Glad plenty laughs, the valleys sing,
  Reviving commerce lifts her head.

5 To thee we pay our grateful songs;
  Thy kind protection still implore:
O may our hearts, and lives, and tongues,
  Confess thy goodness, and adore.

ANNE STEELE.

1102 *Give peace, O God.*

1 O GOD of love, O King of peace,
Make wars throughout the world to cease;
The wrath of sinful man restrain;
Give peace, O God, give peace again.

2 Remember, Lord, thy works of old,
The wonders that our fathers told;
Remember not our sin's dark stain;
Give peace, O God, give peace again.

3 Whom shall we trust but thee, O Lord?
Where rest but on thy faithful word?
None ever called on thee in vain;
Give peace, O God, give peace again.

4 Where saints and angels dwell above,
All hearts are knit in holy love;
O bind us in that heavenly chain;
Give peace, O God, give peace again.

SIR HENRY W. BAKER.

DUKE STREET. L. M. JOHN HATTON.

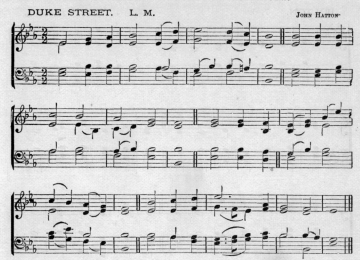

1103 *God, the nation's guardian.*

1 GREAT God! beneath whose piercing eye
The earth's extended kingdoms lie;
Whose favoring smile upholds them all,
Whose anger smites them, and they fall;

2 We bow before thy heavenly throne;
Thy power we see, thy greatness own;
Yet, cherished by thy milder voice,
Our bosoms tremble and rejoice.

3 Thy kindness to our fathers shown
Their children's children long shall own;
To thee, with grateful hearts, shall raise
The tribute of exulting praise.

4 Led on by thine unerring aid,
Secure the paths of life we tread;
And, freely as the vital air,
Thy first and noblest bounties share.

5 Great God, our Guardian, Guide, and
Friend!
O still thy sheltering arm extend;
Preserved by thee for ages past,
For ages let thy kindness last!
WILLIAM ROSCOE, ALT.

1104 *In time of war.*

1 Now may the God of grace and power
Attend his people's humble cry;
Defend them in the needful hour,
And send deliverance from on high.

2 In his salvation is our hope;
And in the name of Israel's God
Our troops shall lift their banners up,
Our navies spread their flags abroad.

3 Some trust in horses trained for war,
And some of chariots make their boasts:
Our surest expectations are
From thee, the Lord of heavenly hosts.

4 Then, save us, Lord, from slavish fear,
And let our trust be firm and strong,
Till thy salvation shall appear,
And hymns of peace conclude our song.
ISAAC WATTS.

1105 *Trust in our fathers' God.*

1 To thee, O God, whose guiding hand
Our fathers led across the sea,
And brought them to this barren shore,
Where they might freely worship thee,

2 To thee, O God, whose arm sustained
Their footsteps in this desert land,
Where sickness lurked and death assailed,
And foes beset on every hand,—

3 To thee, O God, we lift our eyes,
To thee our grateful voices raise,
And, kneeling at thy gracious throne,
Devoutly join in hymns of praise.

4 Our fathers' God, incline thine ear,
And listen to our heartfelt prayer;
Surround us with thy heavenly grace,
And guard us with thy constant care.

5 Our fathers' God, in thee we'll trust,
Sheltered by thee from every harm;
We'll follow where thy hand shall guide,
And lean on thy sustaining arm.
WILLIAM T. DAVIS.

BOLTON. 7, 6.   JOHN WALSH.

1106   *Household love.*

1 O LOVE, divine and tender!
    That through our homes doth move,
Veiled in the softened splendor
    Of holy household love:
A throne, without thy blessing,
    Were labor without rest,
And cottages, possessing
    Thy blessedness, are blest.

2 God bless these hands united,
    God bless these hearts made one;
Unsevered and unblighted
    May they through life go on:
Here, in earth's home, preparing
    For the bright home above,
And there, forever sharing
    Its joy, where "God is love."
                        JOHN S. B. MONSELL.

[S. M. Tune, Dennis. Page 298.]

1107   *Marriage hymn.*

1 How welcome was the call,
    And sweet the festal lay,

When Jesus deigned in Cana's hall
    To bless the marriage day!

2 And happy was the bride,
    And glad the bridegroom's heart,
For he who tarried at their side
    Bade grief and ill depart.

3 His gracious power divine
    The water vessels knew;
And plenteous was the mystic wine
    The wondering servants drew.

4 O Lord of life and love,
    Come thou again to-day;
And bring a blessing from above
    That ne'er shall pass away.

5 O bless, as erst of old,
    The bridegroom and the bride;
Bless with the holier stream that flowed
    Forth from thy piercéd side.

6 Before thine altar-throne
    This mercy we implore:
As thou dost knit them, Lord, in one,
    So bless them evermore.
                        SIR HENRY W. BAKER.

ST. PETERSBURG. L. M. 61. DIMITRI S. BORTNIANSKY.

1108 *For those in peril on the sea.*

1 ETERNAL Father! strong to save,
Whose arm hath bound the restless wave,
Who bidd'st the mighty ocean deep
Its own appointed limits keep;
O hear us when we cry to thee
For those in peril on the sea.

2 O Christ! whose voice the waters heard,
And hushed their raging at thy word,
Who walkedst on the foaming deep,
And calm amidst its rage didst sleep;
O hear us when we cry to thee
For those in peril on the sea.

3 O Holy Spirit! who didst brood
Upon the chaos dark and rude,
And bid its angry tumult cease,
And give, for wild confusion, peace;
O hear us when we cry to thee
For those in peril on the sea.

4 O Trinity of love and power!
Our brethren shield in danger's hour;
From rock and tempest, fire and foe,
Protect them wheresoe'er they go;
Thus evermore shall rise to thee
Glad hymns of praise from land and sea.
WILLIAM WHITING.

[7, 6, 8. Tune, Penitence. Page 204.]

1109 *Safe with Jesus in the ship.*

1 LORD of earth, and air, and sea,
Supreme in power and grace,
Under thy protection we
Our souls and bodies place.

Bold an unknown land to try,
We launch into the foaming deep;
Rocks, and storms, and deaths defy,
With Jesus in the ship.

2 Who the calm can understand,
In a believer's breast?
In the hollow of His hand
Our souls securely rest:
Winds may rise, and seas may roar;
We on his love our spirits stay;
Him with quiet joy adore
Whom winds and seas obey.
CHARLES WESLEY.

[8. Tune, Desire. Page 399.]

1110 *He holdeth the waters in his hand.*

1 O THOU, who hast spread out the skies,
And measured the depths of the sea,
Our incense of praise shall arise
In joyous thanksgiving to thee.
Forever thy presence is near,
Though heaves our bark far from the
land;
We ride on the deep without fear;
The waters are held in thy hand.

2 Eternity comes in the sound
Of billows that never can sleep;
Jehovah encircles us round;
Omnipotence walks on the deep.
Our Father, we look up to thee,
As on toward the haven we roll;
And faith in our Pilot shall be
An anchor to steady the soul.
HANNAH F. GOULD.

GRATITUDE. L. M.   Rev. Ami Bost, arr. by Thomas Hastings.

1111 *For mariners.*

1 While o'er the deep thy servants sail,
Send thou, O Lord, the prosperous gale;
And on their hearts, where'er they go,
O let thy heavenly breezes blow.

2 If on the morning's wings they fly,
They will not pass beyond thine eye:
The wanderer's prayer thou bend'st to hear,
And faith exults to know thee near.

3 When tempests rock the groaning bark,
O hide them safe in Jesus' ark;
When in the tempting port they ride,
O keep them safe at Jesus' side.

4 If life's wide ocean smile or roar,
Still guide them to the heavenly shore;
And grant their dust in Christ may sleep,
Abroad, at home, or in the deep.
GEORGE BURGESS.

1112 *His way is in the sea.*

Lord of the wide, extensive main,
 Whose power the wind, the sea, controls,
Whose hand doth earth and heaven sustain,
 Whose Spirit leads believing souls;

'Tis here thine unknown paths we trace,
 Which dark to human eyes appear;
While through the mighty waves we pass,
 Faith only sees that God is here.

3 Throughout the deep thy footsteps shine;
 We own thy way is in the sea,
O'erawed by majesty divine,
 And lost in thine immensity.

4 Thy wisdom here we learn to adore;
 Thine everlasting truth we prove;
Amazing heights of boundless power,
 Unfathomable depths of love.
CHARLES WESLEY.

[C. M. Tune, Ortonville. Page 92.]

1113 *God's servants safe by sea or land.*

1 How are thy servants blest, O Lord!
 How sure is their defense!
Eternal Wisdom is their guide,
 Their help, Omnipotence.

2 In foreign realms, and lands remote,
 Supported by thy care,
Through burning climes they pass unhurt
 And breathe in tainted air.

3 When by the dreadful tempest borne
 High on the broken wave,
They know thou art not slow to hear,
 Nor impotent to save.

4 The storm is laid, the winds retire,
 Obedient to thy will;
The sea, that roars at thy command,
 At thy command is still.

5 In midst of dangers, fears, and deaths
 Thy goodness we'll adore;
We'll praise thee for thy mercies past,
 And humbly hope for more.

6 Our life, while thou preserv'st that life,
 Thy sacrifice shall be;
And death, when death shall be our lot,
 Shall join our souls to thee.
JOSEPH ADDISON.

SULLIVAN. 12.   Sir Arthur Seymour Sullivan.

1114 *Save, Lord, or we perish.*

1 WHEN through the torn sail the wild
    tempest is streaming,
When o'er the dark wave the red lightning
    is gleaming,
Nor hope lends a ray, the poor seaman to
    cherish,
We fly to our Maker,—"Save, Lord, or we
    perish!"

2 O Jesus, once tossed on the breast of the
    billow,
Aroused by the shriek of despair from thy
    pillow,
Now seated in glory, the mariner cher
    ish,
Who cries, in his anguish, "Save, Lord, or
    we perish!"

3 And O, when the whirlwind of passion is
    raging,
When sin in our hearts its wild warfare is
    waging,
Arise in thy strength, thy redeeméd to
    cherish,
Rebuke the destroyer, "Save, Lord, or we
    perish!"

REGINALD HEBER.

THEODORA. 7.   Arr. from George Frederick Handel.

1115 *Embarking.*

1 LORD, whom winds and seas obey,
Guide us through the watery way;
In the hollow of thy hand
Hide, and bring us safe to land.

2 Jesus, let our faithful mind
Rest, on thee alone reclined:
Every anxious thought repress;
Keep our souls in perfect peace.

3 Keep the souls whom now we leave;
Bid them to each other cleave;
Bid them walk on life's rough sea;
Bid them come by faith to thee.

4 Save, till all these tempests end,
All who on thy love depend;
Waft our happy spirits o'er;
Land us on the heavenly shore.

CHARLES WESLEY.

MISCELLANEOUS

THE FOLLOWING HYMNS WERE COMPOSED BY CHARLES WESLEY IN EXTREME OLD AGE.
THE SECOND HYMN WAS HIS LAST UTTERANCE IN VERSE, AND
WAS DICTATED ON HIS DEATH-BED.

NEUMARCK.   L. M.

GEORGE NEUMARCK.

1116 *The aged disciple's prayer.*

1 I TOO, forewarned by Jesus' love,
  Must shortly lay my body down;
But ere my soul from earth remove,
  O let me put thine image on!

2 Saviour! thy meek and lowly mind
  Be to thine aged servant given;
And glad I'll drop this tent, to find
  My everlasting house in heaven.

CHARLES WESLEY.

VALE.   L. M. 6l.

J. D. BUCKINGHAM.

1117 *Aged and helpless.*

1 IN age and feebleness extreme,
  Who shall a helpless worm redeem?

Jesus, my only hope thou art,
Strength of my failing flesh and heart:
O could I catch one smile from thee,
And drop into eternity!

CHARLES WESLEY.

DOXOLOGIES.

1 L. M.

PRAISE God, from whom all bless-
ings flow;
Praise him, all creatures here below;
Praise him above, ye heavenly host;
Praise Father, Son, and Holy Ghost!
THOMAS KEN.

2 C. M.

To Father, Son, and Holy Ghost,
The God whom we adore,
Be glory, as it was, is now,
And shall be evermore!
TATE AND BRADY.

3 C. M.

THE God of mercy be adored,
Who calls our souls from death,
Who saves by his redeeming word,
And new-creating breath;
To praise the Father, and the Son,
And Spirit all-divine,—
The One in Three, and Three in
One,—
Let saints and angels join.
ISAAC WATTS.

4 S. M.

To God, the Father, Son,
And Spirit, One in Three,
Be glory, as it was, is now,
And shall forever be.
JOHN WESLEY.

5 L. M. 61.

IMMORTAL honor, endless fame,
Attend the almighty Father's name:
The Saviour Son be glorified,
Who for lost man's redemption died;
And equal adoration, to thee!
Eternal Comforter, to thee!
JOHN DRYDEN.

6 L. P. M.

Now to the great and sacred Three.
The Father, Son, and Spirit, be
Eternal praise and glory given,
Through all the worlds where God is
known,
By all the angels near the throne,
And all the saints in earth and
heaven.
ISAAC WATTS.

7 H. M.

To God the Father's throne
Your highest honors raise;
Glory to God the Son;
To God the Spirit, praise:
With all our powers, eternal King,
Thy everlasting praise we sing.
ISAAC WATTS, ALT.

8 C. P. M.

To Father, Son, and Holy Ghost,
The God whom heaven's triumphant
host
And saints on earth adore;
Be glory as in ages past,
As now it is, and so shall last,
When time shall be no more!
TATE AND BRADY.

9 7.

SING we to our God above,
Praise eternal as his love;
Praise him, all ye heavenly host,
Father, Son, and Holy Ghost!
CHARLES WESLEY.

10 7, 61.

PRAISE the name of God most high.
Praise him, all below the sky;
Praise him, all ye heavenly host,
Father, Son, and Holy Ghost!
As through countless ages past,
Evermore his praise shall last.
UNKNOWN.

11   8, 7, 4.

GREAT Jehovah! we adore thee,
  God the Father, God the Son,
God the Spirit, joined in glory
  On the same eternal throne:
    Endless praises
  To Jehovah, Three in One!
          WILLIAM GOODE.

12   8, 7.

PRAISE the God of our salvation;
  Praise the Father's boundless love;
Praise the Lamb, our expiation;
  Praise the Spirit from above,
Author of the new creation,
  Him by whom our spirits live;
Undivided adoration
  To the one Jehovah give!
          JOSIAH CONDER, ALT.

13   8.

ALL praise to the Father, the Son,
  And Spirit, thrice holy and blest!
The eternal, supreme Three in One,
  Was, is, and shall still be confessed.
          UNKNOWN.

14   7, 6, 8.

FATHER, Son, and Holy Ghost,
  Thy Godhead we adore,
Join we with the heavenly host,
  To praise thee evermore!
Live, by earth and heaven adored,
  The Three in One, the One in
    Three;
  Holy, holy, holy Lord,
    All glory be to thee!
          CHARLES WESLEY.

15   6, 4.

To God, the Father, Son,
  And Spirit, Three in One,
    All praise be given!
Crown him, in every song;
To him your hearts belong:
Let all his praise prolong,
    On earth, in heaven!
          EDWIN F. HATFIELD.

16   7, 8, 7.

To Father, Son, and Spirit,
  Ascribe we equal glory;
One Deity, in Persons Three,
  Let all thy works adore thee:
As was from the beginning,
  Glory to God be given,
By all who know thy name below,
  And all thy hosts in heaven.
          CHARLES WESLEY.

17   7, 6.

To thee be praise forever,
  Thou glorious King of kings!
Thy wondrous love and favor
  Each ransomed spirit sings:
We'll celebrate thy glory,
  With all thy saints above,
And shout the joyful story
  Of thy redeeming love.
          THOMAS HAWEIS.

18   10.

To Father, Son, and Spirit, ever
  blest,
Eternal praise and worship be addressed;
From age to age, ye saints, his name
  adore,
And spread his fame, till time shall
  be no more.
          SIMON BROWNE.

19   11.

O FATHER Almighty, to thee be addressed,
With Christ and the Spirit, one God
  ever blest,
All glory and worship, from earth
  and from heaven,
As was, and is now, and shall ever
  be given.
          UNKNOWN.

OCCASIONAL PIECES AND CHANTS.

NORTHFIELD. C. M. (See Hymn 1.) JEREMIAH INGALLS.

1. O for a thousand tongues, to sing My great Re-deem-er's praise;

(sop.) The

S. & T. The glo-ries of, The glo-ries of my God and King, The
A. & B. The glo-ries of my God and King, The glo-ries of my

tri-umphs of his grace,

glo-ries of my God and King, The tri - - umphs of his grace!
God and King,

BRIDGEWATER. L. M. (See Hymn 69.) LEWIS EDSON.

1. Great God, at-tend, while Zi-on sings The joy that from thy presence springs.

To spend one day, To spend one day with thee on earth, To

To spend one day with thee on earth, To spend one day with

spend one day with thee on earth Ex-ceeds a thousand days of mirth.

thee on earth Ex-ceeds a thou - sand days i' mirth.

425

MAJESTY. C. M. D. (See Hymn 152.) WILLIAM BILLINGS.

1. The Lord de-scend-ed from a-bove, And bowed the heavens most high, And un-der-neath his feet he cast The dark - - - ness of the sky. 2. On cher-u-bim and ser-a-phim Full roy-al-ly he rode, And on the wings of might-y winds Came fly-ing all a-broad, And on the wings of might-y winds Came fly-ing all a-broad.

GENEVA. C. M. (See Hymn 160.) JOHN COLE.

1. When all thy mer-cies, O my God, My
When all thy mer-cies, O my God,
When all thy mercies, O my God,

GENEVA.—(Concluded.)

ris - ing soul sur - veys, Trans - port - ed with the

Trans - port - ed with

view, I'm lost In won - der, love, and praise.

SHERBURNE. C. M. (See Hymn 192.) DANIEL READ.

1. While shepherds watched their flocks by night, All seat- ed on the ground,

The

The angel of the

an - gel of the Lord came down, And glo - - - ry shone a - round, And

The an - gel of the Lord came down, And glo - - - ry

The an - gel of the Lord came down, And

Lord came down, And glo - - - - - - - ry shone a - round, And

glo - - - ry shone around, The angel of the Lord came down, And

shone a - round, And glo - - - ry shone around, The an - gel

glo - - - ry shone around, And glo - - ry shone around, The

glo - - - - - ry shone around, The an - gel of the

glo - - - ry shone a - round, And glo - ry shone a - round.

of the Lord came down, And glo - ry shone a - round..........

an - gel of the Lord came down, And glo - ry shone a - round.

Lord came down, And glo - - - ry shone a - round..........

427

TURNER. C. M. (See Hymn 277.) ABRAHAM MAXIM.

1. Come, Ho-ly Spir-it, heavenly Dove, With all thy quickening powers: Kin-dle a flame of sa-cred love, Kin-dle a flame of sa-cred love In these cold hearts of ours, In these cold hearts of ours.

Kin-dle a flame of sa-cred love, Kin-dle a flame of sa-cred love In these cold hearts .... of ours. Kin-dle a flame of sa-cred love In these cold hearts of ours.

Kin-dle a flame of sa - - cred love In these cold hearts of ours, In these cold hearts of ours.

AYLESBURY. S. M. (See Hymn 310.) JAMES GREEN.

1. Ah, how shall fall-en man Be just be-fore his God?

If he con-tend in right-eous-ness, We sink be-neath his rod.

COME, YE SINNERS. 8, 7. D. (See Hymn 340.) JEREMIAH INGALLS.

1. { Come, ye sin - ners, poor and need - y, Weak and
{ Je - sus read - y stands to save you, Full of
D. C. Glo - ry, hon - or, and sal - va - tion, Christ the

FINE. CHORUS.

wound - ed, sick and sore;
pit - y, love, and power: } Turn to the Lord, and
Lord is come to reign.

seek sal - va - tion, Sound the praise of his dear name;

D. C.

RUSSIA. L. M. (See Hymn 394.) DANIEL READ.

1. My soul be - fore thee prostrate lies; To thee, her Source, my spir - it flies;

S. & T. My wants I mourn, My wants I mourn, My chains I see; O
A. & B. My wants I mourn, My chains I see; O let thy pres - ence

let thy pres - ence set me free, O let thy pres - ence set me free.
set me free.

28   429

DUANE STREET.   L. M. D.   (See Hymn 450.)   Rev. George Coles.

1. Je-sus, my all, to heaven is gone, He whom I fix my hopes up-on;

His track I see, and I'll pur-sue The nar-row way, till him I view.
D. S. The King's highway of ho-li-ness, I'll go, for all his paths are peace.

FINE.

D. S.

2. The way the ho-ly prophets went, The road that leads from banishment,

STAFFORD.   S. M.   (See Hymn 473.)   Daniel Read.

1. Lord, in....... the strength of grace, With a glad heart and free,

My - self, my res - i - due of days, My -

My - self, my res - i -
My - self, my res - i - due of days, My -

self, my res - i - due of days,

due............... of days, I con - se - crate to thee.

self, my res - i - due of days,

CONCORD. S. M. (See Hymn 770.) OLIVER HOLDEN.

1. I love thy king-dom, Lord, The house of thine a-bode,

S. & T. The Church our blest, The Church our blest Re-deem-er saved,
A. & B. The Church our blest Re-deem-er saved...........

The Church our blest Re-deem-er saved With his own pre-cious blood.

EXHORTATION. C. M. (See Hymn 1038.) S. HIBBARD.

1. On Jor-dan's stormy banks I stand, And cast..... a wish-ful eye

To Canaan's fair and hap-py land, Where my pos-ses-sions
To Canaan's fair and hap-py land, Where
To Canaan's fair and hap-py land, Where my pos-ses-sions lie,................

he, To Canaan's fair and hap-py land, Where my pos-ses-sions lie.
my possessions lie.................

To Canaan's fair and hap-py land,

431

OCCASIONAL PIECES AND CHANTS.

VENITE, EXULTEMUS DOMINO.

William Boyce.

Psalm xcv.

1 O COME, let us sing un- | to the | Lord ; ‖ let us heartily rejoice in the | strength of | our sal- | vation.

2 Let us come before his presence | with thanks- | giving, ‖ and show ourselves | glad in | him with | psalms.

3 For the Lord is a | great— | God, ‖ and a great | King a- | bove all | gods.

4 In his hands are all the corners | of the | earth; ‖ and the strength of the | hills is | his— | also.

5 The sea is his, | and he | made it; ‖ and his hands pre- | pared the | dry— | land.

6 O come, let us worship | and fall | down, ‖ and kneel be- | fore the | Lord our | Maker.

7 For he is the | Lord our | God, ‖ and we are the people of his pasture, and the | sheep of | his— | hand.

8 O worship the Lord in the | beauty--of | holiness ; ‖ let the whole earth | stand in | awe of | him.

*9 For he cometh, for he cometh to | judge the | earth, ‖ and with righteousness to judge the world, and the | people | with his | truth.

10 Glory be to the Father, and | to the | Son, ‖ and | to the | Holy | Ghost ;

11 As it was in the beginning, is now, and | ever | shall be, ‖ world | without | end. A- | men.

Begin at middle of the chant.

JUBILATE DEO. (1.)

Gregorian.

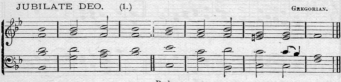

Psalm c.

1 O BE joyful in the Lord, | all ye | lands ; ‖ serve the Lord with gladness, and come before His | presence | with a | song.

2 Be ye sure that the Lord | he is | God ; ‖ it is he that hath made us, and not we ourselves: we are his people, | and the | sheep of--his | pasture.

3 O go your way into his gates with thanksgiving, and into his | courts with | praise ; ‖ be thankful unto him, and | speak good | of his | name.

4 For the Lord is gracious, his mercy is | ever- | lasting ; ‖ and his truth endureth from gener- | ation--to | gener- | ation.

Glory be to the Father, and | to the | Son, ‖ and | to the | Holy | Ghost ;

6 As it was in the beginning, is now, and | ever | shall be, ‖ world | without | end. A- | men.

JUBILATE DEO. (2.)

William Turner.

432

THE LORD'S PRAYER.

L. T. DOWNES.

Matthew vi, 9-13.

1 OUR Father who art in heaven, hallowed | be thy | name. ‖ Thy kingdom come: thy will be done on | earth--as it | is in | heaven.

2 Give us this day our | daily | bread: ‖ and forgive us our trespasses, as we forgive | those who | trespass--a- | gainst us.

3 And lead us not into temptation, but deliver | us from | evil: ‖ for thine is the kingdom, and the power, and the | glory,--for- | ever. A- | men.

GLORIA IN EXCELSIS.

UNKNOWN.

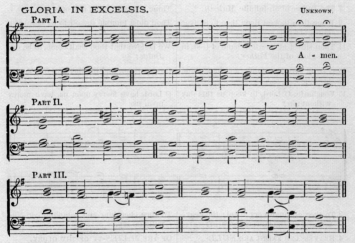

PART I.
GLORY be to | God on | high, ‖ and on earth | peace, good- | will--toward | men.
We praise thee, we bless thee, we | worship | thee, ‖ we glorify thee, we give thanks to | thee for | thy great | glory.

PART II.
O Lord God, | heavenly | King, ‖ God the | Father | Al-— | mighty!
O Lord, the only-begotten Son | Jesus | Christ, ‖ O Lord God, Lamb of | God, Son | of the | Father,

PART III.
That takest away the | sins--of the | world, ‖ have mercy | upon | us.
Thou that takest away the | sins--of the | world, ‖ have mercy | upon | us.
Thou that takest away the | sins--of the | world, ‖ re- | ceive our | prayer.
Thou that sittest at the right hand of | God the | Father, ‖ have mercy | upon | us.

PART I.
For thou | only--art | holy, ‖ thou | only | art the | Lord.
Thou only, O Christ, with the | Holy | Ghost, ‖ art most high in the | glory--of | God the | Father. ‖ A- | men.

TE DEUM LAUDAMUS.

[The CADENCE of each part begins with the word or syllable in *Italics*.]

1 WE praise thee, O God; we acknowledge thee to be the *Lord:*

All the earth doth worship thee, the Father
ever-*lasting.*

3 HOLY—HOLY—HO-*LY:*

LORD GOD OF *SABAOTH:*

5 The glorious company of the apostles
praise *thee:*

The goodly fellowship of the prophets
praise *thee:*

7 The Father of an infinite *Majesty:*

Thine adorable, true, and only *Son:*

9 When thou tookest upon thee to deliver
man,

Thou didst humble thyself to be born of a
Virgin:

11 Thou sittest at the right hand of God, in
the glory of the *Father:*

We believe that thou shalt come, to be our
Judge:

13 O Lord, save thy people, and bless thine
heritage:

Govern them, and lift them up for-*ever.*

15 Vouchsafe, O Lord, to keep us this day
without *sin:*

O Lord, have mercy upon us, have mercy
upon *us.*

2 To thee all angels cry aloud: the heavens and all the powers there-*in:*

To thee cherubim and seraphim con-*tin-*
ually do cry,

4 HEAVEN AND EARTH ARE *FULL*

OF THE *MAJES*-TY OF THY GLORY.

6 The noble army of martyrs praise *thee:*

The holy Church, throughout all the world,
doth acknowledge thee,

8 Also the Holy Ghost, the *Comforter.*

Thou art the King of glory, O Christ; thou
art the everlasting *Son* = of the Father.

10 When thou hadst overcome the sharpness of *death,*

Thou didst open the kingdom of *heaven*
to all believers.

12 We therefore pray thee, help thy servants, whom thou hast redeemed with
thy precious *blood:*

Make them to be numbered with thy saints,
in *glo*-ry everlasting.

14 Day by day we magnify *thee:*

And we worship thy *Name* ever, world
without end.

16 O Lord, let thy mercy be upon us, as
our trust is in *thee:*

O Lord, in thee have I trusted: let me
nev-er be confounded.

BENEDICTUS.

RICHARD FARRANT.

Luke i, 68–71.

1 BLESSED be the Lord | God of | Israel, ‖ for he hath visited | and re- | deemed his | people;

2 And hath raised up a mighty sal- | vation | for us, ‖ in the | house - - of his | servant | David;

3 As he spake by the mouth of his | holy | prophets, ‖ which have been | since the | world be- | gan;

4 That we should be saved | from our | enemies, ‖ and from the | hand of | all that | hate us.

5 Glory be to the Father, and | to the | Son, ‖ and | to the | Holy | Ghost;

6 As it was in the beginning, is now, and | ever | shall be, ‖ world | without | end. A- | men.

DEUS MISEREATUR.

RICHARD FARRANT.

Psalm lxvii.

1 GOD be merciful unto | us, and | bless us; ‖ and show us the light of his counte- nance, and be | merci - -ful | unto | us.

2 That thy way may be | known up- - on | earth; ‖ thy saving | health a- | mong all | nations.

3 Let the people praise | thee, O | God, ‖ yea, let | all the | people | praise thee.

4 O let the nations rejoice | and be | glad; ‖ for thou shalt judge the folk righteous ly, and govern the | nations | upon | earth.

Let the people praise | thee, O | God; ‖ yea, let | all the | people | praise thee.

6 Then shall the earth bring | forth her | increase; ‖ and God, even our own | God, shall | give us - - his | blessing.

7 God | shall— | bless us ; ‖ and all the ends of the | world shall | fear— | him.

8 Glory be to the Father, and | to the | Son, ‖ and | to the | Holy | Ghost;

9 As it was in the beginning, is now, and | ever | shall be, ‖ world | without | end. A- | men.

LÆTATUS SUM.   JOHN ROBINSON.

Psalm cxxii.

1 I WAS glad when they said | unto | me, ‖ Let us go into the | house— | of the | Lord.

2 Our feet shall stand within thy gates, | O Je- | rusalem. ‖ Jerusalem is builded as a city that | is com- | pact to- | gether;

3 Whither the tribes go up; the tribes | of the | Lord, ‖ unto the testimony of Israel to give thanks unto the | name— | of the | Lord.

4 For there are set | thrones of | judgment, ‖ the thrones | of the | house of | David.

5 Pray for the peace of Je- | rusa- | lem; ‖ they shall | prosper | that love | thee.

6 Peace be with- | in thy | walls; ‖ and prosperity with- | in thy | pala- | ces.

7 For my brethren and com- | panions' | sakes, ‖ I will now say, | Peace— | be with- | in thee.

8 Because of the house of the | Lord our | God, ‖ I will | seek, will | seek thy | good.

VIRUM DOLORUM.   REV. WILLIAM FELTON.

Isaiah liii.

1 HE is despised and re- | jected of | men; ‖ a man of sorrows and ac- | quainted | with— | grief.

2 And we hid as it were our | faces | from him; ‖ he was despised, and | we es- | teemed him | not.

3 Surely he hath borne our griefs, and | carried our | sorrows: ‖ yet we did esteem him stricken, | smitten of | God, -- and af- | flicted.

4 But he was wounded for | our trans- | gressions, ‖ he was bruised for | our in- | iqui- | ties;

5 The chastisement of our peace | was up- | on him, ‖ and with his | stripes— | we are | healed.

6 All we like sheep have | gone a- | stray; ‖ we have turned every | one to | his own | way;

7 And the Lord hath | laid on | him | the in- | iquity | of us | all.

8 When thou shalt make his soul an | offering -- for | sin, ‖ he shall see his seed, he | shall pro- | long his | days,

9 And the pleasure of the Lord shall prosper | in his | hand. ‖ He shall see of the travail of his soul, and | shall be | satis- | fied.

OCCASIONAL PIECES AND CHANTS.

MY GOD, MY FATHER.

REV. ARTHUR H. D. TROYTE.

Thy will be done!

1 My God, my Father, *while* I stray
Far from my home on *life's* rough way,
O teach me from my *heart* to say,
    Thy will be done!

2 Though dark my path and sad my lot,
Let me be still and murmur not,
And breathe the prayer divinely taught,
    "Thy will be done!"

3 What though in lonely grief I sigh
For friends beloved, no longer nigh!
Submissive still would I reply,
    "Thy will be done!"

4 Though thou hast called me to resign
What most I prized, it ne'er was mine:
I have but yielded what was thine;
    Thy will be done!

5 Let but my fainting heart be blest
With thy sweet Spirit for its guest,
My God, to thee I leave the rest:
    Thy will be done!

6 Renew my will from day to day;
Blend it with thine, and take away
All that now makes it hard to say,
    "Thy will be done!"

CHARLOTTE ELLIOTT.

THE GOOD DIE NOT.

W. L. REYNOLDS.

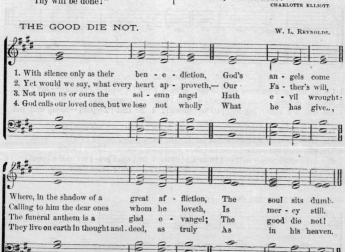

1. With silence only as their ben - e - diction, God's an - gels come
2. Yet would we say, what every heart ap - proveth,— Our Fa - ther's will,
3. Not upon us or ours the sol - emn angel Hath e - vil wrought:
4. God calls our loved ones, but we lose not wholly What he has given,

Where, in the shadow of a great af - fliction, The soul sits dumb.
Calling to him the dear ones whom he loveth, Is mer - cy still.
The funeral anthem is a glad e - vangel; The good die not!
They live on earth in thought and deed, as truly As in his heaven.

JOHN G. WHITTIER.

OCCASIONAL PIECES AND CHANTS.

QUI HABITAT.

UNKNOWN.

Psalm xci.

1 HE that dwelleth in the secret place of the | Most— | High, ‖ shall abide under th | shadow --of | the Al- | mighty.

2 I will say of the Lord, he is my refuge | and my | fortress, ‖ my God, in | him— | will I | trust.

3 Because thou hast made the Lord, which | is my | refuge, ‖ even the Most | High | thy | habi- | tation,

4 There shall no evil be- | fall— | thee, ‖ neither shall any | plague come | nigh thy | dwelling.

5 For he shall give his angels charge | over | thee, ‖ to | keep thee --in | all thy | ways.

6 They shall bear thee up | in their | hands, ‖ lest thou dash thy | foot a- | gainst a | stone.

7 Thou shalt tread upon the | lion and | adder; ‖ the young lion and the dragon shalt | thou | trample | under | feet.

8 Because he hath set his love upon me, therefore will I de- | liver | him: ‖ I will set | him on high, because he hath | known my | Name.

9 He shall call upon me, and I will | answer | him: ‖ I will be with him in trouble; I | will deliver | him, and | honor | him.

10 With long life will I | satis- | fy him, ‖ and | show him | my sal- | vation.

LEVAVI OCULOS.   (1.)

*

Psalm cxxi.

1 I WILL lift up mine eyes un- | to the | hills, ‖ from | whence— | cometh --my | help.

2 My help cometh | from the | Lord, ‖ who | made— | heaven and | earth.

3 He will not suffer thy foot | to be | moved! ‖ he that | keepeth --thee | will not | slumber.

4 Behold, he that keepeth | Is-ra- | el, ‖ shall not | slum- — | ber nor | sleep.

5 The Lord | is thy | keeper; ‖ the Lord is thy shade up- | on thy | right— | hand.

6 The sun shall not smite | thee by | day, ‖ nor the | moon— | by— | night.

7 The Lord shall preserve thee | from all | evil; ‖ he | shall pre- | serve thy | soul.

8 The Lord shall preserve thy going out, and thy | coming in, ‖ from this time fort.. | and | even --for | ever- | more.

LEVAVI OCULOS.   (2.)

J. D. BUCKINGHAM.

TRISAGION.

Unknown.

Holy, holy, holy Lord God of Sabaoth ; heaven and earth are full | of thy | glory.

Hosanna in the highest! Blessed is he that cometh in the name of the Lord. Ho- | sanna | in the | highest!

TERSANCTUS.

Unknown.

Therefore with angels and arch- angels, and with all the company of } heaven, | We laud and magnify thy glorious............... } name,

Ev - er - more prais - - ing thee, and say - ing,

Crescendo.

Ho - - ly, Ho - - ly, Ho - - ly Lord God of Hosts;

f

Heaven and earth are full of........ thy glo - - ry:

p *Cres.* *f*

Glo - ry be to thee, O Lord, Most High. A - men.

THY WILL BE DONE.

ISAAC BAKER WOODBURY.

"Thy will be done."

"THY will be | done !" ‖ In devious way
The hurrying streams of | life may | run ; ‖
Yet still our grateful hearts shall say, |
"Thy will be | done !"

2 "Thy will be | done !" ‖ If o'er us shine
A gladdening and a | prosperous | sun, ‖

This prayer will make it more divine: |
"Thy will be | done !"

3 "Thy will be | done !" ‖ Though
shrouded o'er
Our | path with | gloom, ‖ one comfort
one
Is ours: to breathe, while we adore, |
"Thy will be | done !"

SIR JOHN BOWRING.

A LOWLY SPIRIT.

SAMUEL P. WARREN.

A lowly spirit.

1 FROM the recesses of a lowly spirit
My humble | prayer as- | cends ; ‖ O |
Father, | hear it ; ‖
Upsoaring on the wings of | fear and |
meekness, ‖
For- | give its | weakness.

2 I know, I feel, how mean and | how
un- | worthy ‖
The trembling sacrifice I | pour be- | fore
thee ; ‖
What can I offer in thy | presence |
holy ‖
But | sin and | folly?

3 For in thy sight, who every | bosom |
viewest, ‖
Cold are our warmest vows, and | vain
our | truest ; ‖
Thoughts of a hurrying hour, our | lips
re- | peat them, ‖
Our | hearts for- | get them.

4 We see thy hand ; it leads us, | it sup- |
ports us : ‖
We hear thy voice ; it counsels | and it
courts us ; ‖

And then we turn away; and | still thy |
kindness ‖
Pardons | our— | blindness.

5 Who can resist thy gentle | call, ap- |
pealing ‖
To every generous thought and | grateful
| feeling? ‖
That voice paternal, whispering, | watch-
ing | ever? ‖
My | bosom ? | Never !

6 Father and Saviour! plant within that
bosom
These | seeds of | holiness, ‖ and bid them
| blossom
In | fragrance, ‖ and in beauty | bright
and | vernal, ‖
And | spring e- | ternal.

7 Then place them in those everlasting
gardens,
Where | angels | walk ‖ and seraphs | are
the | wardens ; ‖
Where every flower that creeps through |
death's dark | portal ‖
Be- | comes im- | mortal.

SIR JOHN BOWRING.

OCCASIONAL PIECES AND CHANTS.

DOMINE REFUGIUM. (1.) JOHN BLOW.

[The lines printed in Roman may be read by the minister, and those printed in *Italics* sung by the choir.]

Psalm xc.

1 LORD, thou hast | been our | dwelling-place ‖ in | all— | gener- | ations.
2 *Before the mountains were brought forth, or ever thou hadst formed the earth | and the | world, ‖ even from everlasting to everlasting, | thou— | art— | God.*
3 Thou turnest man | to de- | struction ; ‖ and sayest, Re- | turn, ye | children--of | men.
4 *For a thousand years in thy sight are but as yesterday when | it is | past, ‖ and | as a | watch--in the | night.*
5 Thou carriest them away as with a flood; they are | as a | sleep : ‖ in the morning they are like | grass which | groweth | up.
6 *In the morning it flourisheth, and | groweth | up; ‖ in the evening it is cut | down and | wither- | eth.*
7 For we are consumed | by thine | anger, ‖ and by thy | wrath— | are we | troubled.
8 *Thou hast set our iniquities be- | fore— | thee, ‖ our secret sins in the | light of | thy— | countenance.*
9 For all our days are passed away | in thy | wrath ; ‖ we spend our years | as a | tale--that is | told.
10 *The days of our years are threescore | years and | ten; ‖ and if by reason of strength they be fourscore years, yet is their strength labor and sorrow; for it is soon cut off, | and we | fly a- | way.*
11 Who knoweth the power | of thine | anger? ‖ even according to thy fear, | so— | is thy | wrath.
12 *So teach us to | number--our | days, ‖ that we may apply our | hearts— | unto | wisdom.*
13 Return, O | Lord, how | long? ‖ and let it repent | thee con- | cerning--thy | servants.
14 *O satisfy us early | with thy | mercy; ‖ that we may rejoice and be | glad— | all our | days.*
15 Make us glad according to the days wherein | thou--hast af- | flicted us, ‖ and the years wherein | we have | seen— | evil.
16 *Let thy work appear un- | to thy | servants, ‖ and thy | glory un- | to their | children ;*
*17 And let the beauty of the Lord our God | be up- | on us : ‖ and establish thou the work of our hands upon us; yea, the work of our | hands, es- | tablish thou | it.

* If double chant be used begin at middle of chant.

DOMINE REFUGIUM. (2.) THOMAS MORLEY.

OCCASIONAL PIECES AND CHANTS.

DOMINUS REGIT ME.

LOWELL MASON

Psalm xxiii.

THE Lord is my Shepherd; I | shall not | want; ‖ he maketh me to lie down in green pastures; he leadeth me beside the | still— | waters.

He restoreth my soul; he leadeth me in the paths of righteousness for his | name's— | sake. ‖ Yea, though I walk through the valley of the shadow of death, I will fear no evil, for thou art with me; thy rod and thy staff | they — | comfort me.

Thou preparest a table before me, in the presence of mine enemies; thou anointest my head with oil; my | cup--runneth | over. ‖ Surely goodness and mercy shall follow me all the days of my life; and I will dwell in the house of the | Lord for- | ever. ‖ A- | men.

VENITE AD ME.

UNKNOWN.

Matt. xi, 28–30. Rev. xxii, 17.

1 COME unto me, all ye that labor and are | heavy- | laden, ‖ and | I will | give you | rest.

2 Take my yoke upon you, and learn of me; for I am meek and | lowly--in | heart: ‖ and ye shall find | rest--unto | your— | souls.

3 For my yoke is easy, and my | burden--is | light, ‖ for my yoke is easy, | and my | burden--is | light.

4 And the Spirit and the Bride say, Come. And let him that | heareth,--say, | Come. ‖ And let him that is athirst come; and whosoever will, let him take the | water-- of | life— | freely. A- | men.

GLORIA PATRI.

CHARLES MEINEKE.

Glo - ry be to the Fa-ther, and to the Son, and to the

Ho - ly Ghost, as it was in the be - gin - ning, is

now, and ev - er shall be, world with-out end. A - men. A - men.

442

THE FOUR LAST THINGS

BEETHOVEN AN

Death.

1. We are dy ing day by day; Soon from earth we pass a - way; Lord of
2. In the gloom thy light pro vide, Safe ly through the val ley guide; Thee we

Judgment.

life, to thee we pray; Hear us, ho ly Je - sus
trust, for thou hast died; Hear us, ho ly Je - sus. 3. When thy summons we o -

bey On the dreadful judgment-day, Let not fear our souls dis-may, Hear us, ho ly

Hell. *Unison.*

Je - sus. 4. From the awful place of doom, Where in ray-less outer gloom Dead souls

Heaven.

lie as in a tomb, Save us, ho-ly Je - sus. 5. When thy saints in glory reign, Free from
6. Where, with loved ones gone before, We may

sorrow, free from pain, Pure from every guilty stain, Bring us, ho ly Je - sus.
love thee and a - dore In thy presence ev - ermore, Bring us, ho ly Je - sus.

443

CHANTS.

CHANTS.

7 (SINGLE.)   Rev. Wm. Felton.

13 (SINGLE.)   John Alcock.

8 (SINGLE.)   Gregorian.

14 (SINGLE.)   Unknown.

9 (SINGLE.)   Unknown.

15 (SINGLE.)   Unknown.

10 (SINGLE.)   Unknown.

16 (SINGLE.)   William Crotch.

11 (SINGLE.)   Geo. A. Macfarren.

17 (SINGLE.)   James Turle.

12 (SINGLE.)   Unknown.

18 (SINGLE.)   T——*.

ALPHABETICAL INDEX OF TUNES

Most of the Music included in this Collection is introduced "by permission," either purchased or given. It must, therefore, not be used in any other, without the consent of the authors or of hose who hold the copyright of the Tunes.

446

METRICAL INDEX.

453

INDEX

OF

OCCASIONAL PIECES AND CHANTS.

INDEX OF COMPOSERS

457

INDEX OF AUTHORS OF HYMNS.

DAMS, Mrs. Sarah Flower, *b.* 1805, *d.* 1849. *Hymn* 724.

ADDISON, Joseph, *b.* 1672, *d.* 1719. *Hymns* 138, 160, 180, 412, 1113.

ALEXANDER, Mrs. Cecil Frances, *b.* 1823. *Hymns* 320, 941, 1022.

ALEXANDER, Rev. James Waddell, D.D., *b.* 1804, *d.* 1859. *Hymn* 222.

ALFORD, Rev. Henry, D.D., *b.* 1810, *d.* 1871. *Hymns* 564, 1036, 1062, 1083.

ALLEN, James, *b.* 1734, *d.* 1804. *Hymn* 730.

ALLEN, Jonathan. *Hymn* 342.

AMBROSE OF MILAN, *b.* 340, *d.* 397. *Hymns* 107, 233.

ANDERSON, Mrs. Maria Frances, *b.* 1819. *Hymn* 933.

ANDREW OF CRETE, *b.* 660, *d.* 732. *Hymn* 1047.

ARNOLD, Rev. Gottfried, *b.* 1666, *d.* 1714. *Hymn* 492.

AUBER, Miss Harriet, *b.* 1773, *d.* 1862. *Hymns* 33, 74, 76, 132, 280, 300, 764, 779, 902, 937.

BACON, Rev. Leonard, D.D., *b.* 1802. *Hymn* 925.

BAKER, Rev. Sir Henry Williams, *b.* 1821, *d.* 1877. *Hymns* 91, 638, 734, 891, 1102, 1107.

BAKEWELL, Rev. John, *b.* 1721, *d.* 1819. *Hymn* 246.

BARBAULD, Mrs. Anna Letitia, *b.* 1743, *d.* 1825. *Hymns* 77, 344, 982, 1084.

BARBER, Mary A. S., (about 1840.) *Hymn* 463.

BARING-GOULD, Rev. Sabine, *b.* 1834. *Hymn* 563.

BARTON, Bernard, *b.* 1784, *d.* 1849. *Hymns* 507, 620.

BATHURST, Rev. William Hiley, *b.* 1796. *Hymns* 61, 274, 667, 928, 971, 980.

BAXTER, Mrs. Lydia, *b.* 1809, *d.* 1874. *Hymn* 653.

BAXTER, Rev. Richard, *b.* 1615, *d.* 1691. *Hymn* 669.

BEDDOME, Rev. Benjamin, *b.* 1717, *d.* 1795. *Hymns* 285, 314, 315, 405, 466, 706, 819, 950.

BEHEMB, Rev. M., *b.* 1537, *d.* 1622. *Hymn* 694.

BERNARD OF CLAIRVAUX, *b.* 1091, *d.* 1153. *Hymns* 222, 327, 408, 691, 700, 701, 702.

BERNARD OF CLUNY, (about 1122.) *Hymns* 1058, 1059, 1060, 1061.

BETHUNE, Rev. George W., D.D., *b.* 1805, *d.* 1862. *Hymns* 333, 993.

BICKERSTETH, Rev. Edward H., *b.* 1825. *Hymn* 845.

BLACKLOCK, Rev. Thomas, D.D., *b.* 1721, *d.* 1791. *Hymn* 133.

BOEHM, Anthony Wilhelm, *b.* 1673, *d.* 1722. *Hymn* 327.

BONAR, Rev. Horatius, D.D., *b.* 1808. *Hymns* 426, 434, 576, 603, 655, 728, 754, 796, 855, 957, 994.

BONAR Mrs. Horatius, *Hymn* 741.

BORTHWICK, Miss Jane, *b.* 1825. *Hymns* 352, 654.

BOWLY, Mary Peters, *d.* 1856. *Hymn* 829.

BOURIGNON, Mad. Antoinette, *b.* 1616, *d.* 1680 *Hymn* 457.

BOWRING, Sir John, LL.D., *b.* 1792, *d.* 1872. *Hymns* 150, 204, 290, 328, 935, 978.

BRACKENBURY, Rev. Robert Carr, *b.* 1752, *d.* 1818. *Hymn* 360.

BRADY, Rev. Nicholas, D.D., *b.* 1659, *d.* 1726 *See* Tate and Brady.

BRIDGES, Matthew, *b.* 1800, *d.* 1852. *Hymns* 229, 257, 468.

BROWN, Mrs. Phœbe Hinsdale, *b.* 1783, *d.* 1861. *Hymns* 709, 771.

BRYANT, William Cullen, *b.* 1794, *d.* 1878. *Hymns* 201, 627, 869, 881, 900, 905, 907, 929.

BULFINCH, Rev. Stephen Greenleaf, *b.* 1809, *d.* 1870. *Hymn* 87.

BULLOCK, Rev. William, D.D., *b.* 1798. *Hymn* 1095.

BUNTING, Rev. William Maclardie, *b.* 1805, *d.* 1866. *Hymn* 830.

BURDSALL, Richard, *b.* 1735, *d.* 1824. *Hymn* 330.

BURGESS, Bp. George, D.D., *b.* 1809, *d.* 1866. *Hymns* 579, 1111.

BURLEIGH, William H., *b.* 1812, *d.* 1871. *Hymn* 671.

BURTON, John, *b.* 1803. *Hymn* 282.

BUTTRESS, John, *b.* 1778, *d.* 1820. *Hymn* 298.

CAMERON, William, *b.* 1751, *d.* 1811. *Hymn* 989.

CAMPBELL, Robert, *d.* 1868. *Hymns* 167, 847 *Hymn* 60.

CARLYLE, Rev. Joseph Dacre, *b.* 1759, *d.* 1804. *Hymn* 60.

CARY, Miss Phœbe, *b.* 1825, *d.* 1871. *Hymn* 1053.

CASWALL, Rev. Edward, *b.* 1814, *d.* 1878. *Hymns* 107, 700, 701, 702.

CAWOOD, Rev. John, *b.* 1775, *d.* 1852. *Hymns* 188, 301.

CENNICK, Rev. John, *b.* 1717, *d.* 1755. *Hymns* 450, 697, 720.

CHANDLER, Rev. John, *b.* 1806, *d.* 1876. *Hymns* 129, 219.

CHARLES, Mrs. Elizabeth, (1865.) *Hymns* 205. 233, 1026.

CHORLEY, Henry Fothergill, *b.* 1808, *d.* 1872 *Hymn* 1092.

CLARKE, Rev. James Freeman, D.D., *b.* 1810. *Hymn* 906.

458

INDEX OF AUTHORS OF HYMNS.

460

INDEX OF AUTHORS OF HYMNS.

30

461

INDEX OF AUTHORS OF HYMNS.

INDEX OF SCRIPTURE TEXTS.

Ch.Ver.	Hymn.
8 15	29
8 21	39
8 25	1114
9 23	590,601, 643,666
10 6	799
10 36	898
10 39	540
10 40	709
10 42	609
11 1	43,710
11 28	29,39
12 32	569
12 35	647
12 49	562,936
13 8	951,953
14 17	364
14 27	632
15 2	398
15 18	393,414,806
15 20-24	338,350
17 5	377
18 1	589,689
18 14	484
18 42	201
19 41	405
21 28	913
22 19	833,835,836, 837,840
22 42	537,618,1002
22 44	217,221,234 340,645,886
22 61	543
23 6	246
23 28	234
23 33	206
23 34	221,258
23 42	319,619
24 29	93,102
24 32	712
24 34	235,260
24 36	7
24 39	32

JOHN.

Ch.Ver.	Hymn.
1 4	489
1 9	416
1 14	216,526
1 18	238
1 29	382,822
3 21	475
4 20	36
4 35	598,607
6 21	636
6 37	382
6 48	835
6 63	277
6 68	400,402
7 37	341
9 4	565,572
10 4	46
10 16	793
11 9	570
11 35	203
12 41	56
13 9	533
14 2	1039
14 6	313,318,483, 517,877
14 13	1032

Ch.Ver.	Hymn.
14 16	264,265,266, 275,280,287, 411,424,480, 683
14 19	242
15 5	124,760
16 13	266
16 33	680
17 9	465,468,472, 488
17 21	793
19 2	222
19 30	218,224
19 34	415
20,22	30,263,267, 273
20 25	30
20 27	32
20 28	435
21 15	552
21 17	725
21 20	540

ACTS.

Ch.Ver.	Hymn.
2 1-3	37,268,270, 277
2 24	227
2 39	832
2 42	7?9
3 21	261
4 12	313,332
7 48	44
7 56	680
9 11	710
9 18	309
12 7	422
14 9	398
14 17	139
14 22	496
14 26	939
16 25,26	580,608
16 31	367
17 24	12,44
17 24-28	135
17 28	42,124,126 127
20 35	904
26 18	784

ROMANS.

Ch.Ver.	Hymn.
1 4	6
1 20	38
3 17	337
4 5	367
4 6	418
4 18	626
4 20	667
5 5	378,508
5 6	304
5 8	322
5 15	321
5 17	535
5 20	1048
6 6	519
8 1	422
8 2	482
8 11	668
8 16	271,281,424, 438,439
8 18	1032

Ch.Ver.	Hymn.
8 26	239,706
8 31	591,596
9 28	486
10 15	821
11 4	33
11 12	924
11 27	531
12 15	891,902
13 11	1053,1054
13 12	1070
14 8	110,500,864
14 11	31
14 12	574
14 17	937
15 13	52,59

I. CORINTHIANS.

Ch.Ver.	Hymn.
5 2	220,456,461, 722
2 10	435
3 7	301
3 9	816
3 16	499
6 20	469,474
7 35	39
10 16	835
10 31	484,597
11 3?	833,836
12 3	435
13 1	504
13 12	174
13 13	703
14 1	793
15 20	231,232,233
15 25	245,251, 908,919
15 42	984,995
15 47	207,259
15 52	970,989
15 55	234,260,623, 985,989
16 9	936
16 13	566,567,568

II. CORINTHIANS.

Ch.Ver.	Hymn.
1 22	262
3 6	277
3 15	303,377,381
3 18	491
4 7	1046
5 1	612,1056
5 7	620
5 8	1055
5 11	814
5 14	811,814
5 17	502
6 2	349,361
7 5	798
9 6	904
11 2	511
13 11	265,782,793
13 14	53

GALATIANS.

Ch.Ver.	Hymn.
2 9	791
3 13	18,235,315
4 6	429,438,439, 440,477
4 15	549,561

Ch.Ver.	Hymn.
4 18	560
5 6	446,786
6 2	784,797,801, 804,1068
6 14	204,205, 211,219

EPHESIANS.

Ch.Ver.	Hymn.
1 6	454
1 13	424
1 14	262
1 18	539
1 22	680
2 1	308
2 8	377,385,446, 765
2 12	303
2 14	210
2 20	816,856, 857,859
3 8	356,822
3 15	1033
3 17	502
3 18	433,456,538
3 19	442,456,476
4 3	67
4 5	800
4 8	24,229,230, 231,234,236, 237
4 11	812
4 30	459
5 14	372,555
5 27	795
6 10-18	584,586, 587,588,
6 11	589,1047 543,587, 588,599
6 12	1047
6 16	588,659

PHILIPPIANS.

Ch.Ver.	Hymn.
1 6	936
1 21	669,696, 721,993
1 23	396,1065
2 5	528,586
2 7	422
2 9	822
2 11	31,248
2 13	124
3 7	211,220
3 8	213,708,758, 1042
3 14	476,478,557, 680,1068
4 4	244,493
4 6	728
4 11	664
4 13	814

COLOSSIANS.

Ch.Ver.	Hymn.
1 22	543
3 1	600
3 11	316,525,700, 701,702,736, 741,751,938
3 1?	24,61,448

I. THESS.

Ch.Ver.	Hymn.
4 3	529
4 13	967,971
4 14	960
4 16,17	22,244, 1015,1016, 1019,1028, 1050
5 9	353
5 17	506,589
5 24	534

II. THESS.

Ch.Ver.	Hymn.
1 7,8	1018,1020, 1025

I. TIMOTHY.

Ch.Ver.	Hymn.
1 15	385,441
1 17	126
2 6	35,238
3 16	216,422,540
6 12	599

II. TIMOTHY.

Ch.Ver.	Hymn.
1 6	562
1 9	539
2 3	505,587,588, 593
2 12	256,260,657
2 13	453
4 7	585,955,991
4 8	801

TITUS.

Ch.Ver.	Hymn.
2 13	541
2 14	407
3 2	532
3 5	314,385

HEBREWS.

Ch.Ver.	Hymn.
1 3	148,623
1 6	189
1 14	155,167,356
2 17	254
3 10	390
4 9	78,82,529
4 12	288,311
4 13	139
4 14	243
4 15	254
4 16	498,690,717
6 6	339,374
6 17	523
6 18	656,674
6 19	420,526,663
7 3	250
7 25	258,438
8 8	541
9 5	684
9 14	250
9 24	322
9 27	963,968
10 4	305
10 16	531
10 20	210
10 29	390
10 35	626
11 5	549

INDEX OF SCRIPTURE TEXTS.

466

INDEX OF SUBJECTS.

THE FIGURES REFER TO THE HYMNS.

Abba, Father, 429, 436, 438, 440, 477, 643.

Abide with me, 93.

Accepted time, 361 — See also: *Probation*.

Activity, Calls to, 563-567, 607.

Adoption:—.
  Assurance of, 428, 429, 436, 438-440.
  Joy of, 426, 429, 826.
  Love of, 419, 434.
  Prayer of, 426, 440, 826.

Adoration — See *Christ, God, Holy Spirit, Trinity*.

Advent—See *Christ*.

Advocate—See *Christ*.

Afflictions:—
  Blessings of, 177, 671, 761, 768.
  Comfort in, 661, 671, 672, 755, 759, 761, 767, 777, 798, 1002, 1072.
  Courage in, 648, 761.
  Prayer during, 645, 670, 689.
  Refuge in, 665, 670, 674, 689.
  Submission in, 667.

Angels:—
  Adoring Christ, 246.
  At the advent of Christ, 24, 188, 189, 190, 192, 195.
  At the coronation of Christ, 58, 226, 237, 245, 248, 249.
  At the resurrection of Christ, 227, 234, 235, 237.
  Joy of, 125, 194, 304, 315, 332, 340, 414, 759.
  Ministry of, 52, 97, 134, 144, 155, 158, 167, 217, 356, 444, 485, 547, 969, 980, 1001, 1004, 1070, 1083.
  Song of, 2, 10, 34, 42, 47, 48, 56, 58, 194, 195, 259, 340, 444, 563, 710, 733, 744, 759, 916, 1000, 1070.
  Worship of, 1069.

Apostles' creed, 118.

Archangels:—
  Trumpet, 1023, 1027.
  Voice, 244.
  Worship of, 18, 38, 144, 1077.

Ark of God, 388.

Ascension of Christ — See *Christ*.

Ashamed of Jesus, 604.

Assurance, 427, 435-438, 757.

Atonement :—26, 325, 327, 364.
  Completed, 210, 215, 218, 219, 223, 224, 260, 338, 340.
  Fullness of, 215, 219, 221, 223, 228, 246, 331, 341.
  Necessary, 210.
  Sufficient, 238, 250, 305.
  Universality of, 26, 32, 210, 221, 238, 331, 332.

Backsliding :—546-563.
  Fear of, 543, 555.
  Lamented, 546-550, 553, 554, 557-561.
  Return from, 380, 546-551, 553, 554, 557-561.

Baptism :—
  Adult, 826, 829-831.
  Infant, 825, 827, 828, 832.
  Of the Holy Spirit, 829, 830, 832.
  Significance of, 829, 831.

Barren fig-tree, 953.

Battle-hymn of the Reformation, 569.

Benediction, Apostolic, 53.

Bereavement, 1002, 1006, 1007.

Bible—See *Scriptures*.

Blind Bartimeus, 201.

Brevity of life—See *Life*.

Brotherly love—See *Saints, Communion of*.

Burdens, 1053.

Calvary, 206, 209, 223, 341, 378, 381, 383, 836, 860.

Canaan, The Heavenly, 1036-1038, 1062, 1076.

Charities and reforms, 890-907.

Charity :—
  Acts of, 891-894, 896-898, 902, 905.
  Institutions of, 1099.
  Rewarded, 902-905.
  Supreme, 504.

Cherubim and Seraphim, 56, 120, 144, 152, 193, 229, 234, 727, 1065.

Chief of sinners, 385.

Children and youth :—872-889.
  Advised, 360.
  Baptism of, 827, 828.
  Consecrated to Christ, 827, 828.
  Hosannas of, 874, 882, 883.
  In heaven, 987, 1007.
  Piety of, 879, 880, 886.
  Praise of, 874, 876, 884-886.
  Prayer of, 872, 873, 875, 878, 884, 885, 889.
  Prayer for, 887, 888.
  Training of, 877.

Choosing Christ, 447.

Christ :—181-261.
  Abiding with believers, 14, 93, 102, 679, 701, 702, 738, 742, 760, 820.
  Adoration of, 31, 35, 64, 66, 181, 188, 190, 245, 246, 255, 315, 332, 409, 680, 842, 852, 908, 1013.
  Advent, first, 185, 188-195.
  Advent, second, 650, 954, 955, 1013-1018, 1023, 1024, 1026.
  Advocate, 110, 239, 251, 253, 258, 378, 440, 720.
  Agony of, 217, 236, 246, 340, 417, 423, 618, 665, 723, 836, 850.
  All in all, 31, 203, 325, 337, 397, 431, 441, 468, 494, 525, 635, 736, 806.
  Ascension of, 14, 229, 236, 237, 245, 261.
  Atonement of, 32, 210, 224, 238, 243, 246, 250, 306, 331, 332, 372, 378, 383, 384, 415, 754.
    See also : *Atonement*.
  Author of faith, 406, 445, 491.
  Benevolence of, 261, 306.
  Blood of, 238, 305, 306, 314, 319, 320, 330, 384, 420, 421, 436, 452, 454, 461, 735, 833.

467

468

INDEX OF SUBJECTS.

Christians—(Continued.)
609, 612, 640, 641, 680, 729, 747, 765, 769, 776.
Love of, for Christ, 241, 356, 434, 452, 516, 604, 605, 703, 725, 803.
Perfection of, 746—See also : *Sanctification*.
Priests and kings, 356, 542.
Race of, 594, 648.
Safety of, 41, 115, 164, 170, 356, 441, 507, 625.
Steadfastness of, 518, 588, 616, 649, 677.
Strangers and pilgrims, 648.
Submission of, 506, 610, 618, 619, 621, 622, 628, 629, 631, 632, 637, 638, 643, 645, 655, 665.
Sufferings of, 486, 608, 610–612, 618, 619, 621, 625, 627–629, 631, 632, 643–645, 655, 657, 658, 676.
Triumph of, 452, 585, 588, 594, 626, 627, 631, 991, 1047, 1061, 1062.
Unity of, 67, 737, 780, 782, 783, 785, 792, 793, 796, 797, 800, 801, 804–806, 844.
Warfare of, 563, 569, 581–584, 587–589, 591, 593, 596, 599, 659, 677, 680, 991, 1046.
Witnesses for Jesus, 805, 814, 911.
Work, 456, 565, 572, 575, 578, 591, 592, 596–598, 602, 603, 605–607, 609, 675, 744, 808, 816, 891–898, 902–905.
Christmas hymns, 181–195.
Church :—763–944.
Afflicted, 777, 778.
Beloved by Christians, 770.
Beloved by God, 764, 766–768, 770, 772, 775, 776, 778.
Bride of Christ, 355, 794.
Extension of, 779.
Foundation of, 766, 776.
Glory of, 769, 777, 795.
God the strength of, 569, 763, 768, 772.
Immovable, 563, 763, 764, 772.
In the desert, 1036.
Joining the, 466, 781, 791.
Members of, 764.
Militant, 563, 564, 566–569.
Missions of—See *Missions*.
Praises of the, 727-

Church—(Continued.)
Prayer for the, 46, 921, 992.
Security of the, 763, 764, 768, 772, 773, 776, 777.
The safety of the nation, 764, 871.
Triumph of the, 563, 564, 585, 763, 765, 767, 778, 971.
Unity of, 765, 780, 783, 785, 787, 790, 800, 806.
Work, 856–944.
Churches :—
Dedication of, 860, 862–865, 867–870.
Erection of, 856, 858.
Laying corner-stone of, 857, 859, 861.
Safety of a nation, 871.
Close of worship, 22, 23, 52, 53, 59.
Comfort for mourners, 487, 627, 632, 671, 684, 967.
Communion :—
At the Lord's Table—See *Lord's Supper*.
Of saints—See *Saints*.
With Christ, 833, 846, 849—See also : *Saints*.
With God, 116, 408, 409.
Conference hymn, 798.
Confession of faith, 118, 121, 212.
Of sin, 60, 115, 212, 390.
Conscience :—107, 294, 423, 424, 439, 497, 511, 826.
Prayer for a tender, 511.
Consecration :—456–475.
Entire, 470, 505.
Exhortation to, 220.
Of goods, 467, 892, 903, 904.
Of self, 104, 112, 241, 409, 419, 447, 458, 467, 470, 472–474.
Renewal of, 95, 106, 945.
To Christ, 157, 175, 182, 212, 214, 228, 394, 401, 456, 457, 461, 466–469, 476, 484, 490, 500, 609, 718, 722, 742, 782.
To God, 60, 83, 95, 103, 106, 112, 128, 394, 419, 458–460, 470, 472–475, 478, 685, 726, 946, 951.
To the Church, 770.
To the ministry, 808, 811, 814.
Consolation :—
In Christ's sympathy, 611, 624.
In grief, 611, 624, 688.
In sickness, 612.
Sought, 664.
See also : *Afflictions*.
Contentment, 675, 696, 747.
Contrition, 60, 550, 558, 794.
Conversion, Joys of, 12, 442, 444, 447, 450.

Conviction—See *Sinners*.
Courage, 583, 634, 664, 699.
Covenant :—
New, 531, 833, 837.
Renewed, 771, 945.
Cross :—
And crown, 236, 256, 487, 493, 601, 638, 640, 657, 666, 680, 786, 798, 914, 1032, 1053.
Bearing the, 505, 531, 590, 593, 601, 632, 643, 664, 666, 695, 715, 742, 1040.
Glorying in the, 204, 211, 219, 727, 814.
Lessons of the, 204, 205, 207–209, 211–214, 219–221, 727.
Power of the, 208, 209, 213, 221, 240, 492, 582, 846.
Salvation through the, 204, 212–214, 219–221, 223, 338.
Soldiers of the, 582, 593.
Victory of the, 251, 276.
Crosses and blessings, 615.
Crowned with thorns, 222.
Crowns of glory, 205, 971, 1001, 1014.

Day :—
Of grace, —See *Probation*.
Of life, 1026.
Of rest and gladness, 72.
Of wrath, 1023.
Day-spring, The, 195.
Day-star, 111.
De profundis, 403, 665, 681.
Death :—967–1012.
Confidence in, 141, 156, 171, 180, 228, 333, 427, 613, 619, 634, 721, 967, 973–976, 979, 982, 985.
Conquered, 228, 232, 969–971, 973, 979, 981, 985, 988, 989, 993.
Fear of, overcome, 156, 704, 967, 970, 971, 975, 976, 980, 998.
Nearness of, 113, 367, 366, 373.
Of children, 986, 987, 1006–1008.
Of friends, 967, 974, 977, 1002, 1009.
Of infants, 986, 987.
Of pastor, 991, 992.
Of saints, 969–971, 974, 975, 979, 980, 982–985, 990, 997, 999–1004, 1010–1012.
Prayer in prospect of, 110, 115, 959–962, 964–966, 968.

470

INDEX OF SUBJECTS.

INDEX OF SUBJECTS.

Sinai, 206, 787.

Sin :—
Deceitfulness of, 559.
Load of, 495.
Original, 486, 495.
Rest from, 534.
Salvation from, 522, 528, 532, 540.
Work of, 339, 365.
See also : *Depravity.*

Sinners :—302–417.
Convicted, 305, 308, 309, 314, 344, 379, 380, 389, 391–397, 412, 414, 423.
Contrite, 339, 380, 403–405, 410, 412, 414, 458, 551, 553, 554, 558.
Confessing, 305, 369, 379, 380, 389, 391, 393, 396–298, 403, 404, 412, 414, 425, 444, 559, 656, 737.
Depravity of, 302, 305, 306, 309, 310, 356, 411.
Doomed, 189, 308, 314, 356, 369, 375, 376.
Exhorted, 308, 327, 335–339, 342, 343, 345–348, 353, 354, 356, 360–362, 364, 365, 367, 369–371, 373, 374, 376, 487, 1029.
Invited, 189, 302, 323, 326, 340, 341, 344, 349–351, 355, 357, 362–364, 369–371.
Lost condition of, 303, 304, 306, 308, 309, 320, 347, 356, 358, 360, 365, 371, 377, 380–382, 385, 386, 392, 393, 395, 399, 405, 425.
Refuge in Christ, 302, 307, 310, 312–314, 316, 318–320, 327, 334, 337, 359, 363, 368, 385, 386, 391, 393, 395, 401, 408, 411, 415–417, 420–422, 450.
Seeking pardon, 302, 303, 309, 311, 359, 368, 377, 380, 382, 390, 391, 393, 394, 397–399, 403, 406, 407, 414, 425, 428, 444.
Slavery of, 302, 311, 331, 363, 382, 399, 402, 413, 422, 450, 727, 895, 899–901.
Surrender of, 28, 307, 339, 352, 369, 372, 393, 397, 401, 409, 447, 462.
Warned, 335, 336, 343, 345, 349, 353, 354, 357, 358, 360, 361, 365, 366, 371, 373, 375, 376.
Sleep, 102–105, 108, 112, 113.
Soldiers, Christian, 563, 566–569, 587, 588, 825.
Solitude, 709, 713.
Son of the carpenter, 592.
Song of Moses and the Lamb, 4, 680.

Sowing and reaping, 55, 301, 575, 579, 598, 731, 903, 1081.
Spirit—See *Holy Spirit.*
Star :—
In the East, 182, 186, 300, 935, 989.
Of Bethlehem, 187, 907.
Starry heavens, 138, 293, 628, 788, 978, 1034.
Storms, 613, 656, 678, 731, 931, 957, 973, 982, 998, 1073, 1111.
Sufferings and death of Christ, 204–224.
Sunday-schools :—
Anniversary of, 878.
See also : *Children.*
Supper of the Lamb, 12.

Tabor, or Hermon, 200, 206.
Teachers, Prayer for, 881.
Te Deum Laudamus, 120, 144.
Temptation :—
Of Christ, 209, 254, 417, 723.
Of Christians, 342, 543, 570, 624, 639, 646, 680, 716.
Prayer under, 651, 716.
Ter Sanctus, 40, 48, 56, 72, 136, 144.
Thanksgiving :—51, 52, 99, 121, 232, 478, 946.
Hymns, 1083–1087, 1093, 1101.
Thy will be done, 464, 517, 537, 590, 618, 628, 654, 716, 800, 971, 1002.
Time and eternity, 945–997.
Too late, 375, 376.
Transfiguration of Christ, 198–200.
Trials, 203, 655, 654, 715, 717, 728.
Trinity :—
Adoration of, 16, 35, 121, 130, 136, 137, 144, 411.
Invocation of, 35, 91, 129.
Praise to the, 6, 16, 34, 35, 72, 118, 121, 139, 144, 470.
Prayer to the — See *Prayer.*
Worship of the, 10, 16, 34, 48, 56, 411.
Trust :—
In Christ, 115, 178, 254, 325, 359, 415, 453, 466, 477, 483, 556, 570, 595, 625, 626, 635, 637, 653, 654, 656, 669, 721, 1046, 1115.
In God, 69, 128, 141, 161, 165, 173, 175, 180, 302, 493, 541, 569, 614, 620, 622, 626, 629, 630, 637, 639, 761.

Trust—(*Continued.*)
In providence, 141, 164, 496, 510, 544, 569, 596, 613, 614, 617, 622, 623, 626, 627, 629, 641, 649, 664, 672, 673, 682, 801.
Trumpet :—
Gospel, 72, 326, 331.
Judgment, 994, 996, 1000, 1017–1019, 1023, 1028, 1029.
Types, 199, 305.

Unbelief, 161, 302, 303, 377, 513.
Unfaithfulness lamented—
See *Backsliding.*
Unseen but loved, 714, 733.

Vanity of earth, 358, 647, 662, 708, 741, 758.
Vows to God, 43, 106, 447, 460, 466, 467.

Waiting on God, 497, 529, 633, 786.
Walking with God, 507.
Wanderer :—
Exhorted, 906.
Invited, 370, 371, 603.
Rest of the, 623.
Restored, 370.
Warfare, Christian — See *Christians.*
Warnings, 335 — See *Sinners.*
Watchfulness, 555, 571, 574, 580, 581, 587, 753, 968, 1015.
Watching and praying, 505, 543, 555, 574, 576, 580, 581, 750, 753, 954, 1024, 1047.
Watchmen, 821, 823, 921, 935.
Watch-night, 945–948, 952–956.
Weeping, 1010, 1067.
Witness of our own spirits, 356, 437.
Witness of the Holy Spirit, 424, 429, 438.
Witnesses, Cloud of, 594, 1046.
Working and giving, 904.
World :—
Delusive, 456, 662, 708, 722, 960, 978.
Enmity of, 667, 752.
Renounced, 456, 613, 647, 685, 696, 758, 826, 1075.
Unsatisfying, 358, 647, 1031.
Worship :—1–117.
Blessings of, 67, 75, 88.
Calls to, 2–5, 8, 9, 11, 13, 16, 17, 24, 28, 47, 50, 57, 58, 63, 66, 68, 88, 145, 152, 153, 189, 191.

31

HYMNS FOR SOCIAL WORSHIP.

FIRST LINES OF STANZAS.

FIRST LINES OF STANZAS.

484

FIRST LINES OF STANZAS.

487

FIRST LINES OF HYMNS.

FIRST LINES OF HYMNS.

490

FIRST LINES OF HYMNS.

494

FIRST LINES OF HYMNS.

THE RITUAL.

* * *

Baptism.

[Let every adult person, and the parents of every child to be baptized, have the choice of either sprinkling, pouring, or immersion.]

[We will on no account whatever make a charge for administering Baptism.]

Order for the Administration of Baptism to Infants.

The Minister, coming to the Font, which is to be filled with pure Water, shall use the following:

Dearly Beloved, forasmuch as all men are conceived and born in sin, and that our Saviour Christ saith, Except a man be born of water and of the Spirit he cannot enter into the kingdom of God; I beseech you to call upon God the Father, through our Lord Jesus Christ, that having, of his bounteous mercy, redeemed *this child* by the blood of his Son, he will grant that *he*, being baptized with water, may also be baptized with the Holy Ghost, be received into Christ's holy Church, and become *a lively Member* of the same.

Then shall the Minister say,

Let us pray.

Almighty and Everlasting God, who of thy great mercy hast condescended to enter into covenant relations with man, wherein thou hast included children as partakers of its gracious benefits, declaring that of such is thy kingdom; and in thy ancient Church didst appoint divers baptisms, figuring thereby the renewing of the Holy Ghost; and by thy well-beloved Son Jesus Christ gavest commandment to thy holy Apostles to go into all the world and disciple all nations, baptizing them in the name of the Father, and of the Son, and of the Holy Ghost:

we beseech thee, that of thine infinite mercy thou wilt look upon *this child:* wash *him* and sanctify *him;* that *he*, being saved by thy grace, may be received into Christ's holy Church, and being steadfast in faith, joyful through hope, and rooted in love, may so overcome the evils of this present world that finally *he* may attain to everlasting life, and reign with thee, world without end, through Jesus Christ our Lord. *Amen.*

O merciful God, grant that all carnal affections may die in *him*, and that all things belonging to the Spirit may live and grow in *him*. *Amen.*

Grant that *he* may have power and strength to have victory, and to triumph against the devil, the world, and the flesh. *Amen.*

Grant that whosoever is dedicated to thee by our Office and Ministry may also be endued with heavenly virtues, and everlastingly rewarded through thy mercy, O blessed Lord God, who dost live and govern all things, world without end. *Amen.*

Almighty, Everliving God, whose most dearly beloved Son Jesus Christ, for the forgiveness of our sins, did shed out of his most precious side both water and blood, regard, we beseech thee, our supplications. Sanctify this water for this Holy Sacrament; and grant that *this child*, now to be baptized, may receive the fullness of thy grace, and ever remain in the number of thy faithful and elect children, through Jesus Christ our Lord. *Amen.*

Then shall the Minister address the Parents or Guardians as follows:

Dearly beloved, forasmuch as *this child is* now presented by you for Christian Baptism, you must remember that it is your part and duty to see that *he* be taught, as soon as *he* shall be able to learn, the nature and end of this Holy Sacrament. And that *he* may know these things the better, you shall call upon *him* to give reverent attendance upon the appointed means of grace, such as the ministry of the word, and the public and private worship of God; and further, you shall provide that *he* shall read the Holy Scriptures, and learn the Lord's Prayer, the Ten Commandments, the Apostles' Creed, the Catechism, and all other things which a Christian ought to know and believe to his soul's health, in order that *he* may be brought up to lead a virtuous and holy life, remembering always that baptism doth represent unto us that inward purity which disposeth us to follow the example of our Saviour Christ; that as he died and rose again for us, so should we, who are baptized, die unto sin and rise again unto righteousness, continually mortifying all corrupt affections, and daily proceeding in all virtue and godliness.

Do you therefore solemnly engage to fulfill these duties, so far as in you lies, the Lord being your helper?

Ans. We do.

Then shall the People stand up, and the Minister shall say :

Hear the words of the Gospel, written by St. Mark. [Chap. x, 13–16.]

They brought young children to Christ, that he should touch them. And his disciples rebuked those that brought them. But when Jesus saw it, he was much displeased, and said unto them, Suffer the little children to come unto me, and forbid them not, for of such is the kingdom of God. Verily I say unto you, Whosoever shall not receive the kingdom of God as a little child, he shall not enter therein. And he took them up in his arms, put his hands upon them, and blessed them.

Then the Minister shall take the Child into his hands, and say to the friends of the Child,

Name this child.

And then, naming it after them, he shall sprinkle or pour Water upon it, or, if desired, immerse it in Water, saying,

N., I baptize thee in the name of the Father, and of the Son, and of the Holy Ghost. *Amen.*

Then shall the Minister offer the following Prayer, the people kneeling :

O God of infinite mercy, the Father of all the faithful seed, be pleased to grant unto *this child* an understanding mind and a sanctified heart. May thy providence lead *him* through the dangers, temptations, and ignorance of *his* youth, that *he* may never run into folly, nor into the evils of an unbridled appetite. We pray thee so to order the course of *his* life, that by good education, by holy examples, and by thy restraining and renewing grace, *he* may be led to serve thee faithfully all *his* days; so that, when *he* has glorified thee in *his* generation, and *has* served the Church on earth, *he* may be received into thine eternal kingdom, through Jesus Christ our Lord. *Amen.*

Almighty and most merciful Father, let thy loving mercy and compassion descend upon *these*, thy *servant* and *handmaid*, the *parents* [or guardians] of *this child*. Grant unto *them*, we beseech thee, thy Holy Spirit, that *they* may, like Abraham, command *their* household to keep the way of the Lord. Direct *their* actions, and sanctify *their hearts*, words, and purposes, that *their* whole family may be united to our Lord Jesus Christ in the bands of faith, obedience, and charity; and that they all, being in this life thy holy children by adoption and grace, may be admitted into the Church of the first-born in heaven, through the merits of thy dear Son, our Saviour and Redeemer. *Amen.*

Then may the Minister offer extemporary Prayer.

Then shall be said, all kneeling :

Our Father who art in heaven, hallowed be thy name. Thy kingdom come. Thy will be done in earth, as it is in heaven. Give us this day our daily bread: and forgive us our trespasses, as we forgive them that trespass against us: and lead us not into temptation, but deliver us from evil: for thine is the kingdom, and the power, and the glory, forever. *Amen.*

ORDER FOR THE ADMINISTRATION OF BAPTISM TO SUCH AS ARE OF RIPER YEARS.

DEARLY BELOVED, forasmuch as all men are conceived and born in sin; and that which is born of the flesh is flesh, and they that are in the flesh cannot please God, but live in sin, committing many actual transgressions; and our Saviour Christ saith, Except a man be born of water and of the Spirit he cannot enter into the kingdom of God: I beseech you to call upon God the Father, through our Lord Jesus Christ, that of his bounteous goodness he will grant to *these persons* that which by nature *they* cannot have; that *they*, being baptized with water, may also be baptized with the Holy Ghost, and, being received into Christ's holy Church, may continue lively *Members* of the same.

Then shall the Minister say,

Let us pray.

Almighty and Immortal God, the aid of all that need, the helper of all that flee to thee for succor, the life of them that believe, and the resurrection of the dead: we call upon thee for *these persons*, that *they*, coming to thy Holy Baptism, may also be filled with thy Holy Spirit. Receive *them*, O Lord, as thou hast promised by thy well-beloved Son, saying, Ask, and ye shall receive; seek, and ye shall find; knock, and it shall be opened unto you; so give now unto us that ask; let us that seek, find; open the gate unto us that knock; that *these persons* may enjoy the everlasting benediction of thy heavenly washing, and may come to the eternal kingdom which thou hast promised, by Christ our Lord. *Amen.*

Then shall the People stand up, and the Minister shall say.

Hear the words of the Gospel, written by St. John. [Chap. iii, 1–8.]

There was a man of the Pharisees, named Nicodemus, a ruler of the Jews: the same came to Jesus by night, and said unto him, Rabbi, we know that thou art a teacher come from God; for no man can do these miracles that thou doest except God be with him. Jesus answered and said unto him, Verily, verily, I say unto thee, Except a man be born again, he cannot see the kingdom of God. Nicodemus saith unto him, How can a man be born when he is old? Can he enter the second time into his mother's womb, and be born? Jesus answered, Verily, verily, I say unto thee, Except a man be born of water and of the Spirit he cannot enter into the kingdom of God.

That which is born of the flesh is flesh, and that which is born of the Spirit is spirit. Marvel not that I said unto thee, Ye must be born again. The wind bloweth where it listeth, and thou hearest the sound thereof, but canst not tell whence it cometh, and whither it goeth; so is every one that is born of the Spirit.

Then the Minister shall speak to the Persons to be baptized on this wise:

Well Beloved, who *have* come hither desiring to receive Holy Baptism, you have heard how the Congregation hath prayed that our Lord Jesus Christ would vouchsafe to receive you, to bless you, and to give you the kingdom of heaven, and everlasting life. And our Lord Jesus Christ hath promised in his holy word to grant all those things that we have prayed for: which promise he for his part will most surely keep and perform.

Wherefore, after this promise made by Christ, you must also faithfully, for your part, promise in the presence of this whole Congregation, that you will renounce the devil and all his works, and constantly believe God's holy word, and obediently keep his commandments.

Then shall the Minister demand of each of the Persons to be baptized:

Quest. Dost thou renounce the devil and all his works, the vain pomp and glory of the world, with all covetous desires of the same, and the carnal desires of the flesh, so that thou wilt not follow nor be led by them?

Ans. I renounce them all.

Quest. Dost thou believe in God the Father Almighty, Maker of heaven and earth;

And in Jesus Christ his only begotten Son our Lord; and that he was conceived by the Holy Ghost, born of the Virgin Mary; that he suffered under Pontius Pilate, was crucified, dead, and buried; that he rose again the third day; that he ascended into heaven, and sitteth on the right hand of God the Father Almighty; and from thence shall come again at the end of the world, to judge the quick and the dead?

And dost thou believe in the Holy Ghost; the holy catholic * Church; the communion of saints; the forgiveness of

* The one universal Church of Christ.

sins; the resurrection of the body; and everlasting life after death?

Ans. All this I steadfastly believe.

Quest. Wilt thou be baptized in this faith?

Ans. Such is my desire.

Quest. Wilt thou then obediently keep God's holy will and commandments, and walk in the same all the days of thy life?

Ans. I will endeavor so to do, God being my helper.

Then shall the Minister say:

O Merciful God, grant that all carnal affections may die in *these persons*, and that all things belonging to the Spirit may live and grow in *them. Amen.*

Grant that *they* may have power and strength to have victory, and triumph against the devil, the world, and the flesh. *Amen.*

Grant that *they*, being here dedicated to thee by our Office and Ministry, may also be endued with heavenly virtues, and everlastingly rewarded, through thy mercy, O blessed Lord God, who dost live and govern all things, world without end. *Amen.*

Almighty, Everliving God, whose most dearly beloved Son Jesus Christ, for the forgiveness of our sins, did shed out of his most precious side both water and blood; and gave commandment to his disciples that they should go teach all nations, and baptize them in the name of the Father, and of the Son, and of the Holy Ghost; regard, we beseech thee, our supplications; and grant that the *persons* now to be baptized may recieve the fullness of thy grace, and ever remain in the number of thy faithful and elect children, through Jesus Christ our Lord. *Amen.*

Then shall the Minister ask the name of each Person to be baptized, and shall sprinkle or pour Water upon him (or, if he shall desire it, shall immerse him in Water), saying:

N., I baptize thee in the name of the Father, and of the Son, and of the Holy Ghost. *Amen.*

Then shall be said the Lord's Prayer, all kneeling:

Our Father who art in heaven, hallowed be thy name. Thy kingdom come. Thy will be done in earth, as it is in heaven. Give us this day our daily bread: and forgive us our trespasses as we forgive them that trespass against us: and lead us not into temptation, but deliver us from evil: for thine is the kingdom, and the power, and the glory, forever. *Amen.*

Then may the Minister conclude with extemporary Prayer.

Reception of Members.

FORM FOR RECEIVING PERSONS INTO THE CHURCH AS PROBATIONERS.

Those who are to be received into the Church as Probationers shall be called forward by name, and the Minister, addressing the Congregation, shall say:

DEARLY BELOVED BRETHREN, that none may be admitted hastily into the Church, we receive all persons seeking fellowship with us on profession of faith into a preparatory membership on trial, in which proof may be made, both to themselves and to the Church, of the sincerity and depth of their convictions and of the strength of their purpose to lead a new life.

The persons here present desire to be so admitted. You will hear their answers to the questions put to them, and if you make no objection they will be received.

It is needful, however, that you be reminded of your responsibility, as having previously entered this holy fellowship, and as now representing the Church into which they seek admission. Remembering their inexperience, and how much they must learn in order to become good soldiers of Jesus Christ, see to it that they find in you holy examples of life, and loving help in the true serving of their Lord and ours. I beseech you so to order your own lives that these new disciples may take no detriment from you, but that it may ever be cause for thanksgiving to God that they were led into this fellowship.

Then addressing the Persons seeking Admission on Probation, the Minister shall say:

Dearly Beloved, you have, by the grace of God, made your decision to follow Christ and to serve him. Your confidence in so doing is not to be based on any notion of fitness or worthiness in yourselves, but solely on the merits of our Lord Jesus Christ, and on his death and intercession for us.

That the Church may know your purpose, you will answer the questions I am now to ask you.

Have you an earnest desire to be saved from your sins?

Ans. 1 have.

Will you guard yourselves against all things contrary to the teaching of God's word, and endeavor to lead a holy life, following the commandments of God?

Ans. I will endeavor so to do.

Are you purposed to give reverent attendance upon the appointed means of grace in the ministry of the word, and in the private and public worship of God?

Ans. I am so determined, with the help of God.

No objection being offered, the Minister shall then announce that the Candidates are admitted as Probationers and shall assign them to classes.

Then shall the Minister offer extemporary prayer.

FORM FOR RECEIVING PERSONS INTO THE CHURCH AFTER PROBATION.

Upon the day appointed, all that are to be received into the Church shall be called forward, and the Minister, addressing the Congregation, shall say:

DEARLY BELOVED BRETHREN, the Scriptures teach us that the Church is the household of God, the body of which Christ is the head; and that it is the design of the Gospel to bring together in one all who are in Christ. The fellowship of the Church is the communion that its Members enjoy one with another. The ends of this fellowship are, the maintenance of sound doctrine and of the ordinances of Christian worship, and the exercise of that power of godly admonition and discipline which Christ has committed to his Church for the promotion of holiness. It is the duty of all men to unite in this fellowship; for it is only those that " be planted in the house of the Lord" that "shall flourish in the courts of our God." Its more particular duties are, to promote peace and

unity; to bear one another's burdens; to prevent each other's stumbling; to seek the intimacy of friendly society among themselves; to continue steadfast in the faith and worship of the Gospel; and to pray and sympathize with each other. Among its privileges are, peculiar incitements to holiness from the hearing of God's word and sharing in Christ's ordinances; the being placed under the watchful care of Pastors; and the enjoyment of the blessings which are promised only to those who are of the Household of Faith. Into this holy fellowship the *persons* before you, who *have* already received the Sacrament of Baptism, and *have* been under the care of *proper leaders* for six months on trial, *come* seeking admission. We now propose, in the fear of God, to question *them* as to *their* faith and purposes, that you may know that *they are* proper persons to be admitted into the Church.

Then, addressing the Applicants for Admission, the Minister shall say:

Dearly Beloved, you are come hither seeking the great privilege of union with the Church our Saviour has purchased with his own blood. We rejoice in the grace of God vouchsafed unto you in that he has called you to be his *followers,* and that thus far you have run well. You have heard how blessed are the privileges, and how solemn are the duties, of membership in Christ's Church; and before you are fully admitted thereto, it is proper that you do here publicly renew your vows, confess your faith, and declare your purpose, by answering the following questions:

Do you here, in the presence of God and of this Congregation, renew the solemn promise contained in the Baptismal Covenant, ratifying and confirming the same, and acknowledging *yourselves* bound faithfully to observe and keep that covenant?

Ans. I do.

Have you saving faith in the Lord Jesus Christ?

Ans. I trust I have.

Do you believe in the Doctrines of the Holy Scriptures, as set forth in the Articles of Religion of the Methodist Episcopal Church?

Ans. I do.

...heerfully be governed by ...f the Methodist Episcopal ...d sacred the Ordinances of ...ndeavor, as much as in you lies, ...omote the welfare of your brethren ...nd the advancement of the Redeemer's kingdom?

Ans. I will.

Will you contribute of your earthly substance, according to your ability, to the support of the Gospel and the various benevolent enterprises of the Church?

Ans. I will.

Then the Minister, addressing the Church, shall say:

Brethren, *these persons* having given satisfactory responses to our inquiries, have any of you reason to allege why *they* should not be received into Full membership in the Church?

No objection being alleged, the Minister shall say to the Candidates:

We welcome you to the communion of the Church of God; and, in testimony of our Christian affection and the cordiality with which we receive you, I hereby extend to you the right hand of fellowship: and may God grant that you may be a faithful and useful member of the Church militant till you are called to the fellowship of the Church triumphant; which is "without fault before the throne of God."

Then shall the Minister offer extemporary Prayer.

The Lord's Supper.

[Whenever practicable, let none but the pure, unfermented juice of the grape be used in administering the Lord's Supper.]

[Let persons who have scruples concerning the receiving of the Sacrament of the Lord's Supper kneeling be permitted to receive it either standing or sitting.]

[No person shall be admitted to the Lord's Supper among us who is guilty of any practice for which we would exclude a Member of our Church.]

ORDER FOR THE ADMINISTRATION OF THE LORD'S SUPPER.

The Elder shall say one or more of these Sentences, during the reading of which the Persons appointed for that purpose shall receive the Alms for the Poor:

LET your light so shine before men, that they may see your good works, and glorify your Father which is in heaven. [Matt. v, 16.]

Lay not up for yourselves treasures upon earth, where moth and rust doth corrupt, and where thieves break through and steal: but lay up for yourselves treasures in heaven, where neither moth nor rust doth corrupt, and where thieves do not break through nor steal. [Matt. vi, 19, 20.]

Whatsoever ye would that men should do to you, do ye even so to them: for this is the law and the prophets. [Matt. vii, 12.]

Not every one that saith unto me, Lord, Lord, shall enter into the kingdom of heaven; but he that doeth the will of my Father which is in heaven. [Matt. vii, 21.]

Zaccheus stood, and said unto the Lord; Behold, Lord, the half of my goods I give to the poor: and if I have taken anything from any man by false accusation, I restore him fourfold. [Luke xix, 8.]

He which soweth sparingly shall reap also sparingly; and he which soweth bountifully shall reap also bountifully. Every man according as he purposeth in his heart, so let him give: not grudgingly, or of necessity, for God loveth a cheerful giver. [2 Cor. ix, 6, 7.]

As we have therefore opportunity, let us do good unto all men, especially unto them who are of the household of faith. [Gal. vi, 10.]

Godliness with contentment is great gain; for we brought nothing into this world, and it is certain we can carry nothing out. [1 Tim. vi, 6, 7.]

Charge them that are rich in this world, that they be not high-minded, nor trust in uncertain riches, but in the living God, who giveth us richly all things to enjoy; that they do good, that they be rich in good works, ready to distribute, willing to communicate; laying up in store for themselves a good foundation against the time to come, that they may lay hold on eternal life. [1 Tim. vi, 17-19.]

God is not unrighteous to forget your work and labor of love, which ye have showed toward his name, in that ye have ministered to the saints, and do minister. [Heb. vi, 10.]

To do good, and to communicate, forget not: for with such sacrifices God is well pleased. [Heb. xiii, 16.]

Whoso hath this world's good, and seeth his brother have need, and shutteth up his bowels of compassion from him, how dwelleth the love of God in him? [i John iii, 17.]

He that hath pity upon the poor, lendeth unto the Lord; and that which he hath given will he pay him again. [Prov. xix, 17.]

Blessed is he that considereth the poor: the Lord will deliver him in time of trouble. [Psa. xli, 1.]

Thou shalt open thine hand wide unto thy brother, to thy poor. [Deut. xv, 11.]

After which the Elder shall give the following Invitation, the People standing :

If any man sin, we have an advocate with the Father, Jesus Christ the righteous: and he is the propitiation for our sins: and not for ours only, but also for the sins of the whole world.

Wherefore ye that do truly and earnestly repent of your sins, and are in love and charity with your neighbors, and intend to lead a new life, following the commandments of God, and walking from henceforth in his holy ways, draw near with faith, and take this Holy Sacrament to your comfort; and, devoutly kneeling, make your humble confession to Almighty God.

Then shall this general Confession be made by the Minister in the name of all those who are minded to receive the Holy Communion, both he and all the People devoutly kneeling, and saying :

Almighty God, Father of our Lord Jesus Christ, Maker of all things, Judge of all men, we acknowledge and bewail our manifold sins and wickedness, which we from time to time most grievously have committed, by thought, word, and deed, against thy Divine Majesty, provoking most justly thy wrath and indignation against us. We do earnestly repent, and are heartily sorry for these our misdoings; the remembrance of them is grievous unto us. Have mercy upon us, have mercy upon us, most merciful Father; for thy Son, our Lord Jesus Christ's sake, forgive us all that is past; and grant that we may ever hereafter serve and please thee in newness of life, to the

honor and glory of thy name, through Jesus Christ our Lord. *Amen.*

Then shall the Elder say,

Almighty God, our heavenly Father, who of thy great mercy hast promised forgiveness of sins to all them that with hearty repentance and true faith turn unto thee, have mercy upon us; pardon and deliver us from all our sins; confirm and strengthen us in all goodness; and bring us to everlasting life, through Jesus Christ our Lord. *Amen.*

The Collect.

Almighty God, unto whom all hearts are open, all desires known, and from whom no secrets are hid, cleanse the thoughts of our hearts by the inspiration of thy Holy Spirit, that we may perfectly love thee, and worthily magnify thy holy name through Jesus Christ our Lord. *Amen.*

Then shall the Elder say,

We do not presume to come to this thy table, O merciful Lord, trusting in our own righteousness, but in thy manifold and great mercies. We are not worthy so much as to gather up the crumbs under thy table. But thou art the same Lord, whose property is always to have mercy. Grant us, therefore, gracious Lord, so to eat the flesh of thy dear Son Jesus Christ, and to drink his blood, that we may live and grow thereby; and that, being washed through his most precious blood, we may evermore dwell in him, and he in us. *Amen.*

Then the Elder shall offer the Prayer of Consecration, as followeth:

Almighty God, our heavenly Father, who of thy tender mercy didst give thine only Son Jesus Christ to suffer death upon the cross for our redemption; who made there, by his oblation of himself once offered, a full, perfect, and sufficient sacrifice, oblation, and satisfaction for the sins of the whole world; and did institute, and in his holy Gospel command us to continue, a perpetual memory of his precious death until his coming again: hear us, O merciful Father, we most humbly beseech thee, and grant that we, receiving these thy creatures of bread and wine, according to thy Son our Saviour Jesus Christ's holy institution, in remembrance of his death and passion, may be partakers of his most blessed body and blood; who, in the same night that he was betrayed, took bread; (1) and when he had given thanks, he broke it, and gave it to his disciples, saying, Take, eat; this is my body which is given for you; do this in remembrance of me.

(1)Here the Elder may take the plate of bread in his hand.

Likewise after supper he took (2) the cup; and when he had given thanks he gave it to them, saying, Drink ye all of this; for this is my blood of the New Testament, which is shed for you, and for many, for the remission of sins; do this, as oft as ye shall drink it, in remembrance of me. *Amen.*

(2)Here he may take the cup in his hand.

Then shall the Minister receive the Communion in both kinds, and proceed to deliver the same to the other Ministers, if any be present; after which he shall say:

It is very meet, right, and our bounden duty that we should at all times and in all places give thanks unto thee, O Lord, holy Father, Almighty, Everlasting God.

Therefore with angels and archangels, and with all the company of heaven, we laud and magnify thy glorious name, evermore praising thee, and saying, Holy, Holy, Holy, Lord God of hosts, heaven and earth are full of thy glory. Glory be to thee, O Lord most high! *Amen.*

The Minister shall then proceed to administer the Communion to the People in order, kneeling, into their uncovered hands; and when he delivereth the Bread, he shall say:

The body of our Lord Jesus Christ, which was given for *thee,* preserve *thy* soul and *body* unto everlasting life. Take and eat this in remembrance that Christ died for *thee;* and feed on him in *thy* heart by faith, with thanksgiving.

And the Minister that delivereth the Cup shall say:

The blood of our Lord Jesus Christ, which was shed for *thee,* preserve *thy* soul and *body* unto everlasting life.

Drink this in remembrance that Christ's blood was shed for *thee,* and be thankful.

[if the Consecrated bread or wine be all spent before all have communed, the Elder may Consecrate more by repeating the Prayer of Consecration.]

[When all have communed, the Minister shall return to the Lord's table and place upon it what remaineth of the Consecrated elements, covering the same with a fair linen cloth.]

Then shall the Elder say the Lord's Prayer; the People kneeling, and repeating after him every petition.

Our Father who art in heaven, hallowed be thy name. Thy kingdom come. Thy will be done in earth, as it is in heaven. Give us this day our daily bread: and forgive us our trespasses, as we forgive them that trespass against us: and lead us not into temptation, but deliver us from evil: for thine is the kingdom, and the power, and the glory, forever. *Amen.*

After which shall be said as followeth:

O Lord, our heavenly Father, we thy humble servants desire thy Fatherly goodness mercifully to accept this our sacrifice of praise and thanksgiving; most humbly beseeching thee to grant, that, by the merits and death of thy Son Jesus Christ, and through faith in his blood, we and thy whole Church may obtain remission of our sins, and all other benefits of his passion. And here we offer and present unto thee, O Lord, ourselves, our souls and bodies, to be a reasonable, holy, and lively sacrifice unto thee; humbly beseeching thee that all we who are partakers of this Holy Communion may be filled with thy grace and heavenly benediction. And although we be unworthy, through our manifold sins, to offer unto thee any sacrifice, yet we beseech thee to accept this our bounden duty and service; not weighing our merits, but pardoning our offenses, through Jesus Christ our Lord; by whom, and with whom, in the unity of the Holy Ghost, all honor and glory be unto thee, O Father Almighty, world without end. *Amen.*

*Then shall be said or sung:**

Glory be to God on high, and on earth peace, good-will toward men! We praise thee, we bless thee, we worship thee, we glorify thee, we give thanks to thee for thy great glory, O Lord God, heavenly King, God the Father Almighty!

O Lord, the only begotten Son Jesus Christ: O Lord God, Lamb of God, Son of the Father, that takest away the sins of the world, have mercy upon us. Thou that takest away the sins of the world, have mercy upon us. Thou that takest away the sins of the world, receive our prayer. Thou that sittest at the right hand of God the Father, have mercy upon us. For thou only art holy; thou only art the Lord; thou only, O Christ, with the Holy Ghost, art most high in the glory of God the Father. *Amen.*

Then the Elder, if he see it expedient, may put up an extemporary Prayer; and afterward shall let the People depart with this Blessing:

The peace of God, which passeth all understanding, keep your hearts and minds in the knowledge and love of God, and of his Son Jesus Christ our Lord: and the blessing of God Almighty, the Father, the Son, and the Holy Ghost, be among you, and remain with you always. *Amen.*

N. B.—If the Elder be straitened for time in the usual administration of the Holy Communion, he may omit any part of the service except the Invitation, the Confession, and the Prayer of Consecration: and in its administration to the Sick he may omit any part of the service except the Confession, the Prayer of Consecration, and the usual sentences in delivering the Bread and Wine, closing with the Lord's Prayer, *extempore* supplication, and the Benediction.

* "Gloria in Excelsis," see page 433, of this book.